Elementary and Intermediate
Algebra
Concepts and Applications

VOLUME II

BITTENGER • ELLENBOGEN • JOHNSON

A Custom Edition for Math 152, 152A, 152B and 153 at Ohlone College

Taken from:

Elementary and Intermediate Algebra: Concepts and Applications, Fourth Edition
by Marvin L. Bittenger, David J. Ellenbogen, and Barbara L. Johnson

Beginning and Intermediate Algebra with Applications & Visualization
by Gary Rockswold and Terry A. Kreiger

PEARSON
Custom
Publishing

PEARSON
Addison
Wesley

Taken from:

Elementary and Intermediate Algebra: Concepts and Applications, Fourth Edition
by Marvin L. Bittenger, David J. Ellenbogen, and Barbara L. Johnson
Copyright © 2006 by Pearson Education, Inc.
Published by Addison Wesley
Boston, Massachusetts 02116

Beginning and Intermediate Algebra with Applications & Visualization
by Gary K. Rockswold and Terry A. Kreiger
Copyright © 2005 by Pearson Education, Inc.
Published by Addison Wesley

This special edition published in cooperation with Pearson Custom Publishing.

Printed in the United States of America

10 9 8 7 6 5 4 3 2 1

ISBN 0-536-94121-1

2005360319

KK

Please visit our web site at *www.pearsoncustom.com*

PEARSON CUSTOM PUBLISHING
75 Arlington Street, Suite 300, Boston, MA 02116
A Pearson Education Company

Contents

Sequences, Series, and the Binomial Theorem

Elementary Algebra Review

8

Systems of Linear Equations and Problem Solving

AN APPLICATION

King Street Printing recently charged 1.9¢ per sheet of paper, but 2.4¢ per sheet for paper made of recycled fibers. Darren's bill for 150 sheets of paper was $3.41. How many sheets of each type were used?

This problem appears as Exercise 15 in Section 8.3.

Nancy Plunkett
WASTE REDUCTION MANAGER
Williston, Vermont

I regularly use algebra whenever I create spreadsheets to track the costs and performance of recycling and composting programs and to compile survey data. I also use it to convert volumes of different materials to weight and to calculate rates of change in program participation.

*T*he most difficult part of problem solving is almost always translating the problem situation to mathematical language. Once a problem has been translated, the rest is usually straightforward. In this chapter, we study systems of equations *and how to solve them using graphing, substitution, elimination, and matrices. Systems of equations often provide the easiest way to model real-world situations in fields such as psychology, sociology, business, education, engineering, and science.*

8.1 Systems of Equations in Two Variables

Translating   •   Identifying Solutions   •
Solving Systems Graphically

Translating

Problems involving two unknown quantities are often solved most easily if we can first translate the situation to two equations in two unknowns.

EXAMPLE 1

Bottled-water consumption. Americans are buying more bottled water than ever before. At the time of this writing, the average American buys more bottled water than milk, coffee, or beer. In 2003, the average American purchased 76.4 gal of soft drinks and water. The amount of water was only 4.3 gal less than half of the amount of soft drinks. (*Source*: Based on data from www.beveragemarketing.com) How many gallons of water and how many of soft drinks did the average American buy in 2003?

Solution

1. **Familiarize.** We have already seen problems in which we need to look up certain formulas or the meaning of certain words. Here we simply observe that the words *per person* mean the same thing as the amount consumed by the *average American*.

   Often problems contain information that has no bearing on the situation being discussed. In this case, the fact that more water is bought than milk, coffee, or beer is irrelevant to the question being asked. Instead we focus on the amounts of water and soft drinks consumed. Rather than guess and check, let's proceed to the next step, using *w* to represent the average number of gallons of bottled water purchased and *s* for the average number of gallons of soft drinks purchased in 2003.

Study Skills _____

Speak Up

Don't be hesitant to ask questions in class at appropriate times. Most instructors welcome questions and encourage students to ask them. Other students in your class probably have the same questions you do.

2. Translate.   There are two statements to translate. First we look at the total number of gallons purchased by the average American:

Rewording: The amount of   plus   the amount of   was   76.4.
water purchased   soft drinks purchased

Translating: w $+$ s $=$ 76.4

The second statement compares the two amounts, w and s:

Rewording: The amount of   was   4.3 gal less than half the
water purchased   amount of soft drinks purchased.

Translating: w $=$ $\frac{1}{2}s - 4.3$

We have now translated the problem to a pair, or **system, of equations**:

$$w + s = 76.4,$$
$$w = \frac{1}{2}s - 4.3.$$

> **System of Equations**
>
> A *system of equations* is a set of two or more equations, in two or more variables, for which a common solution is sought.

Problems like Example 1 *can* be solved using one variable; however, as problems become complicated, you will find that using more than one variable (and more than one equation) is often the preferable approach.

EXAMPLE 2

Purchasing.   Recently the Woods County Art Center purchased 120 stamps for $33.90. If the stamps were a combination of 23¢ postcard stamps and 37¢ first-class stamps, how many of each type were bought?

Solution

1. Familiarize.   To familiarize ourselves with this problem, let's guess that the art center bought 60 stamps at 23¢ each and 60 stamps at 37¢ each. The total cost would then be

$$60 \cdot \$0.23 + 60 \cdot \$0.37 = \$13.80 + \$22.20, \text{ or } \$36.00.$$

Since $\$36.00 \neq \$33.90$, our guess is incorrect. Rather than guess again, let's see how algebra can be used to translate the problem.

2. Translate. We let $p =$ the number of postcard stamps and $f =$ the number of first-class stamps. The information can be organized in a table, which will help with the translating.

Type of Stamp	Postcard	First-class	Total
Number Sold	p	f	120
Price	$0.23	$0.37	
Amount	$0.23p	$0.37f	$33.90

$\rightarrow p + f = 120$

$\rightarrow 0.23p + 0.37f = 33.90$

The first row of the table and the first sentence of the problem indicate that a total of 120 stamps were bought:

$$p + f = 120.$$

Since each postcard stamp cost $0.23 and p stamps were bought, $0.23p$ represents the amount paid, in dollars, for the postcard stamps. Similarly, $0.37f$ represents the amount paid, in dollars, for the first-class stamps. This leads to a second equation:

$$0.23p + 0.37f = 33.90.$$

Multiplying both sides by 100, we can clear the decimals. This gives the following system of equations as the translation:

$$p + f = 120,$$
$$23p + 37f = 3390.$$

We will complete the solutions of Examples 1 and 2 in Section 8.3.

Identifying Solutions

A *solution* of a system of two equations in two variables is an ordered pair of numbers that makes *both* equations true.

EXAMPLE 3   Determine whether $(-4, 7)$ is a solution of the system

$$x + y = 3,$$
$$5x - y = -27.$$

Solution   As discussed in Chapter 3, unless stated otherwise, we use alphabetical order of the variables. Thus we replace x with -4 and y with 7:

$$\frac{x + y = 3}{-4 + 7 \mid 3}$$
$$3 \overset{?}{=} 3 \quad \text{TRUE}$$

$$\frac{5x - y = -27}{5(-4) - 7 \mid -27}$$
$$-20 - 7 \mid$$
$$-27 \overset{?}{=} -27 \quad \text{TRUE}$$

The pair $(-4, 7)$ makes both equations true, so it is a solution of the system. We can also describe the solution by writing $x = -4$ and $y = 7$. Set notation can also be used to list the solution set $\{(-4, 7)\}$.

Solving Systems Graphically

Recall that the graph of an equation is a drawing that represents its solution set. If we graph the equations in Example 3, we find that $(-4, 7)$ is the only point common to both lines. Thus one way to solve a system of two equations is to graph both equations and identify any points of intersection. The coordinates of each point of intersection represent a solution of that system.

$$x + y = 3,$$
$$5x - y = -27$$

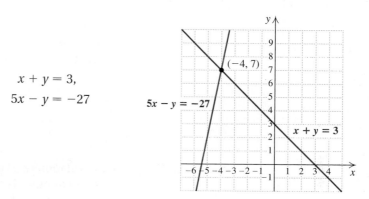

Most pairs of lines have exactly one point in common. We will soon see, however, that this is not always the case.

EXAMPLE 4   Solve each system graphically.

a) $y - x = 1,$ **b)** $y = -3x + 5,$ **c)** $3y - 2x = 6,$
$\quad\ \ y + x = 3$ $\qquad\ y = -3x - 2$ $\qquad\ -12y + 8x = -24$

Solution

a) We graph each equation using any method studied in Chapter 3. All ordered pairs from line L_1 are solutions of the first equation. All ordered pairs from line L_2 are solutions of the second equation. The point of intersection has coordinates that make *both* equations true. Apparently, $(1, 2)$ is the solution. Graphs are not always accurate, so solving by graphing may yield approximate answers. Our check below shows that $(1, 2)$ is indeed the solution.

$$y - x = 1,$$
$$y + x = 3$$

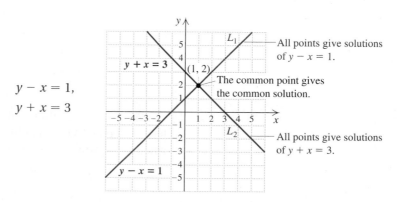

Check:

$$\begin{array}{c|c} y - x = 1 \\ \hline 2 - 1 & 1 \\ 1 \overset{?}{=} 1 & \text{TRUE} \end{array} \qquad \begin{array}{c|c} y + x = 3 \\ \hline 2 + 1 & 3 \\ 3 \overset{?}{=} 3 & \text{TRUE} \end{array}$$

b) We graph the equations. The lines have the same slope, -3, and different y-intercepts, so they are parallel. There is no point at which they cross, so the system has no solution.

$$y = -3x + 5,$$
$$y = -3x - 2$$

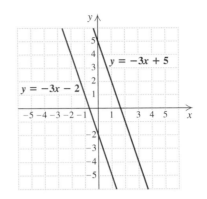

c) We graph the equations and find that the same line is drawn twice. Thus any solution of one equation is a solution of the other. Each equation has an infinite number of solutions, so the system itself has an infinite number of solutions. We check one solution, $(0, 2)$, which is the y-intercept of each equation.

Student Notes _____

Although the system in Example 4(c) is true for an infinite number of ordered pairs, those pairs must be of a certain form. Only pairs that are solutions of $3y - 2x = 6$ or $-12y + 8x = -24$ are solutions of the system. It is incorrect to think that *all* ordered pairs are solutions.

$$3y - 2x = 6,$$
$$-12y + 8x = -24$$

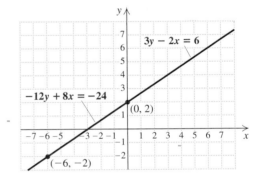

Check:

$$\begin{array}{c|c} 3y - 2x = 6 & \\ \hline 3(2) - 2(0) & 6 \\ 6 - 0 & \\ 6 \overset{?}{=} 6 & \text{TRUE} \end{array}$$

$$\begin{array}{c|c} -12y + 8x = -24 & \\ \hline -12(2) + 8(0) & -24 \\ -24 + 0 & \\ -24 \overset{?}{=} -24 & \text{TRUE} \end{array}$$

You can check that $(-6, -2)$ is another solution of both equations. In fact, any pair that is a solution of one equation is a solution of the other equation as well. Thus the solution set is

$$\{(x, y) \mid 3y - 2x = 6\}$$

or, in words, "the set of all pairs (x, y) for which $3y - 2x = 6$." Since the two equations are equivalent, we could have written instead $\{(x, y) \mid -12y + 8x = -24\}$.

technology connection

On most graphing calculators, an INTERSECT option allows you to find the coordinates of the intersection directly. This is especially useful when equations contain fractions or decimals or when the coordinates of the intersection are not integers. To illustrate, consider the following system:

$$3.45x + 4.21y = 8.39,$$
$$7.12x - 5.43y = 6.18.$$

After solving for y in each equation, we obtain the graph below. Using INTERSECT, we see that, to the nearest hundredth, the coordinates of the intersection are (1.47, 0.79).

$$y_1 = (8.39 - 3.45x)/4.21,$$
$$y_2 = (6.18 - 7.12x)/(-5.43)$$

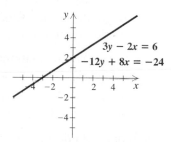

Use a graphing calculator to solve each of the following systems. Make sure that all x- and y-coordinates are correct to the nearest hundredth.

1. $y = -5.43x + 10.89,$
   $y = 6.29x - 7.04$
2. $y = 123.52x + 89.32,$
   $y = -89.22x + 33.76$
3. $2.18x + 7.81y = 13.78,$
   $5.79x - 3.45y = 8.94$
4. $-9.25x - 12.94y = -3.88,$
   $21.83x + 16.33y = 13.69$

When we graph a system of two linear equations in two variables, one of the following three outcomes will occur.

1. The lines have one point in common, and that point is the only solution of the system (see Example 4a). Any system that has *at least* one solution is said to be **consistent**.

2. The lines are parallel, with no point in common, and the system has no solution (see Example 4b). This type of system is called **inconsistent**.

3. The lines coincide, sharing the same graph. Because every solution of one equation is a solution of the other, the system has an infinite number of solutions (see Example 4c). Since it has at least one solution, this type of system is also consistent.

When one equation in a system can be obtained by multiplying both sides of another equation by a constant, the two equations are said to be **dependent**. Thus the equations in Example 4(c) are dependent, but those in Examples 4(a) and 4(b) are **independent**. For systems of three or more equations, the definitions of dependent and independent will be slightly modified.

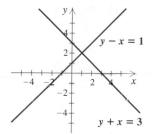

Graphs intersect at one point.
The system is *consistent* and has one solution. Since neither equation is a multiple of the other, they are *independent*.

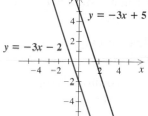

Graphs are parallel.
The system is *inconsistent* because there is no solution. Since the equations are not equivalent, they are *independent*.

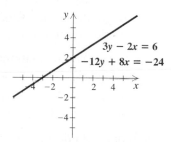

Equations have the same graph.
The system is *consistent* and has an infinite number of solutions. The equations are *dependent* since they are equivalent.

Graphing is helpful when solving systems because it allows us to "see" the solution. It can also be used on systems of nonlinear equations, and in many applications, it provides a satisfactory answer. However, graphing often lacks precision, especially when fraction or decimal solutions are involved. In Section 8.2, we will develop two algebraic methods of solving systems. Both methods produce exact answers.

Exercise Set

⮞ *Concept Reinforcement Classify each statement as either true or false.*

1. Solutions of systems of equations in two variables are ordered pairs.

2. Every system of equations has at least one solution.

3. It is possible for a system of equations to have an infinite number of solutions.

4. The graphs of the equations in a system of two equations may coincide.

5. The graphs of the equations in a system of two equations could be parallel lines.

6. Any system of equations that has at most one solution is said to be consistent.

7. Any system of equations that has more than one solution is said to be inconsistent.

8. If one equation in a system can be obtained by multiplying both sides of another equation in that system by a constant, the two equations are said to be dependent.

Determine whether the ordered pair is a solution of the given system of equations. Remember to use alphabetical order of variables.

9. $(1, 2)$; $4x - y = 2$,
  $10x - 3y = 4$

10. $(-1, -2)$; $2x + y = -4$,
  $x - y = 1$

11. $(2, 5)$; $y = 3x - 1$,
  $2x + y = 4$

12. $(-1, -2)$; $x + 3y = -7$,
  $3x - 2y = 12$

13. $(1, 5)$; $x + y = 6$,
  $y = 2x + 3$

14. $(5, 2)$; $a + b = 7$,
  $2a - 8 = b$

Aha! 15. $(3, 1)$; $3x + 4y = 13$,
  $6x + 8y = 26$

16. $(4, -2)$; $-3x - 2y = -8$,
  $8 = 3x + 2y$

Solve each system graphically. Be sure to check your solution. If a system has an infinite number of solutions, use set-builder notation to write the solution set. If a system has no solution, state this.

17. $x - y = 3$,
  $x + y = 5$

18. $x + y = 4$,
  $x - y = 2$

19. $3x + y = 5$,
  $x - 2y = 4$

20. $2x - y = 4$,
  $5x - y = 13$

21. $4y = x + 8$,
  $3x - 2y = 6$

22. $4x - y = 9$,
  $x - 3y = 16$

23. $x = y - 1$,
  $2x = 3y$

24. $a = 1 + b$,
  $b = 5 - 2a$

25. $x = -3$,
  $y = 2$

26. $x = 4$,
  $y = -5$

27. $t + 2s = -1$,
  $s = t + 10$

28. $b + 2a = 2$,
  $a = -3 - b$

29. $2b + a = 11$,
  $a - b = 5$

30. $y = -\frac{1}{3}x - 1$,
  $4x - 3y = 18$

31. $y = -\frac{1}{4}x + 1$,
  $2y = x - 4$

32. $6x - 2y = 2$,
  $9x - 3y = 1$

33. $y - x = 5$,
  $2x - 2y = 10$

34. $y = -x - 1$,
  $4x - 3y = 24$

35. $y = 3 - x$,
  $2x + 2y = 6$

36. $2x - 3y = 6$,
  $3y - 2x = -6$

37. For the systems in the odd-numbered exercises 17–35, which are consistent?

38. For the systems in the even-numbered exercises 18–36, which are consistent?

39. For the systems in the odd-numbered exercises 17–35, which contain dependent equations?

40. For the systems in the even-numbered exercises 18–36, which contain dependent equations?

Translate each problem situation to a system of equations. Do not attempt to solve, but save for later use.

41. The sum of two numbers is 50. The first number is 25% of the second number. What are the numbers?

42. The sum of two numbers is 40. The first number is 60% of the second number. What are the numbers?

43. *Nontoxic furniture polish.* A nontoxic wood furniture polish can be made by mixing mineral (or olive) oil with vinegar. To make a 16-oz batch for a squirt bottle, Mabel uses an amount of mineral oil that is 4 oz more than twice the amount of vinegar. How much of each ingredient is required?
Sources: Based on information from Chittenden Solid Waste District and *Clean House, Clean Planet* by Karen Logan

44. *Scholastic Aptitude Test.* Many high-school students take the Scholastic Aptitude Test. Each student receives two scores, a *verbal* score and a *math* score. In 2002–2003, the average total score of students was 1026, with the average math score exceeding the verbal score by 12 points. What was the average verbal score and what was the average math score?
Source: College Entrance Examination Board

45. *Geometry.* Two angles are supplementary.* One angle is 3° less than twice the other. Find the measures of the angles.

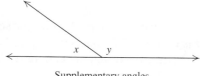

Supplementary angles

46. *Geometry.* Two angles are complementary.[†] The sum of the measures of the first angle and half the second angle is 64°. Find the measures of the angles.

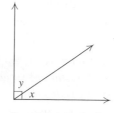

Complementary angles

47. *Basketball scoring.* Wilt Chamberlain once scored 100 points, setting a record for points scored in an NBA game. Chamberlain took only two-point shots and (one-point) foul shots and made a total of 64 shots. How many shots of each type did he make?

48. *Basketball scoring.* The Fenton College Cougars made 40 field goals in a recent basketball game, some 2-pointers and the rest 3-pointers. Altogether the 40 baskets counted for 89 points. How many of each type of field goal was made?

49. *Retail sales.* Paint Town sold 45 paintbrushes, one kind at $8.50 each and another at $9.75 each. In all, $398.75 was taken in for the brushes. How many of each kind were sold?

50. *Retail sales.* Mountainside Fleece sold 40 neckwarmers. Polarfleece neckwarmers sold for $9.90 each and wool ones sold for $12.75 each. In all, $421.65 was taken in for the neckwarmers. How many of each type were sold?

51. *Sales of pharmaceuticals.* In 2004, the Diabetic Express charged $27.06 for a vial of Humulin insulin and $34.39 for a vial of Novolin Velosulin insulin. If a total of $1565.57 was collected for 50 vials of insulin, how many vials of each type were sold?

52. *Fundraising.* The St. Mark's Community Barbecue served 250 dinners. A child's plate cost $3.50 and an adult's plate cost $7.00. A total of $1347.50 was collected. How many of each type of plate was served?

53. *Court dimensions.* The perimeter of a standard basketball court is 288 ft. The length is 44 ft longer than the width. Find the dimensions.

$P = 288$ ft

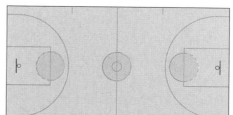

54. *Court dimensions.* The perimeter of a standard tennis court used for doubles is 228 ft. The width is 42 ft less than the length. Find the dimensions.

55. Write a problem for a classmate to solve that requires writing a system of two equations. Devise the problem so that the solution is "The Lakers made 6 three-point baskets and 31 two-point baskets."

---

*The sum of the measures of two supplementary angles is 180°.
[†]The sum of the measures of two complementary angles is 90°.

56. Write a problem for a classmate to solve that can be translated into a system of two equations. Devise the problem so that the solution is "Arnie took five 3-credit classes and two 4-credit classes."

SKILL MAINTENANCE

Solve. [2.2]

57. $2(4x - 3) - 7x = 9$ **58.** $6y - 3(5 - 2y) = 4$

59. $4x - 5x = 8x - 9 + 11x$

60. $8x - 2(5 - x) = 7x + 3$

Solve. [2.3]

61. $3x + 4y = 7$, for y

62. $2x - 5y = 9$, for y

SYNTHESIS

Presidential primaries. For Exercises 63 and 64, consider the following graph showing the results of a poll in which Iowans were asked which Democrat candidate for president they favored.

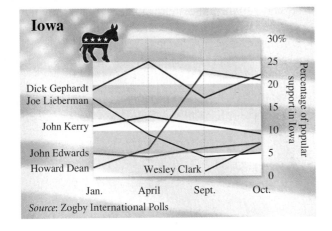

Iowa

Dick Gephardt
Joe Lieberman
John Kerry
John Edwards
Howard Dean
Wesley Clark

Jan.   April   Sept.   Oct.

Percentage of popular support in Iowa
30%
25
20
15
10
5
0

Source: Zogby International Polls

63. At what point in time could it have been said that no one was in fourth place? Explain.

64. At what point in time was there no clear leader? Explain how you reach this conclusion.

65. For each of the following conditions, write a system of equations.
  a) (5, 1) is a solution.
  b) There is no solution.
  c) There is an infinite number of solutions.

66. A system of linear equations has $(1, -1)$ and $(-2, 3)$ as solutions. Determine:
  a) a third point that is a solution, and
  b) how many solutions there are.

67. The solution of the following system is $(4, -5)$. Find A and B.
$$Ax - 6y = 13,$$
$$x - By = -8.$$

Translate to a system of equations. Do not solve.

68. *Ages.* Burl is twice as old as his son. Ten years ago, Burl was three times as old as his son. How old are they now?

69. *Work experience.* Lou and Juanita are mathematics professors at a state university. Together, they have 46 years of service. Two years ago, Lou had taught 2.5 times as many years as Juanita. How long has each taught at the university?

70. *Design.* A piece of posterboard has a perimeter of 156 in. If you cut 6 in. off the width, the length becomes four times the width. What are the dimensions of the original piece of posterboard?

$P = 156$ in.

71. *Nontoxic scouring powder.* A nontoxic scouring powder is made up of 4 parts baking soda and 1 part vinegar. How much of each ingredient is needed for a 16-oz mixture?

Solve graphically.

72. $y = |x|$,   **73.** $x - y = 0$,
      $x + 4y = 15$ $y = x^2$

In Exercises 74–77, use a graphing calculator to solve each system of linear equations for x and y. Round all coordinates to the nearest hundredth.

74. $y = 8.23x + 2.11$,   **75.** $y = -3.44x - 7.72$,
      $y = -9.11x - 4.66$ $y = 4.19x - 8.22$

76. $14.12x + 7.32y = 2.98$,
      $21.88x - 6.45y = -7.22$

77. $5.22x - 8.21y = -10.21$,
      $-12.67x + 10.34y = 12.84$

8.2 | Solving by Substitution or Elimination

The Substitution Method • The Elimination Method •
Comparing Methods

The Substitution Method

Algebraic (nongraphical) methods for solving systems are often superior to graphing, especially when fractions are involved. One algebraic method, the *substitution method*, relies on having a variable isolated.

EXAMPLE 1   Solve the system

$$x + y = 4, \quad (1)$$
$$x = y + 1. \quad (2)$$

For easy reference, we have numbered the equations.

Solution   Equation (2) says that x and $y + 1$ name the same number. Thus we can substitute $y + 1$ for x in equation (1):

$$x + y = 4 \qquad \text{Equation (1)}$$
$$(y + 1) + y = 4. \qquad \text{Substituting } y + 1 \text{ for } x$$

We solve this last equation, using methods learned earlier:

$$(y + 1) + y = 4$$
$$2y + 1 = 4 \qquad \text{Removing parentheses and combining like terms}$$
$$2y = 3 \qquad \text{Subtracting 1 from both sides}$$
$$y = \tfrac{3}{2}. \qquad \text{Dividing by 2}$$

We now return to the original pair of equations and substitute $\tfrac{3}{2}$ for y in either equation so that we can solve for x. For this problem, calculations are slightly easier if we use equation (2):

$$x = y + 1 \qquad \text{Equation (2)}$$
$$= \tfrac{3}{2} + 1 \qquad \text{Substituting } \tfrac{3}{2} \text{ for } y$$
$$= \tfrac{3}{2} + \tfrac{2}{2} = \tfrac{5}{2}.$$

We obtain the ordered pair $\left(\tfrac{5}{2}, \tfrac{3}{2}\right)$. A check ensures that it is a solution:

Check:

$$\begin{array}{c|c} x + y = 4 \\ \hline \tfrac{5}{2} + \tfrac{3}{2} & 4 \\ \tfrac{8}{2} \\ 4 \overset{?}{=} 4 & \text{TRUE} \end{array} \qquad \begin{array}{c|c} x = y + 1 \\ \hline \tfrac{5}{2} & \tfrac{3}{2} + 1 \\ & \tfrac{3}{2} + \tfrac{2}{2} \\ \tfrac{5}{2} \overset{?}{=} \tfrac{5}{2} & \text{TRUE} \end{array}$$

Since $\left(\tfrac{5}{2}, \tfrac{3}{2}\right)$ checks, it is the solution.

The exact solution to Example 1 is difficult to find graphically because it involves fractions. Despite this, the graph shown does serve as a check and provides a visualization of the problem.

Study Skills

Learn from Your Mistakes

Immediately after each quiz or test, write out a step-by-step solution to any questions you missed. Visit your professor during office hours or consult with a tutor for help with problems that are still giving you trouble. Misconceptions tend to resurface if they are not corrected as soon as possible.

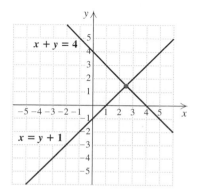

A visualization of Example 1.
Note that the coordinates of the intersection are not obvious.

If neither equation in a system has a variable alone on one side, we first isolate a variable in one equation and then substitute.

EXAMPLE 2   Solve the system

$$2x + y = 6, \quad (1)$$
$$3x + 4y = 4. \quad (2)$$

Solution   First, we select an equation and solve for one variable. To isolate y, we can subtract $2x$ from both sides of equation (1):

$$2x + y = 6 \quad (1)$$
$$y = 6 - 2x. \quad (3) \quad \text{Subtracting } 2x \text{ from both sides}$$

Next, we proceed as in Example 1, by substituting:

$$3x + 4(6 - 2x) = 4 \qquad \text{Substituting } 6 - 2x \text{ for } y \text{ in equation (2).}$$
$$\text{Use parentheses!}$$
$$3x + 24 - 8x = 4 \qquad \text{Distributing to remove parentheses}$$
$$3x - 8x = 4 - 24 \qquad \text{Subtracting 24 from both sides}$$
$$-5x = -20$$
$$x = 4. \qquad \text{Dividing both sides by } -5$$

A visualization of Example 2

Next, we substitute 4 for x in either equation (1), (2), or (3). It is easiest to use equation (3) because it has already been solved for y:

$$y = 6 - 2x$$
$$= 6 - 2(4)$$
$$= 6 - 8 = -2.$$

The pair $(4, -2)$ appears to be the solution. We check in equations (1) and (2).

Check:

$$\frac{2x + y = 6}{\begin{array}{c|c} 2(4) + (-2) & 6 \\ 8 - 2 & \\ & 6 \stackrel{?}{=} 6 \quad \text{TRUE} \end{array}}$$

$$\frac{3x + 4y = 4}{\begin{array}{c|c} 3(4) + 4(-2) & 4 \\ 12 - 8 & \\ & 4 \stackrel{?}{=} 4 \quad \text{TRUE} \end{array}}$$

Since $(4, -2)$ checks, it is the solution.

Some systems have no solution, as we saw graphically in Section 8.1. How do we recognize such systems if we are solving by an algebraic method?

EXAMPLE 3   Solve the system

$$y = -3x + 5, \quad (1)$$
$$y = -3x - 2. \quad (2)$$

Solution   We solved this system graphically in Example 4(b) of Section 8.1, and found that the lines are parallel and the system has no solution. Let's now

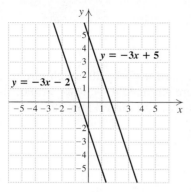

A visualization of Example 3

try to solve the system by substitution. Proceeding as in Example 1, we substitute $-3x - 2$ for y in the first equation:

$$-3x - 2 = -3x + 5 \qquad \text{Substituting } -3x - 2 \text{ for } y \text{ in equation (1)}$$

$$-2 = 5. \qquad \text{Adding } 3x \text{ to both sides; } -2 = 5 \text{ is a contradiction.}$$

When we add $3x$ to get the x-terms on one side, the x-terms drop out and the result is a contradiction—an equation that is always false. When solving algebraically yields a contradiction, we state that the system has no solution.

The Elimination Method

The *elimination method* for solving systems of equations makes use of the *addition principle*: If $a = b$, then $a + c = b + c$. Consider the following system:

$$2x - 3y = 0, \qquad (1)$$
$$-4x + 3y = -1. \qquad (2)$$

To see why the elimination method works well with this system, notice the $-3y$ in one equation and the $3y$ in the other. These terms are opposites. If we add all terms on the left side of the equations, the sum of $-3y$ and $3y$ is 0, so in effect, the variable y is "eliminated."

To use the addition principle with a system, note that according to equation (2), $-4x + 3y$ and -1 are the same number. Thus we can work vertically and add $-4x + 3y$ to the left side of equation (1) and -1 to the right side:

$$\begin{array}{ll} 2x - 3y = 0 & (1) \\ \underline{-4x + 3y = -1} & (2) \\ -2x + 0y = -1. & \text{Adding} \end{array}$$

This eliminates the variable y, and leaves an equation with just one variable, x, for which we solve:

$$-2x = -1$$
$$x = \tfrac{1}{2}.$$

Next, we substitute $\tfrac{1}{2}$ for x in equation (1) and solve for y:

$$2 \cdot \tfrac{1}{2} - 3y = 0 \qquad \text{Substituting. We also could have used equation (2).}$$
$$1 - 3y = 0$$
$$-3y = -1, \text{ so } y = \tfrac{1}{3}.$$

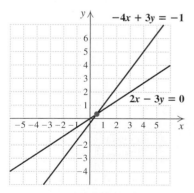

A visualization of the solution of
$$2x - 3y = 0,$$
$$-4x + 3y = -1$$

Check:

$$\begin{array}{c|c} 2x - 3y = 0 & \\ \hline 2\left(\tfrac{1}{2}\right) - 3\left(\tfrac{1}{3}\right) & 0 \\ 1 - 1 & \\ 0 \overset{?}{=} 0 & \text{TRUE} \end{array} \qquad \begin{array}{c|c} -4x + 3y = -1 & \\ \hline -4\left(\tfrac{1}{2}\right) + 3\left(\tfrac{1}{3}\right) & -1 \\ -2 + 1 & \\ -1 \overset{?}{=} -1 & \text{TRUE} \end{array}$$

Since $\left(\tfrac{1}{2}, \tfrac{1}{3}\right)$ checks, it is the solution. See also the graph at left.

To eliminate a variable, we must sometimes multiply before adding.

EXAMPLE 4   Solve the system

$$5x + 4y = 22, \qquad (1)$$
$$-3x + 8y = 18. \qquad (2)$$

Solution   If we add the left sides of the two equations, we will not eliminate a variable. However, if the $4y$ in equation (1) were changed to $-8y$, we would. To accomplish this change, we multiply both sides of equation (1) by -2:

$$
\begin{array}{ll}
-10x - 8y = -44 & \text{Multiplying both sides of equation (1) by } -2 \\
\underline{-3x + 8y = \quad 18} & \\
-13x + \quad 0 = -26 & \text{Adding} \\
\qquad\quad x = 2. & \text{Solving for } x
\end{array}
$$

Then

$$
\begin{array}{ll}
-3 \cdot 2 + 8y = 18 & \text{Substituting 2 for } x \text{ in equation (2)} \\
\quad -6 + 8y = 18 & \\
\qquad\left.\begin{array}{l} 8y = 24 \\ \; y = 3. \end{array}\right\} & \text{Solving for } y
\end{array}
$$

Student Notes

It is wise to double-check each step of your work as you go along, rather than checking all steps after reaching the end of a problem. Finding and correcting an error as it occurs will save you time in the long run. One common error is to forget to multiply *both* sides of the equation when you use the multiplication principle.

We obtain $(2, 3)$, or $x = 2$, $y = 3$. We leave it to the student to confirm that this checks and is the solution.

Sometimes we must multiply twice in order to make two terms become opposites.

EXAMPLE 5   Solve the system

$$2x + 3y = 17, \qquad (1)$$
$$5x + 7y = 29. \qquad (2)$$

Solution   We multiply so that the x-terms are eliminated.

$$
\begin{array}{l}
2x + 3y = 17, \quad\xrightarrow[\text{sides by 5}]{\text{Multiplying both}}\quad 10x + 15y = \quad 85 \\[1em]
5x + 7y = 29 \quad\xrightarrow[\text{sides by} -2]{\text{Multiplying both}}\quad \underline{-10x - 14y = -58} \\[0.5em]
\qquad\qquad\qquad\qquad\qquad\qquad\qquad 0 + \; y = \quad 27 \qquad \text{Adding} \\
\qquad\qquad\qquad\qquad\qquad\qquad\qquad\qquad\quad y = \quad 27
\end{array}
$$

Next, we substitute to find x:

$$
\begin{array}{ll}
2x + 3 \cdot 27 = 17 & \text{Substituting 27 for } y \text{ in equation (1)} \\
\quad 2x + 81 = 17 & \\
\qquad\left.\begin{array}{l} 2x = -64 \\ \; x = -32. \end{array}\right\} & \text{Solving for } x
\end{array}
$$

Check:

$$
\begin{array}{c|c}
\underline{\quad 2x + 3y = 17 \quad} & \\
2(-32) + 3(27) \;\big|\; 17 & \\
\quad -64 + 81 \;\big|\; & \\
\qquad 17 \overset{?}{=} 17 \quad \text{TRUE} &
\end{array}
\qquad
\begin{array}{c|c}
\underline{\quad 5x + 7y = 29 \quad} & \\
5(-32) + 7(27) \;\big|\; 29 & \\
\quad -160 + 189 \;\big|\; & \\
\qquad 29 \overset{?}{=} 29 \quad \text{TRUE} &
\end{array}
$$

We obtain $(-32, 27)$, or $x = -32$, $y = 27$, as the solution.

EXAMPLE 6

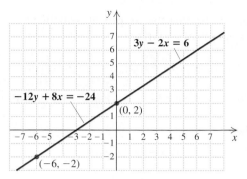

A visualization of Example 6

Solve the system

$$3y - 2x = 6, \qquad (1)$$
$$-12y + 8x = -24. \qquad (2)$$

Solution   We graphed this system in Example 4(c) of Section 8.1, and found that the lines coincide and the system has an infinite number of solutions. Suppose we were to solve this system using the elimination method:

$$12y - 8x = 24 \qquad \text{Multiplying both sides of equation (1) by 4}$$
$$\underline{-12y + 8x = -24}$$
$$0 = 0. \qquad \text{We obtain an identity; } 0 = 0 \text{ is always true.}$$

Note that both variables have been eliminated and what remains is an identity—that is, an equation that is always true. Any pair that is a solution of equation (1) is also a solution of equation (2). The equations are dependent and the solution set is infinite:

$$\{(x, y) \mid 3y - 2x = 6\}, \quad \text{or equivalently,} \quad \{(x, y) \mid -12y + 8x = -24\}.$$

Rules for Special Cases

When solving a system of two linear equations in two variables:

1. If an identity is obtained, such as $0 = 0$, then the system has an infinite number of solutions. The equations are dependent and, since a solution exists, the system is consistent.*
2. If a contradiction is obtained, such as $0 = 7$, then the system has no solution. The system is inconsistent.

Should decimals or fractions appear, it often helps to *clear* before solving.

EXAMPLE 7

Solve the system

$$0.2x + 0.3y = 1.7,$$
$$\tfrac{1}{7}x + \tfrac{1}{5}y = \tfrac{29}{35}.$$

Solution   We have

$$0.2x + 0.3y = 1.7, \rightarrow \text{Multiplying both sides by } 10 \rightarrow 2x + 3y = 17$$
$$\tfrac{1}{7}x + \tfrac{1}{5}y = \tfrac{29}{35} \rightarrow \text{Multiplying both sides by } 35 \rightarrow 5x + 7y = 29.$$

We multiplied both sides of the first equation by 10 to clear the decimals. Multiplication by 35, the least common denominator, clears the fractions in the second equation. The problem now happens to be identical to Example 5. The solution is $(-32, 27)$, or $x = -32, y = 27$.

---

*Consistent systems and dependent equations are discussed in greater detail in Section 8.4.

Comparing Methods

The following table is a summary that compares the graphical, substitution, and elimination methods for solving systems of equations.

CONNECTING THE CONCEPTS

We now have three different methods for solving systems of equations. Each method has certain strengths and weaknesses, as outlined below.

Method	Strengths	Weaknesses
Graphical	Solutions are displayed graphically. Can be used with any system that can be graphed.	Inexact when solutions involve numbers that are not integers. Solution may not appear on the part of the graph drawn.
Substitution	Yields exact solutions. Easy to use when a variable is alone on one side.	Introduces extensive computations with fractions when solving more complicated systems. Solutions are not displayed graphically.
Elimination	Yields exact solutions. Easy to use when fractions or decimals appear in the system. The preferred method for systems of 3 or more equations in 3 or more variables (see Section 8.4).	Solutions are not displayed graphically.

Before selecting a method to use, try to remember the strengths and weaknesses of each method. If possible, begin solving the system mentally to help discover the method that seems best suited for that particular system. Selecting the "best" method for a problem is a bit like selecting one of three different saws with which to cut a piece of wood. The "best" choice depends on what kind of wood is being cut and what type of cut is being made, as well as your skill level with each saw.

Note that each of the three methods was introduced using a rather simple example. As the examples became more complicated, additional steps were required in order to "turn" the new problem into a more familiar format. This is a common approach in mathematics: We perform one or more steps to make a "new" problem resemble a problem we already know how to solve.

Exercise Set

8.2

FOR EXTRA HELP

| Student's Solutions Manual | Digital Video Tutor CD 4 Videotape 8 | AW Math Tutor Center | MathXL Tutorials on CD | Math XL MathXL | MyMathLab MyMathLab |

👉 *Concept Reinforcement*   *In each of Exercises 1–6, match the system listed with the choice from the column on the right that would be a subsequent step in solving the system.*

1. _____ $-2x + 3y = 7,$
$2x + 5y = -8$

2. _____ $x = 4y - 5,$
$5x + 7y = 2$

3. _____ $3x + 4y = 13,$
$4x - 2y = 5$

4. _____ $8x + 6y = -15,$
$5x - 3y = 8$

5. _____ $y = 4x - 7,$
$6x + 3y = 19$

6. _____ $y = \frac{2}{3}x + 4,$
$y = -\frac{1}{5}x + 4$

a) $3x + 4y = 13,$
$8x - 4y = 10$

b) The lines intersect at $(0, 4)$.

c) $6x + 3(4x - 7) = 19$

d) $8y = -1$

e) $5(4y - 5) + 7y = 2$

f) $8x + 6y = -15,$
$10x - 6y = 16$

For Exercises 7–54, if a system has an infinite number of solutions, use set-builder notation to write the solution set. If a system has no solution, state this.

Solve using the substitution method.

7. $y = 5 - 4x,$
$2x - 3y = 13$

8. $2y + x = 9,$
$x = 3y - 3$

9. $3x + 5y = 3,$
$x = 8 - 4y$

10. $9x - 2y = 3,$
$3x - 6 = y$

11. $3s - 4t = 14,$
$5s + t = 8$

12. $m - 2n = 16,$
$4m + n = 1$

13. $4x - 2y = 6,$
$2x - 3 = y$

14. $t = 4 - 2s,$
$t + 2s = 6$

15. $-5s + t = 11,$
$4s + 12t = 4$

16. $5x + 6y = 14,$
$-3y + x = 7$

17. $2x + 2y = 2,$
$3x - y = 1$

18. $4p - 2q = 16,$
$5p + 7q = 1$

19. $x - 4y = 3,$
$5x + 3y = 4$

20. $2a + 2b = 5,$
$3a - b = 7$

21. $2x - 3 = y,$
$y - 2x = 1$

22. $a - 2b = 3,$
$3a = 6b + 9$

Solve using the elimination method.

23. $x + 3y = 7,$
$-x + 4y = 7$

24. $2x + y = 6,$
$x - y = 3$

25. $2x - y = -3,$
$x + y = 9$

26. $x - 2y = 6,$
$-x + 3y = -4$

27. $9x + 3y = -3,$
$2x - 3y = -8$

28. $6x - 3y = 18,$
$6x + 3y = -12$

29. $5x + 3y = 19,$
$2x - 5y = 11$

30. $3x + 2y = 3,$
$9x - 8y = -2$

31. $5r - 3s = 24,$
$3r + 5s = 28$

32. $5x - 7y = -16,$
$2x + 8y = 26$

33. $6s + 9t = 12,$
$4s + 6t = 5$

34. $10a + 6b = 8,$
$5a + 3b = 2$

35. $\frac{1}{2}x - \frac{1}{6}y = 3,$
$\frac{2}{5}x + \frac{1}{2}y = 2$

36. $\frac{1}{3}x + \frac{1}{5}y = 7,$
$\frac{1}{6}x - \frac{2}{5}y = -4$

37. $\frac{x}{2} + \frac{y}{3} = \frac{7}{6},$
$\frac{2x}{3} + \frac{3y}{4} = \frac{5}{4}$

38. $\frac{2x}{3} + \frac{3y}{4} = \frac{11}{12},$
$\frac{x}{3} + \frac{7y}{18} = \frac{1}{2}$

Aha! **39.** $12x - 6y = -15,$
$-4x + 2y = 5$

40. $8s + 12t = 16,$
$6s + 9t = 12$

41. $0.2a + 0.3b = 1,$
$0.3a - 0.2b = 4$

42. $-0.4x + 0.7y = 1.3,$
$0.7x - 0.3y = 0.5$

Solve using any appropriate method.

43. $a - 2b = 16,$
$b + 3 = 3a$

44. $5x - 9y = 7,$
$7y - 3x = -5$

45. $10x + y = 306,$
$10y + x = 90$

46. $3(a - b) = 15,$
$4a = b + 1$

47. $3y = x - 2,$
$x = 2 + 3y$

48. $x + 2y = 8,$
$x = 4 - 2y$

49. $3s - 7t = 5,$
$7t - 3s = 8$

50. $2s - 13t = 120,$
$-14s + 91t = -840$

51. $0.05x + 0.25y = 22,$
$0.15x + 0.05y = 24$

52. $2.1x - 0.9y = 15,$
$-1.4x + 0.6y = 10$

53. $13a - 7b = 9,$
$2a - 8b = 6$

54. $3a - 12b = 9,$
$14a - 11b = 5$

55. Describe a procedure that can be used to write an inconsistent system of equations.

56. Describe a procedure that can be used to write a system that has an infinite number of solutions.

SKILL MAINTENANCE

Solve. [2.5]

57. The fare for a taxi ride from Johnson Street to Elm Street is \$5.20. If the rate of the taxi is \$1.00 for the first $\frac{1}{2}$ mi and 30¢ for each additional $\frac{1}{4}$ mi, how far is it from Johnson Street to Elm Street?

58. A student's average after 4 tests is 78.5. What score is needed on the fifth test in order to raise the average to 80?

59. *Home remodeling.* In a recent year, Americans spent \$35 billion to remodel bathrooms and kitchens. Twice as much was spent on kitchens as on bathrooms. How much was spent on each?
Source: *Indianapolis Star*

60. A 480-m wire is cut into three pieces. The second piece is three times as long as the first. The third is four times as long as the second. How long is each piece?

61. *Car rentals.* Badger Rent-A-Car rents a compact car at a daily rate of \$34.95 plus 10¢ per mile. A sales representative is allotted \$80 for car rental for one day. How many miles can she travel on the \$80 budget?

62. *Car rentals.* Badger rents midsized cars at a rate of \$43.95 plus 10¢ per mile. A tourist has a car-rental budget of \$90 for one day. How many miles can he travel on the \$90?

SYNTHESIS

63. Some systems are more easily solved by substitution and some are more easily solved by elimination. What guidelines could be used to help someone determine which method to use?

64. Explain how it is possible to solve Exercise 39 mentally.

65. If $(1, 2)$ and $(-3, 4)$ are two solutions of $f(x) = mx + b$, find m and b.

66. If $(0, -3)$ and $\left(-\frac{3}{2}, 6\right)$ are two solutions of $px - qy = -1$, find p and q.

67. Determine a and b for which $(-4, -3)$ is a solution of the system
$$ax + by = -26,$$
$$bx - ay = 7.$$

68. Solve for x and y in terms of a and b:
$$5x + 2y = a,$$
$$x - y = b.$$

Solve.

69. $\dfrac{x + y}{2} - \dfrac{x - y}{5} = 1,$
$\dfrac{x - y}{2} + \dfrac{x + y}{6} = -2$

70. $3.5x - 2.1y = 106.2,$
$4.1x + 16.7y = -106.28$

Each of the following is a system of nonlinear equations. However, each is reducible to linear, *since an appropriate substitution (say, u for 1/x and v for 1/y) yields a linear system. Make such a substitution, solve for the new variables, and then solve for the original variables.*

71. $\dfrac{2}{x} + \dfrac{1}{y} = 0,$
$\dfrac{5}{x} + \dfrac{2}{y} = -5$

72. $\dfrac{1}{x} - \dfrac{3}{y} = 2,$
$\dfrac{6}{x} + \dfrac{5}{y} = -34$

73. A student solving the system
$$17x + 19y = 102,$$
$$136x + 152y = 826$$
graphs both equations on a graphing calculator and gets the following screen. The student then (incorrectly) concludes that the equations are dependent and the solution set is infinite. How can algebra be used to convince the student that a mistake has been made?

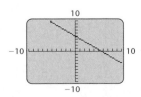

COLLABORATIVE

CORNER

How Many Two's? How Many Three's?

Focus: Systems of linear equations

Time: 20 minutes

Group size: 3

The box score at right, from the 2004 NBA All-Star game, contains information on how many field goals and free throws each player attempted and made. For example, the line "Kidd 4-6 3-4 14" means that the East's Jason Kidd made 4 field goals out of 6 attempts and 3 free throws out of 4 attempts, for a total of 14 points. (Each free throw is worth 1 point and each field goal is worth either 2 or 3 points, depending on how far from the basket it was shot.)

ACTIVITY

1. Work as a group to develop a system of two equations in two unknowns that can be used to determine how many 2-pointers and how many 3-pointers were made by the West.
2. Each group member should solve the system from part (1) in a different way: one person

algebraically, one person by making a table and methodically checking all combinations of 2- and 3-pointers, and one person by guesswork. Compare answers when this has been completed.

3. Determine, as a group, how many 2- and 3-pointers the East made.

East (132)
Iverson 1-6 1-4 3, McGrady 5-11 2-4 13, J.O'Neal 7-13 2-4 16, Carter 5-7 0-0 11, Wallace 2-5 0-0 4, Martin 8-10 1-2 17, Kidd 4-6 3-4 14, Magloire 9-16 1-2 19, Artest 3-5 1-2 7, Davis 3-9 0-0 7, Redd 5-12 0-0 13, Pierce 4-8 0-0 8
Totals 56-108 11-22 132

West (136)
Bryant 9-12 0-1 20, Francis 6-9 0-0 13, Garnett 6-14 0-0 12, Duncan 6-11 2-4 14, Yao Ming 8-14 0-0 16, S.O'Neal 12-19 0-1 24, Allen 6-13 3-4 16, Cassell 2-3 0-0 4, Nowitzki 1-3 0-0 4, Stojakovic 2-5 0-0 5, Kirilenko 1-3 0-0 2, Brad Miller 4-5 0-0 8
Totals 63-111 5-10 136

| East | 33 | 31 | 37 | 31 | — | 132 |
| West | 31 | 27 | 45 | 33 | — | 136 |

8.3   Solving Applications: Systems of Two Equations

Total-Value and Mixture Problems   •   Motion Problems

You are in a much better position to solve problems now that you know how systems of equations can be used. Using systems often makes the translating step easier.

EXAMPLE 1   Bottled-water consumption.   Americans are buying more bottled water than ever before. At the time of this writing, the average American buys more bottled water than milk, coffee, or beer. In 2003, the average American purchased 76.4 gal of soft drinks and water. The amount of water was only 4.3 gal less than

Study Skills _____

Expect to be Challenged

Do not be surprised if your success rate drops some as you work on real-world problems. *This is normal.* Your success rate will increase as you gain experience with these types of problems and use some of the study skills already listed.

half of the amount of soft drinks. (*Source*: Based on data from www.beveragemarketing.com) How many gallons of water and how many of soft drinks did the average American buy in 2003?

Solution   The *Familiarize* and *Translate* steps have been done in Example 1 of Section 8.1. The resulting system of equations is

$$w + s = 76.4,$$
$$w = \frac{1}{2}s - 4.3,$$

where w is the number of gallons of water and s is the number of gallons of soft drinks purchased by the average American in 2003.

3. **Carry out.**   We solve the system of equations. Since one equation already has a variable isolated, let's use the substitution method:

$$w + s = 76.4$$

$$\frac{1}{2}s - 4.3 + s = 76.4 \qquad \text{Substituting } \frac{1}{2}s - 4.3 \text{ for } w$$

$$\frac{3}{2}s - 4.3 = 76.4 \qquad \text{Combining like terms}$$

$$\frac{3}{2}s = 80.7 \qquad \text{Adding 4.3 to both sides}$$

$$s = \frac{2}{3} \cdot 80.7 \qquad \text{Multiplying both sides by } \frac{2}{3}: \frac{2}{3} \cdot \frac{3}{2} = 1$$

$$s = 53.8. \qquad \text{Simplifying}$$

Next, using either of the original equations, we substitute and solve for w:

Student Notes _____

It is very important that you clearly label precisely what each variable represents. Not only will this assist you in writing equations, but it will help you to identify and state solutions.

$$w = \frac{1}{2} \cdot 53.8 - 4.3 = 26.9 - 4.3 = 22.6.$$

4. **Check.**   The sum of 53.8 and 22.6 is 76.4, so the total consumed is correct. Since 4.3 less than half of 53.8 is 26.9 − 4.3, or 22.6, the numbers check.

5. **State.**   In 2003, the average American purchased 22.6 gal of bottled water and 53.8 gal of soft drinks.

Total-Value and Mixture Problems

EXAMPLE 2

Purchasing.   Recently the Woods County Art Center purchased 120 stamps for $33.90. If the stamps were a combination of 23¢ postcard stamps and 37¢ first-class stamps, how many of each type were bought?

Solution   The *Familiarize* and *Translate* steps were completed in Example 2 of Section 8.1.

3. **Carry out.**   We are to solve the system of equations

$$p + f = 120, \qquad (1)$$
$$23p + 37f = 3390, \qquad (2) \qquad \text{Working in cents rather than dollars}$$

where p is the number of postcard stamps bought and f is the number of first-class stamps bought. Because both equations are in the form

$Ax + By = C$, let's use the elimination method to solve the system. We can eliminate p by multiplying both sides of equation (1) by -23 and adding them to the corresponding sides of equation (2):

$$-23p - 23f = -2760 \qquad \text{Multiplying both sides of equation (1) by } -23$$
$$\underline{23p + 37f = 3390}$$
$$14f = 630 \qquad \text{Adding}$$
$$f = 45. \qquad \text{Solving for } f$$

To find p, we substitute 45 for f in equation (1) and then solve for p:

$$p + f = 120 \qquad \text{Equation (1)}$$
$$p + 45 = 120 \qquad \text{Substituting 45 for } f$$
$$p = 75. \qquad \text{Solving for } p$$

We obtain (45, 75), or $f = 45$ and $p = 75$.

4. Check. We check in the original problem. Recall that f is the number of first-class stamps and p the number of postcard stamps.

Number of stamps: $f + p = 45 + 75 = 120$

Cost of first-class stamps: $\$0.37f = 0.37 \times 45 = \$16.65$

Cost of postcard stamps: $\$0.23p = 0.23 \times 75 = \underline{\$17.25}$

$$\text{Total} = \$33.90$$

The numbers check.

5. State. The art center bought 45 first-class stamps and 75 postcard stamps.

Example 2 involved two types of items (first-class stamps and postcard stamps), the quantity of each type bought, and the total value of the items. We refer to this type of problem as a *total-value problem*.

EXAMPLE 3   Blending teas.   Sonya's House of Tea sells loose Lapsang Souchong tea for 95¢ an ounce and Assam Gingia for $1.43 an ounce. Sonya wants to make a 20-oz mixture of the two types, called Dragon Blend, that sells for $1.10 an ounce. How much tea of each type should Sonya use?

Solution

1. Familiarize. This problem is similar to Example 2. Rather than postcard stamps and first-class stamps, we have ounces of Assam Gingia and ounces of Lapsang Souchong. Instead of a different price for each type of stamp, we have a different price per ounce for each type of tea. Finally, rather than knowing the total cost of the stamps, we know the weight and the price per ounce of the mixture. Thus we can find the total value of the blend by multiplying 20 ounces times $1.10, or 110¢ per ounce. Although we could make and check a guess, we proceed to let $l = $ the number of ounces of Lapsang Souchong and $a = $ the number of ounces of Assam Gingia.

2. **Translate.**   Since a 20-oz batch is being made, we must have

$$l + a = 20.$$

To find a second equation, note that the total value of the 20-oz blend must match the combined value of the separate ingredients:

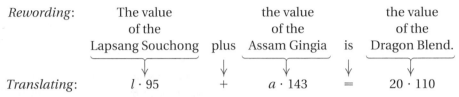

Rewording:	The value of the Lapsang Souchong	plus	the value of the Assam Gingia	is	the value of the Dragon Blend.
Translating:	$l \cdot 95$	$+$	$a \cdot 143$	$=$	$20 \cdot 110$

These equations can also be obtained from a table.

	Lapsang Souchong	**Assam Gingia**	**Dragon Blend**	
Number of Ounces	l	a	20	→ $l + a = 20$
Price per Ounce	95¢	143¢	110¢	
Value of Tea	$95l$	$143a$	$20 \cdot 110$, or 2200¢	→ $95l + 143a = 2200$

We have translated to a system of equations:

$$l + \quad a = 20, \qquad (1)$$
$$95l + 143a = 2200. \qquad (2)$$

3. **Carry out.**   We can solve using substitution. When equation (1) is solved for l, we have $l = 20 - a$. Substituting $20 - a$ for l in equation (2), we find a:

$95(20 - a) + 143a = 2200$	Substituting
$1900 - 95a + 143a = 2200$	Using the distributive law
$48a = 300$	Combining like terms; subtracting 1900 from both sides
$a = 6.25.$	Dividing both sides by 48

We have $a = 6.25$ and, from equation (1) above, $l + a = 20$. Thus, $l = 13.75$.

4. **Check.**   If 13.75 oz of Lapsang Souchong and 6.25 oz of Assam Gingia are combined, a 20-oz blend will result. The value of 13.75 oz of Lapsang Souchong is 13.75(95¢) or 1306.25¢. The value of 6.25 oz of Assam Gingia is 6.25(143¢), or 893.75¢. Thus the combined value of the blend is 1306.25¢ + 893.75¢, or 2200¢, which is $22. A 20-oz blend priced at $1.10 an ounce would also be worth $22, so our answer checks.

5. **State.**   The Dragon Blend should be made by combining 13.75 oz of Lapsang Souchong with 6.25 oz of Assam Gingia.

EXAMPLE 4   Student loans.   Ranjay's student loans totaled $9600. Part was a Perkins loan made at 5% interest and the rest was a Stafford Loan made at 8% interest. After one year, Ranjay's loans accumulated $633 in interest. What was the original amount of each loan?

Solution

1. **Familiarize.** We begin with a guess. If $7000 was borrowed at 5% and $2600 was borrowed at 8%, the two loans would total $9600. The interest would then be 0.05($7000), or $350, and 0.08($2600), or $208, for a total of only $558 in interest. Our guess was wrong, but checking the guess familiarized us with the problem. More than $2600 was borrowed at the higher rate.

2. **Translate.** We let p = the amount of the Perkins loan and f = the amount of the Stafford Loan. Next, we organize a table in which the entries in each column come from the formula for simple interest:

$$Principal \cdot Rate \cdot Time = Interest.$$

	Perkins Loan	Stafford Loan	Total	
Principal	p	f	$9600	→ $p + f = 9600$
Rate of Interest	5%	8%		
Time	1 yr	1 yr		
Interest	$0.05p$	$0.08f$	$633	→ $0.05p + 0.08f = 633$

The total amount borrowed is found in the first row of the table:

$$p + f = 9600.$$

A second equation, representing the accumulated interest, can be found in the last row:

$$0.05p + 0.08f = 633, \quad or \quad 5p + 8f = 63{,}300. \qquad Clearing\ decimals$$

3. **Carry out.** The system can be solved by elimination:

$$
\begin{array}{ll}
p + f = 9600, \\
5p + 8f = 63{,}300.
\end{array}
\quad
\begin{array}{c}
\longrightarrow Multiplying\ both \longrightarrow \\
sides\ by\ -5
\end{array}
\quad
\begin{array}{l}
-5p - 5f = -48{,}000 \\
\underline{5p + 8f = 63{,}300} \\
3f = 15{,}300
\end{array}
$$

$$p + f = 9600 \longleftarrow f = 5100$$
$$p + 5100 = 9600$$
$$p = 4500.$$

We find that $p = 4500$ and $f = 5100$.

4. **Check.** The total amount borrowed is $4500 + $5100, or $9600. The interest on $4500 at 5% for 1 yr is 0.05($4500), or $225. The interest on $5100 at 8% for 1 yr is 0.08($5100), or $408. The total amount of interest is $225 + $408, or $633, so the numbers check.

5. **State.**   The Perkins loan was for $4500 and the Stafford loan was for $5100.

Before proceeding to Example 5, briefly scan Examples 2–4 for similarities. Note that in each case, one of the equations in the system is a simple sum while the other equation represents a sum of products. Example 5 continues this pattern with what is commonly called a *mixture problem*.

Problem-Solving Tip

When solving a problem, see if it is patterned or modeled after a problem that you have already solved.

EXAMPLE 5   Mixing fertilizers.   Sky Meadow Gardening, Inc., carries two brands of fertilizer containing nitrogen and water. "Gently Green" is 5% nitrogen and "Sun Saver" is 15% nitrogen. Sky Meadow Gardening needs to combine the two types of solutions in order to make 90 L of a solution that is 12% nitrogen. How much of each brand should be used?

Solution

1. **Familiarize.**   We make a drawing and then make a guess to gain familiarity with the problem.

Suppose that 40 L of Gently Green and 50 L of Sun Saver are mixed. The resulting mixture will be the right size, 90 L, but will it be the right strength? To find out, note that 40 L of Gently Green would contribute $0.05(40) = 2$ L of nitrogen to the mixture while 50 L of Sun Saver would contribute $0.15(50) = 7.5$ L of nitrogen to the mixture. The total amount of nitrogen in the mixture would then be $2 + 7.5$, or 9.5 L. But we want 12% of 90, or 10.8 L, to be nitrogen. Thus our guess of 40 L and 50 L is incorrect. Still, checking our guess has familiarized us with the problem.

2. **Translate.**   Let g = the number of liters of Gently Green and s = the number of liters of Sun Saver. The information can be organized in a table.

	Gently Green	Sun Saver	Mixture	
Number of Liters	g	s	90	→ $g + s = 90$
Percent of Nitrogen	5%	15%	12%	
Amount of Nitrogen	$0.05g$	$0.15s$	0.12×90, or 10.8 liters	→ $0.05g + 0.15s = 10.8$

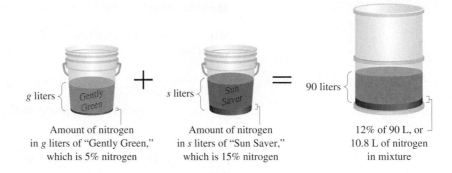

Amount of nitrogen in *g* liters of "Gently Green," which is 5% nitrogen	Amount of nitrogen in *s* liters of "Sun Saver," which is 15% nitrogen	12% of 90 L, or 10.8 L of nitrogen in mixture

If we add *g* and *s* in the first row, we get one equation. It represents the total amount of mixture: $g + s = 90$.

If we add the amounts of nitrogen listed in the third row, we get a second equation. This equation represents the amount of nitrogen in the mixture: $0.05g + 0.15s = 10.8$.

After clearing decimals, we have translated the problem to the system

$$g + s = 90 \qquad (1)$$
$$5g + 15s = 1080. \qquad (2)$$

3. Carry out.   We use the elimination method to solve the system:

$-5g - 5s = -450$	Multiplying both sides of
$\underline{5g + 15s = 1080}$	equation (1) by -5
$10s = 630$	Adding
$s = 63;$	Solving for *s*
$g + 63 = 90$	Substituting into equation (1)
$g = 27.$	Solving for *g*

4. Check.   Remember, *g* is the number of liters of Gently Green and *s* is the number of liters of Sun Saver.

Total amount of mixture: $g + s = 27 + 63 = 90$

Total amount of nitrogen: 5% of 27 + 15% of 63 = 1.35 + 9.45 = 10.8

Percentage of nitrogen in mixture: $\dfrac{\text{Total amount of nitrogen}}{\text{Total amount of mixture}} = \dfrac{10.8}{90} = 12\%$

The numbers check in the original problem.

5. State.   Sky Meadow Gardening should mix 27 L of Gently Green with 63 L of Sun Saver.

Motion Problems

When a problem deals with distance, speed (rate), and time, recall the following.

Distance, Rate, and Time Equations

If r represents rate, t represents time, and d represents distance, then:

$$d = rt, \qquad r = \frac{d}{t}, \quad \text{and} \quad t = \frac{d}{r}.$$

Be sure to remember at least one of these equations. The others can be obtained by multiplying or dividing on both sides as needed.

EXAMPLE 6   Train travel.   A Vermont Railways freight train, loaded with logs, leaves Boston, heading to Washington D.C. at a speed of 60 km/h. Two hours later, an Amtrak® Metroliner leaves Boston, bound for Washington D.C., on a parallel track at 90 km/h. At what point will the Metroliner catch up to the freight train?

Solution

1. **Familiarize.**   Let's make a guess—say, 180 km—and check to see if it is correct. The freight train, traveling 60 km/h, would travel 180 km in $\frac{180}{60} = 3$ hr. The Metroliner, traveling 90 km/h, would cover 180 km in $\frac{180}{90} = 2$ hr. Since 3 hr is *not* two hours more than 2 hr, our guess of 180 km is incorrect. Although our guess is wrong, we see that the time that the trains are running and the point at which they meet are both unknown. We let $t = $ the number of hours that the freight train is running before they meet and $d = $ the distance at which the trains meet. Since the freight train has a 2-hr head start, the Metroliner runs for $t - 2$ hours before catching up to the freight train, at which point both trains have traveled the same distance.

60 km/h
d kilometers
t hours

90 km/h
d kilometers
t − 2 hours

Trains meet here

2. **Translate.**   We can organize the information in a chart. Each row is determined by the formula *Distance = Rate · Time*.

	Distance	Rate	Time	
Freight Train	d	60	t	→$d = 60t$
Metroliner	d	90	$t - 2$	→$d = 90(t - 2)$

Using *Distance = Rate · Time* twice, we get two equations:

$$d = 60t, \qquad (1)$$
$$d = 90(t - 2). \qquad (2)$$

3. Carry out. We solve the system using substitution:

$$60t = 90(t - 2) \qquad \text{Substituting } 60t \text{ for } d \text{ in equation (2)}$$
$$60t = 90t - 180$$
$$-30t = -180$$
$$t = 6.$$

The time for the freight train is 6 hr, which means that the time for the Metroliner is $6 - 2$, or 4 hr. Remember that it is distance, not time, that the problem asked for. Thus for $t = 6$, we have $d = 60 \cdot 6 = 360$ km.

4. Check. At 60 km/h, the freight train will travel $60 \cdot 6$, or 360 km, in 6 hr. At 90 km/h, the Metroliner will travel $90 \cdot (6 - 2) = 360$ km in 4 hr. The numbers check.

5. State. The freight train will catch up to the Metroliner at a point 360 km from Boston.

EXAMPLE 7

Jet travel. A Boeing 747-400 jet flies 4 hr west with a 60-mph tailwind. Returning *against* the wind takes 5 hr. Find the speed of the plane with no wind.

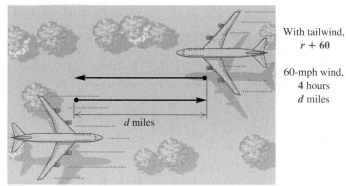

With tailwind,
$r + 60$

60-mph wind,
4 hours
d miles

Into headwind,
$r - 60$

60-mph wind,
5 hours
d miles

d miles

Solution

1. Familiarize. We imagine the situation and make a drawing. Note that the wind *speeds up* the jet on the outbound flight, but *slows down* the jet on the return flight. Since the distances traveled each way must be the same, we can check a guess of the jet's speed with no wind. Suppose the speed of the jet with no wind is 400 mph. The jet would then fly $400 + 60 = 460$ mph with the wind and $400 - 60 = 340$ mph into the wind. In 4 hr, the jet would travel $460 \cdot 4 = 1840$ mi with the wind and $340 \cdot 5 = 1700$ mi against the wind. Since $1840 \neq 1700$, our guess of 400 mph is incorrect. Rather than guess again, let's have $r =$ the speed, in miles per hour, of the jet in still air. Then $r + 60 =$ the jet's speed with the wind and $r - 60 =$ the jet's speed against the wind. We also let $d =$ the distance traveled, in miles.

2. **Translate.**   The information can be organized in a chart. The distances traveled are the same, so we use *Distance = Rate* (or *Speed*) · *Time*. Each row of the chart gives an equation.

	Distance	Rate	Time	
With Wind	d	$r + 60$	4	→ $d = (r + 60)4$
Against Wind	d	$r - 60$	5	→ $d = (r - 60)5$

The two equations constitute a system:

$$d = (r + 60)4, \qquad (1)$$
$$d = (r - 60)5. \qquad (2)$$

3. **Carry out.**   We solve the system using substitution:

$(r - 60)5 = (r + 60)4$ Substituting $(r - 60)5$ for d in equation (1)

$5r - 300 = 4r + 240$ Using the distributive law

$r = 540.$ Solving for r

4. **Check.**   When $r = 540$, the speed with the wind is $540 + 60 = 600$ mph, and the speed against the wind is $540 - 60 = 480$ mph. The distance with the wind, $600 \cdot 4 = 2400$ mi, matches the distance into the wind, $480 \cdot 5 = 2400$ mi, so we have a check.

5. **State.**   The speed of the plane with no wind is 540 mph.

Tips for Solving Motion Problems

1. Draw a diagram using an arrow or arrows to represent distance and the direction of each object in motion.
2. Organize the information in a chart.
3. Look for times, distances, or rates that are the same. These often can lead to an equation.
4. Translating to a system of equations allows for the use of two variables.
5. Always make sure that you have answered the question asked.

Exercise Set

8.3

1.–14. For Exercises 1–14, solve Exercises 41–54 from p. 515.

15. *Printing.*   King Street Printing recently charged 1.9¢ per sheet of paper, but 2.4¢ per sheet for paper made of recycled fibers. Darren's bill for 150 sheets of paper was $3.41. How many sheets of each type were used?

16. *Photocopying.*   Quick Copy recently charged 6¢ a page for copying pages that can be machine-fed and 18¢ a page for copying pages that must be hand-placed on the copier. If Lea's bill for 90 copies was $9.24, how many copies of each type were made?

17. *Lighting.*   Booth Bros. Hardware charges $7.50 for a General Electric Biax Energy Saver light bulb and $5 for an SLi Lighting Cool White Energy Saver bulb. If Paul County Hospital purchased 200 such bulbs for $1150, how many of each type did they purchase?

18. *Office supplies.*   Barlow's Office Supply charges $16.75 for a box of Erase-A-Gel™ pens and $14.25 for a box of Icy™ automatic pencils. If Letsonville Community College purchased 120 such boxes for $1790, how many boxes of each type did they purchase?

19. *Sales.*   Staples® recently sold a black Apple Stylewriter II ink cartridge for $30.86 and a black HP Designjet 10PS cartridge for $43.58. At the start of a recent fall semester, a total of 50 of these cartridges was sold for a total of $1733.80. How many of each type were purchased?

20. *Sales.*   Staples® recently sold a wirebound graph-paper notebook for $2.50 and a college-ruled note-book made of recycled paper for $2.30. At the start of a recent spring semester, a combination of 50 of these notebooks was sold for a total of $118.60. How many of each type were sold?

21. *Blending coffees.*   The Bean Counter charges $9.00 per pound for Kenyan French Roast coffee and $8.00 per pound for Sumatran coffee. How much of each type should be used to make a 20-lb blend that sells for $8.40 per pound?

22. *Mixed nuts.*   Oh Nuts! sells cashews for $6.75 per pound and Brazil nuts for $5.00 per pound. How much of each type should be used to make a 50-lb mixture that sells for $5.70 per pound?

23. *Catering.*   Casella's Catering is planning a wedding reception. The bride and groom would like to serve a nut mixture containing 25% peanuts. Casella has available mixtures that are either 40% or 10% peanuts. How much of each type should be mixed to get a 20-lb mixture that is 25% peanuts?

24. *Ink remover.*   Etch Clean Graphics uses one cleanser that is 25% acid and a second that is 50% acid. How many liters of each should be mixed to get 30 L of a solution that is 40% acid?

25. *Blending granola.*   Deep Thought Granola is 25% nuts and dried fruit. Oat Dream Granola is 10% nuts and dried fruit. How much of Deep

Thought and how much of Oat Dream should be mixed to form a 20-lb batch of granola that is 19% nuts and dried fruit?

26. *Livestock feed.* Soybean meal is 16% protein and corn meal is 9% protein. How many pounds of each should be mixed to get a 350-lb mixture that is 12% protein?

27. *Student loans.* Lomasi's two student loans totaled $12,000. One of her loans was at 6% simple interest and the other at 9%. After one year, Lomasi owed $855 in interest. What was the amount of each loan?

28. *Investments.* An executive nearing retirement made two investments totaling $15,000. In one year, these investments yielded $1432 in simple interest. Part of the money was invested at 9% and the rest at 10%. How much was invested at each rate?

29. *Automotive maintenance.* "Arctic Antifreeze" is 18% alcohol and "Frost No-More" is 10% alcohol. How many liters of each should be mixed to get 20 L of a mixture that is 15% alcohol?

30. *Chemistry.* E-Chem Testing has a solution that is 80% base and another that is 30% base. A technician needs 150 L of a solution that is 62% base. The 150 L will be prepared by mixing the two solutions on hand. How much of each should be used?

31. *Octane ratings.* The octane rating of a gasoline is a measure of the amount of isooctane in the gas. The 2002 Dodge Neon RT requires 91-octane gasoline. How much 87-octane gas and 93-octane gas should Kasey mix in order to make 12 gal of 91-octane gas for her Neon RT?
Sources: Champlain Electric and Petroleum Equipment; Goss Dodge

32. *Octane ratings.* The octane rating of a gasoline is a measure of the amount of isooctane in the gas. The 2005 Chrysler Crossfire requires 93-octane gasoline. How much 87-octane gas and 95-octane gas should Ken mix in order to make 10 gal of 93-octane gas for his Crossfire?
Sources: Champlain Electric and Petroleum Equipment; Freedom Chrysler Plymouth

33. *Food science.* The following bar graph shows the milk fat percentages in three dairy products. How many pounds each of whole milk and cream should be mixed to form 200 lb of milk for cream cheese?

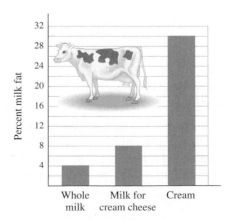

34. *Food science.* How much lowfat (1% fat) milk and how much whole milk (4% fat) should be mixed to make 5 gal of reduced fat (2% fat) milk?

35. *Train travel.* A train leaves Danville Junction and travels north at a speed of 75 km/h. Two hours later, an express train leaves on a parallel track and travels north at 125 km/h. How far from the station will they meet?

36. *Car travel.* Two cars leave Salt Lake City, traveling in opposite directions. One car travels at a speed of 80 km/h and the other at 96 km/h. In how many hours will they be 528 km apart?

37. *Boating.* Mia's motorboat took 3 hr to make a trip downstream with a 6-mph current. The return trip against the same current took 5 hr. Find the speed of the boat in still water.

38. *Canoeing.* Alvin paddled for 4 hr with a 6-km/h current to reach a campsite. The return trip against the same current took 10 hr. Find the speed of Alvin's canoe in still water.

39. *Point of no return.* A plane flying the 3458-mi trip from New York City to London has a 50-mph tailwind. The flight's *point of no return* is the point at which the flight time required to return to New York is the same as the time required to continue to London. If the speed of the plane in still air is 360 mph, how far is New York from the point of no return?

40. *Point of no return.* A plane is flying the 2553-mi trip from Los Angeles to Honolulu into a 60-mph headwind. If the speed of the plane in still air is 310 mph, how far from Los Angeles is the plane's point of no return? (See Exercise 39.)

41. *Architecture.* The rectangular ground floor of the John Hancock building has a perimeter of 860 ft. The length is 100 ft more than the width. Find the length and the width.

$x + 100$

x

42. *Real estate.* The perimeter of a rectangular oceanfront lot is 190 m. The width is one fourth of the length. Find the dimensions.

43. *Real estate.* In 1996, the Simon Property Group and the DeBartolo Realty Corporation merged to form the largest real estate company in the United States, owning 183 shopping centers in 32 states. Prior to merging, Simon owned twice as many properties as DeBartolo. How many properties did each company own before the merger?

DeBartolo shareholders would receive 0.68 share of Simon common stock for each share of DeBartolo common stock. Simon also would agree to repay $1.5 billion in DeBartolo debt. At Tuesday's closing price of $ 23.625 a share for common stock, the transaction is valued at roughly $3 billion.

Executives say the proposed company, Simon DeBartolo Group, would be the largest real estate company in the United States, worth $7.5 billion.

Not included in the deal: DeBartolo's ownership stake in the San Francisco 49ers, or the Indiana Pacers, owned separately by the Simon

44. *Hockey rankings.* Hockey teams receive 2 points for a win and 1 point for a tie. The Wildcats once won a championship with 60 points. They won 9 more games than they tied. How many wins and how many ties did the Wildcats have?

45. *Radio airplay.* Roscoe must play 12 commercials during his 1-hr radio show. Each commercial is either 30 sec or 60 sec long. If the total commercial time during that hour is 10 min, how many commercials of each type does Roscoe play?

46. *Video rentals.* J. P.'s Video rents general-interest films for $3.00 each and children's films for $1.50 each. In one day, a total of $213 was taken in from the rental of 77 videos. How many of each type of video was rented?

47. *Making change.* Cecilia makes a $9.25 purchase at the bookstore with a $20 bill. The store has no bills and gives her the change in quarters and fifty-cent pieces. There are 30 coins in all. How many of each kind are there?

48. *Teller work.* Ashford goes to a bank and gets change for a $50 bill consisting of all $5 bills and $1 bills. There are 22 bills in all. How many of each kind are there?

49. In what ways are Examples 3 and 4 similar? In what sense are their systems of equations similar?

50. Write at least three study tips of your own for someone beginning this exercise set.

SKILL MAINTENANCE

Evaluate.

51. $2x - 3y + 12$, for $x = 5$ and $y = 2$ [1.1]

52. $7x - 4y + 9$, for $x = 2$ and $y = 3$ [1.1]

53. $5a - 7b + 3c$, for $a = -2$, $b = 3$, and $c = 1$ [1.1], [1.8]

54. $3a - 8b - 2c$, for $a = -4$, $b = -1$, and $c = 3$ [1.1], [1.8]

55. $4 - 2y + 3z$, for $y = \frac{1}{3}$ and $z = \frac{1}{4}$ [1.3]

56. $3 - 5y + 4z$, for $y = \frac{1}{2}$ and $z = \frac{1}{5}$ [1.3]

SYNTHESIS

57. Suppose that in Example 3 you are asked only for the amount of Assam Gingia needed for the Dragon Blend. Would the method of solving the problem change? Why or why not?

58. Write a problem similar to Example 2 for a class-mate to solve. Design the problem so that the solution is "The florist sold 14 hanging plants and 9 flats of petunias."

59. *Recycled paper.* Unable to purchase 60 reams of paper that contains 20% post-consumer fiber, the Naylor School bought paper that was either 0% post-consumer fiber or 30% post-consumer fiber. How many reams of each should be purchased in order to use the same amount of post-consumer fiber as if the 20% post-consumer fiber paper were available?

60. *Retail.* Some of the world's best and most expensive coffee is Hawaii's Kona coffee. In order for coffee to be labeled "Kona Blend," it must contain at least 30% Kona beans. Bean Town Roasters has 40 lb of Mexican coffee. How much Kona coffee must they add if they wish to market it as Kona Blend?

61. *Automotive maintenance.* The radiator in Michelle's car contains 6.3 L of antifreeze and water. This mixture is 30% antifreeze. How much of this mixture should she drain and replace with pure antifreeze so that there will be a mixture of 50% antifreeze?

62. *Exercise.* Natalie jogs and walks to school each day. She averages 4 km/h walking and 8 km/h jogging. From home to school is 6 km and Natalie makes the trip in 1 hr. How far does she jog in a trip?

63. *Book sales.* A limited edition of a book published by a historical society was offered for sale to members. The cost was one book for $12 or two books for $20 (maximum of two per member). The society sold 880 books, for a total of $9840. How many members ordered two books?

64. The tens digit of a two-digit positive integer is 2 more than three times the units digit. If the digits are interchanged, the new number is 13 less than half the given number. Find the given integer. (*Hint*: Let $x =$ the tens-place digit and $y =$ the units-place digit; then $10x + y$ is the number.)

65. *Wood stains.* Williams' Custom Flooring has 0.5 gal of stain that is 20% brown and 80% neutral. A customer orders 1.5 gal of a stain that is 60% brown and 40% neutral. How much pure brown stain and how much neutral stain should be added to the original 0.5 gal in order to make up the order?*

66. *Train travel.* A train leaves Union Station for Central Station, 216 km away, at 9 A.M. One hour later, a train leaves Central Station for Union Station. They meet at noon. If the second train had started at 9 A.M. and the first train at 10:30 A.M., they would still have met at noon. Find the speed of each train.

67. *Fuel economy.* Grady's station wagon gets 18 miles per gallon (mpg) in city driving and 24 mpg in highway driving. The car is driven 465 mi on 23 gal of gasoline. How many miles were driven in the city and how many were driven on the highway?

68. *Biochemistry.* Industrial biochemists routinely use a machine to mix a buffer of 10% acetone by adding 100% acetone to water. One day, instead of adding 5 L of acetone to create a vat of buffer, a machine added 10 L. How much additional water was needed to bring the concentration down to 10%?

---

*This problem was suggested by Professor Chris Burditt of Yountville, California.

69. See Exercise 65 above. Let $x =$ the amount of pure brown stain added to the original 0.5 gal. Find a function $P(x)$ that can be used to determine the percentage of brown stain in the 1.5-gal mixture. On a graphing calculator, draw the graph of P and use INTERSECT to confirm the answer to Exercise 65.

70. *Gender.*   Phil and Phyllis are siblings. Phyllis has twice as many brothers as she has sisters. Phil has the same number of brothers as sisters. How many girls and how many boys are in the family?

8.4	**Systems of Equations in Three Variables**

Identifying Solutions   •   Solving Systems in Three Variables   •
Dependency, Inconsistency, and Geometric Considerations

CONNECTING THE CONCEPTS

As often happens in mathematics, once an idea is thoroughly understood, it can be extended to increasingly more complicated problems. This is precisely the situation for the material in Sections 8.4–8.7: We will extend the elimination method of Section 8.2 to systems of three equations in three unknowns. Although we will not do so in this text, the approach that we use can

be further extended to systems with four equations in four unknowns, five equations in five unknowns, and so on.

Another common occurrence in mathematics is the streamlining of a sequence of steps that are used repeatedly. In Sections 8.6 and 8.7, we develop different notations that streamline the calculations of Sections 8.2 and 8.4.

Some problems translate directly to two equations. Others more naturally call for a translation to three or more equations. In this section, we learn how to solve systems of three linear equations. Later, we will use such systems in problem-solving situations.

Identifying Solutions

A **linear equation in three variables** is an equation equivalent to one in the form $Ax + By + Cz = D$, where A, B, C, and D are real numbers. We refer to the form $Ax + By + Cz = D$ as *standard form* for a linear equation in three variables.

A solution of a system of three equations in three variables is an ordered triple (x, y, z) that makes *all three* equations true.

EXAMPLE 1   Determine whether $\left(\frac{3}{2}, -4, 3\right)$ is a solution of the system

$$4x - 2y - 3z = 5,$$
$$-8x - y + z = -5,$$
$$2x + y + 2z = 5.$$

Solution   We substitute $\left(\frac{3}{2}, -4, 3\right)$ into the three equations, using alphabetical order:

$$\begin{array}{r|l} 4x - 2y - 3z = 5 \\ \hline 4 \cdot \frac{3}{2} - 2(-4) - 3 \cdot 3 & 5 \\ 6 + 8 - 9 \\ 5 \overset{?}{=} 5 \quad \text{TRUE} \end{array} \qquad \begin{array}{r|l} -8x - y + z = -5 \\ \hline -8 \cdot \frac{3}{2} - (-4) + 3 & -5 \\ -12 + 4 + 3 \\ -5 \overset{?}{=} -5 \quad \text{TRUE} \end{array}$$

$$\begin{array}{r|l} 2x + y + 2z = 5 \\ \hline 2 \cdot \frac{3}{2} + (-4) + 2 \cdot 3 & 5 \\ 3 - 4 + 6 \\ 5 \overset{?}{=} 5 \quad \text{TRUE} \end{array}$$

The triple makes all three equations true, so it is a solution.

Solving Systems in Three Variables

Graphical methods for solving linear equations in three variables are problematic, because a three-dimensional coordinate system is required and the graph of a linear equation in three variables is a plane. The substitution method *can* be used but becomes very cumbersome unless one or more of the equations has only two variables. Fortunately, the elimination method allows us to manipulate a system of three equations in three variables so that a simpler system of two equations in two variables is formed. Once that simpler system has been solved, we can substitute into one of the three original equations and solve for the third variable.

EXAMPLE 2   Solve the following system of equations:

$$\begin{aligned} x + y + z &= 4, &(1) \\ x - 2y - z &= 1, &(2) \\ 2x - y - 2z &= -1. &(3) \end{aligned}$$

Solution   We select *any* two of the three equations and work to get one equation in two variables. Let's add equations (1) and (2):

$$\begin{array}{ll} x + y + z = 4 & (1) \\ \underline{x - 2y - z = 1} & (2) \\ 2x - y \phantom{{}+{}} = 5. & (4) \quad \text{Adding to eliminate } z \end{array}$$

Next, we select a different pair of equations and eliminate the *same variable* that we did above. Let's use equations (1) and (3) to again eliminate z. Be careful here! A common error is to eliminate a different variable in this step.

$$\begin{array}{l} x + y + z = 4, \\ 2x - y - 2z = -1 \end{array} \xrightarrow[\text{of equation (1) by 2}]{\text{Multiplying both sides}} \begin{array}{ll} 2x + 2y + 2z = 8 \\ \underline{2x - y - 2z = -1} \\ 4x + y \phantom{{}+{}} = 7 & (5) \end{array}$$

Now we solve the resulting system of equations (4) and (5). That solution will give us two of the numbers in the solution of the original system.

$$2x - y = 5 \quad (4)$$

$$\underline{4x + y = 7} \quad (5)$$

$$6x \quad = 12 \quad \text{Adding}$$

$$x = 2$$

Note that we now have two equations in two variables. Had we not eliminated the same variable in both of the above steps, this would not be the case.

We can use either equation (4) or (5) to find y. We choose equation (5):

$$4x + y = 7 \qquad (5)$$

$$4 \cdot 2 + y = 7 \qquad \text{Substituting 2 for } x \text{ in equation (5)}$$

$$8 + y = 7$$

$$y = -1.$$

We now have $x = 2$ and $y = -1$. To find the value for z, we use any of the original three equations and substitute to find the third number, z. Let's use equation (1) and substitute our two numbers in it:

$$x + y + z = 4 \qquad (1)$$

$$2 + (-1) + z = 4 \qquad \text{Substituting 2 for } x \text{ and } -1 \text{ for } y$$

$$1 + z = 4$$

$$z = 3.$$

We have obtained the triple $(2, -1, 3)$. It should check in *all three* equations:

$$\dfrac{x + y + z = 4}{2 + (-1) + 3 \mid 4}$$
$$4 \overset{?}{=} 4 \quad \text{TRUE}$$

$$\dfrac{x - 2y - z = 1}{2 - 2(-1) - 3 \mid 1}$$
$$1 \overset{?}{=} 1 \quad \text{TRUE}$$

$$\dfrac{2x - y - 2z = -1}{2 \cdot 2 - (-1) - 2 \cdot 3 \mid -1}$$
$$-1 \overset{?}{=} -1 \quad \text{TRUE}$$

The solution is $(2, -1, 3)$.

Solving Systems of Three Linear Equations

To use the elimination method to solve systems of three linear equations:

1. Write all equations in the standard form $Ax + By + Cz = D$.
2. Clear any decimals or fractions.
3. Choose a variable to eliminate. Then select two of the three equations and work to get one equation in which the selected variable is eliminated.
4. Next, use a different pair of equations and eliminate the same variable that you did in step (3).
5. Solve the system of equations that resulted from steps (3) and (4).
6. Substitute the solution from step (5) into one of the original three equations and solve for the third variable. Then check.

EXAMPLE 3   Solve the system

$$4x - 2y - 3z = 5, \qquad (1)$$
$$-8x - y + z = -5, \qquad (2)$$
$$2x + y + 2z = 5. \qquad (3)$$

Student Notes

Because solving systems of three equations can be lengthy, it is important that you use plenty of paper, work in pencil, and double-check each step as you proceed.

Solution

1., 2. The equations are already in standard form with no fractions or decimals.

3. Next, select a variable to eliminate. We decide on y because the y-terms are opposites of each other in equations (2) and (3). We add:

$$-8x - y + z = -5 \qquad (2)$$
$$\underline{2x + y + 2z = 5} \qquad (3)$$
$$-6x \quad + 3z = 0. \qquad (4) \qquad \text{Adding}$$

4. We use another pair of equations to create a second equation in x and z. That is, we eliminate the same variable, y, as in step (3). We use equations (1) and (3):

$$\begin{array}{l} 4x - 2y - 3z = 5, \\ 2x + y + 2z = 5 \end{array} \xrightarrow[\text{of equation (3) by 2}]{\text{Multiplying both sides}} \begin{array}{l} 4x - 2y - 3z = 5 \\ \underline{4x + 2y + 4z = 10} \\ 8x \quad + z = 15. \qquad (5) \end{array}$$

5. Now we solve the resulting system of equations (4) and (5). That allows us to find two parts of the ordered triple.

$$\begin{array}{l} -6x + 3z = 0, \\ 8x + z = 15 \end{array} \xrightarrow[\text{of equation (5) by } -3]{\text{Multiplying both sides}} \begin{array}{l} -6x + 3z = 0 \\ \underline{-24x - 3z = -45} \\ -30x \quad = -45 \\ \qquad x = \frac{-45}{-30} = \frac{3}{2} \end{array}$$

We use equation (5) to find z:

$$8x + z = 15$$
$$8 \cdot \tfrac{3}{2} + z = 15 \qquad \text{Substituting } \tfrac{3}{2} \text{ for } x$$
$$12 + z = 15$$
$$z = 3.$$

6. Finally, we use any of the original equations and substitute to find the third number, y. We choose equation (3):

$$2x + y + 2z = 5 \qquad (3)$$
$$2 \cdot \tfrac{3}{2} + y + 2 \cdot 3 = 5 \qquad \text{Substituting } \tfrac{3}{2} \text{ for } x \text{ and } 3 \text{ for } z$$
$$3 + y + 6 = 5$$
$$y + 9 = 5$$
$$y = -4.$$

The solution is $\left(\tfrac{3}{2}, -4, 3\right)$. The check was performed as Example 1.

Sometimes, certain variables are missing at the outset.

EXAMPLE 4   Solve the system

$$x + y + z = 180, \quad (1)$$
$$x \quad - z = -70, \quad (2)$$
$$2y - z = 0. \quad (3)$$

Solution

1., 2. The equations appear in standard form with no fractions or decimals.

3., 4. Note that there is no y in equation (2). Thus, at the outset, we already have y eliminated from one equation. We need another equation with y eliminated, so we use equations (1) and (3):

$$
\begin{array}{l}
x + y + z = 180, \\
2y - z = 0
\end{array}
\quad \xrightarrow[\text{of equation (1) by } -2]{\text{Multiplying both sides}} \quad
\begin{array}{r}
-2x - 2y - 2z = -360 \\
2y - z = 0 \\
\hline
-2x \quad - 3z = -360. \quad (4)
\end{array}
$$

5., 6. Now we solve the resulting system of equations (2) and (4):

$$
\begin{array}{l}
x - z = -70, \\
-2x - 3z = -360
\end{array}
\quad \xrightarrow[\text{of equation (2) by } 2]{\text{Multiplying both sides}} \quad
\begin{array}{r}
2x - 2z = -140 \\
-2x - 3z = -360 \\
\hline
-5z = -500 \\
z = 100.
\end{array}
$$

Continuing as in Examples 2 and 3, we get the solution $(30, 50, 100)$. The check is left to the student.

Dependency, Inconsistency, and Geometric Considerations

Each equation in Examples 2, 3, and 4 has a graph that is a plane in three dimensions. The solutions are points common to the planes of each system. Since three planes can have an infinite number of points in common or no points at all in common, we need to generalize the concept of *consistency*.

Planes intersect at one point. System is *consistent* and has one solution.

Planes intersect along a common line. System is *consistent* and has an infinite number of solutions.

Three parallel planes. System is *inconsistent;* it has no solution.

Planes intersect two at a time, with no point common to all three. System is *inconsistent;* it has no solution.

> *Consistency*
>
> A system of equations that has at least one solution is said to be **consistent**.
>
> A system of equations that has no solution is said to be **inconsistent**.

EXAMPLE 5   Solve:

$$y + 3z = 4, \qquad (1)$$
$$-x - y + 2z = 0, \qquad (2)$$
$$x + 2y + z = 1. \qquad (3)$$

Solution   The variable x is missing in equation (1). By adding equations (2) and (3), we can find a second equation in which x is missing:

$$-x - y + 2z = 0 \qquad (2)$$
$$\underline{x + 2y + z = 1} \qquad (3)$$
$$y + 3z = 1. \qquad (4) \qquad \text{Adding}$$

Equations (1) and (4) form a system in y and z. We solve as before:

$$y + 3z = 4, \quad \xrightarrow[\text{of equation (1) by } -1]{\text{Multiplying both sides}} \quad -y - 3z = -4$$
$$y + 3z = 1 \qquad\qquad\qquad\qquad\qquad \underline{y + 3z = 1}$$
$$\text{This is a contradiction.} \xrightarrow{} 0 = -3. \qquad \text{Adding}$$

Since we end up with a *false* equation, or contradiction, we know that the system has no solution. It is *inconsistent*.

The notion of *dependency* from Section 8.1 can also be extended.

EXAMPLE 6   Solve:

$$2x + y + z = 3, \qquad (1)$$
$$x - 2y - z = 1, \qquad (2)$$
$$3x + 4y + 3z = 5. \qquad (3)$$

Solution   Our plan is to first use equations (1) and (2) to eliminate z. Then we will select another pair of equations and again eliminate z:

$$2x + y + z = 3$$
$$\underline{x - 2y - z = 1}$$
$$3x - y = 4. \qquad (4)$$

Next, we use equations (2) and (3) to eliminate z again:

$$x - 2y - z = 1, \quad \xrightarrow[\text{of equation (2) by } 3]{\text{Multiplying both sides}} \quad 3x - 6y - 3z = 3$$
$$3x + 4y + 3z = 5 \qquad\qquad\qquad\qquad \underline{3x + 4y + 3z = 5}$$
$$6x - 2y = 8. \qquad (5)$$

We now try to solve the resulting system of equations (4) and (5):

$$3x - y = 4,$$ $$6x - 2y = 8$$ $\xrightarrow{\text{Multiplying both sides of equation (4) by } -2}$ $$-6x + 2y = -8$$ $$6x - 2y = 8$$ $$0 = 0. \quad (6)$$

Equation (6), which is an identity, indicates that equations (1), (2), and (3) are *dependent*. This means that the original system of three equations is equivalent to a system of two equations. One way to see this is to observe that two times equation (1), minus equation (2), is equation (3). Thus removing equation (3) from the system does not affect the solution of the system.* In writing an answer to this problem, we simply state that "the equations are dependent."

Recall that when dependent equations appeared in Section 8.1, the solution sets were always infinite in size and were written in set-builder notation. There, all systems of dependent equations were *consistent*. This is not always the case for systems of three or more equations. The following figures illustrate some possibilities geometrically.

 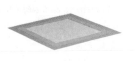 

The planes intersect along a common line. The equations are *dependent* and the system is *consistent*. There is an infinite number of solutions.

The planes coincide. The equations are *dependent* and the system is *consistent*. There is an infinite number of solutions.

Two planes coincide. The third plane is parallel. The equations are *dependent* and the system is *inconsistent*. There is no solution.

Exercise Set

8.4

↪ *Concept Reinforcement* *Classify each statement as either true or false.*

1. $3x + 5y + 4z = 7$ is a linear equation in three variables.

2. It is not difficult to solve a system of three equations in three unknowns by graphing.

3. Every system of three equations in three unknowns has at least one solution.

4. If, when we are solving a system of three equations, a false equation results from adding a multiple of one equation to another, the system is inconsistent.

*A set of equations is dependent if at least one equation can be expressed as a sum of multiples of other equations in that set.

5. If, when we are solving a system of three equations, an identity results from adding a multiple of one equation to another, the equations are dependent.

6. Whenever a system of three equations contains dependent equations, there is an infinite number of solutions.

7. Determine whether $(2, -1, -2)$ is a solution of the system

$$x + y - 2z = 5,$$
$$2x - y - z = 7,$$
$$-x - 2y + 3z = 6.$$

8. Determine whether $(1, -2, 3)$ is a solution of the system

$$x + y + z = 2,$$
$$x - 2y - z = 2,$$
$$3x + 2y + z = 2.$$

Solve each system. If a system's equations are dependent or if there is no solution, state this.

9. $2x - y + z = 10,$
$4x + 2y - 3z = 10,$
$x - 3y + 2z = 8$

10. $x + y + z = 6,$
$2x - y + 3z = 9,$
$-x + 2y + 2z = 9$

11. $x - y + z = 6,$
$2x + 3y + 2z = 2,$
$3x + 5y + 4z = 4$

12. $2x - y - 3z = -1,$
$2x - y + z = -9,$
$x + 2y - 4z = 17$

13. $6x - 4y + 5z = 31,$
$5x + 2y + 2z = 13,$
$x + y + z = 2$

14. $2x - 3y + z = 5,$
$x + 3y + 8z = 22,$
$3x - y + 2z = 12$

15. $x + y + z = 0,$
$2x + 3y + 2z = -3,$
$-x - 2y - z = 1$

16. $3a - 2b + 7c = 13,$
$a + 8b - 6c = -47,$
$7a - 9b - 9c = -3$

17. $2x + y - 3z = -4,$
$4x - 2y + z = 9,$
$3x + 5y - 2z = 5$

18. $4x + y + z = 17,$
$x - 3y + 2z = -8,$
$5x - 2y + 3z = 5$

19. $2x + y + 2z = 11,$
$3x + 2y + 2z = 8,$
$x + 4y + 3z = 0$

20. $2x + y + z = -2,$
$2x - y + 3z = 6,$
$3x - 5y + 4z = 7$

21. $-2x + 8y + 2z = 4,$
$x + 6y + 3z = 4,$
$3x - 2y + z = 0$

22. $x - y + z = 4,$
$5x + 2y - 3z = 2,$
$4x + 3y - 4z = -2$

23. $4x - y - z = 4,$
$2x + y + z = -1,$
$6x - 3y - 2z = 3$

24. $a + 2b + c = 1,$
$7a + 3b - c = -2,$
$a + 5b + 3c = 2$

25. $r + \frac{3}{2}s + 6t = 2,$
$2r - 3s + 3t = 0.5,$
$r + s + t = 1$

26. $5x + 3y + \frac{1}{2}z = \frac{7}{2},$
$0.5x - 0.9y - 0.2z = 0.3,$
$3x - 2.4y + 0.4z = -1$

27. $4a + 9b = 8,$
$8a + 6c = -1,$
$6b + 6c = -1$

28. $3p + 2r = 11,$
$q - 7r = 4,$
$p - 6q = 1$

29. $x + y + z = 57,$
$-2x + y = 3,$
$x - z = 6$

30. $x + y + z = 105,$
$10y - z = 11,$
$2x - 3y = 7$

31. $a - 3c = 6,$
$b + 2c = 2,$
$7a - 3b - 5c = 14$

32. $2a - 3b = 2,$
$7a + 4c = \frac{3}{4},$
$2c - 3b = 1$

Aha! **33.** $x + y + z = 83,$
$y = 2x + 3,$
$z = 40 + x$

34. $l + m = 7,$
$3m + 2n = 9,$
$4l + n = 5$

35. $x + z = 0,$
$x + y + 2z = 3,$
$y + z = 2$

36. $x + y = 0,$
$x + z = 1,$
$2x + y + z = 2$

37. $x + y + z = 1,$
$-x + 2y + z = 2,$
$2x - y = -1$

38. $y + z = 1,$
$x + y + z = 1,$
$x + 2y + 2z = 2$

39. Describe a method for writing an inconsistent system of three equations in three variables.

40. Abbie recommends that a frustrated classmate double- and triple-check each step of work when attempting to solve a system of three equations. Is this good advice? Why or why not?

SKILL MAINTENANCE

Translate each sentence to mathematics. [1.1]

41. One number is twice another.

42. The sum of two numbers is three times the first number.

43. The sum of three consecutive numbers is 45.

44. One number plus twice another number is 17.

45. The sum of two numbers is five times a third number.

46. The product of two numbers is twice their sum.

SYNTHESIS

▢ **47.** Is it possible for a system of three linear equations to have exactly two ordered triples in its solution set? Why or why not?

▢ **48.** Describe a procedure that could be used to solve a system of four equations in four variables.

Solve.

49. $\dfrac{x+2}{3} - \dfrac{y+4}{2} + \dfrac{z+1}{6} = 0,$

$\dfrac{x-4}{3} + \dfrac{y+1}{4} - \dfrac{z-2}{2} = -1,$

$\dfrac{x+1}{2} + \dfrac{y}{2} + \dfrac{z-1}{4} = \dfrac{3}{4}$

50. $w + x + y + z = 2,$
$w + 2x + 2y + 4z = 1,$
$w - x + y + z = 6,$
$w - 3x - y + z = 2$

51. $w + x - y + z = 0,$
$w - 2x - 2y - z = -5,$
$w - 3x - y + z = 4,$
$2w - x - y + 3z = 7$

For Exercises 52 and 53, let u represent $1/x$, *v represent* $1/y$, *and w represent* $1/z$. *Solve for u, v, and w, and then solve for x, y, and z.*

52. $\dfrac{2}{x} - \dfrac{1}{y} - \dfrac{3}{z} = -1,$

$\dfrac{2}{x} - \dfrac{1}{y} + \dfrac{1}{z} = -9,$

$\dfrac{1}{x} + \dfrac{2}{y} - \dfrac{4}{z} = 17$

53. $\dfrac{2}{x} + \dfrac{2}{y} - \dfrac{3}{z} = 3,$

$\dfrac{1}{x} - \dfrac{2}{y} - \dfrac{3}{z} = 9,$

$\dfrac{7}{x} - \dfrac{2}{y} + \dfrac{9}{z} = -39$

Determine k so that each system is dependent.

54. $x - 3y + 2z = 1,$
$2x + y - z = 3,$
$9x - 6y + 3z = k$

55. $5x - 6y + kz = -5,$
$x + 3y - 2z = 2,$
$2x - y + 4z = -1$

In each case, three solutions of an equation in x, y, and z are given. Find the equation.

56. $Ax + By + Cz = 12;$
$\left(1, \frac{3}{4}, 3\right), \left(\frac{4}{3}, 1, 2\right),$ and $(2, 1, 1)$

57. $z = b - mx - ny;$
$(1, 1, 2), (3, 2, -6),$ and $\left(\frac{3}{2}, 1, 1\right)$

58. Write an inconsistent system of equations that contains dependent equations.

CORNER

Finding the Preferred Approach

COLLABORATIVE

Focus: Systems of three linear equations

Time: 10–15 minutes

Group size: 3

Consider the six steps outlined on p. 183 along with the following system:

$2x + 4y = 3 - 5z,$

$0.3x = 0.2y + 0.7z + 1.4,$

$0.04x + 0.03y = 0.07 + 0.04z.$

ACTIVITY

1. Working independently, each group member should solve the system above. One person should begin by eliminating x, one should first eliminate y, and one should first eliminate z. Write neatly so that others can follow your steps.

2. Once all group members have solved the system, compare your answers. If the answers do not check, exchange notebooks and check each other's work. If a mistake is detected, allow the person who made the mistake to make the repair.

3. Decide as a group which of the three approaches above (if any) ranks as easiest and which (if any) ranks as most difficult. Then compare your rankings with the other groups in the class.

8.5 Solving Applications: Systems of Three Equations

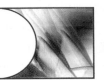

Applications of Three Equations in Three Unknowns

Solving systems of three or more equations is important in many applications. Such systems arise in the natural and social sciences, business, and engineering. In mathematics, purely numerical applications also arise.

EXAMPLE 1   The sum of three numbers is 4. The first number minus twice the second, minus the third is 1. Twice the first number minus the second, minus twice the third is -1. Find the numbers.

Solution

1. **Familiarize.**   There are three statements involving the same three numbers. Let's label these numbers x, y, and z.

2. **Translate.**   We can translate directly as follows.

The sum of the three numbers is 4.
$$x + y + z = 4$$

The first number minus twice the second minus the third is 1.
$$x - 2y - z = 1$$

Twice the first number minus the second minus twice the third is -1.
$$2x - y - 2z = -1$$

We now have a system of three equations:

$$x + y + z = 4,$$
$$x - 2y - z = 1,$$
$$2x - y - 2z = -1.$$

3. **Carry out.**   We need to solve the system of equations. Note that we found the solution, $(2, -1, 3)$, in Example 2 of Section 8.4.

4. **Check.**   The first statement of the problem says that the sum of the three numbers is 4. That checks, because $2 + (-1) + 3 = 4$. The second statement says that the first number minus twice the second, minus the third is 1: $2 - 2(-1) - 3 = 1$. That checks. The check of the third statement is left to the student.

5. **State.**   The three numbers are 2, -1, and 3.

Study Skills

Keeping Math Relevant

Finding applications of math in your everyday life is a great study aid. Try to extend this idea to the newspapers, periodicals, and books that you read. Look with a critical eye at graphs and their labels. Not only will this help with your math, it will make you a more informed citizen.

EXAMPLE 2   Architecture.   In a triangular cross section of a roof, the largest angle is 70° greater than the smallest angle. The largest angle is twice as large as the remaining angle. Find the measure of each angle.

Solution

1. Familiarize.   The first thing we do is make a drawing, or a sketch.

Student Notes ___

It is quite likely that you are expected to remember that the sum of the measures of the angles in any triangle is 180°. You may want to ask your instructor which other formulas from geometry and elsewhere you are expected to know.

Since we don't know the size of any angle, we use x, y, and z to represent the three measures, from smallest to largest. Recall that the measures of the angles in any triangle add up to 180°.

2. Translate.   This geometric fact about triangles gives us one equation:

$$x + y + z = 180.$$

Two of the statements can be translated almost directly.

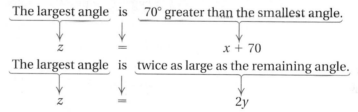

We now have a system of three equations:

$$
\begin{aligned}
x + y + z &= 180, \\
x + 70 &= z, \\
2y &= z;
\end{aligned}
\quad \text{or} \quad
\begin{aligned}
x + y + z &= 180, \\
x \quad\ - z &= -70, \\
2y - z &= 0.
\end{aligned}
\quad
\begin{array}{l}
\text{Rewriting in} \\
\text{standard form}
\end{array}
$$

3. Carry out.   The system was solved in Example 4 of Section 8.4. The solution is (30, 50, 100).

4. Check.   The sum of the numbers is 180, so that checks. The measure of the largest angle, 100°, is 70° greater than the measure of the smallest angle, 30°, so that checks. The measure of the largest angle is also twice the measure of the remaining angle, 50°. Thus we have a check.

5. State.   The angles in the triangle measure 30°, 50°, and 100°.

EXAMPLE 3   Cholesterol levels.   Recent studies indicate that a child's intake of cholesterol should be no more than 300 mg per day. By eating 1 egg, 1 cupcake, and 1 slice of pizza, a child consumes 302 mg of cholesterol. A child who eats 2 cupcakes and 3 slices of pizza takes in 65 mg of cholesterol. By eating 2 eggs and 1 cupcake, a child consumes 567 mg of cholesterol. How much cholesterol is in each item?

Solution

1. **Familiarize.**   After reading the problem, it becomes clear that an egg contains considerably more cholesterol than the other foods. Let's guess that one egg contains 200 mg of cholesterol and one cupcake contains 50 mg. Because of the second sentence in the problem, it would follow that a slice of pizza contains 52 mg of cholesterol since $200 + 50 + 52 = 302$.

   To see if our guess satisfies the other statements in the problem, we find the amount of cholesterol that 2 cupcakes and 3 slices of pizza would contain: $2 \cdot 50 + 3 \cdot 52 = 256$. Since this does not match the 65 mg listed in the fourth sentence of the problem, our guess was incorrect. Rather than guess again, we examine how we checked our guess and let g, c, and $s =$ the number of milligrams of cholesterol in an egg, a cupcake, and a slice of pizza, respectively.

2. **Translate.**   Rewording some of the sentences, we can translate as follows:

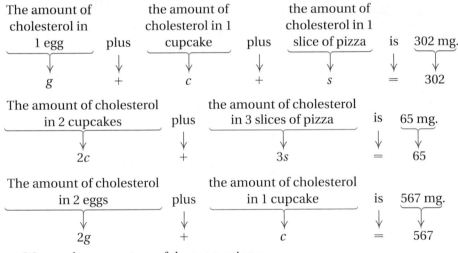

We now have a system of three equations:

$$g + c + \ \ s = 302,$$
$$2c + 3s = 65,$$
$$2g + c \ \ \ \ \ \ = 567.$$

3. **Carry out.**   We solve and get $g = 274$, $c = 19$, and $s = 9$.

4. **Check.**   The sum of 274, 19, and 9 is 302 so the total cholesterol in 1 egg, 1 cupcake, and 1 slice of pizza checks. Two cupcakes and three slices of pizza would contain $2 \cdot 19 + 3 \cdot 9 = 65$ mg, while two eggs and one cupcake would contain $2 \cdot 274 + 19 = 567$ mg of cholesterol. The answer checks.

5. **State.**   An egg contains 274 mg of cholesterol, a cupcake contains 19 mg of cholesterol, and a slice of pizza contains 9 mg of cholesterol.

Exercise Set

8.5

Solve.

1. The sum of three numbers is 57. The second is 3 more than the first. The third is 6 more than the first. Find the numbers.

2. The sum of three numbers is 5. The first number minus the second plus the third is 1. The first minus the third is 3 more than the second. Find the numbers.

3. The sum of three numbers is 26. Twice the first minus the second is 2 less than the third. The third is the second minus three times the first. Find the numbers.

4. The sum of three numbers is 105. The third is 11 less than ten times the second. Twice the first is 7 more than three times the second. Find the numbers.

5. *Geometry.* In triangle *ABC*, the measure of angle *B* is three times that of angle *A*. The measure of angle *C* is 20° more than that of angle *A*. Find the angle measures.

6. *Geometry.* In triangle *ABC*, the measure of angle *B* is twice the measure of angle *A*. The measure of angle *C* is 80° more than that of angle *A*. Find the angle measures.

7. *Health insurance.* In 2004, UNICARE® health insurance for adults under the age of 30 cost $121/month for a couple, $107/month for an adult with one child, and $164/month for a couple with one child. On the basis of the information given, find the monthly rate for an individual adult, a spouse, and a child.
Source: UNICARE Life and Health Insurance Company® advertisement

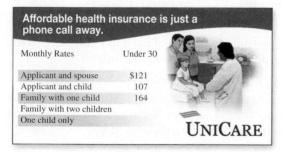

8. *Health insurance.* In 2004, UNICARE® health insurance cost $160/month for a 35–39-year-old adult and spouse, $145/month for a 35–39-year-old adult with one child, and $245/month for a 39-year-old adult with a spouse and child. On the basis of the information given, find the monthly rates for a 39-year-old adult, a 39-year-old's spouse, and a 39-year-old's child.
Source: UNICARE Life and Insurance Company® advertisement

9. *Nutrition.* Most nutritionists now agree that a healthy adult diet should include 25–35 g of fiber each day. A breakfast of 2 bran muffins, 1 banana, and a 1-cup serving of Wheaties® contains 9 g of fiber; a breakfast of 1 bran muffin, 2 bananas, and a 1-cup serving of Wheaties® contains 10.5 g of fiber; and a breakfast of 2 bran muffins and a 1-cup serving of Wheaties® contains 6 g of fiber. How much fiber is in each of these foods?
Sources: usda.gov and InteliHealth.com

10. *Nutrition.* Refer to Exercise 9. A breakfast consisting of 2 pancakes and a 1-cup serving of strawberries contains 4.5 g of fiber, whereas a breakfast of 2 pancakes and a 1-cup serving of Cheerios® contains 4 g of fiber. When a meal consists of 1 pancake, a 1-cup serving of Cheerios®, and a 1-cup serving of strawberries, it contains 7 g of fiber. How much fiber is in each of these foods?
Source: InteliHealth.com

Aha! **11.** *Automobile pricing.* The basic model of a 2004 Jeep Grand Cherokee Laredo (2WD) with a power sunroof cost $25,495. When equipped with 4WD and a sunroof, the vehicle's price rose to $27,465. The cost of the basic model with 4WD was $26,665. Find the basic price, the cost of 4WD, and the cost of a sunroof.

12. *Lens production.* When Sight-Rite's three polishing machines, A, B, and C, are all working, 5700 lenses can be polished in one week. When only A and B are working, 3400 lenses can be polished in one week. When only B and C are working, 4200 lenses can be polished in one week. How many lenses can be polished in a week by each machine?

13. *Welding rates.* Elrod, Dot, and Wendy can weld 74 linear feet per hour when working together. Elrod and Dot together can weld 44 linear feet per hour, while Elrod and Wendy can weld 50 linear feet per hour. How many linear feet per hour can each weld alone?

14. *Telemarketing.* Sven, Tillie, and Isaiah can process 740 telephone orders per day. Sven and Tillie together can process 470 orders, while Tillie and Isaiah together can process 520 orders per day. How many orders can each person process alone?

15. *Coffee prices.* Roz works at a Starbucks® coffee shop where a 12-oz cup of coffee costs $1.40, a 16-oz cup costs $1.60, and a 20-oz cup costs $1.70. During one busy period, Roz served 55 cups of coffee, emptying six 144-oz "brewers" while collecting a total of $85.90. How many cups of each size did Roz fill?

12 oz	16 oz	20 oz
$1.40	$1.60	$1.70

16. *Advertising.* In a recent year, U.S. companies spent a total of $106.5 billion on newspaper, television, and radio ads. The total amount spent on television and radio ads was $18.7 billion more than the amount spent on newspaper ads alone. The amount spent on newspaper ads was $28.8 billion more than what was spent on radio ads. How much was spent on each form of advertising?
Sources: NAA (newspapers); McCann–Erickson Inc. (television and radio)

17. *Restaurant management.* McDonald's® recently sold small soft drinks for $1, medium soft drinks for $1.15, and large soft drinks for $1.30. During a lunch-time rush, Chris sold 40 soft drinks for a total of $45.25. The number of small and large drinks, combined, was 10 fewer than the number of medium drinks. How many drinks of each size were sold?

18. *Investments.* A business class divided an imaginary investment of $80,000 among three mutual funds. The first fund grew by 10%, the second by 6%, and the third by 15%. Total earnings were $8850. The earnings from the first fund were $750 more than the earnings from the third. How much was invested in each fund?

19. *Nutrition.* A dietician in a hospital prepares meals under the guidance of a physician. Suppose that for a particular patient a physician prescribes a meal to have 800 calories, 55 g of protein, and 220 mg of vitamin C. The dietician prepares a meal of roast beef, baked potatoes, and broccoli according to the data in the following table.

Serving Size	Calories	Protein (in grams)	Vitamin C (in milligrams)
Roast Beef, 3 oz	300	20	0
Baked Potato, 1	100	5	20
Broccoli, 156 g	50	5	100

How many servings of each food are needed in order to satisfy the doctor's orders?

20. *Nutrition.* Repeat Exercise 19 but replace the broccoli with asparagus, for which a 180-g serving contains 50 calories, 5 g of protein, and 44 mg of vitamin C. Which meal would you prefer eating?

21. *World population growth.*   The world population is projected to be 9.1 billion in 2050. At that time, there are expected to be approximately 3 billion more people in Asia than in Africa. The population for the rest of the world will be approximately 0.1 billion more than half the population of Asia. Find the projected populations of Asia, Africa, and the rest of the world in 2050.
Sources: U.S. Bureau of the Census; *Burlington Free Press* 3/23/04

22. *Crying rate.*   The sum of the average number of times a man, a woman, and a one-year-old child cry each month is 56.7. A woman cries 3.9 more times than a man. The average number of times a one-year-old cries per month is 43.3 more than the average number of times combined that a man and a woman cry. What is the average number of times per month that each cries?

23. *Basketball scoring.*   The New York Knicks recently scored a total of 92 points on a combination of 2-point field goals, 3-point field goals, and 1-point foul shots. Altogether, the Knicks made 50 baskets and 19 more 2-pointers than foul shots. How many shots of each kind were made?

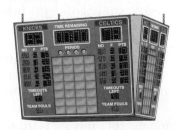

24. *History.*   Find the year in which the first U.S. transcontinental railroad was completed. The following are some facts about the number. The sum of the digits in the year is 24. The ones digit is 1 more than the hundreds digit. Both the tens and the ones digits are multiples of 3.

25. Problems like Exercises 15 and 17 could be classified as total-value problems. How do these problems differ from the total-value problems of Section 8.3?

26. Write a problem for a classmate to solve. Design the problem so that it translates to a system of three equations in three variables.

SKILL MAINTENANCE

Simplify. [1.8]

27. $5(-3) + 7$

28. $-4(-6) + 9$

29. $-6(8) + (-7)$

30. $7(-9) + (-8)$

31. $-7(2x - 3y + 5z)$

32. $-6(4a + 7b - 9c)$

33. $-4(2a + 5b) + 3a + 20b$

34. $3(2x - 7y) + 5x + 21y$

SYNTHESIS

35. Consider Exercise 23. Suppose there were no foul shots made. Would there still be a solution? Why or why not?

36. Consider Exercise 15. Suppose Roz collected $46. Could the problem still be solved? Why or why not?

37. *Health insurance.*   In 2004, UNICARE® health insurance for a 35–39-year-old and his or her spouse cost $160/month. That rate increased to $203/month if a child were included and $243/month if two children were included. The rate dropped to $145/month for just the applicant and one child. Find the separate costs for insuring the applicant, the spouse, the first child, and the second child.
Source: UNICARE Life and Health Insurance Company® advertisement

38. Find a three-digit positive integer such that the sum of all three digits is 14, the tens digit is 2 more than the ones digit, and if the digits are reversed, the number is unchanged.

39. *Ages.*   Tammy's age is the sum of the ages of Carmen and Dennis. Carmen's age is 2 more than the sum of the ages of Dennis and Mark. Dennis's age is four times Mark's age. The sum of all four ages is 42. How old is Tammy?

40. *Ticket revenue.*   A magic show's audience of 100 people consists of adults, students, and children. The ticket prices are $10 for adults, $3 for students, and 50¢ for children. The total amount of money taken in is $100. How many adults, students, and children are in attendance? Does there seem to be some information missing? Do some more careful reasoning.

41. *Sharing raffle tickets.*   Hal gives Tom as many raffle tickets as Tom first had and Gary as many as Gary first had. In like manner, Tom then gives Hal and Gary as many tickets as each then has. Similarly, Gary gives Hal and Tom as many tickets

as each then has. If each finally has 40 tickets, with how many tickets does Tom begin?

42. Find the sum of the angle measures at the tips of the star in this figure.

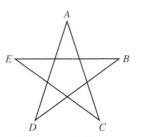

8.6 Elimination Using Matrices

Matrices and Systems   •   Row-Equivalent Operations

In solving systems of equations, we perform computations with the constants. The variables play no important role until the end. Thus we can simplify writing a system by omitting the variables. For example, the system

$$3x + 4y = 5,$$
$$x - 2y = 1$$

simplifies to

$$\begin{array}{ccc} 3 & 4 & 5 \\ 1 & -2 & 1 \end{array}$$

if we do not write the variables, the operation of addition, and the equals signs.

Matrices and Systems

In the example above, we have written a rectangular array of numbers. Such an array is called a **matrix** (plural, **matrices**). We ordinarily write brackets around matrices. The following are matrices:

$$\begin{bmatrix} -3 & 1 \\ 0 & 5 \end{bmatrix}, \begin{bmatrix} 2 & 0 & -1 & 3 \\ -5 & 2 & 7 & -1 \\ 4 & 5 & 3 & 0 \end{bmatrix}, \begin{bmatrix} 2 & 3 \\ 7 & 15 \\ -2 & 23 \\ 4 & 1 \end{bmatrix}$$

 The individual numbers are called *elements* or *entries*.

The **rows** of a matrix are horizontal, and the **columns** are vertical.

$$\begin{bmatrix} 5 & -2 & 2 \\ 1 & 0 & 1 \\ 0 & 1 & 2 \end{bmatrix}$$
⟶ row 1
⟶ row 2
⟶ row 3

↑ column 1   ↑ column 2   ↑ column 3

Let's see how matrices can be used to solve a system.

EXAMPLE 1   Solve the system

$$5x - 4y = -1,$$
$$-2x + 3y = 2.$$

As an aid for understanding, we list the corresponding system in the margin.

$$5x - 4y = -1,$$
$$-2x + 3y = 2$$

Solution We write a matrix using only coefficients and constants, listing x-coefficients in the first column and y-coefficients in the second. Note that in each matrix a dashed line separates the coefficients from the constants:

$$\begin{bmatrix} 5 & -4 & | & -1 \\ -2 & 3 & | & 2 \end{bmatrix}.$$ Consult the notes in the margin for further information.

Our goal is to transform

$$\begin{bmatrix} 5 & -4 & | & -1 \\ -2 & 3 & | & 2 \end{bmatrix} \quad \text{into the form} \quad \begin{bmatrix} a & b & | & c \\ 0 & d & | & e \end{bmatrix}.$$

The variables x and y can then be reinserted to form equations from which we can complete the solution.

We do calculations that are similar to those that we would do if we wrote the entire equations. The first step is to multiply and/or interchange the rows so that each number in the first column below the first number is a multiple of that number. Here that means multiplying Row 2 by 5. This corresponds to multiplying both sides of the second equation by 5.

$$5x - 4y = -1,$$
$$-10x + 15y = 10$$

$$\begin{bmatrix} 5 & -4 & | & -1 \\ -10 & 15 & | & 10 \end{bmatrix} \quad \text{New Row 2} = 5(\text{Row 2 from above})$$

Next, we multiply the first row by 2, add this to Row 2, and write that result as the "new" Row 2. This corresponds to multiplying the first equation by 2 and adding the result to the second equation in order to eliminate a variable. Write out these computations as necessary—we perform them mentally.

$$5x - 4y = -1,$$
$$7y = 8$$

$$\begin{bmatrix} 5 & -4 & | & -1 \\ 0 & 7 & | & 8 \end{bmatrix}$$ $2(5 \quad -4 \ | \ -1) = (10 \quad -8 \ | \ -2)$ and
$(10 \quad -8 \ | \ -2) + (-10 \quad 15 \ | \ 10) = (0 \quad 7 \ | \ 8)$
New Row 2 = 2(Row 1) + (Row 2)

If we now reinsert the variables, we have

$$5x - 4y = -1, \qquad (1)$$
$$7y = 8. \qquad (2)$$

We can now proceed as before, solving equation (2) for y:

$$7y = 8 \qquad (2)$$
$$y = \tfrac{8}{7}.$$

Next, we substitute $\tfrac{8}{7}$ for y in equation (1):

$$5x - 4y = -1 \qquad (1)$$
$$5x - 4 \cdot \tfrac{8}{7} = -1 \qquad \text{Substituting } \tfrac{8}{7} \text{ for } y \text{ in equation (1)}$$
$$x = \tfrac{5}{7}. \qquad \text{Solving for } x$$

The solution is $\left(\tfrac{5}{7}, \tfrac{8}{7}\right)$. The check is left to the student.

EXAMPLE 2   Solve the system

$$2x - y + 4z = -3,$$
$$x \quad\;\; - 4z = 5,$$
$$6x - y + 2z = 10.$$

Solution   We first write a matrix, using only the constants. Where there are missing terms, we must write 0's:

$$2x - y + 4z = -3,$$
$$x \quad\;\; - 4z = 5,$$
$$6x - y + 2z = 10$$

$$\begin{bmatrix} 2 & -1 & 4 & | & -3 \\ 1 & 0 & -4 & | & 5 \\ 6 & -1 & 2 & | & 10 \end{bmatrix}$$

Our goal is to transform the matrix to one of the form

$$ax + by + cz = d,$$
$$ey + fz = g,$$
$$hz = i$$

$$\begin{bmatrix} a & b & c & | & d \\ 0 & e & f & | & g \\ 0 & 0 & h & | & i \end{bmatrix}.$$

A matrix of this form can be rewritten as a system of equations that is equivalent to the original system, and from which a solution can be easily found.

The first step is to multiply and/or interchange the rows so that each number in the first column is a multiple of the first number in the first row. In this case, we do so by interchanging Rows 1 and 2:

$$x \quad\;\; - 4z = 5,$$
$$2x - y + 4z = -3,$$
$$6x - y + 2z = 10$$

$$\begin{bmatrix} 1 & 0 & -4 & | & 5 \\ 2 & -1 & 4 & | & -3 \\ 6 & -1 & 2 & | & 10 \end{bmatrix}$$

This corresponds to interchanging the first two equations.

Next, we multiply the first row by -2, add it to the second row, and replace Row 2 with the result:

$$x \quad\;\; - 4z = 5,$$
$$-y + 12z = -13,$$
$$6x - y + 2z = 10$$

$$\begin{bmatrix} 1 & 0 & -4 & | & 5 \\ 0 & -1 & 12 & | & -13 \\ 6 & -1 & 2 & | & 10 \end{bmatrix}.$$

$-2(1 \;\; 0 \;\; -4 \;|\; 5) = (-2 \;\; 0 \;\; 8 \;|\; -10)$ and
$(-2 \;\; 0 \;\; 8 \;|\; -10) + (2 \;\; -1 \;\; 4 \;|\; -3) = $
$(0 \;\; -1 \;\; 12 \;|\; -13)$

Now we multiply the first row by -6, add it to the third row, and replace Row 3 with the result:

$$x \quad\;\; - 4z = 5,$$
$$-y + 12z = -13,$$
$$-y + 26z = -20$$

$$\begin{bmatrix} 1 & 0 & -4 & | & 5 \\ 0 & -1 & 12 & | & -13 \\ 0 & -1 & 26 & | & -20 \end{bmatrix}.$$

$-6(1 \;\; 0 \;\; -4 \;|\; 5) = (-6 \;\; 0 \;\; 24 \;|\; -30)$ and
$(-6 \;\; 0 \;\; 24 \;|\; -30) + (6 \;\; -1 \;\; 2 \;|\; 10) = $
$(0 \;\; -1 \;\; 26 \;|\; -20)$

Next, we multiply Row 2 by -1, add it to the third row, and replace Row 3 with the result:

$$x \quad\;\; - 4z = 5,$$
$$-y + 12z = -13,$$
$$14z = -7$$

$$\begin{bmatrix} 1 & 0 & -4 & | & 5 \\ 0 & -1 & 12 & | & -13 \\ 0 & 0 & 14 & | & -7 \end{bmatrix}.$$

$-1(0 \;\; -1 \;\; 12 \;|\; -13) = (0 \;\; 1 \;\; -12 \;|\; 13)$
and $(0 \;\; 1 \;\; -12 \;|\; 13) + (0 \;\; -1 \;\; 26 \;|\; -20) = $
$(0 \;\; 0 \;\; 14 \;|\; -7)$

Reinserting the variables gives us

$$x \quad\;\; - 4z = 5,$$
$$-y + 12z = -13,$$
$$14z = -7.$$

We now solve this last equation for z and get $z = -\frac{1}{2}$. Next, we substitute $-\frac{1}{2}$ for z in the preceding equation and solve for y: $-y + 12\left(-\frac{1}{2}\right) = -13$, so $y = 7$. Since there is no y-term in the first equation of this last system, we need only substitute $-\frac{1}{2}$ for z to solve for x: $x - 4\left(-\frac{1}{2}\right) = 5$, so $x = 3$. The solution is $\left(3, 7, -\frac{1}{2}\right)$. The check is left to the student.

The operations used in the preceding example correspond to those used to produce equivalent systems of equations. We call the matrices **row-equivalent** and the operations that produce them **row-equivalent operations**.

Row-Equivalent Operations

Row-Equivalent Operations

Each of the following row-equivalent operations produces a row-equivalent matrix:

a) Interchanging any two rows.
b) Multiplying all elements of a row by a nonzero constant.
c) Replacing a row with the sum of that row and a multiple of another row.

Student Notes

Try to remember that row-equivalent matrices are not *equal*. It is the solutions of the corresponding systems that are the same.

The best overall method for solving systems of equations is by row-equivalent matrices; even computers are programmed to use them. Matrices are part of a branch of mathematics known as linear algebra. They are also studied in many courses in finite mathematics.

 **technology connection**

Row-equivalent operations can be performed on a graphing calculator. For example, to interchange the first and second rows of the matrix, as in step (1) of Example 2 above, we enter the matrix as matrix **A** and select "rowSwap" from the MATRIX MATH menu. Some graphing calculators will not automatically store the matrix produced using a row-equivalent operation, so when several operations are to be performed in succession, it is helpful to store the result of each operation as it is produced. In the window at right, we see both the matrix produced by the rowSwap operation and the indication that this matrix is stored, using **STO▸**, as matrix **B**.

```
rowSwap([A],1,2)→[B]
[[1   0  -4   5]
 [2  -1   4  -3]
 [6  -1   2  10]]
```

1. Use a graphing calculator to proceed through all the steps in Example 2.

8.6 Exercise Set

🖐 *Concept Reinforcement* *Complete each of the following statements.*

1. The rows of a matrix are _____ and the _____ are vertical.

2. Multiplying the numbers in a row of a matrix by a constant corresponds to multiplying both sides of a(n) _____ by a constant.

3. Each number in a matrix is called a(n) _____ or element.

4. The plural of the word matrix is _____ .

5. To solve a system using matrices, we can replace any row by the sum of that row and a(n) _____ of another row.

6. In the final step of solving a system of equations, the leftmost column has zeros in all rows except the _____ one.

Solve using matrices.

7. $9x - 2y = 5,$
   $3x - 3y = 11$

8. $4x + y = 7,$
   $5x - 3y = 13$

9. $x + 4y = 8,$
   $3x + 5y = 3$

10. $x + 4y = 5,$
    $-3x + 2y = 13$

11. $6x - 2y = 4,$
    $7x + y = 13$

12. $3x + 4y = 7,$
    $-5x + 2y = 10$

13. $3x + 2y + 2z = 3,$
    $x + 2y - z = 5,$
    $2x - 4y + z = 0$

14. $4x - y - 3z = 19,$
    $8x + y - z = 11,$
    $2x + y + 2z = -7$

15. $p - 2q - 3r = 3,$
    $2p - q - 2r = 4,$
    $4p + 5q + 6r = 4$

16. $x + 2y - 3z = 9,$
    $2x - y + 2z = -8,$
    $3x - y - 4z = 3$

17. $3p + 2r = 11,$
    $q - 7r = 4,$
    $p - 6q = 1$

18. $4a + 9b = 8,$
    $8a + 6c = -1,$
    $6b + 6c = -1$

19. $2x + 2y - 2z - 2w = -10,$
    $w + y + z + x = -5,$
    $x - y + 4z + 3w = -2,$
    $w - 2y + 2z + 3x = -6$

20. $-w - 3y + z + 2x = -8,$
    $x + y - z - w = -4,$
    $w + y + z + x = 22,$
    $x - y - z - w = -14$

Solve using matrices.

21. *Coin value.* A collection of 42 coins consists of dimes and nickels. The total value is \$3.00. How many dimes and how many nickels are there?

22. *Coin value.* A collection of 43 coins consists of dimes and quarters. The total value is \$7.60. How many dimes and how many quarters are there?

23. *Mixed granola.* Grace sells two kinds of granola. One is worth \$4.05 per pound and the other is worth \$2.70 per pound. She wants to blend the two granolas to get a 15-lb mixture worth \$3.15 per pound. How much of each kind of granola should be used?

24. *Trail mix.* Phil mixes nuts worth \$1.60 per pound with oats worth \$1.40 per pound to get 20 lb of trail mix worth \$1.54 per pound. How many pounds of nuts and how many pounds of oats should be used?

25. *Investments.* Elena receives \$212 per year in simple interest from three investments totaling \$2500. Part is invested at 7%, part at 8%, and part at 9%. There is \$1100 more invested at 9% than at 8%. Find the amount invested at each rate.

26. *Investments.* Miguel receives \$306 per year in simple interest from three investments totaling \$3200. Part is invested at 8%, part at 9%, and part at 10%. There is \$1900 more invested at 10% than at 9%. Find the amount invested at each rate.

📓 27. Explain how you can recognize dependent equations when solving with matrices.

📓 28. Explain how you can recognize an inconsistent system when solving with matrices.

SKILL MAINTENANCE

Simplify. [1.8]

29. $5(-3) - (-7)4$

30. $8(-5) - (-2)9$

31. $-2(5 \cdot 3 - 4 \cdot 6) - 3(2 \cdot 7 - 15) + 4(3 \cdot 8 - 5 \cdot 4)$

32. $6(2 \cdot 7 - 3(-4)) - 4(3(-8) - 10) + 5(4 \cdot 3 - (-2)7)$

SYNTHESIS

 **33.** If the matrices

$$\begin{bmatrix} a_1 & b_1 & \vdots & c_1 \\ d_1 & e_1 & \vdots & f_1 \end{bmatrix} \quad \text{and} \quad \begin{bmatrix} a_2 & b_2 & \vdots & c_2 \\ d_2 & e_2 & \vdots & f_2 \end{bmatrix}$$

share the same solution, does it follow that the corresponding entries are all equal to each other ($a_1 = a_2$, $b_1 = b_2$, etc.)? Why or why not?

34. Explain how the row-equivalent operations make use of the addition, multiplication, and distributive properties.

35. The sum of the digits in a four-digit number is 10. Twice the sum of the thousands digit and the tens digit is 1 less than the sum of the other two digits. The tens digit is twice the thousands digit. The ones digit equals the sum of the thousands digit and the hundreds digit. Find the four-digit number.

36. Solve for x and y:

$$ax + by = c,$$
$$dx + ey = f.$$

8.7 Determinants and Cramer's Rule

Determinants of 2 × 2 Matrices • Cramer's Rule: 2 × 2 Systems • Cramer's Rule: 3 × 3 Systems

Determinants of 2 × 2 Matrices

When a matrix has m rows and n columns, it is called an "m by n" matrix. Thus its *dimensions* are denoted by $m \times n$. If a matrix has the same number of rows and columns, it is called a **square matrix**. Associated with every square matrix is a number called its **determinant**, defined as follows for 2×2 matrices.

---

2 × 2 Determinants

The determinant of a two-by-two matrix $\begin{bmatrix} a & c \\ b & d \end{bmatrix}$ is denoted $\begin{vmatrix} a & c \\ b & d \end{vmatrix}$ and is defined as follows:

$$\begin{vmatrix} a & c \\ b & d \end{vmatrix} = ad - bc.$$

EXAMPLE 1   Evaluate: $\begin{vmatrix} 2 & -5 \\ 6 & 7 \end{vmatrix}$.

Solution   We multiply and subtract as follows:

$$\begin{vmatrix} 2 & -5 \\ 6 & 7 \end{vmatrix} = 2 \cdot 7 - 6 \cdot (-5) = 14 + 30 = 44.$$

Cramer's Rule: 2 × 2 Systems

One of the many uses for determinants is in solving systems of linear equations in which the number of variables is the same as the number of equations and the constants are not all 0. Let's consider a system of two equations:

$$a_1 x + b_1 y = c_1,$$
$$a_2 x + b_2 y = c_2.$$

If we use the elimination method, a series of steps can show that

$$x = \frac{c_1 b_2 - c_2 b_1}{a_1 b_2 - a_2 b_1} \quad \text{and} \quad y = \frac{a_1 c_2 - a_2 c_1}{a_1 b_2 - a_2 b_1}.$$

These fractions can be rewritten using determinants.

Cramer's Rule: 2 × 2 Systems

The solution of the system

$$a_1 x + b_1 y = c_1,$$
$$a_2 x + b_2 y = c_2,$$

if it is unique, is given by

$$x = \frac{\begin{vmatrix} c_1 & b_1 \\ c_2 & b_2 \end{vmatrix}}{\begin{vmatrix} a_1 & b_1 \\ a_2 & b_2 \end{vmatrix}}, \qquad y = \frac{\begin{vmatrix} a_1 & c_1 \\ a_2 & c_2 \end{vmatrix}}{\begin{vmatrix} a_1 & b_1 \\ a_2 & b_2 \end{vmatrix}}.$$

These formulas apply only if the denominator is not 0. If the denominator *is* 0, then one of two things happens:

1. If the denominator is 0 and the numerators are also 0, then the equations in the system are dependent.
2. If the denominator is 0 and at least one numerator is not 0, then the system is inconsistent.

To use Cramer's rule, we find the determinants and compute x and y as shown above. Note that the denominators are identical and the coefficients of x and y appear in the same position as in the original equations. In the numerator of x, the constants c_1 and c_2 replace a_1 and a_2. In the numerator of y, the constants c_1 and c_2 replace b_1 and b_2.

EXAMPLE 2   Solve using Cramer's rule:

$$2x + 5y = 7,$$
$$5x - 2y = -3.$$

Solution   We have

$$x = \frac{\begin{vmatrix} 7 & 5 \\ -3 & -2 \end{vmatrix}}{\begin{vmatrix} 2 & 5 \\ 5 & -2 \end{vmatrix}} \qquad \text{Using Cramer's rule}$$

$$= \frac{7(-2) - (-3)5}{2(-2) - 5 \cdot 5} = -\frac{1}{29}$$

and

$$y = \frac{\begin{vmatrix} 2 & 7 \\ 5 & -3 \end{vmatrix}}{\begin{vmatrix} 2 & 5 \\ 5 & -2 \end{vmatrix}} \qquad \text{Using Cramer's rule}$$

$$= \frac{2(-3) - 5 \cdot 7}{-29} = \frac{41}{29}. \qquad \begin{array}{l}\text{The denominator is the same as in the}\\ \text{expression for } x.\end{array}$$

The solution is $\left(-\frac{1}{29}, \frac{41}{29}\right)$. The check is left to the student.

Cramer's Rule: 3 × 3 Systems

Cramer's rule can be extended for systems of three linear equations. However, before doing so, we must define what a 3 × 3 determinant is.

---

3 × 3 Determinants

The determinant of a three-by-three matrix is defined as follows:

$$\begin{vmatrix} a_1 & b_1 & c_1 \\ a_2 & b_2 & c_2 \\ a_3 & b_3 & c_3 \end{vmatrix} = a_1 \begin{vmatrix} b_2 & c_2 \\ b_3 & c_3 \end{vmatrix} \overset{\text{Subtract.}}{-} a_2 \begin{vmatrix} b_1 & c_1 \\ b_3 & c_3 \end{vmatrix} \overset{\text{Add.}}{+} a_3 \begin{vmatrix} b_1 & c_1 \\ b_2 & c_2 \end{vmatrix}$$

Note that the a's come from the first column. Note too that the 2 × 2 determinants above can be obtained by crossing out the row and the column in which the a occurs.

Student Notes ——

Cramer's rule and the evaluation of determinants rely on patterns. The specific formulas are less important than the patterns that they represent.

For a_1:

$$\begin{vmatrix} \cancel{a_1} & \cancel{b_1} & \cancel{c_1} \\ a_2 & b_2 & c_2 \\ a_3 & b_3 & c_3 \end{vmatrix}$$

For a_2:

$$\begin{vmatrix} \cancel{a_1} & b_1 & c_1 \\ \cancel{a_2} & \cancel{b_2} & \cancel{c_2} \\ a_3 & b_3 & c_3 \end{vmatrix}$$

For a_3:

$$\begin{vmatrix} \cancel{a_1} & b_1 & c_1 \\ a_2 & b_2 & c_2 \\ \cancel{a_3} & \cancel{b_3} & \cancel{c_3} \end{vmatrix}$$

EXAMPLE 3   Evaluate:

$$\begin{vmatrix} -1 & 0 & 1 \\ -5 & 1 & -1 \\ 4 & 8 & 1 \end{vmatrix}.$$

Solution   We have

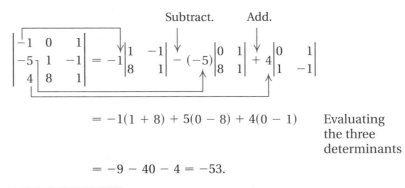

$$= -1(1 + 8) + 5(0 - 8) + 4(0 - 1)$$ Evaluating the three determinants

$$= -9 - 40 - 4 = -53.$$

Cramer's Rule: 3 × 3 Systems

The solution of the system

$$a_1x + b_1y + c_1z = d_1,$$
$$a_2x + b_2y + c_2z = d_2,$$
$$a_3x + b_3y + c_3z = d_3$$

can be found using the following determinants:

$$D = \begin{vmatrix} a_1 & b_1 & c_1 \\ a_2 & b_2 & c_2 \\ a_3 & b_3 & c_3 \end{vmatrix}, \qquad D_x = \begin{vmatrix} d_1 & b_1 & c_1 \\ d_2 & b_2 & c_2 \\ d_3 & b_3 & c_3 \end{vmatrix},$$

D contains only coefficients. In D_x, the d's replace the a's.

$$D_y = \begin{vmatrix} a_1 & d_1 & c_1 \\ a_2 & d_2 & c_2 \\ a_3 & d_3 & c_3 \end{vmatrix}, \qquad D_z = \begin{vmatrix} a_1 & b_1 & d_1 \\ a_2 & b_2 & d_2 \\ a_3 & b_3 & d_3 \end{vmatrix}.$$

In D_y, the d's replace the b's.

In D_z, the d's replace the c's.

If a unique solution exists, it is given by

$$x = \frac{D_x}{D}, \qquad y = \frac{D_y}{D}, \qquad z = \frac{D_z}{D}.$$

EXAMPLE 4   Solve using Cramer's rule:

$$x - 3y + 7z = 13,$$
$$x + y + z = 1,$$
$$x - 2y + 3z = 4.$$

Solution We compute D, D_x, D_y, and D_z:

$$D = \begin{vmatrix} 1 & -3 & 7 \\ 1 & 1 & 1 \\ 1 & -2 & 3 \end{vmatrix} = -10; \qquad D_x = \begin{vmatrix} 13 & -3 & 7 \\ 1 & 1 & 1 \\ 4 & -2 & 3 \end{vmatrix} = 20;$$

$$D_y = \begin{vmatrix} 1 & 13 & 7 \\ 1 & 1 & 1 \\ 1 & 4 & 3 \end{vmatrix} = -6; \qquad D_z = \begin{vmatrix} 1 & -3 & 13 \\ 1 & 1 & 1 \\ 1 & -2 & 4 \end{vmatrix} = -24.$$

Then

$$x = \frac{D_x}{D} = \frac{20}{-10} = -2;$$

$$y = \frac{D_y}{D} = \frac{-6}{-10} = \frac{3}{5};$$

$$z = \frac{D_z}{D} = \frac{-24}{-10} = \frac{12}{5}.$$

The solution is $\left(-2, \frac{3}{5}, \frac{12}{5}\right)$. The check is left to the student.

In Example 4, we need not have evaluated D_z. Once x and y were found, we could have substituted them into one of the equations to find z.

To use Cramer's rule, we divide by D, provided $D \neq 0$. If $D = 0$ and at least one of the other determinants is not 0, then the system is inconsistent. If *all* the determinants are 0, then the equations in the system are dependent.

technology connection

Determinants can be evaluated on most graphing calculators using **2ND** **MATRIX**. After entering a matrix, we select the determinant operation from the MATRIX MATH menu and enter the name of the matrix. The graphing calculator will return the value of the determinant of the matrix. For example, if

$$\mathbf{A} = \begin{bmatrix} 1 & 6 & -1 \\ -3 & -5 & 3 \\ 0 & 4 & 2 \end{bmatrix},$$

we have

```
det([A])
            26
```

1. Confirm the calculations in Example 4.

Exercise Set

8.7

FOR EXTRA HELP

Student's Solutions Manual   Digital Video Tutor CD 4 Videotape 8   Tutor Center AW Math Tutor Center   MathXL Tutorials on CD   MathXL MathXL   MyMathLab MyMathLab

Concept Reinforcement *Classify each of the following as either true or false.*

1. A square matrix has the same number of rows and columns.

2. A 3×4 matrix has 3 rows and 4 columns.

3. Cramer's rule exists only for 2×2 systems.

4. Whenever Cramer's rule yields a denominator that is 0, the system has no solution.

5. Whenever Cramer's rule yields a numerator that is 0, the equations are dependent.

6. Cramer's rule allows us to solve some systems that could not be solved any other way.

Evaluate.

7. $\begin{vmatrix} 5 & 1 \\ 2 & 4 \end{vmatrix}$

8. $\begin{vmatrix} 3 & 2 \\ 2 & -3 \end{vmatrix}$

9. $\begin{vmatrix} 6 & -9 \\ 2 & 3 \end{vmatrix}$

10. $\begin{vmatrix} 3 & 2 \\ -7 & 5 \end{vmatrix}$

11. $\begin{vmatrix} 1 & 4 & 0 \\ 0 & -1 & 2 \\ 3 & -2 & 1 \end{vmatrix}$

12. $\begin{vmatrix} 3 & 0 & -2 \\ 5 & 1 & 2 \\ 2 & 0 & -1 \end{vmatrix}$

13. $\begin{vmatrix} -1 & -2 & -3 \\ 3 & 4 & 2 \\ 0 & 1 & 2 \end{vmatrix}$

14. $\begin{vmatrix} 1 & 2 & 2 \\ 2 & 1 & 0 \\ 3 & 3 & 1 \end{vmatrix}$

15. $\begin{vmatrix} -4 & -2 & 3 \\ -3 & 1 & 2 \\ 3 & 4 & -2 \end{vmatrix}$

16. $\begin{vmatrix} 2 & -1 & 1 \\ 1 & 2 & -1 \\ 3 & 4 & -3 \end{vmatrix}$

Solve using Cramer's rule.

17. $5x + 8y = 1,$
$3x + 7y = 5$

18. $3x - 4y = 6,$
$5x + 9y = 10$

19. $5x - 4y = -3,$
$7x + 2y = 6$

20. $-2x + 4y = 3,$
$3x - 7y = 1$

21. $3x - y + 2z = 1,$
$x - y + 2z = 3,$
$-2x + 3y + z = 1$

22. $3x + 2y - z = 4,$
$3x - 2y + z = 5,$
$4x - 5y - z = -1$

23. $2x - 3y + 5z = 27,$
$x + 2y - z = -4,$
$5x - y + 4z = 27$

24. $x - y + 2z = -3,$
$x + 2y + 3z = 4,$
$2x + y + z = -3$

25. $r - 2s + 3t = 6,$
$2r - s - t = -3,$
$r + s + t = 6$

26. $a - 3c = 6,$
$b + 2c = 2,$
$7a - 3b - 5c = 14$

27. What is it about Cramer's rule that makes it useful?

28. Which version of Cramer's rule do you find more useful: the version for 2×2 systems or the version for 3×3 systems? Why?

SKILL MAINTENANCE

Solve. [2.2]

29. $0.5x - 2.34 + 2.4x = 7.8x - 9$

30. $5x + 7x = -144$

31. A piece of wire 32.8 ft long is to be cut into two pieces, and those pieces are each to be bent to make a square. The length of a side of one square is to be 2.2 ft greater than the length of a side of the other. How should the wire be cut? [2.5]

32. *Inventory.*   The Freeport College store paid $1728 for an order of 45 calculators. The store paid $9 for each scientific calculator. The others, all graphing calculators, cost the store $58 each. How many of each type of calculator was ordered? [8.3]

33. *Insulation.*   The Mazzas' attic required three and a half times as much insulation as did the Kranepools'. Together, the two attics required 36 rolls of insulation. How much insulation did each attic require? [8.3]

34. *Sales of food.*   High Flyin' Wings charges $12 for a bucket of chicken wings and $7 for a chicken dinner. After filling 28 orders for buckets and dinners, High Flyin' Wings had collected $281. How many buckets and how many dinners did they sell? [8.3]

SYNTHESIS

35. Cramer's rule states that if $a_1x + b_1y = c_1$ and $a_2x + b_2y = c_2$ are dependent, then
$$\begin{vmatrix} a_1 & b_1 \\ a_2 & b_2 \end{vmatrix} = 0.$$
Explain why this will always happen.

36. Under what conditions can a 3×3 system of linear equations be consistent but unable to be solved using Cramer's rule?

Solve.

37. $\begin{vmatrix} y & -2 \\ 4 & 3 \end{vmatrix} = 44$

38. $\begin{vmatrix} 2 & x & -1 \\ -1 & 3 & 2 \\ -2 & 1 & 1 \end{vmatrix} = -12$

39. $\begin{vmatrix} m+1 & -2 \\ m-2 & 1 \end{vmatrix} = 27$

40. Show that an equation of the line through (x_1, y_1) and (x_2, y_2) can be written
$$\begin{vmatrix} x & y & 1 \\ x_1 & y_1 & 1 \\ x_2 & y_2 & 1 \end{vmatrix} = 0.$$

8.8 Business and Economic Applications

Break-Even Analysis   •   Supply and Demand

Break-Even Analysis

When a company manufactures x units of a product, it spends money. This is **total cost** and can be thought of as a function C, where $C(x)$ is the total cost of producing x units. When the company sells x units of the product, it takes in money. This is **total revenue** and can be thought of as a function R, where $R(x)$ is the total revenue from the sale of x units. **Total profit** is the money taken in less the money spent, or total revenue minus total cost. Total profit from the production and sale of x units is a function P given by

$$\textbf{Profit} = \textbf{Revenue} - \textbf{Cost,} \quad \text{or} \quad P(x) = R(x) - C(x).$$

If $R(x)$ is greater than $C(x)$, there is a gain and $P(x)$ is positive. If $C(x)$ is greater than $R(x)$, there is a loss and $P(x)$ is negative. When $R(x) = C(x)$, the company breaks even.

There are two kinds of costs. First, there are costs like rent, insurance, machinery, and so on. These costs, which must be paid whether a product is produced or not, are called *fixed costs*. When a product is being produced, there are costs for labor, materials, marketing, and so on. These are called *variable costs*, because they vary according to the amount being produced. The sum of the fixed cost and the variable cost gives the *total cost* of producing a product.

Caution!   Do not confuse "cost" with "price." When we discuss the *cost* of an item, we are referring to what it costs to produce the item. The *price* of an item is what a consumer pays to purchase the item and is used when calculating revenue.

EXAMPLE 1   Manufacturing lamps.   Ergs, Inc., is planning to make a new lamp. Fixed costs will be $90,000, and it will cost $15 to produce each lamp (variable costs). Each lamp sells for $26.

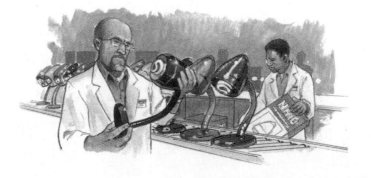

a) Find the total cost $C(x)$ of producing x lamps.

b) Find the total revenue $R(x)$ from the sale of x lamps.

c) Find the total profit $P(x)$ from the production and sale of x lamps.

d) What profit will the company realize from the production and sale of 3000 lamps? of 14,000 lamps?

e) Graph the total-cost, total-revenue, and total-profit functions using the same set of axes. Determine the break-even point.

Solution

a) Total cost is given by

$$C(x) = (\text{Fixed costs}) \text{ plus } (\text{Variable costs}),$$

or $C(x) = \quad 90{,}000 \quad + \quad 15x,$

where x is the number of lamps produced.

b) Total revenue is given by

$R(x) = 26x.$ $26 times the number of lamps sold. We assume that every lamp produced is sold.

c) Total profit is given by

$$P(x) = R(x) - C(x) \qquad \text{Profit is revenue minus cost.}$$
$$= 26x - (90{,}000 + 15x)$$
$$= 11x - 90{,}000.$$

d) Profits will be

$$P(3000) = 11 \cdot 3000 - 90{,}000 = -\$57{,}000$$

when 3000 lamps are produced and sold, and

$$P(14{,}000) = 11 \cdot 14{,}000 - 90{,}000 = \$64{,}000$$

when 14,000 lamps are produced and sold. Thus the company loses money if only 3000 lamps are sold, but makes money if 14,000 are sold.

e) The graphs of each of the three functions are shown below:

$R(x) = 26x,$ This represents the revenue function.

$C(x) = 90{,}000 + 15x,$ This represents the cost function.

$P(x) = 11x - 90{,}000.$ This represents the profit function.

$R(x)$, $C(x)$, and $P(x)$ are all in dollars.

The revenue function has a graph that goes through the origin and has a slope of 26. The cost function has an intercept on the $-axis of 90,000 and has a slope of 15. The profit function has an intercept on the $-axis of −90,000 and has a slope of 11. It is shown by the dashed line. The red dashed line shows a "negative" profit, which is a loss. (That is what is known as "being in the red.") The black dashed line shows a "positive" profit, or gain. (That is what is known as "being in the black.")

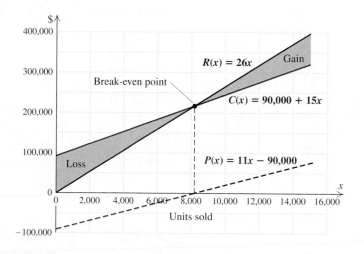

Gains occur where the revenue is greater than the cost. Losses occur where the revenue is less than the cost. The **break-even point** occurs where the graphs of R and C cross. Thus to find the break-even point, we solve a system:

$$R(x) = 26x,$$
$$C(x) = 90,000 + 15x.$$

Since both revenue and cost are in *dollars* and they are equal at the break-even point, the system can be rewritten as

$$d = 26x, \qquad (1)$$
$$d = 90,000 + 15x \qquad (2)$$

and solved using substitution:

$$26x = 90,000 + 15x \qquad \text{Substituting } 26x \text{ for } d \text{ in equation (2)}$$
$$11x = 90,000$$
$$x \approx 8181.8.$$

The firm will break even if it produces and sells about 8182 lamps (8181 will yield a tiny loss and 8182 a tiny gain), and takes in a total of $R(8182) = 26 \cdot 8182 = \$212,732$ in revenue. Note that the x-coordinate of the break-even point can also be found by solving $P(x) = 0$. The break-even point is (8182 lamps, \$212,732).

Supply and Demand

As the price of coffee varies, the amount sold varies. The table and graph below show that *consumers will demand less as the price goes up.*

Demand Function, *D*

Price, *p*, per Kilogram	Quantity, *D(p)* (in millions of kilograms)
$ 8.00	25
9.00	20
10.00	15
11.00	10
12.00	5

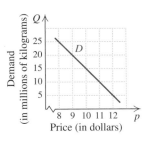

As the price of coffee varies, the amount available varies. The table and graph below show that *sellers will supply more as the price goes up.*

Supply Function, *S*

Price, *p*, per Kilogram	Quantity, *S(p)* (in millions of kilograms)
$ 9.00	5
9.50	10
10.00	15
10.50	20
11.00	25

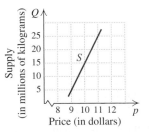

Let's look at the above graphs together. We see that as price increases, demand decreases. As price increases, supply increases. The point of intersection is called the **equilibrium point**. At that price, the amount that the seller will supply is the same amount that the consumer will buy. The situation is analogous to a buyer and a seller negotiating the price of an item. The equilibrium point is the price and quantity that they finally agree on.

Any ordered pair of coordinates from the graph is (price, quantity), because the horizontal axis is the price axis and the vertical axis is the quantity axis. If *D* is a demand function and *S* is a supply function, then the equilibrium point is where demand equals supply:

$$D(p) = S(p).$$

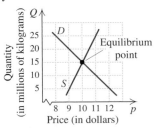

EXAMPLE 2   Find the equilibrium point for the demand and supply functions given:

$$D(p) = 1000 - 60p, \quad (1)$$
$$S(p) = 200 + 4p. \quad (2)$$

Solution   Since both demand and supply are *quantities* and they are equal at the equilibrium point, we rewrite the system as

$$q = 1000 - 60p, \quad (1)$$
$$q = 200 + 4p. \quad (2)$$

We substitute $200 + 4p$ for q in equation (1) and solve:

$200 + 4p = 1000 - 60p$	Substituting $200 + 4p$ for q in equation (1)
$200 + 64p = 1000$	Adding $60p$ to both sides
$64p = 800$	Adding -200 to both sides
$p = \frac{800}{64} = 12.5.$	

Thus the equilibrium price is $12.50 per unit.

To find the equilibrium quantity, we substitute $12.50 into either $D(p)$ or $S(p)$. We use $S(p)$:

$$S(12.5) = 200 + 4(12.5) = 200 + 50 = 250.$$

Thus the equilibrium quantity is 250 units, and the equilibrium point is ($12.50, 250).

Exercise Set

8.8

FOR EXTRA HELP

| Student's Solutions Manual | Digital Video Tutor CD 4 Videotape 8 | AW Math Tutor Center | MathXL Tutorials on CD | MathXL MathXL | MyMathLab MyMathLab |

↝ *Concept Reinforcement*   *In each of Exercises 1–8, match the word or phrase with the most appropriate choice from the column on the right.*

1. ____ Total cost

2. ____ Total revenue

3. ____ Total profit

4. ____ Fixed costs

5. ____ Variable costs

6. ____ Break-even point

7. ____ Equilibrium point

8. ____ Price

a) The amount of money that a company takes in

b) The sum of fixed costs and variable costs

c) The point at which total revenue equals total cost

d) What consumers pay per item

e) The difference between total revenue and total cost

f) What companies spend whether or not a product is produced

g) The point at which supply equals demand

h) The costs that vary according to the number of items produced

For each of the following pairs of total-cost and total-revenue functions, find **(a)** *the total-profit function and* **(b)** *the break-even point.*

9. $C(x) = 45x + 300{,}000$;
   $R(x) = 65x$

10. $C(x) = 25x + 270{,}000$;
   $R(x) = 70x$

11. $C(x) = 10x + 120{,}000$;
   $R(x) = 60x$

12. $C(x) = 30x + 49{,}500$;
   $R(x) = 85x$

13. $C(x) = 40x + 22{,}500$;
   $R(x) = 85x$

14. $C(x) = 20x + 10{,}000$;
   $R(x) = 100x$

15. $C(x) = 22x + 16{,}000$;
   $R(x) = 40x$

16. $C(x) = 15x + 75{,}000$;
   $R(x) = 55x$

Aha! **17.** $C(x) = 75x + 100{,}000$;
   $R(x) = 125x$

18. $C(x) = 20x + 120{,}000$;
   $R(x) = 50x$

Find the equilibrium point for each of the following pairs of demand and supply functions.

19. $D(p) = 1000 - 10p$,
   $S(p) = 230 + p$

20. $D(p) = 2000 - 60p$,
   $S(p) = 460 + 94p$

21. $D(p) = 760 - 13p$,
   $S(p) = 430 + 2p$

22. $D(p) = 800 - 43p$,
   $S(p) = 210 + 16p$

23. $D(p) = 7500 - 25p$,
   $S(p) = 6000 + 5p$

24. $D(p) = 8800 - 30p$,
   $S(p) = 7000 + 15p$

25. $D(p) = 1600 - 53p$,
   $S(p) = 320 + 75p$

26. $D(p) = 5500 - 40p$,
   $S(p) = 1000 + 85p$

Solve.

27. *Computer manufacturing.*   Biz.com Electronics is planning to introduce a new line of computers. The fixed costs for production are $125,300. The variable costs for producing each computer are $450. The revenue from each computer is $800. Find the following.

   a) The total cost $C(x)$ of producing x computers

   b) The total revenue $R(x)$ from the sale of x computers

   c) The total profit $P(x)$ from the production and sale of x computers

   d) The profit or loss from the production and sale of 100 computers; of 400 computers

   e) The break-even point

28. *Manufacturing CD players.*   SoundGen, Inc., is planning to manufacture a new type of CD player. The fixed costs for production are $22,500. The variable costs for producing each CD player are estimated to be $40. The revenue from each CD player is to be $85. Find the following.

   a) The total cost $C(x)$ of producing x CD players

   b) The total revenue $R(x)$ from the sale of x CD players

   c) The total profit $P(x)$ from the production and sale of x CD players

   d) The profit or loss from the production and sale of 3000 CD players; of 400 CD players

   e) The break-even point

29. *Manufacturing caps.*   Martina's Custom Printing is planning on adding painter's caps to its product line. For the first year, the fixed costs for setting up production are $16,404. The variable costs for producing a dozen caps are $6.00. The revenue on each dozen caps will be $18.00. Find the following.

   a) The total cost $C(x)$ of producing x dozen caps

   b) The total revenue $R(x)$ from the sale of x dozen caps

   c) The total profit $P(x)$ from the production and sale of x dozen caps

   d) The profit or loss from the production and sale of 3000 dozen caps; of 1000 dozen caps

   e) The break-even point

30. *Sport coat production.*   Sarducci's is planning a new line of sport coats. For the first year, the fixed costs for setting up production are $10,000. The variable costs for producing each coat are $30. The revenue from each coat is to be $80. Find the following.

   a) The total cost $C(x)$ of producing x coats

   b) The total revenue $R(x)$ from the sale of x coats

   c) The total profit $P(x)$ from the production and sale of x coats

   d) The profit or loss from the production and sale of 2000 coats; of 50 coats

   e) The break-even point

31. In Example 1, the slope of the line representing Revenue is the sum of the slopes of the other two lines. This is not a coincidence. Explain why.

32. Variable costs and fixed costs are often compared to the slope and the y-intercept, respectively, of an equation for a line. Explain why you feel this analogy is or is not valid.

SKILL MAINTENANCE

Solve. [2.2]

33. $3x - 9 = 27$

34. $4x - 7 = 53$

35. $4x - 5 = 7x - 13$

36. $2x + 9 = 8x - 15$

37. $7 - 2(x - 8) = 14$

38. $6 - 4(3x - 2) = 10$

SYNTHESIS

39. Ian claims that since his fixed costs are $1000, he need sell only 20 birdbaths at $50 each in order to break even. Does this sound plausible? Why or why not?

40. In this section, we examined supply and demand functions for coffee. Does it seem realistic to you for the graph of D to have a constant slope? Why or why not?

41. *Yo-yo production.*   Bing Boing Hobbies is willing to produce 100 yo-yo's at $2.00 each and 500 yo-yo's at $8.00 each. Research indicates that the public will buy 500 yo-yo's at $1.00 each and 100 yo-yo's at $9.00 each. Find the equilibrium point.

42. *Loudspeaker production.*   Fidelity Speakers, Inc., has fixed costs of $15,400 and variable costs of $100 for each pair of speakers produced. If the speakers sell for $250 a pair, how many pairs of speakers must be produced (and sold) in order to have enough profit to cover the fixed costs of two additional facilities? Assume that all fixed costs are identical.

Use a graphing calculator to solve.

43. *Dog food production.*   Puppy Love, Inc., will soon begin producing a new line of puppy food. The marketing department predicts that the demand function will be $D(p) = -14.97p + 987.35$ and the supply function will be $S(p) = 98.55p - 5.13$.

a) To the nearest cent, what price per unit should be charged in order to have equilibrium between supply and demand?

b) The production of the puppy food involves $87,985 in fixed costs and $5.15 per unit in variable costs. If the price per unit is the value you found in part (a), how many units must be sold in order to break even?

44. *Computer production.*   Number Cruncher Computers, Inc., is planning a new line of computers, each of which will sell for $970. The fixed costs in setting up production are $1,235,580 and the variable costs for each computer are $697.

a) What is the break-even point? (Round to the nearest whole number.)

b) The marketing department at Number Cruncher is not sure that $970 is the best price. Their demand function for the new computers is given by $D(p) = -304.5p + 374,580$ and their supply function is given by $S(p) = 788.7p - 576,504$. To the nearest dollar, what price p would result in equilibrium between supply and demand?

8 Study Summary

Because so many real-world problems translate into two or more equations in two or more variables, **systems of equations** are studied in great detail (p. 509). Most of the systems studied in this chapter are **consistent**, meaning that they have at least one solution, although we also studied some **inconsistent** systems, for which there is no solution (p. 513). The equations in the systems we solved were **independent**, except for those cases in which one equation could be written as a multiple and/or sum of the other equation(s) (such equations are called **dependent**) (p. 513).

Three methods—graphing, substitution, and elimination—can be used to solve systems of equations (pp. 511, 517, 519). Of the three methods, graphing is the easiest to visualize.

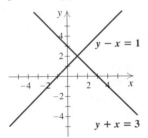

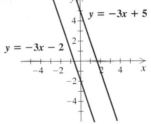

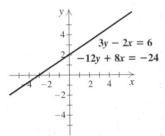

Graphs intersect at one point.	**Graphs are parallel.**	**Equations have the same graph.**
The system is *consistent* and has one solution. Since neither equation is a multiple of the other, they are *independent*.	The system is *inconsistent* because there is no solution. Since the equations are not equivalent, they are *independent*.	The system is *consistent* and has an infinite number of solutions. The equations are *dependent* since they are equivalent.

Graphing is especially useful when working with **revenue, cost,** and **profit** functions to determine a **break-even point** (p. 567). It is also used when working with **supply** and **demand** functions to determine an **equilibrium point** (p. 568).

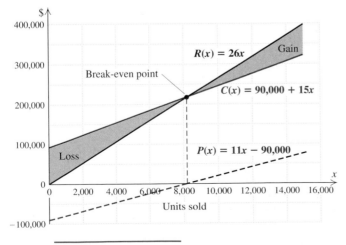

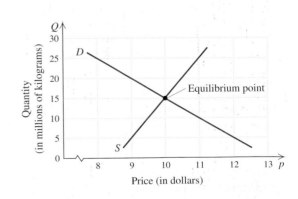

The substitution and elimination methods are the most commonly used methods for solving **total-value**, **mixture**, and **motion problems**.

Total Value

King Street Printing recently charged 1.9¢ per sheet of paper, but 2.4¢ per sheet for paper made of recycled fibers. Darren's bill for 150 sheets of paper was $3.41. How many sheets of each type were used? (Exercise 15, p. 535)

Mixture

Etch Clean Graphics uses one cleanser that is 25% acid and a second that is 50% acid. How many liters of each should be mixed to get 30 L of a solution that is 40% acid? (Exercise 24, p. 535)

Motion

Mia's motorboat took 3 hr to make a trip downstream with a 6-mph current. The return trip against the same current took 5 hr. Find the speed of the boat in still water. (Exercise 37, p. 537)

The elimination method can be extended to systems of three or more equations in three or more variables. One way in which this is accomplished is through the use of **matrices** (singular: **matrix**) (p. 554). A matrix is an array of numbers that are displayed in **rows** and **columns** (p. 554). The individual numbers are called **entries** or **elements** (p. 554).

By using **row-equivalent** operations, we can use matrices to solve systems of equations without needing to continually rewrite all of the variables (p. 557). The solution of systems is streamlined even further when **determinants** are used as part of **Cramer's rule** (pp. 559–562).

Determinant of a 2 × 2 Matrix

$$\begin{vmatrix} a & c \\ b & d \end{vmatrix} = ad - bc$$

Determinant of a 3 × 3 Matrix

$$\begin{vmatrix} a_1 & b_1 & c_1 \\ a_2 & b_2 & c_2 \\ a_3 & b_3 & c_3 \end{vmatrix} = a_1 \begin{vmatrix} b_2 & c_2 \\ b_3 & c_3 \end{vmatrix} - a_2 \begin{vmatrix} b_1 & c_1 \\ b_3 & c_3 \end{vmatrix} + a_3 \begin{vmatrix} b_1 & c_1 \\ b_2 & c_2 \end{vmatrix}$$

Cramer's Rule: 2 × 2 Systems

The solution of the system

$$a_1x + b_1y = c_1,$$
$$a_2x + b_2y = c_2,$$

if it is unique, is given by

$$x = \frac{\begin{vmatrix} c_1 & b_1 \\ c_2 & b_2 \end{vmatrix}}{\begin{vmatrix} a_1 & b_1 \\ a_2 & b_2 \end{vmatrix}}, \quad y = \frac{\begin{vmatrix} a_1 & c_1 \\ a_2 & c_2 \end{vmatrix}}{\begin{vmatrix} a_1 & b_1 \\ a_2 & b_2 \end{vmatrix}}.$$

Cramer's Rule: 3 × 3 Systems

The solution of the system

$$a_1x + b_1y + c_1z = d_1,$$
$$a_2x + b_2y + c_2z = d_2,$$
$$a_3x + b_3y + c_3z = d_3,$$

if it is unique, is given by

$$x = \frac{\begin{vmatrix} d_1 & b_1 & c_1 \\ d_2 & b_2 & c_2 \\ d_3 & b_3 & c_3 \end{vmatrix}}{\begin{vmatrix} a_1 & b_1 & c_1 \\ a_2 & b_2 & c_2 \\ a_3 & b_3 & c_3 \end{vmatrix}}, \quad y = \frac{\begin{vmatrix} a_1 & d_1 & c_1 \\ a_2 & d_2 & c_2 \\ a_3 & d_3 & c_3 \end{vmatrix}}{\begin{vmatrix} a_1 & b_1 & c_1 \\ a_2 & b_2 & c_2 \\ a_3 & b_3 & c_3 \end{vmatrix}}, \quad z = \frac{\begin{vmatrix} a_1 & b_1 & d_1 \\ a_2 & b_2 & d_2 \\ a_3 & b_3 & d_3 \end{vmatrix}}{\begin{vmatrix} a_1 & b_1 & c_1 \\ a_2 & b_2 & c_2 \\ a_3 & b_3 & c_3 \end{vmatrix}}.$$

8 Review Exercises

↩ *Concept Reinforcement*   *Complete each of the following sentences.*

1. The system

$$5x + 3y = 7,$$
$$y = 2x + 1$$

is most easily solved using the _____ method. [8.2]

2. The system

$$-2x + 3y = 8,$$
$$2x + 2y = 7$$

is most easily solved using the _____ method. [8.2]

3. A weakness in using graphs to solve a system is that when solutions involve fractions or decimals, the graph may yield only a(n)_____ solution. [8.2]

4. When one equation in a system is a multiple of another equation in that system, the equations are said to be _____. [8.1]

5. A system for which there is no solution is said to be _____. [8.1]

6. When using elimination to solve a system of two equations, if an identity is obtained, we know that there is a(n) _____ number of solutions. [8.2]

7. When we are graphing to solve a system of two equations, if there is no solution, the lines will be _____. [8.1]

8. When a matrix has the same number of rows and columns, it is said to be _____. [8.7]

9. Cramer's rule is a formula in which the numerator and the denominator of each fraction is a(n) _____. [8.7]

10. At the break-even point, the value of the profit function is _____. [8.8]

For Exercises 11–19, if a system has an infinite number of solutions, use set-builder notation to write the solution set. If a system has no solution, state this.

Solve graphically. [8.1]

11. $3x + 2y = -4,$
$y = 3x + 7$

12. $2x + 3y = 12,$
$4x - y = 10$

Solve using the substitution method. [8.2]

13. $9x - 6y = 2,$
$x = 4y + 5$

14. $y = x + 2,$
$y - x = 8$

15. $x - 3y = -2,$
$7y - 4x = 6$

Solve using the elimination method. [8.2]

16. $8x - 2y = 10,$
$-4y - 3x = -17$

17. $4x - 7y = 18,$
$9x + 14y = 40$

18. $3x - 5y = -4,$
$5x - 3y = 4$

19. $1.5x - 3 = -2y,$
$3x + 4y = 6$

Solve. [8.3]

20. Luther bought two DVD's and one videocassette for $48. If he had purchased one DVD and two videocassettes, he would have spent $3 less. What is the price of a DVD? What is the price of a videocassette?

21. A freight train leaves Houston at midnight traveling north at a speed of 44 mph. One hour later, a passenger train, going 55 mph, travels north from Houston on a parallel track. How many hours will the passenger train travel before it overtakes the freight train?

22. Yolanda wants 14 L of fruit punch that is 10% juice. At the store, she finds punch that is 15% juice and punch that is 8% juice. How much of each should she purchase?

Solve. If a system's equations are dependent or if there is no solution, state this.

23. $x + 4y + 3z = 2,$
$2x + y + z = 10,$
$-x + y + 2z = 8$
[8.4]

24. $4x + 2y - 6z = 34,$
$2x + y + 3z = 3,$
$6x + 3y - 3z = 37$
[8.4]

25. $2x - 5y - 2z = -4,$
$7x + 2y - 5z = -6,$
$-2x + 3y + 2z = 4$
[8.4]

26. $-5x + 5y = -6,$
$2x - 2y = 4$
[8.2]

27. $3x + y = 2,$
$x + 3y + z = 0,$
$x + z = 2$ [8.4]

Solve.

28. In triangle ABC, the measure of angle A is four times the measure of angle C, and the measure of angle B is $45°$ more than the measure of angle C. What are the measures of the angles of the triangle? [8.5]

29. *Nontoxic floor wax.* A nontoxic floor wax can be made from lemon juice and food-grade linseed oil. The amount of oil should be twice the amount of lemon juice. How much of each ingredient is needed to make 32 oz of floor wax? (The mix should be spread with a rag and buffed when dry.) [8.3]

30. *Lumber production.* Denison Lumber can convert logs into either lumber or plywood. In a given day, the mill turns out 42 pallets of plywood and lumber. It makes a profit of $75 on a pallet of lumber and $120 on a pallet of plywood. How many pallets of each type must be produced and sold in order to make a profit of $3735? [8.3]

Solve using matrices. Show your work. [8.6]

31. $3x + 4y = -13,$
$5x + 6y = 8$

32. $3x - y + z = -1,$
$2x + 3y + z = 4,$
$5x + 4y + 2z = 5$

Evaluate. [8.7]

33. $\begin{vmatrix} -2 & 4 \\ -3 & 5 \end{vmatrix}$

34. $\begin{vmatrix} 2 & 3 & 0 \\ 1 & 4 & -2 \\ 2 & -1 & 5 \end{vmatrix}$

Solve using Cramer's rule. Show your work. [8.7]

35. $2x + 3y = 6,$
$x - 4y = 14$

36. $2x + y + z = -2,$
$2x - y + 3z = 6,$
$3x - 5y + 4z = 7$

37. Find the equilibrium point for the demand and supply functions

$$S(p) = 60 + 7p$$

and

$$D(p) = 120 - 13p. \text{ [8.8]}$$

38. Auriel is beginning to produce organic honey. For the first year, the fixed costs for setting up production are $9000. The variable costs for producing each pint of honey are $0.75. The revenue from each pint of honey is $5.25. Find the following. [8.8]

a) The total cost $C(x)$ of producing x pints of honey

b) The total revenue $R(x)$ from the sale of x pints of honey

c) The total profit $P(x)$ from the production and sale of x pints of honey

d) The profit or loss from the production and sale of 1500 pints of honey; of 5000 pints of honey

e) The break-even point

SYNTHESIS

39. How would you go about solving a problem that involves four variables? [8.5]

40. Explain how a system of equations can be both dependent and inconsistent. [8.4]

41. Auriel is quitting a job that pays $27,000 a year to make honey (see Exercise 38). How many pints of honey must she produce and sell in order to make the same amount that she made in the job she left? [8.8]

42. Solve graphically:

$$y = x + 2,$$
$$y = x^2 + 2. \text{ [8.1]}$$

43. The graph of $f(x) = ax^2 + bx + c$ contains the points $(-2, 3)$, $(1, 1)$, and $(0, 3)$. Find a, b, and c and give a formula for the function. [8.5]

8 Chapter Test

1. Solve graphically:
$$2x + y = 8,$$
$$y - x = 2.$$

Solve, if possible, using the substitution method.

2. $x + 3y = -8,$
$4x - 3y = 23$

3. $2x + 4y = -6,$
$y = 3x - 9$

Solve, if possible, using the elimination method.

4. $4x - 6y = 3,$
$6x - 4y = -3$

5. $4y + 2x = 18,$
$3x + 6y = 26$

6. The perimeter of a rectangle is 96. The length of the rectangle is 6 less than twice the width. Find the dimensions of the rectangle.

7. Pepperidge Farm® Goldfish is a snack food for which 40% of its calories come from fat. Rold Gold® Pretzels receive 9% of their calories from fat. How many grams of each would be needed to make 620 g of a snack mix for which 15% of the calories are from fat?

Solve. If a system's equations are dependent or if there is no solution, state this.

8. $-3x + y - 2z = 8,$
$-x + 2y - z = 5,$
$2x + y + z = -3$

9. $6x + 2y - 4z = 15,$
$-3x - 4y + 2z = -6,$
$4x - 6y + 3z = 8$

10. $2x + 2y = 0,$
$4x + 4z = 4,$
$2x + y + z = 2$

11. $3x + 3z = 0,$
$2x + 2y = 2,$
$3y + 3z = 3$

Solve using matrices.

12. $7x - 8y = 10,$
$9x + 5y = -2$

13. $x + 3y - 3z = 12,$
$3x - y + 4z = 0,$
$-x + 2y - z = 1$

Evaluate.

14. $\begin{vmatrix} 4 & -2 \\ 3 & 7 \end{vmatrix}$

15. $\begin{vmatrix} 3 & 4 & 2 \\ 2 & -5 & 4 \\ 4 & 5 & -3 \end{vmatrix}$

16. Solve using Cramer's rule:
$$8x - 3y = 5,$$
$$2x + 6y = 3.$$

17. An electrician, a carpenter, and a plumber are hired to work on a house. The electrician earns $21 per hour, the carpenter $19.50 per hour, and the plumber $24 per hour. The first day on the job, they worked a total of 21.5 hr and earned a total of $469.50. If the plumber worked 2 more hours than the carpenter did, how many hours did each work?

18. Find the equilibrium point for the demand and supply functions
$$D(p) = 79 - 8p \quad \text{and} \quad S(p) = 37 + 6p.$$

19. Kick Back, Inc., is producing a new hammock. For the first year, the fixed costs for setting up production are $40,000. The variable costs for producing each hammock are $25. The revenue from each hammock is $70. Find the following.
   a) The total cost $C(x)$ of producing x hammocks
   b) The total revenue $R(x)$ from the sale of x hammocks
   c) The total profit $P(x)$ from the production and sale of x hammocks
   d) The profit or loss from the production and sale of 300 hammocks; of 900 hammocks
   e) The break-even point

SYNTHESIS

20. The graph of the function $f(x) = mx + b$ contains the points $(-1, 3)$ and $(-2, -4)$. Find m and b.

21. At a county fair, an adult's ticket sold for $5.50, a senior citizen's ticket for $4.00, and a child's ticket for $1.50. On opening day, the number of adults' and senior citizens' tickets sold was 30 more than the number of children's tickets sold. The number of adults' tickets sold was 6 more than four times the number of senior citizens' tickets sold. Total receipts from the ticket sales were $11,219.50. How many of each type of ticket were sold?

9

Inequalities and Problem Solving

AN APPLICATION

The yearly U.S. production of crude oil $C(t)$, in millions of barrels, t years after 1990, can be approximated by the equation

$$C(t) = -53.5t + 2683$$

(*Source*: Based on data from the *Statistical Abstract of the United States* 2003). Determine (using an inequality) those years for which domestic production will be less than 1750 million barrels.

This problem appears as Example 4 in Section 9.1.

Melissa Leadley
OILFIELD SERVICES ENGINEER
Bakersfield, California

When trying to find oil and gas, we are always solving for the unknown. We use math to calculate important information like oil saturation and rock permeability, which can influence multimillion dollar decisions on whether to produce an oil well, stimulate it, or abandon it.

*I*nequalities are mathematical sentences containing symbols such as < (is less than). In this chapter, we use the principles for solving inequalities developed in Chapter 2 to solve compound inequalities. We also combine our knowledge of inequalities and systems of equations to solve systems of inequalities.

9.1 Interval Notation and Applications

Solving Inequalities • Interval Notation • Problem Solving

Solving Inequalities

Recall from Chapter 1 that an **inequality** is any sentence containing $<, >, \le, \ge$, or $\ne$ (see Section 1.4)—for example,

$$-2 < a, \qquad x > 4, \qquad x + 3 \le 6, \qquad 6 - 7y \ge 10y - 4, \quad \text{and} \quad 5x \ne 10.$$

Any replacement for the variable that makes an inequality true is called a **solution**. The set of all solutions is called the **solution set**. When all solutions of an inequality are found, we say that we have **solved** the inequality.

We can use two principles, developed in Chapter 2, to solve inequalities.

The Addition Principle for Inequalities

For any real numbers a, b, and c:

$$a < b \text{ is equivalent to } a + c < b + c;$$
$$a > b \text{ is equivalent to } a + c > b + c.$$

Similar statements hold for $\le$ and $\ge$.

The Multiplication Principle for Inequalities

For any real numbers a and b, and for any *positive* number c,

$$a < b \text{ is equivalent to } ac < bc;$$
$$a > b \text{ is equivalent to } ac > bc.$$

For any real numbers a and b, and for any *negative* number c,

$$a < b \text{ is equivalent to } ac > bc;$$
$$a > b \text{ is equivalent to } ac < bc.$$

Similar statements hold for $\le$ and $\ge$.

The *graph* of an inequality is a visual representation of the inequality's solution set. An inequality in one variable can be graphed on a number line. Inequalities in two variables are graphed on a coordinate plane, and appear later in this chapter.

The solutions of the inequality $x < 4$ are graphed on the following number line:

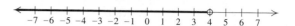

The open dot indicates that 4 is not a solution, and the shading indicates that all real numbers less than 4 are solutions.

We can write the solution set using *set-builder notation* (see Section 2.6):

$$\{x \mid x < 4\}.$$

This is read

"The set of all x such that x is less than 4."

Interval Notation

Another way to write solutions of an inequality in one variable is to use **interval notation**. Interval notation uses parentheses, ( ), and brackets, [ ].

If a and b are real numbers such that $a < b$, we define the **open interval** **(*a, b*)** as the set of all numbers x for which $a < x < b$. Thus,

$(a, b) = \{x \mid a < x < b\}.$ Parentheses are used to exclude endpoints.

Its graph excludes the endpoints:

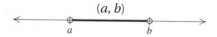

Caution! Do not confuse the *interval* (a, b) with the *ordered pair* (a, b). The context in which the notation appears usually makes the meaning clear.

The **closed interval [*a, b*]** is defined as the set of all numbers x for which $a \le x \le b$. Thus,

$[a, b] = \{x \mid a \le x \le b\}.$ Brackets are used to include endpoints.

Its graph includes the endpoints, as indicated by solid dots*:

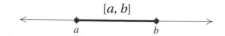

---

*Some books use the graphs ⟵(——)⟶ and ⟵[——]⟶ instead of, respectively, ⟵∘——∘⟶ and ⟵•——•⟶ .

There are two kinds of **half-open intervals**, defined as follows:

1. $(a, b] = \{x \mid a < x \le b\}$. This is open on the left. Its graph is as follows:

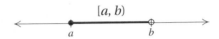

2. $[a, b) = \{x \mid a \le x < b\}$. This is open on the right. Its graph is as follows:

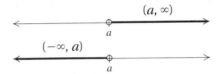

We use the symbols ∞ and $-\infty$ to represent positive and negative infinity, respectively. Thus the notation (a, ∞) represents the set of all real numbers greater than a, and $(-\infty, a)$ represents the set of all real numbers less than a.

The notations $[a, \infty)$ and $(-\infty, a]$ are used when we want to include the endpoint a.

EXAMPLE 1   Graph $y \ge -2$ on a number line and write the solution set using both set-builder and interval notations.

Solution   Using set-builder notation, we write the solution set as $\{y \mid y \ge -2\}$; using interval notation, we write $[-2, \infty)$. To graph the solution, we shade all numbers to the right of -2 and use a solid dot to indicate that -2 is also a solution.

$$\xleftarrow{\hspace{1cm}} \underset{-7 \ -6 \ -5 \ -4 \ -3 \ -2 \ -1 \ \ 0 \ \ 1 \ \ 2 \ \ 3 \ \ 4 \ \ 5 \ \ 6 \ \ 7}{\rule{1pt}{0pt}} \xrightarrow{\hspace{1cm}}$$

EXAMPLE 2   Solve: $16 - 7y \ge 10y - 4$. Write the solution set in both set-builder and interval notation.

Solution

$$16 - 7y \ge 10y - 4$$
$$-16 + 16 - 7y \ge -16 + 10y - 4 \qquad \text{Adding } -16 \text{ to both sides}$$
$$-7y \ge 10y - 20$$
$$-10y + (-7y) \ge -10y + 10y - 20 \qquad \text{Adding } -10y \text{ to both sides}$$
$$-17y \ge -20$$

The symbol must be reversed.

$$-\tfrac{1}{17} \cdot (-17y) \le -\tfrac{1}{17} \cdot (-20) \qquad \begin{array}{l}\text{Multiplying both sides by } -\tfrac{1}{17} \\ \text{or dividing both sides by } -17\end{array}$$

$$y \le \tfrac{20}{17}$$

The solution set is $\left\{y \mid y \leq \frac{20}{17}\right\}$, or $\left(-\infty, \frac{20}{17}\right]$.

> *Caution!*   Remember that whenever we multiply or divide both sides of an inequality by a negative number, we must reverse the inequality symbol.

We can use interval notation to describe the values for which one function's value is greater than another's.

EXAMPLE 3

Let $f(x) = -3(x + 8) - 5x$ and $g(x) = 4x - 9$. Find all values of x for which $f(x) > g(x)$.

Solution   We are looking for values of x for which $f(x) > g(x)$.

$$f(x) > g(x)$$

$-3(x + 8) - 5x > 4x - 9$	Replacing $f(x)$ with $-3(x + 8) - 5x$ and $g(x)$ with $4x - 9$
$-3x - 24 - 5x > 4x - 9$	Using the distributive law
$-24 - 8x > 4x - 9$	
$-24 - 8x + 8x > 4x - 9 + 8x$	Adding $8x$ to both sides
$-24 > 12x - 9$	
$-24 + 9 > 12x - 9 + 9$	Adding 9 to both sides
$-15 > 12x$	
$-\frac{5}{4} > x$	Dividing by 12 and simplifying

The symbol stays the same.

The solution set is $\left\{x \mid -\frac{5}{4} > x\right\}$, or $\left\{x \mid x < -\frac{5}{4}\right\}$, or $\left(-\infty, -\frac{5}{4}\right)$.

technology connection

On most calculators, Example 3 can be checked by graphing $y_1 = -3(x + 8) - 5x > 4x - 9$ ($>$ is often found by pressing **2ND** **MATH**). The solution set is then displayed as an interval (shown by a horizontal line 1 unit above the x-axis).

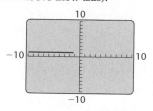

A check can also be made by graphing $y_1 = -3(x + 8) - 5x$ and $y_2 = 4x - 9$ and identifying those x-values for which $y_1 > y_2$.

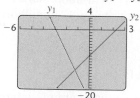

The INTERSECT option helps us find that $y_1 = y_2$ when $x = -1.25$. Note that $y_1 > y_2$ for x-values in the interval $(-\infty, -1.25)$.

Problem Solving

Many problem-solving situations translate to inequalities.

EXAMPLE 4

Domestic oil production.   The yearly U.S. production of crude oil $C(t)$, in millions of barrels, t years after 1990, can be approximated by the equation

$$C(t) = -53.5t + 2683$$

(*Source*: Based on data from the *Statistical Abstract of the United States* 2003). Determine (using an inequality) those years for which domestic production will be less than 1750 million barrels.

Solution

1. **Familiarize.**   We already have a formula. To become more familiar with it, we might make a substitution for t. Suppose we want to predict production after 20 years, in 2010. We substitute 20 for t:

$$C(20) = -53.5 \cdot 20 + 2683 = 1613.$$

We see that by 2010, production will be less than 1750 million barrels. To predict the exact years in which fewer than 1750 million barrels will be produced, we could check other substitutions. Instead, we proceed to the next step.

2. **Translate.**   We are asked to find the years for which U.S. oil production $C(t)$ will be *less than* 1750 million barrels. Thus we have

$$C(t) < 1750.$$

We replace $C(t)$ with $-53.5t + 2683$ to find the times t that solve the inequality:

$$-53.5t + 2683 < 1750. \qquad \text{Substituting}$$

3. **Carry out.**   We solve the inequality:

$$-53.5t + 2683 < 1750$$
$$-53.5t < -933 \qquad \text{Adding } -2683 \text{ to both sides}$$
$$t > 17.44. \qquad \text{Dividing both sides by } -53.5, \text{ reversing the symbol, and rounding}$$

4. **Check.**   A partial check is to substitute a value for t greater than 17.44. We did that in the *Familiarize* step.

5. **State.**   U.S. oil production will fall below 1750 million barrels about 17.4 years after 1990, or in 2007, and will remain below 1750 million for all years after that.

EXAMPLE 5

Job offers.   After graduation, Rose had two job offers in sales:

Uptown Fashions: A salary of $600 per month, plus a commission of 4% of sales;

Ergo Designs: A salary of $800 per month, plus a commission of 6% of sales in excess of $10,000.

If sales always exceed $10,000, for what amount of sales would Uptown Fashions provide higher pay?

Solution

1. **Familiarize.**   Listing the given information in a table will be helpful.

Uptown Fashions Monthly Income	Ergo Designs Monthly Income
$600 salary 4% of sales *Total*: $600 + 4% of sales	$800 salary 6% of sales over $10,000 *Total*: $800 + 6% of sales over $10,000

Next, suppose that Rose sold a certain amount—say, $12,000—in one month. Which plan would be better? Working for Uptown, she would earn $600 plus 4% of $12,000, or

$$600 + 0.04(12,000) = \$1080.$$

Since with Ergo Designs commissions are paid only on sales in excess of $10,000, Rose would earn $800 plus 6% of ($12,000 − $10,000), or

$$800 + 0.06(2000) = \$920.$$

This shows that for monthly sales of $12,000, Uptown pays better. Similar calculations will show that for sales of $30,000 a month, Ergo pays better. To determine *all* values for which Uptown pays more money, we must solve an inequality that is based on the calculations above.

2. **Translate.**   We let S = the amount of monthly sales, in dollars, and will assume $S > 10,000$ so that both plans will pay a commission. Examining the calculations in the *Familiarize* step, we see that monthly income from Uptown is $600 + 0.04S$ and from Ergo is $800 + 0.06(S − 10,000)$. We want to find all values of S for which

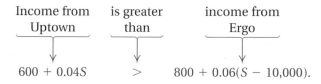

$$600 + 0.04S \quad > \quad 800 + 0.06(S - 10,000).$$

3. **Carry out.**   We solve the inequality:

$$600 + 0.04S > 800 + 0.06(S - 10,000)$$

$600 + 0.04S > 800 + 0.06S - 600$	Using the distributive law
$600 + 0.04S > 200 + 0.06S$	Combining like terms
$400 > 0.02S$	Subtracting 200 and $0.04S$ from both sides
$20,000 > S$, or $S < 20,000$.	Dividing both sides by 0.02

4. **Check.**   The above steps indicate that income from Uptown Fashions is higher than income from Ergo Designs for sales less than $20,000. In the *Familiarize* step, we saw that for sales of $12,000, Uptown pays more. Since $12,000 < 20,000$, this is a partial check.

5. **State.**   When monthly sales are less than $20,000, Uptown Fashions provides the higher pay.

Exercise Set

9.1

 Concept Reinforcement   Classify each of the following as equivalent inequalities, equivalent equations, equivalent expressions, or not equivalent.

1. $x - 7 > -2,\ x > 5$

2. $t + 3 < 1,\ t < 2$

3. $5x + 7 = 6 - 3x,\ 8x + 7 = 6$

4. $2(4x + 1),\ 8x + 2$

5. $-4t \leq 12,\ t \leq -3$

6. $\frac{3}{5}a + \frac{1}{5} = 2,\ 3a + 1 = 10$

7. $6a + 9,\ 3(2a + 3)$

8. $-4x \geq -8,\ x \geq 2$

9. $-\frac{1}{2}x < 7,\ x > 14$

10. $-\frac{1}{3}t \leq -5,\ t \geq 15$

Graph each inequality, and write the solution set using both interval and set-builder notations.

11. $y < 6$

12. $x > 4$

13. $x \geq -4$

14. $t \leq 6$

15. $t > -3$

16. $y < -3$

17. $x \leq -7$

18. $x \geq -6$

Solve. Then graph.

19. $y - 9 > -18$

20. $y - 8 > -14$

21. $y - 20 \leq -6$

22. $x - 11 \leq -2$

23. $9t < -81$

24. $8x \geq 24$

25. $-9x \geq -8.1$

26. $-8y \leq 3.2$

27. $-\frac{3}{4}x \geq -\frac{5}{8}$

28. $-\frac{5}{6}y \leq -\frac{3}{4}$

29. $\dfrac{2x + 7}{5} < -9$

30. $\dfrac{5y + 13}{4} > -2$

31. $\dfrac{3t - 7}{-4} \leq 5$

32. $\dfrac{2t - 9}{-3} \geq 7$

33. Let $f(x) = 2x + 1$ and $g(x) = x + 7$. Find all values of x for which $f(x) \geq g(x)$.

34. Let $f(x) = 5 - x$ and $g(x) = 4x - 5$. Find all values of x for which $f(x) \geq g(x)$.

35. Let $f(x) = 7 - 3x$ and $g(x) = 2x - 3$. Find all values of x for which $f(x) \leq g(x)$.

36. Let $f(x) = 8x - 9$ and $g(x) = 3x - 11$. Find all values of x for which $f(x) \leq g(x)$.

37. Let $f(x) = 2x - 7$ and $g(x) = 5x - 9$. Find all values of x for which $f(x) < g(x)$.

38. Let $f(x) = 0.4x + 5$ and $g(x) = 1.2x - 4$. Find all values of x for which $g(x) \geq f(x)$.

39. Let $f(x) = \frac{3}{8} + 2x$ and $g(x) = 3x - \frac{1}{8}$. Find all values of x for which $g(x) \geq f(x)$.

40. Let $f(x) = 2x + 1$ and $g(x) = -\frac{1}{2}x + 6$. Find all values of x for which $f(x) < g(x)$.

Solve.

41. $4(3y - 2) \geq 9(2y + 5)$

42. $4m + 7 \geq 14(m - 3)$

43. $5(t - 3) + 4t < 2(7 + 2t)$

44. $2(4 + 2x) > 2x + 3(2 - 5x)$

45. $5[3m - (m + 4)] > -2(m - 4)$

46. $8x - 3(3x + 2) - 5 \geq 3(x + 4) - 2x$

47. $19 - (2x + 3) \leq 2(x + 3) + x$

48. $13 - (2c + 2) \geq 2(c + 2) + 3c$

49. $\frac{1}{4}(8y + 4) - 17 < -\frac{1}{2}(4y - 8)$

50. $\frac{1}{3}(6x + 24) - 20 > -\frac{1}{4}(12x - 72)$

51. $2[8 - 4(3 - x)] - 2 \geq 8[2(4x - 3) + 7] - 50$

52. $5[3(7 - t) - 4(8 + 2t)] - 20 \leq -6[2(6 + 3t) - 4]$

Phone rates.   In Vermont, Verizon recently charged customers $13.55 for monthly service plus 2.2¢ per minute for local phone calls between 9 A.M. and 9 P.M. weekdays. The charge for off-peak local calls was 0.5¢ per minute. Calls were free after the total monthly charges reached $39.40.

53. Assume that only peak local calls were made. For how long must a customer speak on the phone if the $39.40 maximum charge is to apply?

54. Assume that only off-peak calls were made. For how long must a customer speak on the phone if the $39.40 maximum charge is to apply?

55. *Checking-account rates.*   The Hudson Bank offers two checking-account plans. Their Anywhere plan charges 20¢ per check whereas their Acu-checking plan costs $2 per month plus 12¢ per check. For what numbers of checks per month will the Acu-checking plan cost less?

56. *Moving costs.*   Musclebound Movers charges $85 plus $40 an hour to move households across town. Champion Moving charges $60 an hour for cross-town moves. For what lengths of time is Champion more expensive?

57. *Wages.*   Toni can be paid in one of two ways:

    Plan A: A salary of $400 per month, plus a commission of 8% of gross sales;

    Plan B: A salary of $610 per month, plus a commission of 5% of gross sales.

    For what amount of gross sales should Toni select plan A?

58. *Wages.*   Branford can be paid for his masonry work in one of two ways:

    Plan A: $300 plus $9.00 per hour;

    Plan B: Straight $12.50 per hour.

    Suppose that the job takes n hours. For what values of n is plan B better for Branford?

59. *Wedding costs.*   The Arnold Inn offers two plans for wedding parties. Under plan A, the inn charges $30 for each person in attendance. Under plan B, the inn charges $1300 plus $20 for each person in excess of the first 25 who attend. For what size parties will plan B cost less? (Assume that more than 25 guests will attend.)

60. *Insurance benefits.*   Bayside Insurance offers two plans. Under plan A, Giselle would pay the first $50 of her medical bills and 20% of all bills after that. Under plan B, Giselle would pay the first $250 of bills, but only 10% of the rest. For what amount of medical bills will plan B save Giselle money? (Assume that her bills will exceed $250.)

61. *Show business.*   Slobberbone receives $750 plus 15% of receipts over $750 for playing a club date. If a club charges a $6 cover charge, how many people must attend in order for the band to receive at least $1200?

62. *Temperature conversion.*   The function
$$C(F) = \tfrac{5}{9}(F - 32)$$
can be used to find the Celsius temperature $C(F)$ that corresponds to $F°$ Fahrenheit.
    a) Gold is solid at Celsius temperatures less than 1063°C. Find the Fahrenheit temperatures for which gold is solid.
    b) Silver is solid at Celsius temperatures less than 960.8°C. Find the Fahrenheit temperatures for which silver is solid.

63. *Manufacturing.*   Ergs, Inc., is planning to make a new kind of lamp. Fixed costs will be $90,000, and variable costs will be $15 for the production of each lamp. The total-cost function for x lamps is
$$C(x) = 90,000 + 15x.$$
The company makes $26 in revenue for each lamp sold. The total-revenue function for x lamps is
$$R(x) = 26x.$$
(See Section 8.8.)
    a) When $R(x) < C(x)$, the company loses money. Find the values of x for which the company loses money.
    b) When $R(x) > C(x)$, the company makes a profit. Find the values of x for which the company makes a profit.

64. *Publishing.*   The demand and supply functions for a locally produced poetry book are approximated by
$$D(p) = 2000 - 60p \quad \text{and}$$
$$S(p) = 460 + 94p,$$
where p is the price in dollars (see Section 8.8).

a) Find those values of p for which demand exceeds supply.

b) Find those values of p for which demand is less than supply.

65. Explain in your own words why the inequality symbol must be reversed when both sides of an inequality are multiplied by a negative number.

66. Why isn't roster notation used to write solutions of inequalities?

SKILL MAINTENANCE

Find the domain of f. [7.2]

67. $f(x) = \dfrac{3}{x-2}$

68. $f(x) = \dfrac{x-5}{4x+12}$

69. $f(x) = \dfrac{5x}{7-2x}$

70. $f(x) = \dfrac{x+3}{9-4x}$

Simplify. [1.8]

71. $9x - 2(x-5)$

72. $8x + 7(2x-1)$

SYNTHESIS

73. A Presto photocopier costs \$510 and an Exact Image photocopier costs \$590. Write a problem that involves the cost of the copiers, the cost per page of photocopies, and the number of copies for which the Presto machine is the more expensive machine to own.

74. Explain how the addition principle can be used to avoid ever needing to multiply or divide both sides of an inequality by a negative number.

Solve for x and y. Assume that a, b, c, d, and m are positive constants.

75. $3ax + 2x \geq 5ax - 4$; assume $a > 1$

76. $6by - 4y \leq 7by + 10$

77. $a(by - 2) \geq b(2y + 5)$; assume $a > 2$

78. $c(6x - 4) < d(3 + 2x)$; assume $3c > d$

79. $c(2 - 5x) + dx > m(4 + 2x)$; assume $5c + 2m < d$

80. $a(3 - 4x) + cx < d(5x + 2)$; assume $c > 4a + 5d$

Determine whether each statement is true or false. If false, give an example that shows this.

81. For any real numbers a, b, c, and d, if $a < b$ and $c < d$, then $a - c < b - d$.

82. For all real numbers x and y, if $x < y$, then $x^2 < y^2$.

83. Are the inequalities
$$x < 3 \quad \text{and} \quad x + \frac{1}{x} < 3 + \frac{1}{x}$$
equivalent? Why or why not?

84. Are the inequalities
$$x < 3 \quad \text{and} \quad 0 \cdot x < 0 \cdot 3$$
equivalent? Why or why not?

Solve. Then graph.

85. $x + 5 \leq 5 + x$

86. $x + 8 < 3 + x$

87. $x^2 > 0$

88. Assume that the graphs of $y_1 = -\frac{1}{2}x + 5$, $y_2 = x - 1$, and $y_3 = 2x - 3$ are as shown below. Solve each inequality, referring only to the figure.

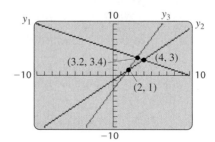

a) $-\frac{1}{2}x + 5 > x - 1$

b) $x - 1 \leq 2x - 3$

c) $2x - 3 \geq -\frac{1}{2}x + 5$

89. Using an approach similar to that in the Technology Connection on p. 581, use a graphing calculator to check your answers to Exercises 19, 35, 51, and 55.

CORNER

Reduce, Reuse, and Recycle

Focus: Inequalities and problem solving
Time: 15–20 minutes
Group size: 2

In the United States, the amount of solid waste (rubbish) being recycled is slowly catching up to the amount being generated. In 1991, each person generated, on average, 4.3 lb of solid waste every day, of which 0.8 lb was recycled. In 2001, each person generated, on average, 4.4 lb of solid waste, of which 1.3 lb was recycled. (*Sources*: U.S. Bureau of the Census, *Statistical Abstract of the United States* 2003, and EPA Municipal Solid Waste Factbook)

ACTIVITY

Assume that the amount of solid waste being generated and the amount recycled are both increasing linearly. One group member should find a linear function w for which $w(t)$ represents the number of pounds of waste generated per person per day t years after 1991. The other group member should find a linear function r for which $r(t)$ represents the number of pounds recycled per person per day t years after 1991. Finally, working together, the group should determine those years for which the amount recycled will meet or exceed the amount generated.

9.2 Intersections, Unions, and Compound Inequalities

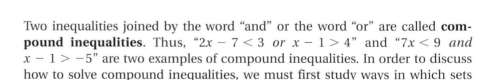

Intersections of Sets and Conjunctions of Sentences   •
Unions of Sets and Disjunctions of Sentences   •   Interval
Notation and Domains

Two inequalities joined by the word "and" or the word "or" are called **compound inequalities**. Thus, "$2x - 7 < 3$ *or* $x - 1 > 4$" and "$7x < 9$ *and* $x - 1 > -5$" are two examples of compound inequalities. In order to discuss how to solve compound inequalities, we must first study ways in which sets can be combined.

Intersections of Sets and Conjunctions of Sentences

The **intersection** of two sets A and B is the set of all elements that are common to both A and B. We denote the intersection of sets A and B as

$$A \cap B.$$

The intersection of two sets is represented by the purple region shown in the figure at left. For example, if $A = \{$all students who are more than $5'4''$ tall$\}$ and $B = \{$all students who weigh more than 120 lb$\}$, then $A \cap B = \{$all students who are more than $5'4''$ tall and weigh more than 120 lb$\}$.

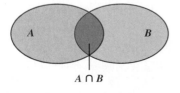

$A \cap B$

EXAMPLE 1   Find the intersection: $\{1, 2, 3, 4, 5\} \cap \{-2, -1, 0, 1, 2, 3\}$.

Solution   The numbers 1, 2, and 3 are common to both sets, so the intersection is $\{1, 2, 3\}$.

────────────

When two or more sentences are joined by the word *and* to make a compound sentence, the new sentence is called a **conjunction** of the sentences. The following is a conjunction of inequalities:

$$-2 < x \quad and \quad x < 1.$$

A number is a solution of a conjunction if it is a solution of *both* of the separate parts. For example, -1 is a solution because it is a solution of $-2 < x$ as well as $x < 1$.

Below we show the graph of $-2 < x$, followed by the graph of $x < 1$, and finally the graph of the conjunction $-2 < x$ and $x < 1$. *Note that the solution set of a conjunction is the intersection of the solution sets of the individual sentences.*

$\{x \mid -2 < x\}$ ← graph line → $(-2, \infty)$

$\{x \mid x < 1\}$ ← graph line → $(-\infty, 1)$

$\{x \mid -2 < x\} \cap \{x \mid x < 1\}$
$= \{x \mid -2 < x \text{ and } x < 1\}$ ← graph line → $(-2, 1)$

Because there are numbers that are both greater than -2 and less than 1, the conjunction $-2 < x$ and $x < 1$ can be abbreviated by $-2 < x < 1$. Thus the interval $(-2, 1)$ can be represented as $\{x \mid -2 < x < 1\}$, the set of all numbers that are *simultaneously* greater than -2 *and* less than 1. Note that for $a < b$,

$a < x \quad and \quad x < b \quad$ **can be abbreviated** $\quad a < x < b$;

and, equivalently,

$b > x \quad and \quad x > a \quad$ **can be abbreviated** $\quad b > x > a.$

EXAMPLE 2   Solve and graph: $-1 \le 2x + 5 < 13$.

Solution   This inequality is an abbreviation for the conjunction

$$-1 \le 2x + 5 \quad and \quad 2x + 5 < 13.$$

The word *and* corresponds to set *intersection*. To solve the conjunction, we solve each of the two inequalities separately and then find the intersection of the solution sets:

$-1 \le 2x + 5$	and	$2x + 5 < 13$
$-6 \le 2x$	and	$2x < 8$ Subtracting 5 from both sides of each inequality
$-3 \le x$	and	$x < 4.$ Dividing both sides of each inequality by 2

We now abbreviate the answer:

$$-3 \le x < 4.$$

The solution set is $\{x \mid -3 \le x < 4\}$, or, in interval notation, $[-3, 4)$. The graph is the intersection of the two separate solution sets.

$\{x \mid -3 \le x\}$

$[-3, \infty)$

$\{x \mid x < 4\}$

$(-\infty, 4)$

$\{x \mid -3 \le x\} \cap \{x \mid x < 4\}$
$= \{x \mid -3 \le x < 4\}$

$[-3, 4)$

The steps in Example 2 are often combined as follows:

$$-1 \le 2x + 5 < 13$$
$$-1 - 5 \le 2x + 5 - 5 < 13 - 5 \qquad \text{Subtracting 5 from all three regions}$$
$$-6 \le 2x < 8$$
$$-3 \le x < 4.$$

Such an approach saves some writing and will prove useful in Section 9.3.

> *Caution!*   The abbreviated form of a conjunction, like $-3 \le x < 4$, can be written only if both inequality symbols point in the same direction. It is *not acceptable* to write a sentence like $-1 > x < 5$ since doing so does not indicate if *both* $-1 > x$ and $x < 5$ must be true or if it is enough for one of the separate inequalities to be true.

EXAMPLE 3   Solve and graph: $2x - 5 \ge -3$ *and* $5x + 2 \ge 17$.

Solution   We first solve each inequality separately, retaining the word *and*:

$$2x - 5 \ge -3 \quad and \quad 5x + 2 \ge 17$$
$$2x \ge 2 \quad and \quad 5x \ge 15$$
$$x \ge 1 \quad and \quad x \ge 3.$$

Next, we find the intersection of the two separate solution sets.

$\{x \mid x \ge 1\}$

$[1, \infty)$

$\{x \mid x \ge 3\}$

$[3, \infty)$

$\{x \mid x \ge 1\} \cap \{x \mid x \ge 3\}$
$= \{x \mid x \ge 3\}$

$[3, \infty)$

The numbers common to both sets are those greater than or equal to 3. Thus the solution set is $\{x \mid x \geq 3\}$, or, in interval notation, $[3, \infty)$. You should check that any number in $[3, \infty)$ satisfies the conjunction whereas numbers outside $[3, \infty)$ do not.

Mathematical Use of the Word "and"

The word "and" corresponds to "intersection" and to the symbol " $\cap$ ". Any solution of a conjunction must make each part of the conjunction true.

Sometimes there is no way to solve both parts of a conjunction at once.

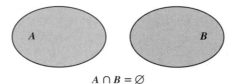

$A \cap B = \varnothing$

When $A \cap B = \varnothing$, A and B are said to be *disjoint*.

EXAMPLE 4   Solve and graph: $2x - 3 > 1$ *and* $3x - 1 < 2$.

Solution   We solve each inequality separately:

$$2x - 3 > 1 \quad and \quad 3x - 1 < 2$$
$$2x > 4 \quad and \quad 3x < 3$$
$$x > 2 \quad and \quad x < 1.$$

The solution set is the intersection of the individual inequalities.

$\{x \mid x > 2\}$ $(2, \infty)$

$\{x \mid x < 1\}$ $(-\infty, 1)$

$\{x \mid x > 2\} \cap \{x \mid x < 1\}$
$= \{x \mid x > 2 \ and \ x < 1\} = \varnothing$ $\varnothing$

Since no number is both greater than 2 and less than 1, the solution set is the empty set, $\varnothing$.

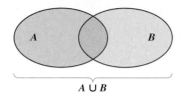

$A \cup B$

Unions of Sets and Disjunctions of Sentences

The **union** of two sets A and B is the collection of elements belonging to A and/or B. We denote the union of A and B by

$$A \cup B.$$

The union of two sets is often pictured as shown at left. For example, if $A =$ {all parents} and $B =$ {all people who are at least 30 yr old}, then $A \cup B =$ {all people who are parents *or* who are at least 30 yr old}. Note that this set includes people who are parents *and* at least 30 yr old.

EXAMPLE 5   Find the union: $\{2, 3, 4\} \cup \{3, 5, 7\}$.

Solution   The numbers in either or both sets are 2, 3, 4, 5, and 7, so the union is $\{2, 3, 4, 5, 7\}$.

Student Notes

Remember that the union or intersection of two sets is itself a set and should be written with set braces.

When two or more sentences are joined by the word *or* to make a compound sentence, the new sentence is called a **disjunction** of the sentences. Here is an example:

$$x < -3 \quad or \quad x > 3.$$

A number is a solution of a disjunction if it is a solution of at least one of the separate parts. For example, -5 is a solution of this disjunction since -5 is a solution of $x < -3$. Below we show the graph of $x < -3$, followed by the graph of $x > 3$, and finally the graph of the disjunction $x < -3$ or $x > 3$. *Note that the solution set of a disjunction is the union of the solution sets of the individual sentences.*

$\{x \mid x < -3\}$
$-6\ -5\ -4\ -3\ -2\ -1\ \ 0\ \ 1\ \ 2\ \ 3\ \ 4\ \ 5\ \ 6$
$(-\infty, -3)$

$\{x \mid x > 3\}$
$-6\ -5\ -4\ -3\ -2\ -1\ \ 0\ \ 1\ \ 2\ \ 3\ \ 4\ \ 5\ \ 6$
$(3, \infty)$

$\{x \mid x < -3\} \cup \{x \mid x > 3\}$
$= \{x \mid x < -3 \ or \ x > 3\}$
$-6\ -5\ -4\ -3\ -2\ -1\ \ 0\ \ 1\ \ 2\ \ 3\ \ 4\ \ 5\ \ 6$
$(-\infty, -3) \cup (3, \infty)$

The solution set of $x < -3$ or $x > 3$ is $\{x \mid x < -3 \ or \ x > 3\}$, or, in interval notation, $(-\infty, -3) \cup (3, \infty)$. There is no simpler way to write the solution.

> ### Mathematical Use of the Word "or"
>
> The word "or" corresponds to "union" and to the symbol " $\cup$ ". For a number to be a solution of a disjunction, it must be in *at least one* of the solution sets of the individual sentences.

EXAMPLE 6   Solve and graph: $7 + 2x < -1$ *or* $13 - 5x \le 3$.

Solution   We solve each inequality separately, retaining the word *or*:

$$7 + 2x < -1 \quad or \quad 13 - 5x \le 3$$
$$2x < -8 \quad or \quad -5x \le -10$$

↑   Dividing by a negative and
↓   reversing the symbol

$$x < -4 \quad or \qquad x \ge 2.$$

To find the solution set of the disjunction, we consider the individual graphs. We graph $x < -4$ and then $x \ge 2$. Then we take the union of the graphs.

$\{x \mid x < -4\}$ (number line: open circle at -4, shaded left) $(-\infty, -4)$

$\{x \mid x \ge 2\}$ (number line: closed circle at 2, shaded right) $[2, \infty)$

$\{x \mid x < -4\} \cup \{x \mid x \ge 2\}$
$= \{x \mid x < -4 \text{ or } x \ge 2\}$ (number line) $(-\infty, -4) \cup [2, \infty)$

The solution set is $\{x \mid x < -4 \text{ or } x \ge 2\}$, or $(-\infty, -4) \cup [2, \infty)$.

> **Caution!**   A compound inequality like
>
> $$x < -4 \quad or \quad x \ge 2,$$
>
> as in Example 6, *cannot* be expressed as $2 \le x < -4$ because to do so would be to say that x is *simultaneously* less than -4 and greater than or equal to 2. No number is both less than -4 *and* greater than 2, but many are less than -4 *or* greater than 2.

EXAMPLE 7   Solve: $-2x - 5 < -2$ *or* $x - 3 < -10$.

Solution   We solve the individual inequalities separately, retaining the word *or*:

$$-2x - 5 < -2 \quad or \quad x - 3 < -10$$
$$-2x < 3 \qquad or \qquad x < -7$$

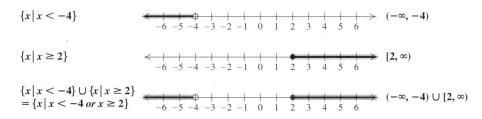

Dividing by a negative and reversing the symbol   Keep the word "or."

$$x > -\tfrac{3}{2} \quad or \qquad x < -7.$$

(number line: from -10 to 2, open circle at -7 shaded left, open circle at $-\tfrac{3}{2}$ shaded right)

The solution set is $\left\{x \mid x < -7 \text{ or } x > -\tfrac{3}{2}\right\}$, or $(-\infty, -7) \cup \left(-\tfrac{3}{2}, \infty\right)$.

EXAMPLE 8   Solve: $3x - 11 < 4$ *or* $4x + 9 \geq 1$.

Solution   We solve the individual inequalities separately, retaining the word *or*:

$$3x - 11 < 4 \quad or \quad 4x + 9 \geq 1$$
$$3x < 15 \quad or \quad 4x \geq -8$$
$$x < 5 \quad or \quad x \geq -2.$$
$$\underset{\text{Keep the word "or."}}{}$$

To find the solution set, we first look at the individual graphs.

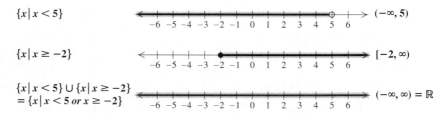

$\{x \mid x < 5\}$ $(-\infty, 5)$

$\{x \mid x \geq -2\}$ $[-2, \infty)$

$\{x \mid x < 5\} \cup \{x \mid x \geq -2\}$
$= \{x \mid x < 5 \ or \ x \geq -2\}$ $(-\infty, \infty) = \mathbb{R}$

Since *all* numbers are less than 5 or greater than or equal to -2, the two sets fill the entire number line. Thus the solution set is $\mathbb{R}$, the set of all real numbers.

Interval Notation and Domains

In Section 7.2, we saw that if $g(x) = \dfrac{5x - 2}{3x - 7}$, then the domain of $g = \{x \mid x$ is a real number *and* $x \neq \frac{7}{3}\}$. We can now represent such a set using interval notation:

$$\left\{x \mid x \text{ is a real number } and \ x \neq \tfrac{7}{3}\right\} = \left(-\infty, \tfrac{7}{3}\right) \cup \left(\tfrac{7}{3}, \infty\right).$$

$$\left(-\infty, \tfrac{7}{3}\right) \cup \left(\tfrac{7}{3}, \infty\right)$$

EXAMPLE 9   Use interval notation to write the domain of f if $f(x) = \sqrt{x + 2}$.

Solution   The expression $\sqrt{x + 2}$ is not a real number when $x + 2$ is negative. Thus the domain of f is the set of all x-values for which $x + 2 \geq 0$:

$$x + 2 \geq 0 \qquad x + 2 \text{ cannot be negative.}$$
$$x \geq -2. \qquad \text{Adding } -2 \text{ to both sides}$$

$$[-2, \infty)$$

We have the domain of $f = \{x \mid x \geq -2\} = [-2, \infty)$.

Exercise Set

9.2

FOR EXTRA HELP

Student's
Solutions
Manual

Digital Video Tutor
CD 5
Videotape 9

AW Math
Tutor Center

MathXL Tutorials
on CD

MathXL

MyMathLab
MyMathLab

Concept Reinforcement   *In each of Exercises 1–10, match the set with the most appropriate choice from the column on the right.*

1. ____ $\{x \mid x < -2 \text{ or } x > 2\}$

2. ____ $\{x \mid x < -2 \text{ and } x > 2\}$

3. ____ $\{x \mid x > -2\} \cap \{x \mid x < 2\}$

4. ____ $\{x \mid x \le -2\} \cup \{x \mid x \ge 2\}$

5. ____ $\{x \mid x \le -2\} \cup \{x \mid x \le 2\}$

6. ____ $\{x \mid x \le -2\} \cap \{x \mid x \le 2\}$

7. ____ $\{x \mid x \ge -2\} \cap \{x \mid x \ge 2\}$

8. ____ $\{x \mid x \ge -2\} \cup \{x \mid x \ge 2\}$

9. ____ $\{x \mid x \le 2\} \text{ and } \{x \mid x \ge -2\}$

10. ____ $\{x \mid x \le 2\} \text{ or } \{x \mid x \ge -2\}$

a)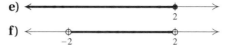

b)

c)

d)

e)

f)

g)

h)

i) $\mathbb{R}$

j) $\varnothing$

Find each indicated intersection or union.

11. $\{5, 9, 11\} \cap \{9, 11, 18\}$

12. $\{2, 4, 8\} \cup \{8, 9, 10\}$

13. $\{0, 5, 10, 15\} \cup \{5, 15, 20\}$

14. $\{2, 5, 9, 13\} \cap \{5, 8, 10\}$

15. $\{a, b, c, d, e, f\} \cap \{b, d, f\}$

16. $\{a, b, c\} \cup \{a, c\}$

17. $\{r, s, t\} \cup \{r, u, t, s, v\}$

18. $\{m, n, o, p\} \cap \{m, o, p\}$

19. $\{3, 6, 9, 12\} \cap \{5, 10, 15\}$

20. $\{1, 5, 9\} \cup \{4, 6, 8\}$

21. $\{3, 5, 7\} \cup \varnothing$

22. $\{3, 5, 7\} \cap \varnothing$

Graph and write interval notation for each compound inequality.

23. $3 < x < 7$

24. $0 \le y \le 4$

25. $-6 \le y \le -2$

26. $-9 \le x < -5$

27. $x < -1 \text{ or } x > 4$

28. $x < -5 \text{ or } x > 1$

29. $x \le -2 \text{ or } x > 1$

30. $x \le -5 \text{ or } x > 2$

31. $-4 \le -x < 2$

32. $x > -7 \text{ and } x < -2$

33. $x > -2 \text{ and } x < 4$

34. $3 > -x \ge -1$

35. $5 > a \text{ or } a > 7$

36. $t \ge 2 \text{ or } -3 > t$

37. $x \ge 5 \text{ or } -x \ge 4$

38. $-x < 3 \text{ or } x < -6$

39. $7 > y \text{ and } y \ge -3$

40. $6 > -x \ge 0$

41. $x < 7 \text{ and } x \ge 3$

42. $x \ge -3 \text{ and } x < 3$

Aha! 43. $t < 2 \text{ or } t < 5$

44. $t > 4 \text{ or } t > -1$

Solve and graph each solution set.

45. $-2 < t + 1 < 8$

46. $-3 < t + 1 \le 5$

47. $2 < x + 3 \text{ and } x + 1 \le 5$

48. $-1 < x + 2 \text{ and } x - 4 < 3$

49. $-7 \leq 2a - 3$ and $3a + 1 < 7$

50. $-4 \leq 3n + 5$ and $2n - 3 \leq 7$

Aha! **51.** $x + 7 \leq -2$ or $x + 7 \geq -3$

52. $x + 5 < -3$ or $x + 5 \geq 4$

53. $5 > \dfrac{x - 3}{4} > 1$

54. $3 \geq \dfrac{x - 1}{2} \geq -4$

55. $-7 \leq 4x + 5 \leq 13$

56. $-4 \leq 2x + 3 \leq 15$

57. $2 \leq f(x) \leq 8$, where $f(x) = 3x - 1$

58. $7 \geq g(x) \geq -2$, where $g(x) = 3x - 5$

59. $-21 \leq f(x) < 0$, where $f(x) = -2x - 7$

60. $4 > g(t) \geq 2$, where $g(t) = -3t - 8$

61. $f(x) \leq 2$ or $f(x) \geq 8$, where $f(x) = 3x - 1$

62. $g(x) \leq -2$ or $g(x) \geq 10$, where $g(x) = 3x - 5$

63. $f(x) < -3$ or $f(x) > 5$, where $f(x) = 2x - 7$

64. $g(x) < -7$ or $g(x) > 7$, where $g(x) = 3x + 5$

65. $6 > 2a - 1$ or $-4 \leq -3a + 2$

66. $3a - 7 > -10$ or $5a + 2 \leq 22$

67. $a + 3 < -2$ and $3a - 4 < 8$

68. $1 - a < -2$ and $2a + 1 > 9$

69. $3x + 2 < 2$ or $4 - 2x < 14$

70. $2x - 1 > 5$ or $3 - 2x \geq 7$

71. $2t - 7 \leq 5$ or $5 - 2t > 3$

72. $5 - 3a \leq 8$ or $2a + 1 > 7$

For $f(x)$ as given, use interval notation to write the domain of f.

73. $f(x) = \dfrac{9}{x + 8}$

74. $f(x) = \dfrac{2}{x + 3}$

75. $f(x) = \sqrt{x - 6}$

76. $f(x) = \sqrt{x - 2}$

77. $f(x) = \dfrac{x + 3}{2x - 8}$

78. $f(x) = \dfrac{x - 1}{3x + 6}$

79. $f(x) = \sqrt{2x + 7}$

80. $f(x) = \sqrt{8 - 5x}$

81. $f(x) = \sqrt{8 - 2x}$

82. $f(x) = \sqrt{10 - 2x}$

83. Why can the conjunction $2 < x$ and $x < 5$ be rewritten as $2 < x < 5$, but the disjunction $2 < x$ or $x < 5$ cannot be rewritten as $2 < x < 5$?

84. Can the solution set of a disjunction be empty? Why or why not?

SKILL MAINTENANCE

Graph.

85. $y = 5$ [3.6]

86. $y = -2$ [3.6]

87. $f(x) = |x|$ [7.3]

88. $g(x) = x - 1$ [7.3]

Solve each system graphically. [8.1]

89. $y = x - 3$,
$y = 5$

90. $y = x + 2$,
$y = -3$

SYNTHESIS

91. What can you conclude about a, b, c, and d, if $[a, b] \cup [c, d] = [a, d]$? Why?

92. What can you conclude about a, b, c, and d, if $[a, b] \cap [c, d] = [a, b]$? Why?

93. Use the accompanying graph of $f(x) = 2x - 5$ to solve $-7 < 2x - 5 < 7$.

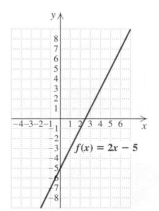

94. Use the accompanying graph of $g(x) = 4 - x$ to solve $4 - x < -2$ or $4 - x > 7$.

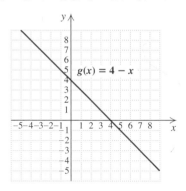

95. *Childless women.* On the basis of trends from the late 1900s, the function given by

$$P(t) = 0.44t + 10.2$$

can be used to estimate the percentage of U.S. women age 40–44, $P(t)$, t years after 1980, who have not given birth. For what years will the percentage of childless 40–44-year-old women be between 19 and 30 percent?

Sources: Based on data from the U.S. Bureau of the Census; *Deseret Morning News*, 11/03

96. *Pressure at sea depth.* The function given by

$$P(d) = 1 + \frac{d}{33}$$

gives the pressure, in atmospheres (atm), at a depth of d feet in the sea. For what depths d is the pressure at least 1 atm and at most 7 atm?

97. *Converting dress sizes.* The function given by

$$f(x) = 2(x + 10)$$

can be used to convert dress sizes x in the United States to dress sizes $f(x)$ in Italy. For what dress sizes in the United States will dress sizes in Italy be between 32 and 46?

98. *Solid-waste generation.* The function given by

$$w(t) = 0.01t + 4.3$$

can be used to estimate the number of pounds of solid waste, $w(t)$, produced daily, on average, by each person in the United States, t years after 1991. For what years will waste production range from 4.5 to 4.75 lb per person per day?

99. *Records in the women's 100-m dash.* Florence Griffith Joyner set a world record of 10.49 sec in the women's 100-m dash in 1988. The function given by

$$R(t) = -0.0433t + 10.49$$

can be used to predict the world record in the women's 100-m dash t years after 1988. Predict (using an inequality) those years for which the world record was between 11.5 and 10.8 sec. (Measure from the middle of 1988.)

Sources: *Guinness Book of World Records* 2004; www.Runnersworld.com

100. *Temperatures of liquids.* The formula

$$C = \tfrac{5}{9}(F - 32)$$

can be used to convert Fahrenheit temperatures F to Celsius temperatures C.

a) Gold is liquid for Celsius temperatures C such that $1063° \leq C < 2660°$. Find a comparable inequality for Fahrenheit temperatures.

b) Silver is liquid for Celsius temperatures C such that $960.8° \leq C < 2180°$. Find a comparable inequality for Fahrenheit temperatures.

101. *Minimizing tolls.* A $3.00 toll is charged to cross the bridge from Sanibel Island to mainland Florida. A six-month pass, costing $15.00, reduces the toll to $0.50. A one-year pass, costing $150, allows for free crossings. How many crossings per year does it take, on average, for two consecutive six-month passes to be the most economical choice? Assume a constant number of trips per month.

Source: www.leewayinfo.com

Solve and graph.

102. $4a - 2 \leq a + 1 \leq 3a + 4$

103. $4m - 8 > 6m + 5$ or $5m - 8 < -2$

104. $x - 10 < 5x + 6 \leq x + 10$

105. $3x < 4 - 5x < 5 + 3x$

Determine whether each sentence is true or false for all real numbers a, b, and c.

106. If $-b < -a$, then $a < b$.

107. If $a \le c$ and $c \le b$, then $b > a$.

108. If $a < c$ and $b < c$, then $a < b$.

109. If $-a < c$ and $-c > b$, then $a > b$.

For f(x) as given, use interval notation to write the domain of f.

110. $f(x) = \dfrac{\sqrt{5 + 2x}}{x - 1}$

111. $f(x) = \dfrac{\sqrt{3 - 4x}}{x + 7}$

112. Let $y_1 = -1$, $y_2 = 2x + 5$, and $y_3 = 13$. Then use the graphs of y_1, y_2, and y_3 to check the solution to Example 2.

113. Let $y_1 = -2x - 5$, $y_2 = -2$, $y_3 = x - 3$, and $y_4 = -10$. Then use the graphs of y_1, y_2, y_3, and y_4 to check the solution to Example 7.

114. Use a graphing calculator to check your answers to Exercises 43–46 and Exercises 63–66.

115. On many graphing calculators, the TEST key provides access to inequality symbols, while the LOGIC option of that same key accesses the conjunction *and* and the disjunction *or*. Thus, if $y_1 = x > -2$ and $y_2 = x < 4$, Exercise 33 can be checked by forming the expression $y_3 = y_1$ *and* y_2. The interval(s) in the solution set appears as a horizontal line 1 unit above the *x*-axis. (Be careful to "deselect" y_1 and y_2 so that only y_3 is drawn.)

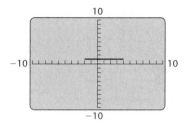

CORNER

Saving on Shipping Costs

Focus: Compound inequalities and solution sets

Time: 20–30 minutes

Group size: 2–3

For Priority Mail, the United States Postal Service charges (at present, in 2005) $3.85 for the first pound plus $0.51 for each pound or part thereof after the first. For UPS Ground Residential shipping, the first pound costs $6.25 and each additional pound or part thereof costs $0.17.*

_____

*This activity is based on an article by Michael Contino in *Mathematics Teacher*, May 1995.

ACTIVITY

1. One group member should determine the function p, where $p(x)$ represents the cost, in dollars, of mailing x pounds as Priority Mail.
2. One member should determine the function r, where $r(x)$ represents the cost, in dollars, of shipping x pounds using UPS Ground.
3. A third member should graph p and r on the same set of axes.
4. Finally, working together, use the graph to determine those weights for which Priority Mail is less expensive than UPS Ground Residential shipping. Express your answer in both set-builder and interval notations.

COLLABORATIVE

9.3 Absolute-Value Equations and Inequalities

Equations with Absolute Value • Inequalities with Absolute Value

Equations with Absolute Value

Recall from Section 1.4 that the absolute value of a number a is the number of units that a is from zero. Another definition uses opposites.

> **Absolute Value**
>
> The absolute value of x, denoted $|x|$, is defined as
> $$|x| = \begin{cases} x, & \text{if } x \geq 0, \\ -x, & \text{if } x < 0. \end{cases}$$
>
> (When x is nonnegative, the absolute value of x is x. When x is negative, the absolute value of x is the opposite of x.)

To better understand this definition, suppose x is -5. Then $|x| = |-5| = 5$, and 5 is the opposite of -5. This shows that when x represents a negative number, the absolute value of x is the opposite of x (which is positive).

Since distance is always nonnegative, we can think of a number's absolute value as its distance from zero on a number line.

EXAMPLE 1 Find the solution set: **(a)** $|x| = 4$; **(b)** $|x| = 0$; **(c)** $|x| = -7$.

Solution

a) We interpret $|x| = 4$ to mean that the number x is 4 units from zero on a number line. There are two such numbers, 4 and -4. Thus the solution set is $\{-4, 4\}$.

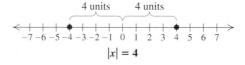

A second way to visualize this problem is to graph $f(x) = |x|$ (see Section 7.3). We also graph $g(x) = 4$. The x-values of the points of intersection are the solutions of $|x| = 4$.

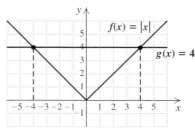

b) We interpret $|x| = 0$ to mean that x is 0 units from zero on a number line. The only number that satisfies this is 0 itself. Thus the solution set is $\{0\}$.

c) Since distance is always nonnegative, it doesn't make sense to talk about a number that is -7 units from zero. Remember: The absolute value of a number is never negative. Thus, $|x| = -7$ has no solution; the solution set is $\varnothing$.

Example 1 leads us to the following principle for solving equations.

The Absolute-Value Principle for Equations

For any positive number p and any algebraic expression X:

a) The solutions of $|X| = p$ are those numbers that satisfy $X = -p$ or $X = p$.

b) The equation $|X| = 0$ is equivalent to the equation $X = 0$.

c) The equation $|X| = -p$ has no solution.

EXAMPLE 2

Find the solution set: **(a)** $|2x + 5| = 13$; **(b)** $|4 - 7x| = -8$.

Solution

a) We use the absolute-value principle, knowing that $2x + 5$ must be either 13 or -13:

$$|X| = p$$
$$|2x + 5| = 13 \qquad \text{Substituting}$$
$$2x + 5 = -13 \quad or \quad 2x + 5 = 13$$
$$2x = -18 \quad or \qquad 2x = 8$$
$$x = -9 \quad or \qquad x = 4.$$

Check: For -9:

$$|2x + 5| = 13$$

$|2(-9) + 5|$	13
$|-18 + 5|$	
$|-13|$	
$13 \overset{?}{=} 13$	TRUE

For 4:

$$|2x + 5| = 13$$

$|2 \cdot 4 + 5|$	13
$|8 + 5|$	
$|13|$	
$13 \overset{?}{=} 13$	TRUE

The number $2x + 5$ is 13 units from zero if x is replaced with -9 or 4. The solution set is $\{-9, 4\}$.

b) The absolute-value principle reminds us that absolute value is always nonnegative. The equation $|4 - 7x| = -8$ has no solution. The solution set is $\varnothing$.

To use the absolute-value principle, we must be sure that the absolute-value expression is alone on one side of the equation.

technology connection

To check Example 2(a), we use the NUM option after pressing **MATH** and let $y_1 = \text{abs}(2x + 5)$ and $y_2 = 13$. Next, using the window $[-12, 8, -2, 18]$, we use the INTERSECT option after pressing **2ND** **CALC** to find the intersections $(-9, 13)$ and $(4, 13)$. The x-coordinates, -9 and 4, are the solutions.

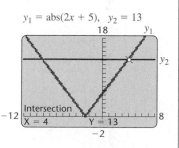

$y_1 = \text{abs}(2x + 5), \quad y_2 = 13$

1. Use a graphing calculator to show that Example 2(b) has no solution.

EXAMPLE 3

Given that $f(x) = 2|x + 3| + 1$, find all x for which $f(x) = 15$.

Solution   Since we are looking for $f(x) = 15$, we substitute:

$$f(x) = 15$$
$$2|x + 3| + 1 = 15 \qquad \text{Replacing } f(x) \text{ with } 2|x + 3| + 1$$
$$2|x + 3| = 14 \qquad \text{Subtracting 1 from both sides}$$
$$|x + 3| = 7 \qquad \text{Dividing both sides by 2}$$
$$x + 3 = -7 \quad or \quad x + 3 = 7 \qquad \text{Using the absolute-value principle}$$
$$\text{for equations}$$
$$x = -10 \quad or \qquad x = 4.$$

We leave it to the student to check that $f(-10) = f(4) = 15$. The solution set is $\{-10, 4\}$.

EXAMPLE 4

Solve: $|x - 2| = 3$.

Solution   Because this equation is of the form $|a - b| = c$, it can be solved in two different ways.

Method 1.   We interpret $|x - 2| = 3$ as stating that the number $x - 2$ is 3 units from zero. Using the absolute-value principle, we replace X with $x - 2$ and p with 3:

$$|X| = p$$
$$|x - 2| = 3$$
$$x - 2 = -3 \quad or \quad x - 2 = 3 \qquad \text{Using the absolute-value principle}$$
$$x = -1 \quad or \qquad x = 5.$$

Method 2.   This approach is helpful in calculus. The expressions $|a - b|$ and $|b - a|$ can be used to represent the *distance between a and b* on the number line. For example, the distance between 7 and 8 is given by $|8 - 7|$ or $|7 - 8|$. From this viewpoint, the equation $|x - 2| = 3$ states that the distance between x and 2 is 3 units. We draw a number line and locate all numbers that are 3 units from 2.

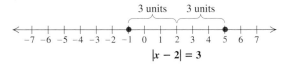

The solutions of $|x - 2| = 3$ are -1 and 5.

Check: The check consists of observing that both methods give the same solutions. The solution set is $\{-1, 5\}$.

Sometimes an equation has two absolute-value expressions. Consider $|a| = |b|$. This means that a and b are the same distance from zero.

If a and b are the same distance from zero, then either they are the same number or they are opposites.

EXAMPLE 5   Solve: $|2x - 3| = |x + 5|$.

Solution   The given equation tells us that $2x - 3$ and $x + 5$ are the same distance from 0. This means that they are either the same number or opposites:

This assumes these numbers are the same.   This assumes these numbers are opposites.

$$2x - 3 = x + 5 \quad or \quad 2x - 3 = -(x + 5)$$
$$x - 3 = 5 \quad or \quad 2x - 3 = -x - 5$$
$$x = 8 \quad or \quad 3x - 3 = -5$$
$$3x = -2$$
$$x = -\tfrac{2}{3}.$$

The check is left to the student. The solutions are 8 and $-\tfrac{2}{3}$ and the solution set is $\left\{-\tfrac{2}{3}, 8\right\}$.

Inequalities with Absolute Value

Our methods for solving equations with absolute value can be adapted for solving inequalities. Inequalities of this sort arise regularly in more advanced courses.

EXAMPLE 6   Solve $|x| < 4$. Then graph.

Solution   The solutions of $|x| < 4$ are all numbers whose *distance from zero is less than* 4. By substituting or by looking at the number line, we can see that numbers like $-3, -2, -1, -\tfrac{1}{2}, -\tfrac{1}{4}, 0, \tfrac{1}{4}, \tfrac{1}{2}, 1, 2$, and 3 are all solutions. In fact, the solutions are all the numbers between -4 and 4. The solution set is $\{x \mid -4 < x < 4\}$. In interval notation, the solution set is $(-4, 4)$. The graph is as follows:

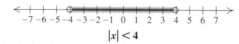

$$|x| < 4$$

We can also visualize Example 6 by graphing $f(x) = |x|$ and $g(x) = 4$, as in Example 1. The solution set consists of all x-values for which $(x, f(x))$ is below the horizontal line $g(x) = 4$. These x-values comprise the interval $(-4, 4)$.

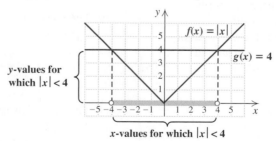

EXAMPLE 7   Solve $|x| \geq 4$. Then graph.

Solution   The solutions of $|x| \geq 4$ are all numbers that are at least 4 units from zero—in other words, those numbers x for which $x \leq -4$ *or* $4 \leq x$. The solution set is $\{x \mid x \le -4 \ or \ x \ge 4\}$. In interval notation, the solution set is $(-\infty, -4] \cup [4, \infty)$. We can check mentally with numbers like $-4.1, -5, 4.1$, and 5. The graph is as follows:

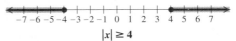

$|x| \ge 4$

As with Examples 1 and 6, Example 7 can be visualized by graphing $f(x) = |x|$ and $g(x) = 4$. The solution set of $|x| \ge 4$ consists of all x-values for which $(x, f(x))$ is on or above the horizontal line $g(x) = 4$. These x-values comprise $(-\infty, -4] \cup [4, \infty)$.

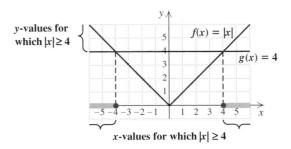

x-values for which $|x| \ge 4$

Examples 1, 6, and 7 illustrate three types of problems in which absolute-value symbols appear. The following is a general principle for solving such problems.

Principles for Solving Absolute-Value Problems

For any positive number p and any expression X:

a) The solutions of $|X| = p$ are those numbers that satisfy $X = -p \ or \ X = p.$

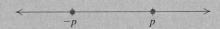

b) The solutions of $|X| < p$ are those numbers that satisfy $-p < X < p.$

c) The solutions of $|X| > p$ are those numbers that satisfy $X < -p \ or \ p < X.$

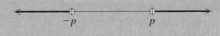

Of course, if p is negative, any value of X will satisfy the inequality $|X| > p$ because absolute value is never negative. (The solution set is $\mathbb{R}$.) By the same reasoning, $|X| < p$ has no solution when p is not positive. (The solution set is $\varnothing$). Thus, $|2x - 7| > -3$ is true for any real number x, and $|2x - 7| < -3$ has no solution.

Note that an inequality of the form $|X| < p$ corresponds to a *con*junction, whereas an inequality of the form $|X| > p$ corresponds to a *dis*junction.

EXAMPLE 8

Solve $|3x - 2| < 4$. Then graph.

Solution   The number $3x - 2$ must be less than 4 units from 0. This is of the form $|X| < p$, so part (b) of the principles listed above applies:

$$|X| < p$$

$|3x - 2| < 4$	Replacing X with $3x - 2$ and p with 4
$-4 < 3x - 2 < 4$	The number $3x - 2$ must be within 4 units of zero.
$-2 < \quad 3x \quad < 6$	Adding 2
$-\frac{2}{3} < \quad x \quad < 2.$	Multiplying by $\frac{1}{3}$

The solution set is $\left\{x \mid -\frac{2}{3} < x < 2\right\}$. In interval notation, the solution set is $\left(-\frac{2}{3}, 2\right)$. The graph is as follows:

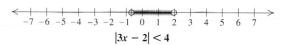

$$|3x - 2| < 4$$

EXAMPLE 9

Given that $f(x) = |4x + 2|$, find all x for which $f(x) \geq 6$.

Solution   We have

$$f(x) \geq 6,$$

or $|4x + 2| \geq 6.$ Substituting

To solve, we use part (c) of the principles listed above. In this case, X is $4x + 2$ and p is 6:

$$|X| \geq p$$

$|4x + 2| \geq 6$	Replacing X with $4x + 2$ and p with 6
$4x + 2 \leq -6 \quad or \quad 6 \leq 4x + 2$	The number $4x + 2$ must be at least 6 units from zero.
$4x \leq -8 \quad or \quad 4 \leq 4x$	Adding -2
$x \leq -2 \quad or \quad 1 \leq x.$	Multiplying by $\frac{1}{4}$

The solution set is $\{x \mid x \leq -2 \ or \ x \geq 1\}$. In interval notation, the solution is $(-\infty, -2] \cup [1, \infty)$. The graph is as follows:

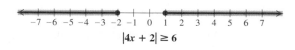

$$|4x + 2| \geq 6$$

---

technology connection

To solve $|4x + 2| \geq 6$, graph $y_1 = \text{abs}(4x + 2)$ and $y_2 = 6$. The x-values on the graph of $y_1 = |4x + 2|$ that are *on or above* the line $y = 6$ solve the inequality.

$y_1 = \text{abs}(4x + 2), \quad y_2 = 6$

1. How can the same graph be used to solve $|4x + 2| < 6$ or $|4x + 2| = 6$?
2. Solve Example 8.

Exercise Set

9.3

▶ *Concept Reinforcement* *Classify each of the following as either true or false.*

1. If x is negative, then $|x| = -x$.

2. $|x|$ is never negative.

3. $|x|$ is always positive.

4. The distance between a and b can be expressed as $|a - b|$.

5. The number a is $|a|$ units from 0.

6. There are two solutions of $|3x - 8| = 17$.

7. There is no solution of $|4x + 9| > -5$.

8. All real numbers are solutions of $|2x - 7| < -3$.

Solve.

9. $|x| = 7$

10. $|x| = 9$

Aha! 11. $|x| = -6$

12. $|x| = -3$

13. $|p| = 0$

14. $|y| = 7.3$

15. $|t| = 5.5$

16. $|m| = 0$

17. $|2x - 3| = 4$

18. $|5x + 2| = 7$

19. $|3x - 5| = -8$

20. $|7x - 2| = -9$

21. $|x - 2| = 6$

22. $|x - 3| = 8$

23. $|x - 5| = 3$

24. $|x - 6| = 1$

25. $|x - 7| = 9$

26. $|x - 4| = 5$

27. $|5x| - 3 = 37$

28. $|2y| - 5 = 13$

29. $7|q| - 2 = 9$

30. $7|z| + 2 = 16$

31. $\left|\dfrac{2x - 1}{3}\right| = 5$

32. $\left|\dfrac{4 - 5x}{6}\right| = 3$

33. $|m + 5| + 9 = 16$

34. $|t - 7| + 1 = 4$

35. $5 - 2|3x - 4| = -5$

36. $3|2x - 5| - 7 = -1$

37. Let $f(x) = |2x + 6|$. Find all x for which $f(x) = 8$.

38. Let $f(x) = |2x + 4|$. Find all x for which $f(x) = 10$.

39. Let $f(x) = |x| - 3$. Find all x for which $f(x) = 5.7$.

40. Let $f(x) = |x| + 7$. Find all x for which $f(x) = 18$.

41. Let $f(x) = \left|\dfrac{3x - 2}{5}\right|$. Find all x for which $f(x) = 2$.

42. Let $f(x) = \left|\dfrac{1 - 2x}{3}\right|$. Find all x for which $f(x) = 1$.

Solve.

43. $|x + 4| = |2x - 7|$

44. $|3x + 5| = |x - 6|$

45. $|x + 4| = |x - 3|$

46. $|x - 9| = |x + 6|$

47. $|3a - 1| = |2a + 4|$

48. $|5t + 7| = |4t + 3|$

Aha! 49. $|n - 3| = |3 - n|$

50. $|y - 2| = |2 - y|$

51. $|7 - a| = |a + 5|$

52. $|6 - t| = |t + 7|$

53. $\left|\frac{1}{2}x - 5\right| = \left|\frac{1}{4}x + 3\right|$

54. $\left|2 - \frac{2}{3}x\right| = \left|4 + \frac{7}{8}x\right|$

Solve and graph.

55. $|a| \le 9$

56. $|x| < 2$

57. $|x| > 8$

58. $|a| \ge 3$

59. $|t| > 0$

60. $|t| \ge 1.7$

61. $|x - 1| < 4$

62. $|x - 1| < 3$

63. $|x + 2| \le 6$

64. $|x + 4| \le 1$

65. $|x - 3| + 2 > 7$

66. $|x - 4| + 5 > 2$

Aha! 67. $|2y - 9| > -5$

68. $|3y - 4| > 8$

69. $|3a - 4| + 2 \ge 8$

70. $|2a - 5| + 1 \ge 9$

71. $|y - 3| < 12$

72. $|p - 2| < 3$

73. $9 - |x + 4| \leq 5$

74. $12 - |x - 5| \leq 9$

75. $|4 - 3y| > 8$

76. $|7 - 2y| < -6$

Aha! **77.** $|5 - 4x| < -6$

78. $7 + |4a - 5| \leq 26$

79. $\left|\dfrac{2 - 5x}{4}\right| \geq \dfrac{2}{3}$

80. $\left|\dfrac{1 + 3x}{5}\right| > \dfrac{7}{8}$

81. $|m + 3| + 8 \leq 14$

82. $|t - 7| + 3 \geq 4$

83. $25 - 2|a + 3| > 19$

84. $30 - 4|a + 2| > 12$

85. Let $f(x) = |2x - 3|$. Find all x for which $f(x) \leq 4$.

86. Let $f(x) = |5x + 2|$. Find all x for which $f(x) \leq 3$.

87. Let $f(x) = 5 + |3x - 4|$. Find all x for which $f(x) \geq 16$.

88. Let $f(x) = |2 - 9x|$. Find all x for which $f(x) \geq 25$.

89. Let $f(x) = 7 + |2x - 1|$. Find all x for which $f(x) < 16$.

90. Let $f(x) = 5 + |3x + 2|$. Find all x for which $f(x) < 19$.

91. Explain in your own words why -7 is not a solution of $|x| < 5$.

92. Explain in your own words why $[6, \infty)$ is only part of the solution of $|x| \geq 6$.

SKILL MAINTENANCE

Solve using substitution or elimination. [8.2]

93. $2x - 3y = 7,$
    $3x + 2y = -10$

94. $3x - 5y = 9,$
    $4x - 3y = 1$

95. $x = -2 + 3y,$
    $x - 2y = 2$

96. $y = 3 - 4x,$
    $2x - y = -9$

Solve graphically. [8.1]

97. $x + 2y = 9,$
    $3x - y = -1$

98. $2x + y = 7,$
    $-3x - 2y = 10$

SYNTHESIS

99. Is it possible for an equation in x of the form $|ax + b| = c$ to have exactly one solution? Why or why not?

100. Explain why the inequality $|x + 5| \geq 2$ can be interpreted as "the number x is at least 2 units from -5."

101. From the definition of absolute value, $|x| = x$ only when $x \geq 0$. Solve $|3t - 5| = 3t - 5$ using this same reasoning.

Solve.

102. $|3x - 5| = x$

103. $|x + 2| > x$

104. $2 \leq |x - 1| \leq 5$

105. $|5t - 3| = 2t + 4$

106. $t - 2 \leq |t - 3|$

Find an equivalent inequality with absolute value.

107. $-3 < x < 3$

108. $-5 \leq y \leq 5$

109. $x \leq -6 \text{ or } 6 \leq x$

110. $x < -4 \text{ or } 4 < x$

111. $x < -8 \text{ or } 2 < x$

112. $-5 < x < 1$

113. x is less than 2 units from 7.

114. x is less than 1 unit from 5.

Write an absolute-value inequality for which the interval shown is the solution.

115.
```
←++++++++++●━━━━━━━━━━●+→
 -7 -6 -5 -4 -3 -2 -1 0 1 2 3 4 5 6 7
```

116.
```
←+○━━━━━━━━━━━━━━━━━○++→
 -5 -4 -3 -2 -1 0 1 2 3 4 5 6 7 8 9
```

117.
```
←○━━━━━━━━━━━○++++++++→
 -7 -6 -5 -4 -3 -2 -1 0 1 2 3 4 5 6 7
```

118.
```
←++●━━━━━━━━━━━━━━━●++→
 0 1 2 3 4 5 6 7 8 9 10 11 12 13 14
```

119. *Bungee jumping.*   A bungee jumper is bouncing up and down so that her distance d above a river satisfies the inequality $|d - 60 \text{ ft}| \leq 10 \text{ ft}$ (see the figure below). If the bridge from which she jumped is 150 ft above the river, how far is the bungee jumper from the bridge at any given time?

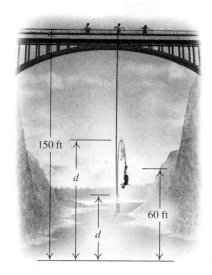

120. *Water level.* Depending on how dry or wet the weather has been, water in a well will rise and fall. The distance d that a well's water level is below the ground satisfies the inequality $|d - 15| \leq 2.5$ (see the figure below).

a) Solve for d.

b) How tall a column of water is in the well at any given time?

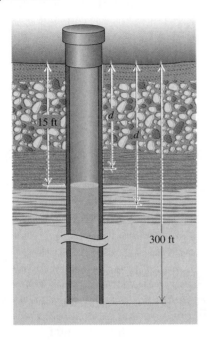

121. Use the accompanying graph of $f(x) = |2x - 6|$ to solve $|2x - 6| \leq 4$.

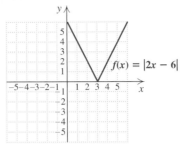

122. Describe a procedure that could be used to solve any equation of the form $g(x) < c$ graphically.

123. Use a graphing calculator to check the solutions to Examples 3 and 5.

124. Use a graphing calculator to check your answers to Exercises 9, 17, 23, 49, 61, 71, 79, and 103.

125. Isabel is using the following graph to solve $|x + 3| < 4$. How can you tell that a mistake has been made in entering $y = \text{abs}(x + 3)$?

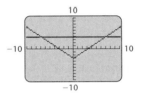

9.4   Inequalities in Two Variables

Graphs of Linear Inequalities • Systems of Linear Inequalities

In Section 2.6, we graphed inequalities in one variable on a number line. Now we graph inequalities in two variables on a plane.

Graphs of Linear Inequalities

When the equals sign in a linear equation is replaced with an inequality sign, a **linear inequality** is formed. Solutions of linear inequalities are ordered pairs.

EXAMPLE 1

Determine whether $(-3, 2)$ and $(6, -7)$ are solutions of the inequality $5x - 4y > 13$.

Study Skills _____

Improve Your Study Skills

The time you spend learning to study better will be returned many times over. Study skills resources such as books and videos are available, your school may offer a class on study skills, or you can find Web sites that offer tips and instruction.

Solution   Below, on the left, we replace x with -3 and y with 2. On the right, we replace x with 6 and y with -7.

$$\begin{array}{c|c} \multicolumn{2}{c}{5x - 4y > 13} \\ \hline 5(-3) - 4 \cdot 2 & 13 \\ -15 - 8 & \\ -23 \overset{?}{>} 13 & \text{FALSE} \end{array}$$

Since $-23 > 13$ is false, $(-3, 2)$ is not a solution.

$$\begin{array}{c|c} \multicolumn{2}{c}{5x - 4y > 13} \\ \hline 5(6) - 4(-7) & 13 \\ 30 + 28 & \\ 58 \overset{?}{>} 13 & \text{TRUE} \end{array}$$

Since $58 > 13$ is true, $(6, -7)$ is a solution.

The graph of a linear equation is a straight line. The graph of a linear inequality is a **half-plane**, with a **boundary** that is a straight line. To find the equation of the boundary line, we simply replace the inequality sign with an equals sign.

EXAMPLE 2

Graph: $y \leq x$.

Solution   We first graph the equation of the boundary, $y = x$. Every solution of $y = x$ is an ordered pair, like $(3, 3)$, in which both coordinates are the same. The graph of $y = x$ is shown on the left below. Since the inequality symbol is $\leq$, the line is drawn solid and is part of the graph of $y \leq x$.

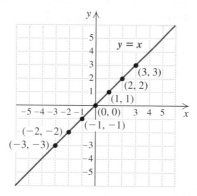 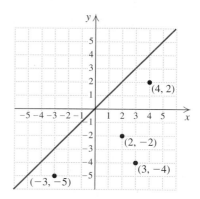

Note that in the graph on the right each ordered pair on the half-plane below $y = x$ contains a y-coordinate that is less than the x-coordinate. All these pairs represent solutions of $y \leq x$. We check one pair, $(4, 2)$, as follows:

$$\begin{array}{c|c} \multicolumn{2}{c}{y \leq x} \\ \hline 2 & 4 \quad \text{TRUE} \end{array}$$

It turns out that *any* point on the same side of $y = x$ as $(4, 2)$ is also a solution. Thus, if one point in a half-plane is a solution, then *all* points in that half-plane are solutions.

We finish drawing the solution set by shading the half-plane below $y = x$. The complete solution set consists of the shaded half-plane as well as the boundary line itself.

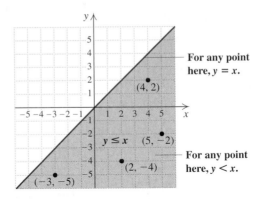

From Example 2, we see that for any inequality of the form $y \le f(x)$ or $y < f(x)$, we shade *below* the graph of $y = f(x)$.

EXAMPLE 3   Graph: $8x + 3y > 24$.

Solution   First, we sketch the graph of $8x + 3y = 24$. Since the inequality sign is $>$, points on this line do not represent solutions of the inequality, so the line is drawn dashed. Points representing solutions of $8x + 3y > 24$ are in either the half-plane above the line or the half-plane below the line. To determine which, we select a point that is not on the line and determine whether it is a solution of $8x + 3y > 24$. Let's use $(1, 1)$ as this *test point*:

$$\begin{array}{c|c} \multicolumn{2}{c}{8x + 3y > 24} \\ \hline 8(1) + 3(1) & 24 \\ 8 + 3 & \\ 11 \overset{?}{>} 24 & \text{\footnotesize FALSE} \end{array}$$

Since $11 > 24$ is *false*, $(1, 1)$ is not a solution. Thus no point in the half-plane containing $(1, 1)$ is a solution. The points in the other half-plane *are* solutions, so we shade that half-plane and obtain the graph shown at right.

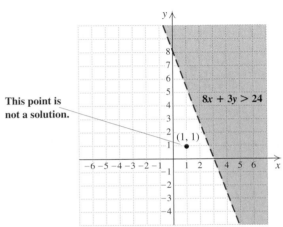

Steps for Graphing Linear Inequalities

1. Replace the inequality sign with an equals sign and graph this line as the boundary. If the inequality symbol is $<$ or $>$, draw the line dashed. If the inequality symbol is $\leq$ or $\geq$, draw the line solid.

2. The graph of the inequality consists of a half-plane on one side of the line and, if the line is solid, the line as well.

   a) If the inequality is of the form $y < mx + b$ or $y \leq mx + b$, shade *below* the line.
      If the inequality is of the form $y > mx + b$ or $y \geq mx + b$, shade *above* the line.

   b) If y is not isolated, either solve for y and graph as in part (a) or simply graph the boundary and use a test point (as in Example 3). If the test point *is* a solution, shade the half-plane containing the point. If it is not a solution, shade the other half-plane.

EXAMPLE 4   Graph: $6x - 2y < 12$.

Solution   We could graph $6x - 2y = 12$ and use a test point, as in Example 3. Instead, let's solve $6x - 2y < 12$ for y:

$$6x - 2y < 12$$
$$-2y < -6x + 12 \qquad \text{Adding } -6x \text{ to both sides}$$
$$y > 3x - 6. \qquad \text{Dividing both sides by } -2 \text{ and reversing the } < \text{ symbol}$$

The graph consists of the half plane above the dashed boundary line $y = 3x - 6$ (see the graph below).

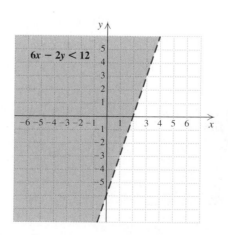

EXAMPLE 5   Graph $x > -3$ on a plane.

Solution   There is a missing variable in this inequality. If we graph the inequality on a line, its graph is as follows:

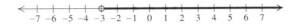

However, we can also write this inequality as $x + 0y > -3$ and graph it on a plane. We can use the same technique as in the examples above. First, we graph the boundary $x = -3$ in the plane, using a dashed line. Then we test some point, say, $(2, 5)$:

$$\frac{x + 0y > -3}{2 + 0 \cdot 5 \;\vert\; -3}$$
$$2 \overset{?}{>} -3 \quad \text{TRUE}$$

Since $(2, 5)$ is a solution, all points in the half-plane containing $(2, 5)$ are solutions. We shade that half-plane. Another approach is to simply note that the solutions of $x > -3$ are all pairs with first coordinates greater than -3.

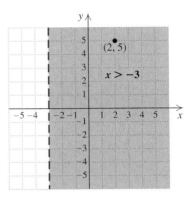

technology connection

On most graphing calculators, an inequality like $y < \frac{6}{5}x + 3.49$ can be drawn by entering $(6/5)x + 3.49$ as y_1, moving the cursor to the GraphStyle icon just to the left of y_1, pressing **ENTER** until ◣ appears, and then pressing **GRAPH**.

Many newer calculators have an INEQUALZ program that is accessed using the **APPS** key. Running this program allows us to write inequalities at the **Y=** screen by pressing **ALPHA** and then one of the five keys just below the screen.

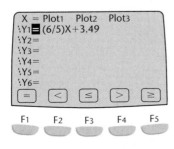

Although the graphs should be identical regardless of the method used, on the newer calculators the boundary line appears dashed when $<$ or $>$ is selected.

$$y_1 < (6/5)x + 3.49, \text{ or}$$
$$\blacktriangleleft\, y_1 = (6/5)x + 3.49$$

Inequalities containing $\leq$ or $\geq$ are handled in a similar manner.

Graph each of the following. Solve for y first if necessary.

1. $y > x + 3.5$ **2.** $7y \leq 2x + 5$
3. $8x - 2y < 11$ **4.** $11x + 13y + 4 \geq 0$

EXAMPLE 6   Graph $y \leq 4$ on a plane.

Solution   The inequality is of the form $y \leq mx + b$ (with $m = 0$), so we shade below the solid horizontal line representing $y = 4$.

This inequality can also be graphed by drawing $y = 4$ and testing a point above or below the line. The student should check that this results in a graph identical to the one at right.

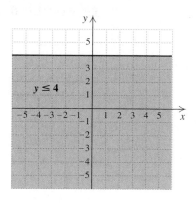

Systems of Linear Inequalities

To graph a system of equations, we graph the individual equations and then find the intersection of the individual graphs. We do the same thing for a system of inequalities, that is, we graph each inequality and find the intersection of the individual graphs.

EXAMPLE 7   Graph the system

$$x + y \leq 4,$$
$$x - y < 4.$$

Solution   To graph $x + y \leq 4$, we graph $x + y = 4$ using a solid line. Since the test point $(0, 0)$ *is* a solution and $(0, 0)$ is below the line, we shade the half-plane below the graph red. The arrows near the ends of the line are another way of indicating the half-plane containing solutions.

Next, we graph $x - y < 4$. We graph $x - y = 4$ using a dashed line and consider $(0, 0)$ as a test point. Again, $(0, 0)$ is a solution, so we shade that side of the line blue. The solution set of the system is the region that is shaded purple (both red and blue) and part of the line $x + y = 4$.

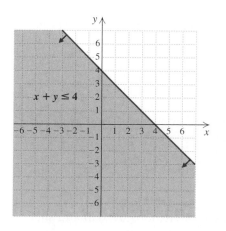
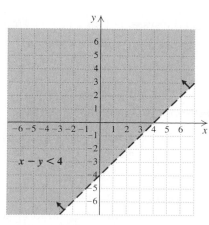
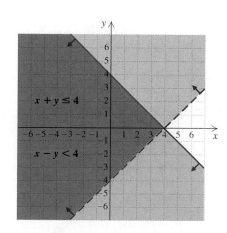

EXAMPLE 8   Graph: $-2 < x \leq 3$.

Student Notes _____

If you don't use differently colored pencils or pens to shade different regions, consider using a pencil to make slashes that tilt in different directions in each region. You may also find it useful to attach arrows to the lines, as in the examples shown.

Solution   This is a system of inequalities:

$$-2 < x,$$
$$x \leq 3.$$

We graph the equation $-2 = x$, and see that the graph of the first inequality is the half-plane to the right of the boundary $-2 = x$. It is shaded red.

We graph the second inequality, starting with the boundary $x = 3$, and find that its graph is the line and also the half-plane to its left. It is shaded blue.

The solution set of the system is the region that is the intersection of the individual graphs. Since it is shaded both blue and red, it appears to be purple. All points in this region have x-coordinates that are greater than -2 but do not exceed 3.

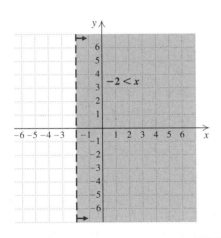
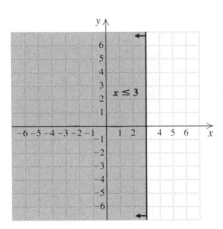
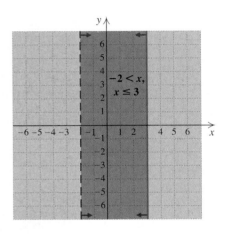

_____

A system of inequalities may have a graph that consists of a polygon and its interior. In Section 9.5, we will have use for the corners, or *vertices* (singular, *vertex*), of such a graph.

EXAMPLE 9   Graph the system of inequalities. Find the coordinates of any vertices formed.

$$6x - 2y \leq 12, \quad (1)$$
$$y - 3 \leq 0, \quad (2)$$
$$x + y \geq 0 \quad (3)$$

Solution   We graph the boundaries

$$6x - 2y = 12,$$
$$y - 3 = 0,$$
and $\quad x + y = 0$

using solid lines. The regions for each inequality are indicated by the arrows near the ends of the lines. We note where the regions overlap and shade the region of solutions purple.

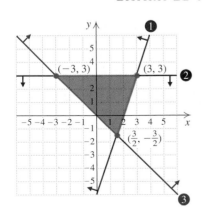

To find the vertices, we solve three different systems of two equations. The system of boundary equations from inequalities (1) and (2) is

$$6x - 2y = 12,$$
$$y - 3 = 0.$$

Solving, we obtain the vertex (3, 3).

The system of boundary equations from inequalities (1) and (3) is

$$6x - 2y = 12,$$
$$x + y = 0.$$

Solving, we obtain the vertex $\left(\frac{3}{2}, -\frac{3}{2}\right)$.

The system of boundary equations from inequalities (2) and (3) is

$$y - 3 = 0,$$
$$x + y = 0.$$

Solving, we obtain the vertex $(-3, 3)$.

 **technology connection**

Systems of inequalities can be graphed by solving for y and then graphing each inequality as in the Technology Connection on p. 610. To graph systems directly using the INEQUALZ application, enter the correct inequalities, press ⬭GRAPH, and then press **ALPHA** and Shades (⬭F1 or ⬭F2). At the SHADES menu, select Ineq Intersection to see the final graph. To find the vertices, or points of intersection, select PoI-Trace from the graph menu.

$y_1 \geq 3x - 6, \quad y_2 \leq 3, \quad y_3 \geq -x$

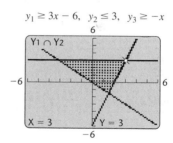

1. Use a graphing calculator to check the solution of Example 7.

$y_1 \geq 3x - 6, \quad y_2 \leq 3, \quad y_3 \geq -x$

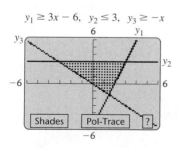

CONNECTING THE CONCEPTS

We have now solved a variety of equations, inequalities, systems of equations, and systems of inequalities. In each case, there are different ways to represent the solution. Below is a list of the different types of problems we have solved, along with illustrations of each type.

Type	*Example*	*Solution*	*Graph*
Linear equations in one variable	$2x - 8 = 3(x + 5)$	A number	
Linear inequalities in one variable	$-3x + 5 > 2$	A set of numbers; an interval	
Linear equations in two variables	$2x + y = 7$	A set of ordered pairs; a line	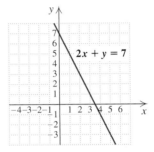
Linear inequalities in two variables	$x + y \geq 4$	A set of ordered pairs; a half-plane	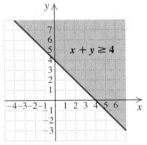
System of equations in two variables	$x + y = 3,$ $5x - y = -27$	An ordered pair or a (possibly empty) set of ordered pairs	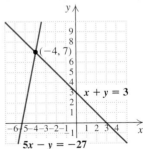
System of inequalities in two variables	$6x - 2y \leq 12,$ $y - 3 \leq 0,$ $x + y \geq 0$	A set of ordered pairs; a region of a plane	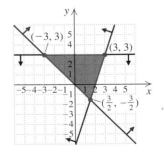

Keeping in mind how these solutions vary and what their graphs look like will help you as you progress further in this book and in mathematics in general.

Exercise Set

9.4

FOR EXTRA HELP

Student's
Solutions
Manual

Digital Video Tutor
CD 5
Videotape 9

Tutor
Center
AW Math
Tutor Center

MathXL Tutorials
on CD

Math XL
MathXL

MyMathLab
MyMathLab

Concept Reinforcement   *In each of Exercises 1–6, match the phrase with the most appropriate choice from the column on the right.*

1. _____ A solution of a linear inequality

2. _____ The graph of a linear inequality

3. _____ The graph of a system of linear inequalities

4. _____ Often a convenient test point

5. _____ The name for the corners of a graph of a system of linear inequalities

6. _____ A dashed line

a) $(0, 0)$

b) Vertices

c) A half-plane

d) The intersection of two or more half-planes

e) An ordered pair that satisfies the inequality

f) Indicates the line is not part of the solution

Determine whether each ordered pair is a solution of the given inequality.

7. $(-4, 2)$; $2x + 3y < -1$

8. $(3, -6)$; $4x + 2y \leq -2$

9. $(8, 14)$; $2y - 3x \geq 9$

10. $(7, 20)$; $3x - y > -1$

Graph on a plane.

11. $y > \frac{1}{2}x$

12. $y > 2x$

13. $y \geq x - 3$

14. $y < x + 3$

15. $y \leq x + 5$

16. $y > x - 2$

17. $x - y \leq 4$

18. $x + y < 4$

19. $2x + 3y < 6$

20. $3x + 4y \leq 12$

21. $2y - x \leq 4$

22. $2y - 3x > 6$

23. $2x - 2y \geq 8 + 2y$

24. $3x - 2 \leq 5x + y$

25. $y \geq 3$

26. $x < -5$

27. $x \leq 6$

28. $y > -3$

29. $-2 < y < 7$

30. $-4 < y < -1$

31. $-4 \leq x \leq 2$

32. $-3 \leq y \leq 4$

33. $0 \leq y \leq 3$

34. $0 \leq x \leq 6$

Graph each system.

35. $y > -x,$
$y < x + 2$

36. $y < x,$
$y > -x + 1$

37. $y \geq x,$
$y \geq 2x - 4$

38. $y \geq x,$
$y \leq -x + 4$

39. $y \leq -3,$
$x \geq -1$

40. $y \geq -3,$
$x \geq 1$

41. $x > -4,$
$y < -2x + 3$

42. $x < 3,$
$y > -3x + 2$

43. $y \leq 5,$
$y \geq -x + 4$

44. $y \geq -2,$
$y \geq x + 3$

45. $x + y \leq 6,$
$x - y \leq 4$

46. $x + y < 1,$
$x - y < 2$

47. $y + 3x > 0,$
$y + 3x < 2$

48. $y - 2x \geq 1,$
$y - 2x \leq 3$

Graph each system of inequalities. Find the coordinates of any vertices formed.

49. $y \leq 2x - 3,$
$y \geq -2x + 1,$
$x \leq 5$

50. $2y - x \leq 2,$
$y - 3x \geq -4,$
$y \geq -1$

51. $x + 2y \leq 12,$
$2x + y \leq 12,$
$x \geq 0,$
$y \geq 0$

52. $x - y \leq 2,$
$x + 2y \geq 8,$
$y \leq 4$

53. $8x + 5y \leq 40,$
$x + 2y \leq 8,$
$x \geq 0,$
$y \geq 0$

54. $4y - 3x \geq -12,$
$4y + 3x \geq -36,$
$y \leq 0,$
$x \leq 0$

55. $y - x \geq 2,$
$y - x \leq 4,$
$2 \leq x \leq 5$

56. $3x + 4y \geq 12,$
$5x + 6y \leq 30,$
$1 \leq x \leq 3$

57. In Example 7, is the point $(4, 0)$ part of the solution set? Why or why not?

58. When graphing linear inequalities, Ron makes a habit of always shading above the line when the symbol $\geq$ is used. Is this wise? Why or why not?

SKILL MAINTENANCE

Solve.

59. *Catering.*   Sandy's Catering needs to provide 10 lb of mixed nuts for a wedding reception. Peanuts cost $2.50 per pound and fancy nuts cost $7 per pound. If $40 has been allocated for nuts, how many pounds of each type should be mixed? [8.3]

60. *Household waste.*   The Hendersons generate two and a half times as much trash as their neighbors, the Savickis. Together, the two households produce 14 bags of trash each month. How much trash does each household produce? [8.3]

61. *Paid admissions.*   There were 203 tickets sold for a volleyball game. For activity-card holders the price was $2.50, and for noncard holders the price was $4. The total amount of money collected was $620. How many of each type of ticket were sold? [8.3]

62. *Paid admissions.*   There were 200 tickets sold for a women's basketball game. Tickets for students were $4 each and for adults were $6 each. The total amount collected was $1060. How many of each type of ticket were sold? [8.3]

63. *Landscaping.*   Grass seed is being spread on a triangular traffic island. If the grass seed can cover an area of 200 ft^2 and the island's base is 16 ft long, how tall a triangle can the seed fill? [2.5]

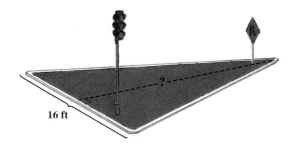

16 ft

64. *Interest rate.*   What rate of interest is required in order for a principal of $1280 to earn $17.60 in half a year? [2.4]

SYNTHESIS

65. Explain how a system of linear inequalities could have a solution set containing exactly one pair.

66. Do all systems of linear inequalities have solutions? Why or why not?

Graph.

67. $x + y > 8,$
   $x + y \leq -2$

68. $x + y \geq 1,$
   $-x + y \geq 2,$
      $x \geq -2,$
      $y \geq 2,$
      $y \leq 4,$
      $x \leq 2$

69. $x - 2y \leq 0,$
   $-2x + \; y \leq 2,$
      $x \leq 2,$
      $y \leq 2,$
   $x + \; y \leq 4$

70. Write four systems of four inequalities that describe a 2-unit by 2-unit square that has (0, 0) as one of the vertices.

71. *Luggage size.*   Unless an additional fee is paid, most major airlines will not check any luggage for which the sum of the item's length, width, and height exceeds 62 in. The U.S. Postal Service will ship a package only if the sum of the package's length and girth (distance around its midsection) does not exceed 130 in. Video Promotions is ordering several 30-in. long cases that will be both mailed and checked as luggage. Using w and h for width and height (in inches), respectively, write and graph an inequality that represents all acceptable combinations of width and height.
Sources: U.S. Postal Service; www.case2go.com

30 in.

CANNES FESTIVAL

VIDEO EQUIPMENT

h

w

Girth

72. *Hockey wins and losses.*   The Skating Stars figure that they need at least 60 points for the season in order to make the playoffs. A win is worth 2 points and a tie is worth 1 point. Graph a system of inequalities that describes the situation. (*Hint*: Let w = the number of wins and t = the number of ties.)

73. *Elevators.*   Many elevators have a capacity of 1 metric ton (1000 kg). Suppose that c children, each weighing 35 kg, and a adults, each 75 kg, are on an elevator. Graph a system of inequalities that indicates when the elevator is overloaded.

74. *Widths of a basketball floor.*   Sizes of basketball floors vary due to building sizes and other constraints such as cost. The length L is to be at most 94 ft and the width W is to be at most 50 ft. Graph a system of inequalities that describes the possible dimensions of a basketball floor.

75. Use a graphing calculator to graph each inequality.
   a) $3x + 6y > 2$
   b) $x - 5y \leq 10$
   c) $13x - 25y + 10 \leq 0$
   d) $2x + 5y > 0$

76. Use a graphing calculator to check your answers to Exercises 35–48. Then use INTERSECT to determine any point(s) of intersection.

CORNER

How Old Is Old Enough?

COLLABORATIVE

Focus: Linear inequalities

Time: 15–25 minutes

Group size: 2

It is not unusual for the ages of a bride and groom to differ significantly. Yet is it possible for the difference in age to be too great? In answer to this question, the following rule of thumb has emerged: *The younger spouse's age should be at least seven more than half the age of the older spouse.* (*Source*: http://home.earthlink.net/ ~mybrainhurts/2002_06_01_archive.html)

ACTIVITY

1. Let b = the age of the bride, in years, and g = the age of the groom, in years. One group member should write an equation for calculating the bride's minimum age if the groom's age is known. The other group member should write an equation for finding the groom's minimum age if the bride's age is known. The equations should look similar.

2. Convert each equation into an inequality by selecting the appropriate symbol from $<$, $>$, $\leq$, and $\geq$. Be sure to reflect the rule of thumb stated above.

3. Graph both inequalities from step 2 as a system of linear inequalities. What does the solution set represent?

4. If your group feels that a minimum or maximum age for marriage should exist, adjust your graph accordingly.

5. Compare your finished graph with those of other groups.

9.5   Applications Using Linear Programming

Objective Functions and Constraints   •   Linear Programming

There are many real-world situations in which we need to find a greatest value (a maximum) or a least value (a minimum). For example, most businesses like to know how to make the *most* profit with the *least* expense possible. Some such problems can be solved using systems of inequalities.

Objective Functions and Constraints

Often a quantity we wish to maximize depends on two or more other quantities. For example, a gardener's profits P might depend on the number of shrubs s and the number of trees t that are planted. If the gardener makes a $10 profit from each shrub and an $18 profit from each tree, the total profit, in dollars, is given by the **objective function**

$$P = 10s + 18t.$$

Thus the gardener might be tempted to simply plant lots of trees since they yield the greater profit. This would be a good idea were it not for the fact that the number of trees and shrubs planted—and thus the total profit—is subject to the demands, or **constraints**, of the situation. For example, to improve drainage, the gardener might be required to plant at least 3 shrubs. Thus the objective function would be subject to the *constraint*

$$s \geq 3.$$

Because of the limited space, the gardener might also be required to plant no more than 10 plants. This would subject the objective function to a *second* constraint:

$$s + t \leq 10.$$

Finally, the gardener might be told to spend no more than $700 on the plants. If the shrubs cost $40 each and the trees cost $100 each, the objective function is subject to a *third* constraint:

The cost of the shrubs plus the cost of the trees cannot exceed $700.

$$40s \qquad + \qquad 100t \qquad \leq \qquad 700$$

In short, the gardener wishes to maximize the objective function

$$P = 10s + 18t,$$

subject to the constraints

$$s \geq 3,$$
$$s + t \leq 10,$$
$$40s + 100t \leq 700,$$
$$s \geq 0, \left.\vphantom{\begin{matrix}a\\b\end{matrix}}\right\}$$ Because the number of trees and
$$t \geq 0. \right.$$ shrubs cannot be negative

These constraints form a system of linear inequalities that can be graphed.

Linear Programming

The gardener's problem is "How many shrubs and trees should be planted, subject to the constraints listed, in order to maximize profit?" To solve such a problem, we use an important result from a branch of mathematics known as **linear programming**.

The Corner Principle

Suppose that an objective function $F = ax + by + c$ depends on x and y (with a, b, and c constant). Suppose also that F is subject to constraints on x and y, which form a system of linear inequalities. If F has a minimum or a maximum value, then it can be found as follows:

1. Graph the system of inequalities and find the vertices.
2. Find the value of the objective function at each vertex. The greatest and the least of those values are the maximum and the minimum of the function, respectively.
3. The ordered pair at which the maximum or minimum occurs indicates the choice of (x, y) for which that maximum or minimum occurs.

This result was proven during World War II, when linear programming was developed to help with shipping troops and supplies from North America to Europe.

EXAMPLE 1   Solve the gardener's problem discussed above.

Solution   We are asked to maximize $P = 10s + 18t$, subject to the constraints

$$s \geq 3,$$
$$s + t \leq 10,$$
$$40s + 100t \leq 700,$$
$$s \geq 0,$$
$$t \geq 0.$$

We graph the system, using the techniques of Section 9.4. The portion of the graph that is shaded represents all pairs that satisfy the constraints. It is sometimes called the *feasible region.*

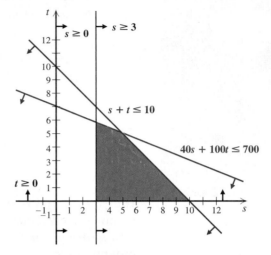

According to the corner principle, P is maximized at one of the vertices of the shaded region. To determine the coordinates of the vertices, we solve the following systems:

$$\left.\begin{array}{r} 40s + 100t = 700, \\ s = 3; \end{array}\right\}$$
The student can verify that the solution of this system is $(3, 5.8)$.

$$\left.\begin{array}{r} s + t = 10, \\ 40s + 100t = 700; \end{array}\right\}$$
The student can verify that the solution of this system is $(5, 5)$.

$$\left.\begin{array}{r} s + t = 10, \\ t = 0; \end{array}\right\}$$
The solution of this system is $(10, 0)$.

$$\left.\begin{array}{r} t = 0, \\ s = 3. \end{array}\right\}$$
The solution of this system is $(3, 0)$.

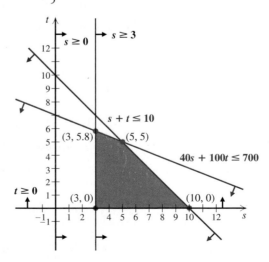

We now find the value of *P* at each vertex.

Vertex (s, t)	Profit P = 10s + 18t	
(3, 5.8)	10(3) + 18(5.8) = 134.4	
(5, 5)	10(5) + 18(5) = 140	←——— Maximum
(10, 0)	10(10) + 18(0) = 100	
(3, 0)	10(3) + 18(0) = 30	←——— Minimum

The greatest value of *P* occurs at (5, 5). Thus profit is maximized at $140 if the gardener plants 5 shrubs and 5 trees. Incidentally, we have also shown that profit is minimized at $30 if 3 shrubs and 0 trees are planted.

EXAMPLE 2   **Test scores.** Corinna is taking a test in which multiple-choice questions are worth 10 points each and short-answer questions are worth 15 points each. It takes her 3 min to answer each multiple-choice question and 6 min to answer each short-answer question. The total time allowed is 60 min, and no more than 16 questions can be answered. Assuming that all her answers are correct, how many items of each type should Corinna answer in order to get the best score?

Solution

1. Familiarize. Tabulating information will help us to see the picture.

Type	Number of Points for Each	Time Required for Each	Number Answered
Multiple-choice	10	3 min	x
Short-answer	15	6 min	y
Total time: 60 min			
Total number of items: 16 or fewer			

Note that we use *x* to represent the number of multiple-choice questions and *y* to represent the number of short-answer questions that are answered.

2. Translate. In this case, it helps to extend the table.

Type	Number of Points for Each	Time Required for Each	Number Answered	Total Time for Each Type	Total Points for Each Type
Multiple-choice	10	3 min	x	$3x$	$10x$
Short-answer	15	6 min	y	$6y$	$15y$
Total			$x + y \leq 16$	$3x + 6y \leq 60$	$10x + 15y$

↑ Because no more than 16 items may be answered

↑ Because the time cannot exceed 60 min

↑ This is what we want to maximize: the total score on the test.

Student Notes _____

It is very important that you clearly label what each variable represents. It is also important to clearly label what the function is that is being maximized or minimized and how that function is evaluated.

Let T represent the total score. We express this as a function of the same variables used in the constraints—in this case, x and y:

$$T = 10x + 15y.$$

We wish to maximize T subject to the constraints listed above:

$$x + y \le 16,$$
$$3x + 6y \le 60,$$
$$\left.\begin{array}{r} x \ge 0, \\ y \ge 0. \end{array}\right\}$$ We include this because the number of questions answered cannot be negative.

3. **Carry out.**   The mathematical manipulation consists of graphing the system and evaluating T at each vertex. The graph is as follows:

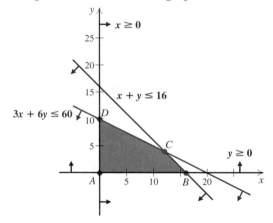

We find the coordinates of each vertex by solving a system of two linear equations. The coordinates of point A are obviously $(0, 0)$. To find the coordinates of point C, we solve the system

$$x + y = 16, \qquad (1)$$
$$3x + 6y = 60, \qquad (2)$$

as follows:

$$-3x - 3y = -48 \qquad \text{Multiplying both sides of equation (1) by } -3$$
$$\underline{3x + 6y = 60}$$
$$3y = 12 \qquad \text{Adding}$$
$$y = 4.$$

Then we find that $x = 12$. Thus the coordinates of vertex C are $(12, 4)$. Point B is the x-intercept of the line given by $x + y = 16$, so B is $(16, 0)$. Point D is the y-intercept of $3x + 6y = 60$, so D is $(0, 10)$. Computing the test score for each ordered pair, we obtain the table at left.

The greatest score in the table is 180, obtained when 12 multiple-choice and 4 short-answer questions are answered.

Vertex (x, y)	Score $T = 10x + 15y$
A $(0, 0)$	0
B $(16, 0)$	160
C $(12, 4)$	180
D $(0, 10)$	150

4. **Check.**   We can check that $T \le 180$ for any other pair in the shaded region. This is left to the student.

5. **State.**   In order to maximize her score, Corinna should answer 12 multiple-choice questions and 4 short-answer questions.

9.5 Exercise Set

FOR EXTRA HELP

Student's Solutions Manual

Digital Video Tutor CD 5 Videotape 9

AW Math Tutor Center

MathXL Tutorials on CD

Math XL
MathXL

MyMathLab
MyMathLab

🐝 *Concept Reinforcement*   *Complete each of the following sentences.*

1. In linear programing, a function is maximized or _____ subject to the demands of a given situation.

2. In linear programming, the function on which the demands are placed is known as the _____ function.

3. In linear programming, the demands arising from the given situation are known as _____.

4. To solve a linear programming problem, we make use of the _____ principle.

5. The shaded portion of a graph that represents all points that satisfy a problem's constraints is known as the _____ region.

6. In linear programming, the corners of the shaded portion of the graph are referred to as _____.

Find the maximum and the minimum values of each objective function and the values of x and y at which they occur.

7. $F = 2x + 14y$,
subject to
$5x + 3y \leq 34$,
$3x + 5y \leq 30$,
$x \geq 0$,
$y \geq 0$

8. $G = 7x + 8y$,
subject to
$3x + 2y \leq 12$,
$2y - x \leq 4$,
$x \geq 0$,
$y \geq 0$

9. $P = 8x - y + 20$,
subject to
$6x + 8y \leq 48$,
$0 \leq y \leq 4$,
$0 \leq x \leq 7$

10. $Q = 24x - 3y + 52$,
subject to
$5x + 4y \leq 20$,
$0 \leq y \leq 4$,
$0 \leq x \leq 3$

11. $F = 2y - 3x$,
subject to
$y \leq 2x + 1$,
$y \geq -2x + 3$,
$x \leq 3$

12. $G = 5x + 2y + 4$,
subject to
$y \leq 2x + 1$,
$y \geq -x + 3$,
$x \leq 5$

13. *Gas mileage.*   Roschelle owns a car and a moped. She has at most 12 gal of gasoline to be used between the car and the moped. The car's tank holds at most 18 gal and the moped's 3 gal. The mileage for the car is 20 mpg and for the moped is 100 mpg. How many gallons of gasoline should each vehicle use if Roschelle wants to travel as far as possible? What is the maximum number of miles?

14. *Lunch-time profits.*   Elrod's lunch cart sells burritos and chili. To stay in business, Elrod must sell at least 10 orders of chili and 30 burritos each day. Because of limited space, no more than 40 orders of chili or 70 burritos can be made. The total number of orders cannot exceed 90. If profit is $1.65 per chili order and $1.05 per burrito, how many of each item should Elrod sell in order to maximize profit?

15. *Milling.*   Johnson Lumber can convert logs into either lumber or plywood. In a given week, the mill can turn out 400 units of production, of which 100 units of lumber and 150 units of plywood are required by regular customers. The profit on a unit of lumber is $20 and on a unit of plywood is $30. How many units of each type should the mill produce in order to maximize profit?

16. *Cycle production.*   Yawaka manufactures motorcycles and bicycles. In order to stay in business, the company determines that the number of bicycles made cannot exceed 3 times the number of motorcycles made. Yawaka lacks the facilities to produce more than 60 motorcycles or more than 120 bicycles. The total production of motorcycles and bicycles cannot exceed 160. The profit on a motorcycle is $1340 and on a bicycle is $200. Find the number of each that should be manufactured in order to maximize profit.

Aha! **17.** *Investing.* Rosa is planning to invest up to $40,000 in corporate or municipal bonds, or both. She must invest from $6000 to $22,000 in corporate bonds, and she does not want to invest more than $30,000 in municipal bonds. The interest on corporate bonds is 8% and on municipal bonds is $7\frac{1}{2}$%. This is simple interest for one year. How much should Rosa invest in each type of bond in order to earn the most interest? What is the maximum interest?

18. *Investing.* Jamaal is planning to invest up to $22,000 in City Bank or the Southwick Credit Union, or both. He wants to invest at least $2000 but no more than $14,000 in City Bank. Because of insurance limitations, he will invest no more than $15,000 in the Southwick Credit Union. The interest in City Bank is 6% and in the credit union is $6\frac{1}{2}$%. This is simple interest for one year. How much should Jamaal invest in each bank in order to earn the most interest? What is the maximum interest?

19. *Test scores.* Phil is about to take a test that contains matching questions worth 10 points each and essay questions worth 25 points each. He must do at least 3 matching questions, but time restricts doing more than 12. Phil must do at least 4 essays, but time restricts doing more than 15. If no more than 20 questions can be answered, how many of each type should Phil do in order to maximize his score? What is this maximum score?

20. *Test scores.* Edy is about to take a test that contains short-answer questions worth 4 points each and word problems worth 7 points each. Edy must do at least 5 short-answer questions, but time restricts doing more than 10. She must do at least 3 word problems, but time restricts doing more than 10. Edy can do no more than 18 questions in total. How many of each type of question must Edy do in order to maximize her score? What is this maximum score?

21. *Grape growing.* Auggie's vineyard consists of 240 acres upon which he wishes to plant Merlot and Cabernet grapes. Profit per acre of Merlot is $400 and profit per acre of Cabernet is $300. Furthermore, the total number of hours of labor available during the harvest season is 3200. Each acre of Merlot requires 20 hr of labor and each acre of Cabernet requires 10 hr of labor. Determine how the land should be divided between Merlot and Cabernet in order to maximize profit.

22. *Coffee blending.* The Coffee Peddler has 1440 lb of Sumatran coffee and 700 lb of Kona coffee. A batch of Hawaiian Blend requires 8 lb of Kona and 12 lb of Sumatran, and yields a profit of $90. A batch of Classic Blend requires 4 lb of Kona and 16 lb of Sumatran, and yields a $55 profit. How many batches of each kind should be made in order to maximize profit? What is the maximum profit? (*Hint*: Organize the information in a table.)

23. *Textile production.* It takes Cosmic Stitching 2 hr of cutting and 4 hr of sewing to make a knit suit. To make a worsted suit, it takes 4 hr of cutting and 2 hr of sewing. At most 20 hr per day are available for cutting and at most 16 hr per day are available for sewing. The profit on a knit suit is $68 and on a worsted suit is $62. How many of each kind of suit should be made in order to maximize profit?

24. *Biscuit production.* The Broad St. Biscuit Factory makes two types of biscuits, Biscuit Jumbos and Mitimite Biscuits. The oven can cook at most 200 biscuits per hour. Jumbos each require 2 oz of flour, Mitimites require 1 oz of flour, and there is at most 1440 oz of flour available. The income from Jumbos is $1.00 and from Mitimites is $0.80. How many of each type of biscuit should be made in order to maximize income? What is the maximum income?

25. Before a student begins work in this section, what three sections of the text would you suggest he or she study? Why?

26. What does the use of the word "constraint" in this section have in common with the use of the word in everyday speech?

SKILL MAINTENANCE

Evaluate. [1.8]

27. $5x^3 - 4x^2 - 7x + 2$, for $x = -2$

28. $6t^3 - 3t^2 + 5t$, for $t = 2$

Simplify. [1.2]

29. $3(2x - 5) + 4(x + 5)$

30. $4(5t - 7) + 6(t + 8)$

31. $6x - 3(x + 2)$

32. $8t - 2(3t - 1)$

SYNTHESIS

33. Explain how Exercises 17 and 18 can be answered by logical reasoning without linear programming.

34. Write a linear programming problem for a classmate to solve. Devise the problem so that profit must be maximized subject to at least two (nontrivial) constraints.

35. *Airplane production.*   Alpha Tours has two types of airplanes, the T3 and the S5, and contracts requiring accommodations for a minimum of 2000 first-class, 1500 tourist-class, and 2400 economy-class passengers. The T3 costs $30 per mile to operate and can accommodate 40 first-class, 40 tourist-class, and 120 economy-class passengers, whereas the S5 costs $25 per mile to operate and can accommodate 80 first-class, 30 tourist-class, and 40 economy-class passengers. How many of each type of airplane should be used in order to minimize the operating cost?

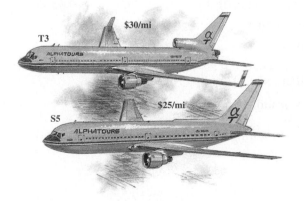

36. *Airplane production.*   A new airplane, the T4, is now available, having an operating cost of $37.50 per mile and accommodating 40 first-class, 40 tourist-class, and 80 economy-class passengers. If the T3 of Exercise 35 were replaced with the T4, how many S5's and how many T4's would be needed in order to minimize the operating cost?

37. *Furniture production.*   P. J. Edward Furniture Design produces chairs and sofas. The chairs require 20 ft of wood, 1 lb of foam rubber, and 2 sq yd of fabric. The sofas require 100 ft of wood, 50 lb of foam rubber, and 20 sq yd of fabric. The company has 1900 ft of wood, 500 lb of foam rubber, and 240 sq yd of fabric. The chairs can be sold for $80 each and the sofas for $1200 each. How many of each should be produced in order to maximize income?

9 Study Summary

Our focus in this chapter has been on **inequalities** and their **solutions** (p. 578). Because most inequalities have an infinite number of solutions, **set-builder notation** and **interval notation** are used to write **solution sets** (p. 579). To solve an inequality, principles similar to those used for solving equations are used (p. 578).

The Addition Principle for Inequalities

For any real numbers a, b, and c:

$$a < b \text{ is equivalent to } a + c < b + c; \quad a > b \text{ is equivalent to } a + c > b + c.$$

The Multiplication Principle for Inequalities

For any real numbers a and b, and for any positive number c,

$$a < b \text{ is equivalent to } ac < bc; \quad a > b \text{ is equivalent to } ac > bc.$$

For any real numbers a and b, and for any *negative* number c,

$$a < b \text{ is equivalent to } ac > bc; \quad a > b \text{ is equivalent to } ac < bc.$$

Similar statements hold for $\leq$ and $\geq$.

These principles can be used, for example, to show that the solution set of $-2x + 7 > 1$ is $\{x \mid x < 3\}$ or $(-\infty, 3)$.

The solution of a **conjunction** like $x + 5 \leq 7$ *and* $2x \geq -3$ is an **intersection** of sets (pp. 587–588). The solution of a **disjunction** like $3x < 12$ *or* $x - 9 > 5$ is a **union** of sets (p. 591). Both conjunctions and disjunctions are **compound inequalities** (p. 587). We use compound inequalities to solve **absolute-value** problems like $|5x + 2| < 9$ (pp. 598–602).

The Absolute-Value Principles for Equations and Inequalities

For any positive number p and any algebraic expression X:

a) The solutions of $|X| = p$ are those numbers that satisfy $X = -p$ *or* $X = p$.
b) The solutions of $|X| < p$ are those numbers that satisfy $-p < X < p$.
c) The solutions of $|X| > p$ are those numbers that satisfy $X < -p$ *or* $p < X$.

If $|X| = 0$, then $X = 0$. If p is negative, then $|X| = p$ and $|X| < p$ have no solution, and any value of X will satisfy $|X| > p$.

Linear inequalities like $2x + 3y \leq 10$ are solved by graphing the **boundary** $2x + 3y = 10$ (pp. 606–607). To determine which **half-plane** is part of the solution set, we use a convenient **test point** (pp. 607, 608). When more than one linear inequality is to be solved at a time, we have a **system of linear inequalities** (p. 611). The solution of such a system requires finding the intersection of two or more half-planes.

Maximization or minimization problems in **linear programming** require us to identify a **feasible region** by solving a system of linear inequalities that represent the **constraints** of the problem (pp. 618–620). The corners, or **vertices**, of the region are then tested in the problem's **objective function** (pp. 612, 618). The **corner principle** states that if a maximum or minimum exists, then it will occur at one of the vertices (p. 619).

9 Review Exercises

↪ *Concept Reinforcement*   *Classify each of the following as either true or false.*

1. The addition and multiplication principles for inequalities are used to write equivalent inequalities. [9.1]

2. It is always true that if $a > b$, then $ac > bc$. [9.1]

3. The solution of $|3x - 5| \leq 8$ is a closed interval. [9.3]

4. The inequality $2 < 5x + 1 < 9$ is equivalent to $2 < 5x + 1$ *or* $5x + 1 < 9$. [9.2]

5. The solution set of a disjunction is the union of two solution sets. [9.2]

6. The equation $|x| = -p$ has no solution when p is positive. [9.3]

7. $|f(x)| > 3$ is equivalent to $f(x) < -3$ *or* $f(x) > 3$. [9.3]

8. A test point is used to determine whether the line in a linear inequality is drawn solid or dashed. [9.4]

9. The graph of a system of linear inequalities is always a half-plane. [9.4]

10. The corner principle states that every objective function has a maximum or minimum value. [9.5]

Graph each inequality and write the solution set using both set-builder and interval notations. [9.1]

11. $x \leq -2$

12. $a + 7 \leq -14$

13. $y - 5 \geq -12$

14. $4y > -15$

15. $-0.3y < 9$

16. $-6x - 5 < 4$

17. $-\frac{1}{2}x - \frac{1}{4} > \frac{1}{2} - \frac{1}{4}x$

18. $0.3y - 7 < 2.6y + 15$

19. $-2(x - 5) \geq 6(x + 7) - 12$

20. Let $f(x) = 3x - 5$ and $g(x) = 11 - x$. Find all values of x for which $f(x) \leq g(x)$. [9.1]

Solve. [9.1]

21. Rose can choose between two summer jobs. She can work as a checker in a discount store for $8.40 an hour, or she can mow lawns for $12.00 an hour. In order to mow lawns, she must buy a $450 lawnmower. For how many hours must Rose work in order for the mowing to be more profitable than checking?

22. Clay is going to invest $9000, part at 3% and the rest at 3.5%. What is the most he can invest at 3% and still be guaranteed $300 in interest each year?

23. Find the intersection:

$\{1, 2, 5, 6, 9\} \cap \{1, 3, 5, 9\}$. [9.2]

24. Find the union:

$\{1, 2, 5, 6, 9\} \cup \{1, 3, 5, 9\}$. [9.2]

Graph and write interval notation. [9.2]

25. $x \leq 3$ *and* $x > -5$

26. $x \leq 3$ *or* $x > -5$

Solve and graph each solution set. [9.2]

27. $-4 < x + 8 \leq 5$

28. $-15 < -4x - 5 < 0$

29. $3x < -9$ *or* $-5x < -5$

30. $2x + 5 < -17$ *or* $-4x + 10 \leq 34$

31. $2x + 7 \leq -5$ *or* $x + 7 \geq 15$

32. $f(x) < -5$ *or* $f(x) > 5$, where $f(x) = 3 - 5x$

For $f(x)$ as given, use interval notation to write the domain of f. [9.2]

33. $f(x) = \dfrac{2x}{x - 8}$

34. $f(x) = \sqrt{x + 5}$

35. $f(x) = \sqrt{8 - 3x}$

Solve. [9.3]

36. $|x| = 5$

37. $|t| \geq 3.5$

38. $|x - 3| = 7$

39. $|2x + 5| < 12$

40. $|3x - 4| \geq 15$

41. $|2x + 5| = |x - 9|$

42. $|5n + 6| = -8$

43. $\left| \dfrac{x + 4}{6} \right| \leq 2$

44. $2|x - 5| - 7 > 3$

45. Let $f(x) = |3x - 5|$. Find all x for which $f(x) < 0$. [9.3]

46. Graph $x - 2y \geq 6$ on a plane. [9.4]

Graph each system of inequalities. Find the coordinates of any vertices formed. [9.4]

47. $x + 3y > -1$,
$x + 3y < 4$

48. $x - 3y \leq 3$,
$x + 3y \geq 9$,
$y \leq 6$

49. Find the maximum and the minimum values of

$F = 3x + y + 4$

subject to

$y \leq 2x + 1$,
$x \leq 7$,
$y \geq 3$.   [9.5]

50. Custom Computers has two manufacturing plants. The Oregon plant cannot produce more than 60 computers a week, while the Ohio plant cannot produce more than 120 computers a week. The Electronics Outpost sells at least 160 Custom computers each week. It costs $40 to ship a computer to The Electronics Outpost from the Oregon plant and $25 to ship from the Ohio plant. How many computers should be shipped from each plant in order to minimize cost? [9.5]

SYNTHESIS

51. Explain in your own words why $|X| = p$ has two solutions when p is positive and no solution when p is negative. [9.3]

52. Explain why the graph of the solution of a system of linear inequalities is the intersection, not the union, of the individual graphs. [9.4]

53. Solve: $|2x + 5| \leq |x + 3|$. [9.3]

54. Classify as true or false: If $x < 3$, then $x^2 < 9$. If false, give an example showing why. [9.1]

55. Just-For-Fun manufactures marbles with a 1.1-cm diameter and a ± 0.03-cm manufacturing tolerance, or allowable variation in diameter. Write the tolerance as an inequality with absolute value. [9.3]

9 Chapter Test

Graph each inequality and write the solution set using both set-builder and interval notations.

1. $x - 2 < 10$

2. $-0.6y < 30$

3. $-4y - 3 \geq 5$

4. $3a - 5 \leq -2a + 6$

5. $3(7 - x) < 2x + 5$

6. $-8(2x + 3) + 6(4 - 5x) \geq 2(1 - 7x) - 4(4 + 6x)$

7. Let $f(x) = -5x - 1$ and $g(x) = -9x + 3$. Find all values of x for which $f(x) > g(x)$.

8. Lia can rent a van for either $40 with unlimited mileage or $30 with 100 free miles and an extra charge of 15¢ for each mile over 100. For what numbers of miles traveled would the unlimited mileage plan save Lia money?

9. A refrigeration repair company charges $80 for the first half-hour of work and $60 for each additional hour. Blue Mountain Camp has budgeted $200 to repair its walk-in cooler. For what lengths of a service call will the budget not be exceeded?

10. Find the intersection:

$\{1, 3, 5, 7, 9\} \cap \{3, 5, 11, 13\}$.

11. Find the union:

$\{1, 3, 5, 7, 9\} \cup \{3, 5, 11, 13\}$.

12. Write the domain of f using interval notation if $f(x) = \sqrt{8 - 2x}$.

Solve and graph each solution set.

13. $-2 < x - 3 < 5$

14. $-11 \leq -5t - 2 < 0$

15. $3x - 2 < 7 \text{ or } x - 2 > 4$

16. $-3x > 12 \text{ or } 4x > -10$

17. $-\frac{1}{3} \leq \frac{1}{6}x - 1 < \frac{1}{4}$

18. $|x| = 13$

19. $|a| > 7$

20. $|3x - 1| < 7$

21. $|-5t - 3| \geq 10$

22. $|2 - 5x| = -12$

23. $g(x) < -3 \text{ or } g(x) > 3$, where $g(x) = 4 - 2x$

24. Let $f(x) = |x + 10|$ and $g(x) = |x - 12|$. Find all values of x for which $f(x) = g(x)$.

Graph the system of inequalities. Find the coordinates of any vertices formed.

25. $x + y \geq 3$,
$x - y \geq 5$

26. $2y - x \geq -7$,
$2y + 3x \leq 15$,
$y \leq 0$,
$x \leq 0$

27. Find the maximum and the minimum values of

$F = 5x + 3y$

subject to

$x + y \leq 15$,
$1 \leq x \leq 6$,
$0 \leq y \leq 12$.

28. Sassy Salon makes $12 on each manicure and $18 on each haircut. A manicure takes 30 minutes and a haircut takes 50 minutes, and there are 5 stylists who each work 6 hours a day. If the salon can schedule 50 appointments a day, how many should be manicures and how many haircuts in order to maximize profit? What is the maximum profit?

SYNTHESIS

Solve. Write the solution set using interval notation.

29. $|2x - 5| \leq 7 \text{ and } |x - 2| \geq 2$

30. $7x < 8 - 3x < 6 + 7x$

31. Write an absolute-value inequality for which the interval shown is the solution.

1–9   Cumulative Review

1. Evaluate
$$\frac{2x - y^2}{x + y}$$
for $x = 3$ and $y = -4$. [1.8]

2. Convert to scientific notation: 391,000,000. [4.8]

3. Determine the slope and the y-intercept for the line given by $7x - 4y = 12$. [3.6]

4. Find an equation for the line that passes through the points $(-1, 7)$ and $(2, -3)$. [3.7]

5. Solve the system
$$5x - 2y = -23,$$
$$3x + 4y = 7. \ [8.2]$$

6. Solve the system
$$-3x + 4y + \ z = -5,$$
$$x - 3y - \ z = 6,$$
$$2x + 3y + 5z = -8. \ [8.4]$$

7. Folsom Elementary School sold 45 pizzas for a fundraiser. Small pizzas sold for $7.00 each and large pizzas for $10.00 each. The total amount of funds received from the sale was $402. How many of each size pizza were sold? [8.3]

8. The sum of three numbers is 20. The first number is 3 less than twice the third number. The second number minus the third number is -7. What are the numbers? [8.5]

9. Trex Company makes decking material from waste wood fibers and reclaimed polyethylene. Its sales rose from $49.2 million in 1998 to $191 million in 2003. Calculate the rate at which sales were rising. [3.4]
Source: U.S. Securities and Exchange Commission

10. In 1989, the average length of a visit to a physician in an HMO was 15.4 min; and in 1998, it was 17.9 min. Let V represent the average length of a visit t years after 1989. [7.3]
Sources: Rutgers University Study and National Center for Health Statistics
   a) Find a linear function $V(t)$ that fits the data.
   b) Use the function of part (a) to predict the average length of a visit in 2005.

11. If
$$f(x) = \frac{x - 2}{x - 5},$$
find (a) $f(3)$ and (b) the domain of f. [7.1], [7.2]

Solve.

12. $8x = 1 + 16x^2$ [5.7]

13. $144 = 49y^2$ [5.7]

14. $20 > 2 - 6x$ [9.1]

15. $\frac{1}{3}x - \frac{1}{5} \geq \frac{1}{5}x - \frac{1}{3}$ [9.1]

16. $-8 < x + 2 < 15$ [9.2]

17. $3x - 2 < -6 \ or \ x + 3 > 9$ [9.2]

18. $|x| > 6.4$ [9.3]

19. $|3x - 2| \leq 14$ [9.3]

20. $\frac{8}{n} - \frac{2}{n} = 3$ [6.6]

21. $\frac{6}{x - 5} = \frac{2}{2x}$ [6.6]

22. $\frac{3x}{x - 2} - \frac{6}{x + 2} = \frac{24}{x^2 - 4}$ [6.6]

23. $\frac{3x^2}{x + 2} + \frac{5x - 22}{x - 2} = \frac{-48}{x^2 - 4}$ [6.6]

24. Let $f(x) = |3x - 5|$. Find all values of x for which $f(x) = 2$. [9.3]

25. Write the domain of f using interval notation if $f(x) = \sqrt{x - 9}$. [9.2]

Solve.

26. $5m - 3n = 4m + 12$, for n [2.3]

27. $P = \dfrac{4a}{a + b}$, for a [7.5]

Graph on a plane.

28. $4x \geq 5y + 12$ [9.4]

29. $y = \frac{1}{3}x - 2$ [3.6]

Perform the indicated operations and simplify.

30. $(2x^2 - 8x + 7) + (6x - 3x^3 + 9x^2 - 4)$ [4.3]

31. $(8x^3y^2)(-3xy^2)$ [4.6]

32. $(3a + b - 2c) - (-4b + 3c - 2a)$ [4.6]

33. $(5x^2 - 2x + 1)(3x^2 + x - 2)$ [4.4]

34. $(3x^2 + y)^2$ [4.6]

35. $(2x^2 - y)(2x^2 + y)$ [4.6]

36. $(-5m^3n^2 - 3mn^3) + (-4m^2n^2 + 4m^3n^2) - (2mn^3 - 3m^2n^2)$ [4.6]

37. $\dfrac{y^2 - 36}{2y + 8} \cdot \dfrac{y + 4}{y + 6}$ [6.2]

38. $\dfrac{x^4 - 1}{x^2 - x - 2} \div \dfrac{x^2 + 1}{x - 2}$ [6.2]

39. $\dfrac{5ab}{a^2 - b^2} + \dfrac{a + b}{a - b}$ [6.4]

40. $\dfrac{2}{m + 1} + \dfrac{3}{m - 5} - \dfrac{m^2 - 1}{m^2 - 4m - 5}$ [6.4]

41. $y - \dfrac{2}{3y}$ [6.4]

42. Simplify: $\dfrac{\dfrac{1}{x} - \dfrac{1}{y}}{x + y}$. [6.5]

43. Divide: $(9x^3 + 5x^2 + 2) \div (x + 2)$. [4.7]

Factor.

44. $4x^3 - 14x^2$ [5.1]

45. $x^2 + 8x - 84$ [5.2]

46. $16y^2 - 81$ [5.4]

47. $64x^3 + 8$ [5.5]

48. $t^2 - 16t + 64$ [5.4]

49. $x^6 - x^2$ [5.4]

50. $0.027b^3 - 0.008c^3$ [5.5]

51. $20x^2 - 7x - 3$ [5.3]

52. $3t^2 + 17t - 28$ [5.3]

53. $x^5 - x^3y + x^2y - y^2$ [5.1]

54. If $f(x) = x^2 - 4$ and $g(x) = x^2 - 7x + 10$, find the domain of f/g. [7.4]

55. A digital data circuit can transmit a particular set of data in 4 sec. An analog phone circuit can transmit the same data in 20 sec. How long would it take, working together, for both circuits to transmit the data? [6.7]

56. The floor area of a rental trailer is rectangular. The length is 3 ft more than the width. A rug of area 54 ft^2 exactly fills the floor of the trailer. Find the perimeter of the trailer. [5.8]

57. The sum of the squares of three consecutive even integers is equal to 8 more than three times the square of the second number. Find the integers. [5.8]

58. *Logging.*   The volume of wood V in a tree trunk varies jointly as the height h and the square of the girth g (girth is distance around). If the volume is 35 ft^3 when the height is 20 ft and the girth is 5 ft, what is the height when the volume is 85.75 ft^3 and the girth is 7 ft? [7.5]

SYNTHESIS

59. Multiply: $(x - 4)^3$. [4.4]

60. Solve: $x^4 + 225 = 34x^2$. [5.7]

Solve.

61. $4 \leq |3 - x| \leq 6$ [9.2], [9.3]

62. $\dfrac{18}{x - 9} + \dfrac{10}{x + 5} = \dfrac{28x}{x^2 - 4x - 45}$ [6.6]

63. $16x^3 = x$ [5.7]

10

Exponents and Radicals

AN APPLICATION

The function given by $f(x) = 262 \cdot 2^{x/12}$ can be used to determine the frequency, in cycles per second, of a musical note that is x half-steps above a piano's middle C. Show that the G that is 7 half-steps (a perfect 5th) above middle C has a frequency that is about 1.5 times that of middle C.

This problem appears as Exercise 113 in Section 10.2.

R. J. Malloy
GUITAR MAKER
Englewood, Florida

Music is mathematics with a soul. From determining what thickness and length of a string will produce the vibrations of a pure C note to determining how a new bracing system will affect the tone of a guitar, I use math constantly. Even the shape of a violin is determined by algebraic formulas that are 500 years old and based on the speed of sound through solid materials.

*I*n this chapter, we learn about square roots, cube roots, fourth roots, and so on. These roots are studied in connection with the manipulation of radical expressions and the solution of real-world applications. Exponents that are fractions are also studied and used to ease some of our work with radicals. The chapter closes with an examination of the complex-number system.

10.1 Radical Expressions and Functions

Square Roots and Square-Root Functions • Expressions of the Form $\sqrt{a^2}$ • Cube Roots • Odd and Even nth Roots

In this section, we consider roots, such as square roots and cube roots. We look at the symbolism that is used and ways in which symbols can be manipulated to get equivalent expressions. All of this will be important in problem solving.

Square Roots and Square-Root Functions

When a number is multiplied by itself, we say that the number is squared. Often we need to know what number was squared in order to produce some value a. If such a number can be found, we call that number a *square root* of a.

> **Square Root**
> The number c is a *square root* of a if $c^2 = a$.

For example,

9 has -3 and 3 as square roots because $(-3)^2 = 9$ and $3^2 = 9$.

25 has -5 and 5 as square roots because $(-5)^2 = 25$ and $5^2 = 25$.

-4 does not have a real-number square root because there is no real number c for which $c^2 = -4$.

Note that every positive number has two square roots, whereas 0 has only itself as a square root. Negative numbers do not have real-number square roots, although later in this chapter we introduce the *complex-number* system in which such square roots do exist.

EXAMPLE 1   Find the two square roots of 64.

Solution   The square roots are 8 and -8, because $8^2 = 64$ and $(-8)^2 = 64$.

Whenever we refer to *the* square root of a number, we mean the nonnegative square root of that number. This is often referred to as the *principal square root* of the number.

Student Notes _____

It is important to remember the difference between *the* square root of 9 and *a* square root of 9. *A* square root of 9 means either 3 or -3, whereas *the* square root of 9, denoted $\sqrt{9}$, means the principal square root of 9, or 3.

Principal Square Root

The *principal square root* of a nonnegative number is its nonnegative square root. The symbol $\sqrt{}$ is called a *radical sign* and is used to indicate the principal square root of the number over which it appears.

EXAMPLE 2   Simplify each of the following.

a) $\sqrt{25}$ **b)** $\sqrt{\dfrac{25}{64}}$

c) $-\sqrt{64}$ **d)** $\sqrt{0.0049}$

Solution

a) $\sqrt{25} = 5$ $\sqrt{}$ indicates the principal square root. Note that $\sqrt{25} \neq -5$.

b) $\sqrt{\dfrac{25}{64}} = \dfrac{5}{8}$ Since $\left(\dfrac{5}{8}\right)^2 = \dfrac{25}{64}$

c) $-\sqrt{64} = -8$ Since $\sqrt{64} = 8$, $-\sqrt{64} = -8$.

d) $\sqrt{0.0049} = 0.07$ $(0.07)(0.07) = 0.0049$. Note too that $0.0049 = \dfrac{49}{10{,}000}$ and $\sqrt{49/10{,}000} = \dfrac{7}{100}$.

In addition to being read as "the principal square root of *a*," $\sqrt{a}$ is also read as "the square root of *a*," "root *a*," or "radical *a*." Any expression in which a radical sign appears is called a *radical expression*. The following are radical expressions:

$$\sqrt{5}, \qquad \sqrt{a}, \qquad -\sqrt{3x}, \qquad \sqrt{\dfrac{y^2 + 7}{y}}, \qquad \sqrt{x} + 8.$$

The expression under the radical sign is called the **radicand**. In the expressions above, the radicands are 5, a, $3x$, $(y^2 + 7)/y$, and x.

All but the most basic calculators give values for square roots. These values are, for the most part, approximations. For example, on many calculators, if you enter 5 and then press $\sqrt{}$, a number like

2.23606798

appears, depending on how the calculator rounds. (On some calculators, the $\sqrt{}$ key is pressed first.) The exact value of $\sqrt{5}$, for example, is not given by any repeating or terminating decimal. In general, for any whole number a that is not a perfect square, $\sqrt{a}$ is a nonterminating, nonrepeating decimal. We discussed such *irrational numbers* in Chapter 1.

The square-root function, given by

$$f(x) = \sqrt{x},$$

has the interval $[0, \infty)$ as its domain. We can draw its graph by selecting convenient values for x and calculating the corresponding outputs. Once these ordered pairs have been graphed, a smooth curve can be drawn.

$$f(x) = \sqrt{x}$$

x	$\sqrt{x}$	$(x, f(x))$
0	0	(0, 0)
1	1	(1, 1)
4	2	(4, 2)
9	3	(9, 3)

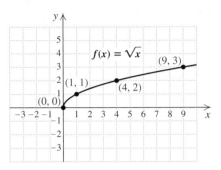

EXAMPLE 3   For each function, find the indicated function value.

a) $f(x) = \sqrt{3x - 2};\ f(1)$ **b)** $g(z) = -\sqrt{6z + 4};\ g(3)$

Solution

a) $f(1) = \sqrt{3 \cdot 1 - 2}$ Substituting

$ = \sqrt{1} = 1$ Simplifying

b) $g(3) = -\sqrt{6 \cdot 3 + 4}$ Substituting

$ = -\sqrt{22}$ Simplifying. This is the most exact way to write the answer.

$ \approx -4.69041576$ Using a calculator to write an approximate answer

Expressions of the Form $\sqrt{a^2}$

It is tempting to write $\sqrt{a^2} = a$, but the next example shows that, as a rule, this is untrue.

EXAMPLE 4   Evaluate $\sqrt{a^2}$ for the following values: **(a)** 5; **(b)** 0; **(c)** -5.

Solution

a) $\sqrt{5^2} = \sqrt{25} = 5$

$\underset{\textstyle \text{Same}}{\underline{}}$

b) $\sqrt{0^2} = \sqrt{0} = 0$

$\underset{\textstyle \text{Same}}{\underline{}}$

c) $\sqrt{(-5)^2} = \sqrt{25} = 5$

$\underset{\textstyle \text{Opposites}}{\underline{}}$ Note that $\sqrt{(-5)^2} \neq -5$.

You may have noticed that evaluating $\sqrt{a^2}$ is just like evaluating $|a|$.

> **Simplifying $\sqrt{a^2}$**
>
> For any real number a,
>
> $$\sqrt{a^2} = |a|.$$
>
> (The principal square root of a^2 is the absolute value of a.)

When a radicand is the square of a variable expression, like $(x + 5)^2$ or $36t^2$, absolute-value signs are needed when simplifying. We use absolute-value signs unless we know that the expression being squared is nonnegative. This assures that our result is never negative.

EXAMPLE 5   Simplify each expression. Assume that the variable can represent any real number.

a) $\sqrt{(x + 1)^2}$ b) $\sqrt{x^2 - 8x + 16}$

c) $\sqrt{a^8}$ d) $\sqrt{t^6}$

Solution

a) $\sqrt{(x + 1)^2} = |x + 1|$ Since $x + 1$ might be negative (for example, if $x = -3$), absolute-value notation is necessary.

b) $\sqrt{x^2 - 8x + 16} = \sqrt{(x - 4)^2} = |x - 4|$ Since $x - 4$ might be negative, absolute-value notation is necessary.

c) Note that $(a^4)^2 = a^8$ and that a^4 is never negative. Thus,

$$\sqrt{a^8} = a^4.$$ Absolute-value notation is unnecessary here.

d) Note that $(t^3)^2 = t^6$. Thus,

$$\sqrt{t^6} = |t^3|.$$ Since t^3 might be negative, absolute-value notation is necessary.

EXAMPLE 6   Simplify each expression. Assume that no radicands were formed by raising negative quantities to even powers.

a) $\sqrt{y^2}$ b) $\sqrt{a^{10}}$ c) $\sqrt{9x^2 - 6x + 1}$

Solution

a) $\sqrt{y^2} = y$ We are assuming that y is nonnegative, so no absolute-value notation is necessary. When y *is* negative, $\sqrt{y^2} \neq y$.

b) $\sqrt{a^{10}} = a^5$ Assuming that a^5 is nonnegative. Note that $(a^5)^2 = a^{10}$.

c) $\sqrt{9x^2 - 6x + 1} = \sqrt{(3x - 1)^2} = 3x - 1$ Assuming that $3x - 1$ is nonnegative

---

technology connection

To see the necessity of the absolute-value signs, let y_1 represent the left side and y_2 the right side of each of the following equations. Then use a graph or table to determine whether these equations are true.

1. $\sqrt{x^2} \stackrel{?}{=} x$

2. $\sqrt{x^2} \stackrel{?}{=} |x|$

3. $x \stackrel{?}{=} |x|$

Cube Roots

We often need to know what number was cubed in order to produce a certain value. When such a number is found, we say that we have found a *cube root*. For example,

2 is the cube root of 8 because $2^3 = 2 \cdot 2 \cdot 2 = 8$;

-4 is the cube root of -64 because $(-4)^3 = (-4)(-4)(-4) = -64$.

> ### Cube Root
>
> The number c is the *cube root* of a if $c^3 = a$. In symbols, we write $\sqrt[3]{a}$ to denote the cube root of a.

Because each real number has only one cube root, a function can be formed. The cube-root function, given by

$$f(x) = \sqrt[3]{x},$$

has $\mathbb{R}$ as its domain and $\mathbb{R}$ as its range. To draw its graph, we select convenient values for x and calculate the corresponding outputs. Once these ordered pairs have been graphed, a smooth curve is drawn. Note that the cube root of a positive number is positive, and the cube root of a negative number is negative.

$$f(x) = \sqrt[3]{x}$$

x	$\sqrt[3]{x}$	$(x, f(x))$
0	0	$(0, 0)$
1	1	$(1, 1)$
8	2	$(8, 2)$
-1	-1	$(-1, -1)$
-8	-2	$(-8, -2)$

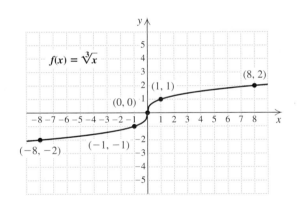

EXAMPLE 7   For each function, find the indicated function value.

a) $f(y) = \sqrt[3]{y};\ f(125)$

b) $g(x) = \sqrt[3]{x - 1};\ g(-26)$

Solution

a) $f(125) = \sqrt[3]{125} = 5$ Since $5 \cdot 5 \cdot 5 = 125$

b) $g(-26) = \sqrt[3]{-26 - 1}$
   $= \sqrt[3]{-27}$
   $= -3$ Since $(-3)(-3)(-3) = -27$

EXAMPLE 8   Simplify: $\sqrt[3]{-8y^3}$.

Solution

$$\sqrt[3]{-8y^3} = -2y \qquad \text{Since } (-2y)(-2y)(-2y) = -8y^3$$

Odd and Even *n*th Roots

The fourth root of a number a is the number c for which $c^4 = a$. There are also 5th roots, 6th roots, and so on. We write $\sqrt[n]{a}$ for the nth root. The number n is called the *index* (plural, *indices*). When the index is 2, we do not write it.

EXAMPLE 9   Find each of the following.

a) $\sqrt[5]{32}$

b) $\sqrt[5]{-32}$

c) $-\sqrt[5]{32}$

d) $-\sqrt[5]{-32}$

Solution

a) $\sqrt[5]{32} = 2$ Since $2^5 = 32$

b) $\sqrt[5]{-32} = -2$ Since $(-2)^5 = -32$

c) $-\sqrt[5]{32} = -2$ Taking the opposite of $\sqrt[5]{32}$

d) $-\sqrt[5]{-32} = -(-2) = 2$ Taking the opposite of $\sqrt[5]{-32}$

Note that every number has exactly one real root when n is odd. Odd roots of positive numbers are positive and odd roots of negative numbers are negative. Absolute-value signs are not used when finding odd roots.

EXAMPLE 10   Find each of the following.

a) $\sqrt[7]{x^7}$

b) $\sqrt[9]{(t-1)^9}$

Solution

a) $\sqrt[7]{x^7} = x$

b) $\sqrt[9]{(t-1)^9} = t - 1$

When the index n is even, we say that we are taking an *even root*. Every positive real number has two real nth roots when n is even—one positive and one negative. For example, the fourth roots of 16 are -2 and 2. Negative numbers do not have real nth roots when n is even.

When n is even, the notation $\sqrt[n]{a}$ indicates the nonnegative nth root. Thus, to write even nth roots, absolute-value signs are often required.

EXAMPLE 11   Simplify each expression, if possible. Assume that variables can represent any real number.

a) $\sqrt[4]{16}$ **b)** $-\sqrt[4]{16}$

c) $\sqrt[4]{-16}$ **d)** $\sqrt[4]{81x^4}$

e) $\sqrt[6]{(y+7)^6}$

Solution

a) $\sqrt[4]{16} = 2$ Since $2^4 = 16$

b) $-\sqrt[4]{16} = -2$ Taking the opposite of $\sqrt[4]{16}$

c) $\sqrt[4]{-16}$ cannot be simplified. $\sqrt[4]{-16}$ is not a real number.

d) $\sqrt[4]{81x^4} = |3x|$, or $3|x|$ Use absolute-value notation since x could represent a negative number.

e) $\sqrt[6]{(y+7)^6} = |y+7|$ Use absolute-value notation since $y+7$ is negative for $y < -7$.

We summarize as follows.

Simplifying nth Roots

n	a	$\sqrt[n]{a}$	$\sqrt[n]{a^n}$
Even	Positive	Positive	a
Even	Negative	Not a real number	$-a$
Odd	Positive	Positive	a
Odd	Negative	Negative	a

EXAMPLE 12   Determine the domain of $g(x) = \sqrt[6]{7 - 3x}$.

Solution   Since the index is even, the radicand, $7 - 3x$, must be nonnegative. We solve the inequality:

$7 - 3x \geq 0$ We cannot find the 6th root of a negative number.

$-3x \geq -7$

$x \leq \frac{7}{3}.$ Multiplying both sides by $-\frac{1}{3}$ and reversing the inequality

Thus,

$$\text{Domain of } g = \left\{ x \,\middle|\, x \leq \tfrac{7}{3} \right\}$$
$$= \left(-\infty, \tfrac{7}{3} \right].$$

technology connection

To enter cube or higher roots on a graphing calculator, select options 4 or 5 of the **MATH** menu. The characters $6\sqrt[x]{}$ indicate the sixth root.

1. Use a **TABLE** or **GRAPH** and **TRACE** to check the solution of Example 12.

Exercise Set

10.1

🖢 *Concept Reinforcement*   *Select the appropriate word to complete each of the following.*

1. Every positive number has _____ square root(s).
   one/two

2. The principal square root is never _____.
   negative/positive

3. For any _____ number a, we have negative/positive
   $\sqrt{a^2} = a$.

4. For any _____ number a, we have negative/positive
   $\sqrt{a^2} = -a$.

5. If a is a whole number that is not a perfect square, then $\sqrt{a}$ is a(n) _____ number.
   irrational/rational

6. The domain of the function f given by $f(x) = \sqrt[3]{x}$ is the set of all _____ numbers.
   whole/real/positive

7. If $\sqrt[4]{x}$ is a real number, then x must be _____.
   negative/positive/nonnegative

8. If $\sqrt[3]{x}$ is negative, then x must be _____.
   negative/positive

For each number, find all of its square roots.

9. 49

10. 81

11. 144

12. 9

13. 400

14. 2500

15. 900

16. 225

Simplify.

17. $-\sqrt{\dfrac{36}{49}}$

18. $-\sqrt{\dfrac{361}{9}}$

19. $\sqrt{441}$

20. $\sqrt{196}$

21. $-\sqrt{\dfrac{16}{81}}$

22. $-\sqrt{\dfrac{81}{144}}$

23. $\sqrt{0.04}$

24. $\sqrt{0.36}$

25. $-\sqrt{0.0025}$

26. $\sqrt{0.0144}$

Identify the radicand and the index for each expression.

27. $5\sqrt{p^2 + 4}$

28. $-7\sqrt{y^2 - 8}$

29. $x^2y^3\sqrt[3]{\dfrac{x}{y + 4}}$

30. $a^2b^3\sqrt[3]{\dfrac{a}{a^2 - b}}$

For each function, find the specified function value, if it exists.

31. $f(t) = \sqrt{5t - 10};\ f(6), f(2), f(1), f(-1)$

32. $g(x) = \sqrt{x^2 - 25};\ g(-6), g(3), g(6), g(13)$

33. $t(x) = -\sqrt{2x + 1};\ t(4), t(0), t(-1), t\left(-\tfrac{1}{2}\right)$

34. $p(z) = \sqrt{2z^2 - 20};\ p(4), p(3), p(-5), p(0)$

35. $f(t) = \sqrt{t^2 + 1};\ f(0), f(-1), f(-10)$

36. $g(x) = -\sqrt{(x + 1)^2};\ g(-3), g(4), g(-5)$

37. $g(x) = \sqrt{x^3 + 9};\ g(-2), g(-3), g(3)$

38. $f(t) = \sqrt{t^3 - 10};\ f(2), f(3), f(4)$

Simplify. Remember to use absolute-value notation when necessary. If a root cannot be simplified, state this.

39. $\sqrt{36x^2}$

40. $\sqrt{25t^2}$

41. $\sqrt{(-6b)^2}$

42. $\sqrt{(-7c)^2}$

43. $\sqrt{(8 - t)^2}$

44. $\sqrt{(a + 3)^2}$

45. $\sqrt{y^2 + 16y + 64}$

46. $\sqrt{x^2 - 4x + 4}$

47. $\sqrt{4x^2 + 28x + 49}$

48. $\sqrt{9x^2 - 30x + 25}$

49. $\sqrt[4]{256}$

50. $-\sqrt[4]{625}$

51. $\sqrt[5]{-1}$

52. $-\sqrt[5]{3^5}$

53. $\sqrt[5]{-\dfrac{32}{243}}$

54. $\sqrt[5]{-\dfrac{1}{32}}$

55. $\sqrt[6]{x^6}$

56. $\sqrt[8]{y^8}$

57. $\sqrt[4]{(6a)^4}$

58. $\sqrt[4]{(7b)^4}$

59. $\sqrt[10]{(-6)^{10}}$

60. $\sqrt[12]{(-10)^{12}}$

61. $\sqrt[414]{(a + b)^{414}}$

62. $\sqrt[1976]{(2a + b)^{1976}}$

63. $\sqrt{a^{22}}$ **64.** $\sqrt{x^{10}}$

65. $\sqrt{-25}$ **66.** $\sqrt{-16}$

Simplify. Assume that no radicands were formed by raising negative quantities to even powers.

67. $\sqrt{16x^2}$ **68.** $\sqrt{25t^2}$

69. $\sqrt{(3t)^2}$ **70.** $\sqrt{(7c)^2}$

71. $\sqrt{(a+1)^2}$ **72.** $\sqrt{(5+b)^2}$

73. $\sqrt{4x^2+8x+4}$ **74.** $\sqrt{9x^2+36x+36}$

75. $\sqrt{9t^2-12t+4}$ **76.** $\sqrt{25t^2-20t+4}$

77. $\sqrt[3]{27}$ **78.** $-\sqrt[3]{64}$

79. $\sqrt[4]{16x^4}$ **80.** $\sqrt[4]{81x^4}$

81. $\sqrt[3]{-216}$ **82.** $-\sqrt[5]{-100,000}$

83. $-\sqrt[3]{-125y^3}$ **84.** $-\sqrt[3]{-64x^3}$

85. $\sqrt{t^{18}}$ **86.** $\sqrt{a^{14}}$

87. $\sqrt{(x-2)^8}$ **88.** $\sqrt{(x+3)^{10}}$

For each function, find the specified function value, if it exists.

89. $f(x) = \sqrt[3]{x+1}$; $f(7), f(26), f(-9), f(-65)$

90. $g(x) = -\sqrt[3]{2x-1}$; $g(0), g(-62), g(-13), g(63)$

91. $g(t) = \sqrt[4]{t-3}$; $g(19), g(-13), g(1), g(84)$

92. $f(t) = \sqrt[4]{t+1}$; $f(0), f(15), f(-82), f(80)$

Determine the domain of each function described.

93. $f(x) = \sqrt{x-6}$ **94.** $g(x) = \sqrt{x+8}$

95. $g(t) = \sqrt[4]{t+8}$ **96.** $f(x) = \sqrt[4]{x-9}$

97. $g(x) = \sqrt[4]{2x-10}$ **98.** $g(t) = \sqrt[3]{2t-6}$

99. $f(t) = \sqrt[5]{8-3t}$ **100.** $f(t) = \sqrt[6]{4-3t}$

101. $h(z) = -\sqrt[6]{5z+2}$ **102.** $d(x) = -\sqrt[4]{7x-5}$

Aha! **103.** $f(t) = 7 + \sqrt[8]{t^8}$ **104.** $g(t) = 9 + \sqrt[6]{t^6}$

105. Explain how to write the negative square root of a number using radical notation.

106. Does the square root of a number's absolute value always exist? Why or why not?

SKILL MAINTENANCE

Simplify. Do not use negative exponents in your answer. [4.1], [4.8]

107. $(a^3b^2c^5)^3$ **108.** $(5a^7b^8)(2a^3b)$

109. $(2a^{-2}b^3c^{-4})^{-3}$ **110.** $(5x^{-3}y^{-1}z^2)^{-2}$

111. $\dfrac{8x^{-2}y^5}{4x^{-6}z^{-2}}$ **112.** $\dfrac{10a^{-6}b^{-7}}{2a^{-2}c^{-3}}$

SYNTHESIS

113. Under what conditions does the nth root of x^3 exist? Explain your reasoning.

114. Under what conditions does the nth root of x^2 exist? Explain your reasoning.

115. *Dairy farming.* As a calf grows, it needs more milk for nourishment. The number of pounds of milk, M, required by a calf weighing x pounds can be estimated using the formula
$$M = -5 + \sqrt{6.7x - 444}.$$
Estimate the number of pounds of milk required by a calf of the given weight: **(a)** 300 lb; **(b)** 100 lb; **(c)** 200 lb; **(d)** 400 lb.
Source: www.ext.vt.edu

116. *Spaces in a parking lot.* A parking lot has attendants to park the cars. The number N of stalls needed for waiting cars before attendants can get to them is given by the formula $N = 2.5\sqrt{A}$, where A is the number of arrivals in peak hours. Find the number of spaces needed for the given number of arrivals in peak hours: **(a)** 25; **(b)** 36; **(c)** 49; **(d)** 64.

Determine the domain of each function described. Then draw the graph of each function.

117. $f(x) = \sqrt{x} + 5$ **118.** $g(x) = \sqrt{x+5}$

119. $g(x) = \sqrt{x} - 2$ **120.** $f(x) = \sqrt{x-2}$

121. Find the domain of f if
$$f(x) = \frac{\sqrt{x+3}}{\sqrt[4]{2-x}}.$$

122. Find the domain of g if
$$g(x) = \frac{\sqrt[4]{5-x}}{\sqrt[6]{x+4}}.$$

123. Find the domain of F if $F(x) = \dfrac{x}{\sqrt{x^2-5x-6}}$.

124. Use a graphing calculator to check your answers to Exercises 39, 45, and 57. On some graphing calculators, a MATH key is needed to enter higher roots.

125. Use a graphing calculator to check your answers to Exercises 117 and 118. (See Exercise 124.)

10.2   Rational Numbers as Exponents

Rational Exponents • Negative Rational Exponents •
Laws of Exponents • Simplifying Radical Expressions

In Chapter 1, we considered the natural numbers as exponents. Our discussion of exponents was expanded in Chapter 4 to include all integers. We now expand the study still further—to include all rational numbers. This will give meaning to expressions like $a^{1/3}$, $7^{-1/2}$, and $(3x)^{4/5}$. Such notation will help us simplify certain radical expressions.

Rational Exponents

Consider $a^{1/2} \cdot a^{1/2}$. If we still want to add exponents when multiplying, it must follow that $a^{1/2} \cdot a^{1/2} = a^{1/2+1/2}$, or a^1. This suggests that $a^{1/2}$ is a square root of a. Similarly, $a^{1/3} \cdot a^{1/3} \cdot a^{1/3} = a^{1/3+1/3+1/3}$, or a^1, so $a^{1/3}$ should mean $\sqrt[3]{a}$.

$$a^{1/n} = \sqrt[n]{a}$$

$a^{1/n}$ means $\sqrt[n]{a}$. When a is nonnegative, n can be any natural number greater than 1. When a is negative, n must be odd.

Note that the denominator of the exponent becomes the index and the base becomes the radicand.

EXAMPLE 1   Write an equivalent expression using radical notation.

a) $x^{1/2}$

b) $(-8)^{1/3}$

c) $(abc)^{1/5}$

d) $(25x^{16})^{1/2}$

Solution

a) $x^{1/2} = \sqrt{x}$

b) $(-8)^{1/3} = \sqrt[3]{-8} = -2$

c) $(abc)^{1/5} = \sqrt[5]{abc}$

The denominator of the exponent becomes the index. The base becomes the radicand. Recall that for square roots, the index 2 is understood without being written.

d) $(25x^{16})^{1/2} = 25^{1/2}x^8 = \sqrt{25} \cdot x^8 = 5x^8$

EXAMPLE 2   Write an equivalent expression using exponential notation.

a) $\sqrt[5]{9xy}$

b) $\sqrt[7]{\dfrac{x^3y}{4}}$

c) $\sqrt{5x}$

Solution   Parentheses are required to indicate the base.

a) $\sqrt[5]{9xy} = (9xy)^{1/5}$

b) $\sqrt[7]{\dfrac{x^3y}{4}} = \left(\dfrac{x^3y}{4}\right)^{1/7}$ The index becomes the denominator of the exponent. The radicand becomes the base.

c) $\sqrt{5x} = (5x)^{1/2}$ The index 2 is understood without being written. We assume $x \geq 0$.

How shall we define $a^{2/3}$? If the property for multiplying exponents is to hold, we must have $a^{2/3} = (a^{1/3})^2$ and $a^{2/3} = (a^2)^{1/3}$. This would suggest that $a^{2/3} = (\sqrt[3]{a})^2$ and $a^{2/3} = \sqrt[3]{a^2}$. We make our definition accordingly.

> **Positive Rational Exponents**
>
> For any natural numbers m and n ($n \neq 1$) and any real number a for which $\sqrt[n]{a}$ exists,
>
> $$a^{m/n} \quad \text{means} \quad (\sqrt[n]{a})^m, \quad \text{or} \quad \sqrt[n]{a^m}.$$

EXAMPLE 3   Write an equivalent expression using radical notation and simplify.

a) $27^{2/3}$

b) $25^{3/2}$

Solution

a) $27^{2/3}$ means $(\sqrt[3]{27})^2$ or, equivalently, $\sqrt[3]{27^2}$. Let's see which is easier to simplify:

$$(\sqrt[3]{27})^2 = 3^2 \qquad\qquad \sqrt[3]{27^2} = \sqrt[3]{729}$$
$$= 9; \qquad\qquad\qquad\quad = 9.$$

Student Notes

It is important to remember both meanings of $a^{m/n}$. When the root of the base a is known, $(\sqrt[n]{a})^m$ is generally easier to work with. When it is not known, $\sqrt[n]{a^m}$ is often more convenient.

The simplification on the left is probably easier for most people.

b) $25^{3/2}$ means $(\sqrt[2]{25})^3$ or, equivalently, $\sqrt[2]{25^3}$ (the index 2 is normally omitted). Since $\sqrt{25}$ is more commonly known than $\sqrt{25^3}$, we use that form:

$$25^{3/2} = (\sqrt{25})^3 = 5^3 = 125.$$

EXAMPLE 4   Write an equivalent expression using exponential notation.

a) $\sqrt[3]{9^4}$

b) $(\sqrt[4]{7xy})^5$

Solution

a) $\sqrt[3]{9^4} = 9^{4/3}$

b) $(\sqrt[4]{7xy})^5 = (7xy)^{5/4}$ The index becomes the denominator of the fraction that is the exponent.

Negative Rational Exponents

Recall from Section 4.8 that $x^{-2} = 1/x^2$. Negative rational exponents behave similarly.

Negative Rational Exponents

For any rational number m/n and any nonzero real number a for which $a^{m/n}$ exists,

$$a^{-m/n} \text{ means } \frac{1}{a^{m/n}}.$$

Caution!   A negative exponent does not indicate that the expression in which it appears is negative: $a^{-1} \neq -a$.

EXAMPLE 5

Write an equivalent expression with positive exponents and, if possible, simplify.

a) $9^{-1/2}$

b) $(5xy)^{-4/5}$

c) $64^{-2/3}$

d) $4x^{-2/3}y^{1/5}$

e) $\left(\dfrac{3r}{7s}\right)^{-5/2}$

Solution

a) $9^{-1/2} = \dfrac{1}{9^{1/2}}$ $9^{-1/2}$ is the reciprocal of $9^{1/2}$.

Since $9^{1/2} = \sqrt{9} = 3$, the answer simplifies to $\dfrac{1}{3}$.

b) $(5xy)^{-4/5} = \dfrac{1}{(5xy)^{4/5}}$ $(5xy)^{-4/5}$ is the reciprocal of $(5xy)^{4/5}$.

c) $64^{-2/3} = \dfrac{1}{64^{2/3}}$ $64^{-2/3}$ is the reciprocal of $64^{2/3}$.

Since $64^{2/3} = (\sqrt[3]{64})^2 = 4^2 = 16$, the answer simplifies to $\dfrac{1}{16}$.

d) $4x^{-2/3}y^{1/5} = 4 \cdot \dfrac{1}{x^{2/3}} \cdot y^{1/5} = \dfrac{4y^{1/5}}{x^{2/3}}$

e) In Section 4.8, we found that $(a/b)^{-n} = (b/a)^n$. This property holds for *any* negative exponent:

$$\left(\frac{3r}{7s}\right)^{-5/2} = \left(\frac{7s}{3r}\right)^{5/2}.$$ Writing the reciprocal of the base and changing the sign of the exponent

Laws of Exponents

The same laws hold for rational exponents as for integer exponents.

Laws of Exponents

For any real numbers a and b and any rational exponents m and n for which a^m, a^n, and b^m are defined:

1. $a^m \cdot a^n = a^{m+n}$ In multiplying, add exponents if the bases are the same.

2. $\dfrac{a^m}{a^n} = a^{m-n}$ In dividing, subtract exponents if the bases are the same. (Assume $a \neq 0$.)

3. $(a^m)^n = a^{m \cdot n}$ To raise a power to a power, multiply the exponents.

4. $(ab)^m = a^m b^m$ To raise a product to a power, raise each factor to the power and multiply.

EXAMPLE 6   Use the laws of exponents to simplify.

a) $3^{1/5} \cdot 3^{3/5}$

b) $\dfrac{a^{1/4}}{a^{1/2}}$

c) $(7.2^{2/3})^{3/4}$

d) $(a^{-1/3}b^{2/5})^{1/2}$

Solution

a) $3^{1/5} \cdot 3^{3/5} = 3^{1/5+3/5} = 3^{4/5}$ Adding exponents

b) $\dfrac{a^{1/4}}{a^{1/2}} = a^{1/4-1/2} = a^{1/4-2/4}$ Subtracting exponents after finding a common denominator

$\qquad\qquad = a^{-1/4}$, or $\dfrac{1}{a^{1/4}}$ $a^{-1/4}$ is the reciprocal of $a^{1/4}$.

c) $(7.2^{2/3})^{3/4} = 7.2^{(2/3)(3/4)} = 7.2^{6/12}$ Multiplying exponents

$\qquad\qquad = 7.2^{1/2}$ Using arithmetic to simplify the exponent

d) $(a^{-1/3}b^{2/5})^{1/2} = a^{(-1/3)(1/2)} \cdot b^{(2/5)(1/2)}$ Raising a product to a power and multiplying exponents

$\qquad\qquad = a^{-1/6}b^{1/5}$, or $\dfrac{b^{1/5}}{a^{1/6}}$

Simplifying Radical Expressions

Many radical expressions contain radicands or factors of radicands that are powers. When these powers and the index share a common factor, rational exponents can be used to simplify the expression.

> **To Simplify Radical Expressions**
> 1. Convert radical expressions to exponential expressions.
> 2. Use arithmetic and the laws of exponents to simplify.
> 3. Convert back to radical notation as needed.

EXAMPLE 7 Use rational exponents to simplify. Do not use exponents that are fractions in the final answer.

a) $\sqrt[6]{(5x)^3}$

b) $\sqrt[5]{t^{20}}$

c) $\left(\sqrt[3]{ab^2c}\right)^{12}$

d) $\sqrt{\sqrt[3]{x}}$

Solution

a) $\sqrt[6]{(5x)^3} = (5x)^{3/6}$ Converting to exponential notation

$\qquad\qquad\quad = (5x)^{1/2}$ Simplifying the exponent

$\qquad\qquad\quad = \sqrt{5x}$ Returning to radical notation

b) $\sqrt[5]{t^{20}} = t^{20/5}$ Converting to exponential notation

$\qquad\quad = t^4$ Simplifying the exponent

c) $\left(\sqrt[3]{ab^2c}\right)^{12} = (ab^2c)^{12/3}$ Converting to exponential notation

$\qquad\qquad\quad = (ab^2c)^4$ Simplifying the exponent

$\qquad\qquad\quad = a^4b^8c^4$ Using the laws of exponents

d) $\sqrt{\sqrt[3]{x}} = \sqrt{x^{1/3}}$ Converting the radicand to exponential notation

$\qquad\quad = (x^{1/3})^{1/2}$ Try to go directly to this step.

$\qquad\quad = x^{1/6}$ Using the laws of exponents

$\qquad\quad = \sqrt[6]{x}$ Returning to radical notation

technology connection

One way to check Example 7(a) is to let $y_1 = (5x)^{3/6}$ and $y_2 = \sqrt{5x}$. Then use (GRAPH) or (TABLE) to see if $y_1 = y_2$. An alternative is to let $y_3 = y_2 - y_1$ and see if $y_3 = 0$. Check Example 7(a) using one of these two methods.

1. Why are rational exponents especially useful when working on a graphing calculator?

Exercise Set

10.2

↪ *Concept Reinforcement* *In each of Exercises 1–8, match the expression with the equivalent expression from the column on the right.*

1. ____ $x^{2/5}$

2. ____ $x^{5/2}$

3. ____ $x^{-5/2}$

4. ____ $x^{-2/5}$

5. ____ $x^{1/5} \cdot x^{2/5}$

6. ____ $(x^{1/5})^{5/2}$

7. ____ $\sqrt[5]{x^4}$

8. ____ $\left(\sqrt[4]{x}\right)^5$

a) $x^{3/5}$

b) $\left(\sqrt[5]{x}\right)^4$

c) $\sqrt{x^5}$

d) $x^{1/2}$

e) $\dfrac{1}{(\sqrt{x})^5}$

f) $\sqrt[4]{x^5}$

g) $\sqrt[5]{x^2}$

h) $\dfrac{1}{(\sqrt[5]{x})^2}$

Note: Assume for all exercises that even roots are of nonnegative quantities and that all denominators are nonzero.

Write an equivalent expression using radical notation and, if possible, simplify.

9. $x^{1/6}$ **10.** $y^{1/5}$

11. $16^{1/2}$ **12.** $8^{1/3}$

13. $81^{1/4}$ **14.** $64^{1/6}$

15. $9^{1/2}$ **16.** $25^{1/2}$

17. $(xyz)^{1/3}$ **18.** $(ab)^{1/4}$

19. $(a^2b^2)^{1/5}$ **20.** $(x^3y^3)^{1/4}$

21. $t^{2/5}$ **22.** $b^{3/2}$

23. $16^{3/4}$ **24.** $4^{7/2}$

25. $27^{4/3}$ **26.** $9^{5/2}$

27. $(81x)^{3/4}$ **28.** $(125a)^{2/3}$

29. $(25x^4)^{3/2}$ **30.** $(9y^6)^{3/2}$

Write an equivalent expression using exponential notation.

31. $\sqrt[3]{20}$ **32.** $\sqrt[3]{19}$

33. $\sqrt{17}$ **34.** $\sqrt{6}$

35. $\sqrt{x^3}$ **36.** $\sqrt{a^5}$

37. $\sqrt[5]{m^2}$ **38.** $\sqrt[5]{n^4}$

39. $\sqrt[4]{cd}$ **40.** $\sqrt[3]{xy}$

41. $\sqrt[5]{xy^2z}$ **42.** $\sqrt[7]{x^3y^2z^2}$

43. $\left(\sqrt{3mn}\right)^3$ **44.** $\left(\sqrt[3]{7xy}\right)^4$

45. $\left(\sqrt[7]{8x^2y}\right)^5$ **46.** $\left(\sqrt[6]{2a^5b}\right)^7$

47. $\dfrac{2x}{\sqrt[3]{z^2}}$ **48.** $\dfrac{3a}{\sqrt[5]{c^2}}$

Write an equivalent expression with positive exponents and, if possible, simplify.

49. $x^{-1/3}$ **50.** $y^{-1/4}$

51. $(2rs)^{-3/4}$ **52.** $(5xy)^{-5/6}$

53. $\left(\dfrac{1}{16}\right)^{-3/4}$ **54.** $\left(\dfrac{1}{8}\right)^{-2/3}$

55. $\dfrac{2c}{a^{-3/5}}$ **56.** $\dfrac{3b}{a^{-5/7}}$

57. $5x^{-2/3}y^{4/5}z$ **58.** $2a^{3/4}b^{-1/2}c^{2/3}$

59. $3^{-5/2}a^3b^{-7/3}$ **60.** $2^{-1/3}x^4y^{-2/7}$

61. $\left(\dfrac{2ab}{3c}\right)^{-5/6}$ **62.** $\left(\dfrac{7x}{8yz}\right)^{-3/5}$

63. $\dfrac{6a}{\sqrt[4]{b}}$ **64.** $\dfrac{7x}{\sqrt[3]{z}}$

Use the laws of exponents to simplify. Do not use negative exponents in any answers.

65. $7^{3/4} \cdot 7^{1/8}$ **66.** $11^{2/3} \cdot 11^{1/2}$

67. $\dfrac{3^{5/8}}{3^{-1/8}}$ **68.** $\dfrac{8^{7/11}}{8^{-2/11}}$

69. $\dfrac{5.2^{-1/6}}{5.2^{-2/3}}$ **70.** $\dfrac{2.3^{-3/10}}{2.3^{-1/5}}$

71. $(10^{3/5})^{2/5}$ **72.** $(5^{5/4})^{3/7}$

73. $a^{2/3} \cdot a^{5/4}$ **74.** $x^{3/4} \cdot x^{1/3}$

Aha!   **75.** $(64^{3/4})^{4/3}$ **76.** $(27^{-2/3})^{3/2}$

77. $(m^{2/3}n^{-1/4})^{1/2}$ **78.** $(x^{-1/3}y^{2/5})^{1/4}$

Use rational exponents to simplify. Do not use fraction exponents in the final answer.

79. $\sqrt[6]{x^4}$ **80.** $\sqrt[6]{a^2}$

81. $\sqrt[4]{a^{12}}$ **82.** $\sqrt[3]{x^{15}}$

83. $\sqrt[5]{a^{10}}$ **84.** $\sqrt[6]{x^{18}}$

85. $\left(\sqrt[7]{xy}\right)^{14}$ **86.** $\left(\sqrt[3]{ab}\right)^{15}$

87. $\sqrt[4]{(7a)^2}$ **88.** $\sqrt[8]{(3x)^2}$

89. $\left(\sqrt[8]{2x}\right)^6$ **90.** $\left(\sqrt[10]{3a}\right)^5$

91. $\sqrt[3]{\sqrt[6]{a}}$ **92.** $\sqrt[4]{\sqrt{x}}$

93. $\sqrt[4]{(xy)^{12}}$ **94.** $\sqrt{(ab)^6}$

95. $\left(\sqrt[5]{a^2b^4}\right)^{15}$ **96.** $\left(\sqrt[3]{x^2y^5}\right)^{12}$

97. $\sqrt[3]{\sqrt[4]{xy}}$ **98.** $\sqrt[5]{\sqrt{2a}}$

99. If $f(x) = (x + 5)^{1/2}(x + 7)^{-1/2}$, find the domain of f. Explain how you found your answer.

100. Explain why $\sqrt[3]{x^6} = x^2$ for any value of x, whereas $\sqrt[2]{x^6} = x^3$ only when $x \geq 0$.

SKILL MAINTENANCE

Simplify.

101. $3x(x^3 - 2x^2) + 4x^2(2x^2 + 5x)$ [4.3], [4.4]

102. $5t^3(2t^2 - 4t) - 3t^4(t^2 - 6t)$ [4.3], [4.4]

103. $(3a - 4b)(5a + 3b)$ [4.5]

104. $(7x - y)^2$ [4.5]

105. *Real estate taxes.* For homes under $100,000, the property transfer tax in Vermont is 0.5% of the selling price. Find the selling price of a home that had a transfer tax of $467.50. [2.4]

106. What numbers are their own squares? [5.8]

SYNTHESIS

107. Let $f(x) = 5x^{-1/3}$. Under what condition will we have $f(x) > 0$? Why?

108. If $g(x) = x^{3/n}$, in what way does the domain of g depend on whether n is odd or even?

Use rational exponents to simplify.

109. $\sqrt{x\sqrt[3]{x^2}}$

110. $\sqrt[4]{\sqrt[3]{8x^3y^6}}$

111. $\sqrt[12]{p^2 + 2pq + q^2}$

Music. The function given by $f(x) = k2^{x/12}$ can be used to determine the frequency, in cycles per second, of a musical note that is x half-steps above a note with frequency k.*

112. The frequency of concert A for a trumpet is 440 cycles per second. Find the frequency of the A that is two octaves (24 half-steps) above concert A (few trumpeters can reach this note.)

113. Show that the G that is 7 half-steps (a "perfect fifth") above middle C (262 cycles per second) has a frequency that is about 1.5 times that of middle C.

---
*This application was inspired by information provided by Dr. Homer B. Tilton of Pima Community College East.

114. Show that the C sharp that is 4 half-steps (a "major third") above concert A (see Exercise 112) has a frequency that is about 25% greater than that of concert A.

115. *Baseball.* The statistician Bill James has found that a baseball team's winning percentage P can be approximated by

$$P = \frac{r^{1.83}}{r^{1.83} + \sigma^{1.83}},$$

where r is the total number of runs scored by that team and σ is the total number of runs scored by their opponents. During a recent season, the San Francisco Giants scored 799 runs and their opponents scored 749 runs. Use James's formula to predict the Giants' winning percentage (the team actually won 55.6% of their games).
Source: M. Bittinger, *One Man's Journey Through Mathematics*. Boston: Addison-Wesley, 2004

116. *Road pavement messages.* In a psychological study, it was determined that the proper length L of the letters of a word printed on pavement is given by

$$L = \frac{0.000169d^{2.27}}{h},$$

where d is the distance of a car from the lettering and h is the height of the eye above the surface of the road. All units are in meters. This formula says that if a person is h meters above the surface of the road and is to be able to recognize a message d meters away, that message will be the most recognizable if the length of the letters is L. Find L to the nearest tenth of a meter, given d and h.

a) $h = 1$ m, $d = 60$ m
b) $h = 0.9906$ m, $d = 75$ m
c) $h = 2.4$ m, $d = 80$ m
d) $h = 1.1$ m, $d = 100$ m

117. *Dating fossils.* The function $r(t) = 10^{-12} 2^{-t/5700}$ expresses the ratio of carbon isotopes to carbon atoms in a fossil that is t years old. What ratio of carbon isotopes to carbon atoms would be present in a 1900-year-old bone?

118. *Physics.* The equation $m = m_0(1 - v^2 c^{-2})^{-1/2}$, developed by Albert Einstein, is used to determine the mass m of an object that is moving v meters per second and has mass m_0 before the motion begins. The constant c is the speed of light, approximately 3×10^8 m/sec. Suppose that a particle with mass 8 mg is accelerated to a speed of $\frac{9}{5} \times 10^8$ m/sec. Without using a calculator, find the new mass of the particle.

119. Using a graphing calculator, select the **MODE** SIMUL and the FORMAT ExprOff. Then graph

$$y_1 = x^{1/2}, \qquad y_2 = 3x^{2/5},$$
$$y_3 = x^{4/7}, \quad \text{and} \quad y_4 = \frac{1}{5} x^{3/4}.$$

Looking only at coordinates, match each graph with its equation.

CORNER

Are Equivalent Fractions Equivalent Exponents?

Focus: Functions and rational exponents

Time: 10–20 minutes

Group size: 3

Materials: Graph paper

In arithmetic, we have seen that $\frac{1}{3}, \frac{1}{6} \cdot 2$, and $2 \cdot \frac{1}{6}$ all represent the same number. Interestingly,

$$f(x) = x^{1/3},$$
$$g(x) = (x^{1/6})^2, \quad \text{and}$$
$$h(x) = (x^2)^{1/6}$$

represent three *different* functions.

ACTIVITY

1. Selecting a variety of values for x and using the definition of positive rational exponents, one group member should graph f, a second group member should graph g, and a third group member should graph h. Be sure to check whether negative x-values are in the domain of the function.

2. Compare the three graphs and check each other's work. How and why do the graphs differ?

3. Decide as a group which graph, if any, would best represent the graph of $k(x) = x^{2/6}$. Then be prepared to explain your reasoning to the entire class. (*Hint*: Study the definition of $a^{m/n}$ on p. 446 carefully.)

10.3 Multiplying Radical Expressions

Multiplying Radical Expressions • Simplifying by Factoring •
Multiplying and Simplifying

Multiplying Radical Expressions

Note that $\sqrt{4}\,\sqrt{25} = 2 \cdot 5 = 10$. Also $\sqrt{4 \cdot 25} = \sqrt{100} = 10$. Likewise,
$$\sqrt[3]{27}\,\sqrt[3]{8} = 3 \cdot 2 = 6 \quad \text{and} \quad \sqrt[3]{27 \cdot 8} = \sqrt[3]{216} = 6.$$

These examples suggest the following.

> **The Product Rule for Radicals**
> For any real numbers $\sqrt[n]{a}$ and $\sqrt[n]{b}$,
> $$\sqrt[n]{a} \cdot \sqrt[n]{b} = \sqrt[n]{a \cdot b}.$$
> (The product of two nth roots is the nth root of the product of the two radicands.)

Rational exponents can be used to derive this rule:
$$\sqrt[n]{a} \cdot \sqrt[n]{b} = a^{1/n} \cdot b^{1/n} = (a \cdot b)^{1/n} = \sqrt[n]{a \cdot b}.$$

EXAMPLE 1   Multiply.

a) $\sqrt{3} \cdot \sqrt{5}$ **b)** $\sqrt{x+3}\,\sqrt{x-3}$

c) $\sqrt[3]{4} \cdot \sqrt[3]{5}$ **d)** $\sqrt[4]{\dfrac{y}{5}} \cdot \sqrt[4]{\dfrac{7}{x}}$

Solution

a) When no index is written, roots are understood to be square roots with an unwritten index of two. We apply the product rule:
$$\sqrt{3} \cdot \sqrt{5} = \sqrt{3 \cdot 5}$$
$$= \sqrt{15}.$$

b) $\sqrt{x+3}\,\sqrt{x-3} = \sqrt{(x+3)(x-3)}$ The product of two square roots is
$$= \sqrt{x^2 - 9}$$ the square root of the product.

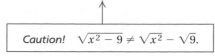

Caution! $\sqrt{x^2 - 9} \neq \sqrt{x^2} - \sqrt{9}$.

technology connection

To check Example 1(b), let
$y_1 = \sqrt{x+3}\,\sqrt{x-3}$ and
$y_2 = \sqrt{x^2 - 9}$ and compare:

$y_1 = \sqrt{(x+3)}\sqrt{(x-3)}$

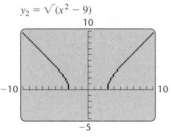

$y_2 = \sqrt{(x^2 - 9)}$

Because $y_1 = y_2$ for all x-values that can be used in *both* y_1 and y_2, Example 1(b) *is* correct.

1. Why do the graphs above differ in appearance? (*Hint*: What are the domains of the two related functions?)

c) Both $\sqrt[3]{4}$ and $\sqrt[3]{5}$ have indices of three, so to multiply we can use the product rule:

$$\sqrt[3]{4} \cdot \sqrt[3]{5} = \sqrt[3]{4 \cdot 5} = \sqrt[3]{20}.$$

d) $\sqrt[4]{\dfrac{y}{5}} \cdot \sqrt[4]{\dfrac{7}{x}} = \sqrt[4]{\dfrac{y}{5} \cdot \dfrac{7}{x}} = \sqrt[4]{\dfrac{7y}{5x}}$ In Section 7.4, we discuss other ways to write answers like this.

Caution!   The product rule for radicals applies only when radicals have the same index:

$$\sqrt[n]{a} \cdot \sqrt[m]{b} \neq \sqrt[nm]{a \cdot b}.$$

Simplifying by Factoring

The number p is a *perfect square* if there exists a rational number q for which $q^2 = p$. We say that p is a *perfect cube* if $q^3 = p$ for some rational number q. In general, p is a *perfect nth power* if $q^n = p$ for some rational number q. Thus, 16 and $\frac{1}{10,000}$ are both perfect 4th powers since $2^4 = 16$ and $\left(\frac{1}{10}\right)^4 = \frac{1}{10,000}$.

The product rule allows us to simplify $\sqrt[n]{ab}$ whenever ab contains a factor that is a perfect nth power.

Using the Product Rule to Simplify
$$\sqrt[n]{ab} = \sqrt[n]{a} \cdot \sqrt[n]{b}.$$
($\sqrt[n]{a}$ and $\sqrt[n]{b}$ must both be real numbers.)

To illustrate, suppose we wish to simplify $\sqrt{20}$. Since this is a *square* root, we check to see if there is a factor of 20 that is a perfect square. There is one, 4, so we express 20 as $4 \cdot 5$ and use the product rule:

$$\sqrt{20} = \sqrt{4 \cdot 5} \quad \text{Factoring the radicand (4 is a perfect square)}$$
$$= \sqrt{4} \cdot \sqrt{5} \quad \text{Factoring into two radicals}$$
$$= 2\sqrt{5}. \quad \text{Finding the square root of 4}$$

To Simplify a Radical Expression with Index n by Factoring
1. Express the radicand as a product in which one factor is the largest perfect nth power possible.
2. Take the nth root of each factor.
3. Simplification is complete when no radicand has a factor that is a perfect nth power.

It is often safe to assume that a radicand does not represent a negative number raised to an even power. We will henceforth make this assumption— unless functions are involved—and discontinue use of absolute-value notation when taking even roots.

EXAMPLE 2   Simplify by factoring: **(a)** $\sqrt{200}$; **(b)** $\sqrt{18x^2y}$; **(c)** $\sqrt[3]{72}$; **(d)** $\sqrt[4]{162x^6}$.

Solution

a) $\sqrt{200} = \sqrt{100 \cdot 2}$ 100 is the largest perfect-square factor of 200.

$\quad\quad = \sqrt{100} \cdot \sqrt{2} = 10\sqrt{2}$

b) $\sqrt{18x^2y} = \sqrt{9 \cdot 2 \cdot x^2 \cdot y}$ $9x^2$ is the largest perfect-square factor of $18x^2y$.

$\quad\quad = \sqrt{9x^2} \cdot \sqrt{2y}$ Factoring into two radicals

$\quad\quad = 3x\sqrt{2y}$ Taking the square root of $9x^2$

c) $\sqrt[3]{72} = \sqrt[3]{8 \cdot 9}$ 8 is the largest perfect-cube (third-power) factor of 72.

$\quad\quad = \sqrt[3]{8} \cdot \sqrt[3]{9} = 2\sqrt[3]{9}$

Let's look at this example another way. We write a complete factorization and look for triples of factors. Each triple of factors makes a cube:

$$\sqrt[3]{72} = \sqrt[3]{\underline{2 \cdot 2 \cdot 2} \cdot 3 \cdot 3}\quad\quad \text{Each triple of factors is a cube.}$$

$$= 2\sqrt[3]{3 \cdot 3} = 2\sqrt[3]{9}.$$

d) $\sqrt[4]{162x^6} = \sqrt[4]{81 \cdot 2 \cdot x^4 \cdot x^2}$ $81 \cdot x^4$ is the largest perfect fourth-power factor of $162x^6$.

$\quad\quad = \sqrt[4]{81x^4} \cdot \sqrt[4]{2x^2}$ Factoring into two radicals

$\quad\quad = 3x\sqrt[4]{2x^2}$ Taking fourth roots

Let's look at this example another way. We write a complete factorization and look for quadruples of factors. Each quadruple makes a perfect fourth power:

$$\sqrt[4]{162x^6} = \sqrt[4]{\underline{3 \cdot 3 \cdot 3 \cdot 3} \cdot 2 \cdot \underline{x \cdot x \cdot x \cdot x} \cdot x \cdot x}\quad\quad \begin{array}{l}\text{Each quadruple}\\\text{of factors is a}\\\text{power of 4.}\end{array}$$

$$= 3 \cdot x \cdot \sqrt[4]{2 \cdot x \cdot x}$$

$$= 3x\sqrt[4]{2x^2}.$$

EXAMPLE 3   If $f(x) = \sqrt{3x^2 - 6x + 3}$, find a simplified form for $f(x)$. Assume that x can be any real number.

technology connection

To use a graphing calculator to check Example 3, let
$y_1 = \sqrt{(3x^2 - 6x + 3)}$,
$y_2 = \text{abs}(x - 1)\ \sqrt{3}$, and
$y_3 = (x - 1)\ \sqrt{3}$. Do the graphs all coincide? Why or why not?

Solution

$f(x) = \sqrt{3x^2 - 6x + 3}$

$\quad\quad = \sqrt{3(x^2 - 2x + 1)}$ Factoring the radicand; $x^2 - 2x + 1$ is a perfect square.

$\quad\quad = \sqrt{(x - 1)^2 \cdot 3}$

$\quad\quad = \sqrt{(x - 1)^2} \cdot \sqrt{3}$ Factoring into two radicals

$\quad\quad = |x - 1|\sqrt{3}$ Finding the square root of $(x - 1)^2$

EXAMPLE 4   Simplify: **(a)** $\sqrt{x^7y^{11}z^9}$; **(b)** $\sqrt[3]{16a^7b^{14}}$.

Solution

a) There are many ways to factor $x^7y^{11}z^9$. Because of the square root (index of 2), we identify the largest exponents that are multiples of 2:

$$\sqrt{x^7y^{11}z^9} = \sqrt{x^6 \cdot x \cdot y^{10} \cdot y \cdot z^8 \cdot z}$$ Using the largest even powers of x, y, and z

$$= \sqrt{x^6}\,\sqrt{y^{10}}\,\sqrt{z^8}\,\sqrt{xyz}$$ Factoring into several radicals

$$= x^{6/2}\,y^{10/2}\,z^{8/2}\sqrt{xyz}$$ Converting to rational exponents

$$= x^3y^5z^4\sqrt{xyz}.$$

Check: $(x^3y^5z^4\sqrt{xyz})^2 = (x^3)^2(y^5)^2(z^4)^2(\sqrt{xyz})^2$

$$= x^6 \cdot y^{10} \cdot z^8 \cdot xyz = x^7y^{11}z^9$$

Our check shows that $x^3y^5z^4\sqrt{xyz}$ is the square root of $x^7y^{11}z^9$.

b) There are many ways to factor $16a^7b^{14}$. Because of the cube root (index of 3), we identify factors with the largest exponents that are multiples of 3:

$$\sqrt[3]{16a^7b^{14}} = \sqrt[3]{8 \cdot 2 \cdot a^6 \cdot a \cdot b^{12} \cdot b^2}$$ Using the largest perfect-cube factors; 6 and 12 are multiples of 3

$$= \sqrt[3]{8}\,\sqrt[3]{a^6}\,\sqrt[3]{b^{12}}\,\sqrt[3]{2ab^2}$$ Factoring into several radicals

$$= 2\ a^{6/3}\ b^{12/3}\sqrt[3]{2ab^2}$$ Converting to rational exponents

$$= 2a^2b^4\sqrt[3]{2ab^2}$$

As a check, let's redo the problem using a complete factorization of the radicand:

$$\sqrt[3]{16a^7b^{14}} = \sqrt[3]{\underline{2 \cdot 2 \cdot 2} \cdot 2 \cdot \underline{a \cdot a \cdot a} \cdot \underline{a \cdot a \cdot a} \cdot a \cdot \underline{b \cdot b \cdot b} \cdot \underline{b \cdot b \cdot b} \cdot \underline{b \cdot b \cdot b} \cdot \underline{b \cdot b \cdot b} \cdot b \cdot b}$$

Each triple of factors makes a cube.

$$= 2 \cdot a \cdot a \cdot b \cdot b \cdot b \cdot b \cdot \sqrt[3]{2 \cdot a \cdot b \cdot b}$$
$$= 2a^2b^4\sqrt[3]{2ab^2}.$$ Our answer checks.

> *Remember*: To simplify an nth root, identify factors in the radicand with exponents that are multiples of n.

Multiplying and Simplifying

We have used the product rule for radicals to find products and also to simplify radical expressions. For some radical expressions, it is possible to do both: First find a product and then simplify.

EXAMPLE 5   Multiply and simplify.

a) $\sqrt{15}\,\sqrt{6}$ **b)** $3\sqrt[3]{25}\cdot 2\sqrt[3]{5}$ **c)** $\sqrt[4]{8x^3y^5}\,\sqrt[4]{4x^2y^3}$

Solution

a) $\sqrt{15}\,\sqrt{6} = \sqrt{15\cdot 6}$ Multiplying radicands

$\qquad\qquad = \sqrt{90} = \sqrt{9\cdot 10}$ 9 is a perfect square.

$\qquad\qquad = 3\sqrt{10}$

b) $3\sqrt[3]{25}\cdot 2\sqrt[3]{5} = 3\cdot 2\cdot\sqrt[3]{25\cdot 5}$ Using a commutative law; multiplying radicands

$\qquad\qquad\qquad = 6\cdot\sqrt[3]{125}$ 125 is a perfect cube.

$\qquad\qquad\qquad = 6\cdot 5,\text{ or } 30$

c) $\sqrt[4]{8x^3y^5}\,\sqrt[4]{4x^2y^3} = \sqrt[4]{32x^5y^8}$ Multiplying radicands

$\qquad\qquad\qquad = \sqrt[4]{16x^4y^8\cdot 2x}$ Identifying perfect fourth-power factors

$\qquad\qquad\qquad = \sqrt[4]{16}\,\sqrt[4]{x^4}\,\sqrt[4]{y^8}\,\sqrt[4]{2x}$ Factoring into radicals

$\qquad\qquad\qquad = 2xy^2\sqrt[4]{2x}$ Finding the fourth roots; assume $x \geq 0$.

The checks are left to the student.

Student Notes _____

To multiply $\sqrt{x}\cdot\sqrt{x}$, remember what $\sqrt{x}$ represents and go directly to the product, x. Too often students unnecessarily write $\sqrt{x}\cdot\sqrt{x} = \sqrt{x^2} = x$.

Exercise Set

10.3

FOR EXTRA HELP

Student's Solutions Manual   Digital Video Tutor CD 5 Videotape 10   AW Math Tutor Center   MathXL Tutorials on CD   MathXL   MyMathLab

 Concept Reinforcement   *Classify each of the following statements as either true or false.*

1. For any real numbers $\sqrt[n]{a}$ and $\sqrt[n]{b}$,
$\sqrt[n]{a}\cdot\sqrt[n]{b} = \sqrt[n]{ab}$.

2. For any real numbers $\sqrt[n]{a}$ and $\sqrt[n]{b}$,
$\sqrt[n]{a} + \sqrt[n]{b} = \sqrt[n]{a+b}$.

3. For any real numbers $\sqrt[n]{a}$ and $\sqrt[m]{b}$,
$\sqrt[n]{a}\cdot\sqrt[m]{b} = \sqrt[nm]{ab}$.

4. For $x > 0$, $\sqrt{x^2 - 9} = x - 3$.

5. The expression $\sqrt[3]{X}$ is not simplified if X contains a factor that is a perfect cube.

6. It is often possible to simplify $\sqrt{A\cdot B}$ even though $\sqrt{A}$ and $\sqrt{B}$ cannot be simplified.

Multiply.

7. $\sqrt{5}\,\sqrt{7}$ **8.** $\sqrt{10}\,\sqrt{7}$

9. $\sqrt[3]{7}\,\sqrt[3]{2}$ **10.** $\sqrt[3]{2}\,\sqrt[3]{5}$

11. $\sqrt[4]{6}\,\sqrt[4]{3}$ **12.** $\sqrt[4]{8}\,\sqrt[4]{9}$

13. $\sqrt{2x}\,\sqrt{13y}$ **14.** $\sqrt{5a}\,\sqrt{6b}$

15. $\sqrt[5]{8y^3}\,\sqrt[5]{10y}$ **16.** $\sqrt[5]{9t^2}\,\sqrt[5]{2t}$

17. $\sqrt{y-b}\,\sqrt{y+b}$ **18.** $\sqrt{x-a}\,\sqrt{x+a}$

19. $\sqrt[3]{0.7y}\,\sqrt[3]{0.3y}$ **20.** $\sqrt[3]{0.5x}\,\sqrt[3]{0.2x}$

21. $\sqrt[5]{x-2}\,\sqrt[5]{(x-2)^2}$

22. $\sqrt[4]{x-1}\,\sqrt[4]{x^2+x+1}$

23. $\sqrt{\dfrac{7}{t}}\sqrt{\dfrac{s}{11}}$

24. $\sqrt{\dfrac{x}{6}}\sqrt{\dfrac{7}{y}}$

25. $\sqrt[7]{\dfrac{x-3}{4}}\sqrt[7]{\dfrac{5}{x+2}}$

26. $\sqrt[6]{\dfrac{a}{b-2}}\sqrt[6]{\dfrac{3}{b+2}}$

Simplify by factoring.

27. $\sqrt{18}$ **28.** $\sqrt{50}$ **29.** $\sqrt{27}$

30. $\sqrt{45}$ **31.** $\sqrt{8}$ **32.** $\sqrt{75}$

33. $\sqrt{198}$ **34.** $\sqrt{325}$ **35.** $\sqrt{36a^4b}$

36. $\sqrt{175y^8}$ **37.** $\sqrt[3]{8x^3y^2}$ **38.** $\sqrt[3]{27ab^6}$

39. $\sqrt[3]{-16x^6}$ **40.** $\sqrt[3]{-32a^6}$

Find a simplified form of $f(x)$. Assume that x can be any real number.

41. $f(x) = \sqrt[3]{125x^5}$

42. $f(x) = \sqrt[3]{16x^6}$

43. $f(x) = \sqrt{49(x-3)^2}$

44. $f(x) = \sqrt{81(x-1)^2}$

45. $f(x) = \sqrt{5x^2 - 10x + 5}$

46. $f(x) = \sqrt{2x^2 + 8x + 8}$

Simplify. Assume that no radicands were formed by raising negative numbers to even powers.

47. $\sqrt{a^6b^7}$ **48.** $\sqrt{x^6y^9}$

49. $\sqrt[3]{x^5y^6z^{10}}$ **50.** $\sqrt[3]{a^6b^7c^{13}}$

51. $\sqrt[5]{-32a^7b^{11}}$ **52.** $\sqrt[4]{16x^5y^{11}}$

53. $\sqrt[5]{x^{13}y^8z^{17}}$ **54.** $\sqrt[5]{a^6b^8c^9}$

55. $\sqrt[3]{-80a^{14}}$ **56.** $\sqrt[4]{810x^9}$

Multiply and simplify.

57. $\sqrt{6}\sqrt{3}$ **58.** $\sqrt{15}\sqrt{5}$

59. $\sqrt{15}\sqrt{21}$ **60.** $\sqrt{10}\sqrt{14}$

61. $\sqrt[3]{9}\sqrt[3]{3}$ **62.** $\sqrt[3]{2}\sqrt[3]{4}$

Aha! 63. $\sqrt{18a^3}\sqrt{18a^3}$ **64.** $\sqrt{75x^7}\sqrt{75x^7}$

65. $\sqrt[3]{5a^2}\sqrt[3]{2a}$ **66.** $\sqrt[3]{7x}\sqrt[3]{3x^2}$

67. $\sqrt{2x^5}\sqrt{10x^2}$ **68.** $\sqrt{5a^7}\sqrt{15a^3}$

69. $\sqrt[3]{s^2t^4}\sqrt[3]{s^4t^6}$ **70.** $\sqrt[3]{x^2y^4}\sqrt[3]{x^2y^6}$

71. $\sqrt[3]{(x+5)^2}\sqrt[3]{(x+5)^4}$

72. $\sqrt[3]{(a-b)^5}\sqrt[3]{(a-b)^7}$

73. $\sqrt[4]{20a^3b^7}\sqrt[4]{4a^2b^5}$

74. $\sqrt[4]{9x^7y^2}\sqrt[4]{9x^2y^9}$

75. $\sqrt[5]{x^3(y+z)^6}\sqrt[5]{x^3(y+z)^4}$

76. $\sqrt[5]{a^3(b-c)^4}\sqrt[5]{a^7(b-c)^4}$

77. Why do we need to know how to multiply radical expressions before learning how to simplify radical expressions?

78. Why is it incorrect to say that, in general, $\sqrt{x^2} = x$?

SKILL MAINTENANCE

Perform the indicated operation and, if possible, simplify. [6.4]

79. $\dfrac{3x}{16y} + \dfrac{5y}{64x}$

80. $\dfrac{2}{a^3b^4} + \dfrac{6}{a^4b}$

81. $\dfrac{4}{x^2-9} - \dfrac{7}{2x-6}$

82. $\dfrac{8}{x^2-25} - \dfrac{3}{2x-10}$

Simplify. [4.1]

83. $\dfrac{9a^4b^7}{3a^2b^5}$ **84.** $\dfrac{12a^2b^7}{4ab^2}$

SYNTHESIS

85. Explain why it is true that $\sqrt[n]{ab} = \sqrt[n]{a}\cdot\sqrt[n]{b}$.

86. Is the equation $\sqrt{(2x+3)^8} = (2x+3)^4$ always, sometimes, or never true? Why?

87. *Radar range.* The function given by
$$R(x) = \frac{1}{2}\sqrt[4]{\frac{x\cdot 3.0\times 10^6}{\pi^2}}$$
can be used to determine the maximum range $R(x)$, in miles, of an ARSR-3 surveillance radar with a peak power of x watts. Determine the maximum radar range when the peak power is 5×10^4 watts.
Source: Introduction to RADAR Techniques, Federal Aviation Administration, 1988

88. *Speed of a skidding car.*   Police can estimate the speed at which a car was traveling by measuring its skid marks. The function given by

$$r(L) = 2\sqrt{5L}$$

can be used, where L is the length of a skid mark, in feet, and $r(L)$ is the speed, in miles per hour. Find the exact speed and an estimate (to the nearest tenth mile per hour) for the speed of a car that left skid marks **(a)** 20 ft long; **(b)** 70 ft long; **(c)** 90 ft long. See also Exercise 102.

89. *Wind chill temperature.*   When the temperature is T degrees Celsius and the wind speed is v meters per second, the *wind chill temperature,* T_{W}, is the temperature (with no wind) that it feels like. Here is a formula for finding wind chill temperature:

$$T_{\text{W}} = 33 - \frac{(10.45 + 10\sqrt{v} - v)(33 - T)}{22}.$$

Estimate the wind chill temperature (to the nearest tenth of a degree) for the given actual temperatures and wind speeds.

a) $T = 7°C$, $v = 8\,\text{m/sec}$
b) $T = 0°C$, $v = 12\,\text{m/sec}$
c) $T = -5°C$, $v = 14\,\text{m/sec}$
d) $T = -23°C$, $v = 15\,\text{m/sec}$

Simplify. Assume that all variables are nonnegative.

90. $\left(\sqrt{r^3 t}\right)^7$

91. $\left(\sqrt[3]{25x^4}\right)^4$

92. $\left(\sqrt[3]{a^2 b^4}\right)^5$

93. $\left(\sqrt{a^3 b^5}\right)^7$

Draw and compare the graphs of each group of equations.

94. $f(x) = \sqrt{x^2 - 2x + 1}$,
     $g(x) = x - 1$,
     $h(x) = |x - 1|$

95. $f(x) = \sqrt{x^2 + 2x + 1}$,
     $g(x) = x + 1$,
     $h(x) = |x + 1|$

96. If $f(t) = \sqrt{t^2 - 3t - 4}$, what is the domain of f?

97. What is the domain of g, if $g(x) = \sqrt{x^2 - 6x + 8}$?

Solve.

98. $\sqrt[3]{5x^{k+1}}\ \sqrt[3]{25x^k} = 5x^7$, for k

99. $\sqrt[5]{4a^{3k+2}}\ \sqrt[5]{8a^{6-k}} = 2a^4$, for k

100. Use a graphing calculator to check your answers to Exercises 21 and 41.

101. Rony is puzzled. When he uses a graphing calculator to graph $y = \sqrt{x} \cdot \sqrt{x}$, he gets the following screen. Explain why Rony did not get the complete line $y = x$.

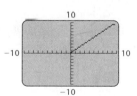

102. Does a car traveling twice as fast as another car leave a skid mark that is twice as long? (See Exercise 88.) Why or why not?

10.4 Dividing Radical Expressions

Dividing and Simplifying   •   Rationalizing Denominators and
Numerators (Part 1)

Dividing and Simplifying

Study Skills

Professors Are Human

Even the best professors
sometimes make mistakes. If, as
you review your notes, you find
that something doesn't make
sense, it may be due to your
instructor having made a mistake.
If, after double-checking, you still
perceive a mistake, politely ask
him or her about it. In doing so,
you may be helping *everyone* in
your class enormously.

Just as the root of a product can be expressed as the product of two roots, the
root of a quotient can be expressed as the quotient of two roots. For example,

$$\sqrt[3]{\frac{27}{8}} = \frac{3}{2} \quad \text{and} \quad \frac{\sqrt[3]{27}}{\sqrt[3]{8}} = \frac{3}{2}.$$

This example suggests the following.

> **The Quotient Rule for Radicals**
> For any real numbers $\sqrt[n]{a}$ and $\sqrt[n]{b}$, $b \neq 0$,
> $$\sqrt[n]{\frac{a}{b}} = \frac{\sqrt[n]{a}}{\sqrt[n]{b}}.$$

Remember that an nth root is simplified when its radicand has no factors
that are perfect nth powers. Recall too that we assume that no radicands represent negative quantities raised to an even power.

EXAMPLE 1   Simplify by taking the roots of the numerator and the denominator.

a) $\sqrt[3]{\frac{27}{125}}$ b) $\sqrt{\frac{25}{y^2}}$

Solution

a) $\sqrt[3]{\frac{27}{125}} = \frac{\sqrt[3]{27}}{\sqrt[3]{125}} = \frac{3}{5}$ Taking the cube roots of the numerator and
the denominator

b) $\sqrt{\frac{25}{y^2}} = \frac{\sqrt{25}}{\sqrt{y^2}} = \frac{5}{y}$ Taking the square roots of the numerator and the
denominator. Assume $y > 0$.

As in Section 10.3, any radical expressions appearing in the answers should
be simplified as much as possible.

EXAMPLE 2   Simplify: **(a)** $\sqrt{\dfrac{16x^3}{y^8}}$; **(b)** $\sqrt[3]{\dfrac{27y^{14}}{8x^3}}$.

Solution

a) $\sqrt{\dfrac{16x^3}{y^8}} = \dfrac{\sqrt{16x^3}}{\sqrt{y^8}}$

$= \dfrac{\sqrt{16x^2 \cdot x}}{\sqrt{y^8}}$

$= \dfrac{4x\sqrt{x}}{y^4}$ Simplifying the numerator and the denominator

b) $\sqrt[3]{\dfrac{27y^{14}}{8x^3}} = \dfrac{\sqrt[3]{27y^{14}}}{\sqrt[3]{8x^3}}$

$= \dfrac{\sqrt[3]{27y^{12}y^2}}{\sqrt[3]{8x^3}}$ y^{12} is the largest perfect-cube factor of y^{14}.

$= \dfrac{\sqrt[3]{27y^{12}}\,\sqrt[3]{y^2}}{\sqrt[3]{8x^3}}$

$= \dfrac{3y^4\sqrt[3]{y^2}}{2x}$ Simplifying the numerator and the denominator

If we read from right to left, the quotient rule tells us that to divide two radical expressions that have the same index, we can divide the radicands.

EXAMPLE 3

Student Notes

When writing radical signs, pay careful attention to what is included as the radicand. Each of the following represents a *different* number:

$\sqrt{\dfrac{5 \cdot 2}{3}}, \quad \dfrac{\sqrt{5 \cdot 2}}{3}, \quad \dfrac{\sqrt{5} \cdot 2}{3}.$

Divide and, if possible, simplify.

a) $\dfrac{\sqrt{80}}{\sqrt{5}}$

b) $\dfrac{5\sqrt[3]{32}}{\sqrt[3]{2}}$

c) $\dfrac{\sqrt{72xy}}{2\sqrt{2}}$

d) $\dfrac{\sqrt[4]{18a^9b^5}}{\sqrt[4]{3b}}$

Solution

a) $\dfrac{\sqrt{80}}{\sqrt{5}} = \sqrt{\dfrac{80}{5}} = \sqrt{16} = 4$

> Because the indices match, we can divide the radicands.

b) $\dfrac{5\sqrt[3]{32}}{\sqrt[3]{2}} = 5\sqrt[3]{\dfrac{32}{2}} = 5\sqrt[3]{16}$

$= 5\sqrt[3]{8 \cdot 2}$ 8 is the largest perfect-cube factor of 16.

$= 5\sqrt[3]{8}\,\sqrt[3]{2} = 5 \cdot 2\sqrt[3]{2}$

$= 10\sqrt[3]{2}$

c) $\dfrac{\sqrt{72xy}}{2\sqrt{2}} = \dfrac{1}{2}\sqrt{\dfrac{72xy}{2}}$

> Because the indices match, we can divide the radicands.

$$= \dfrac{1}{2}\sqrt{36xy} = \dfrac{1}{2} \cdot 6\sqrt{xy}$$

$$= 3\sqrt{xy}$$

d) $\dfrac{\sqrt[4]{18a^9b^5}}{\sqrt[4]{3b}} = \sqrt[4]{\dfrac{18a^9b^5}{3b}}$

$$= \sqrt[4]{6a^9b^4} = \sqrt[4]{a^8b^4}\,\sqrt[4]{6a}$$

Note that 8 is the largest power less than 9 that is a multiple of the index 4.

$$= a^2b\sqrt[4]{6a}$$

Partial check: $(a^2b)^4 = a^8b^4$

Rationalizing Denominators and Numerators (Part 1)*

When a radical expression appears in a denominator, it can be useful to find an equivalent expression in which the denominator no longer contains a radical.[†] The procedure for finding such an expression is called **rationalizing the denominator**. We carry this out by multiplying by 1 in either of two ways.

One way is to multiply by 1 *under* the radical to make the denominator of the radicand a perfect power.

EXAMPLE 4 Rationalize each denominator.

a) $\sqrt{\dfrac{7}{3}}$ **b)** $\sqrt[3]{\dfrac{5}{16}}$

Solution

a) We multiply by 1 under the radical, using $\frac{3}{3}$. We do this so that the denominator of the radicand will be a perfect square:

$$\sqrt{\dfrac{7}{3}} = \sqrt{\dfrac{7}{3} \cdot \dfrac{3}{3}}$$ Multiplying by 1 under the radical

$$= \sqrt{\dfrac{21}{9}}$$ The denominator, 9, is now a perfect square.

$$= \dfrac{\sqrt{21}}{\sqrt{9}}$$ Using the quotient rule for radicals

$$= \dfrac{\sqrt{21}}{3}.$$

---

*Denominators and numerators with two terms are rationalized in Section 10.5.
[†]See Exercise 73 on p. 664.

b) Note that $16 = 4^2$. Thus, to make the denominator a perfect cube, we multiply under the radical by $\frac{4}{4}$:

$$\sqrt[3]{\frac{5}{16}} = \sqrt[3]{\frac{5}{4 \cdot 4} \cdot \frac{4}{4}} \qquad \text{Since the index is 3, we need 3 identical factors in the denominator.}$$

$$= \sqrt[3]{\frac{20}{4^3}} \qquad \text{The denominator is now a perfect cube.}$$

$$= \frac{\sqrt[3]{20}}{\sqrt[3]{4^3}}$$

$$= \frac{\sqrt[3]{20}}{4}.$$

Another way to rationalize a denominator is to multiply by 1 *outside* the radical.

EXAMPLE 5   Rationalize each denominator.

a) $\sqrt{\dfrac{4}{5b}}$

b) $\dfrac{\sqrt[3]{a}}{\sqrt[3]{9x}}$

c) $\dfrac{3x}{\sqrt[5]{2x^2y^3}}$

Solution

a) We rewrite the expression as a quotient of two radicals. Then we simplify and multiply by 1:

$$\sqrt{\frac{4}{5b}} = \frac{\sqrt{4}}{\sqrt{5b}} = \frac{2}{\sqrt{5b}} \qquad \text{We assume } b > 0.$$

$$= \frac{2}{\sqrt{5b}} \cdot \frac{\sqrt{5b}}{\sqrt{5b}} \qquad \text{Multiplying by 1}$$

$$= \frac{2\sqrt{5b}}{(\sqrt{5b})^2} \qquad \text{Try to do this step mentally.}$$

$$= \frac{2\sqrt{5b}}{5b}.$$

b) To rationalize the denominator $\sqrt[3]{9x}$, note that $9x$ is $3 \cdot 3 \cdot x$. In order for this radicand to be a cube, we need another factor of 3 and two more factors of x. Thus we multiply by 1, using $\sqrt[3]{3x^2}/\sqrt[3]{3x^2}$:

$$\frac{\sqrt[3]{a}}{\sqrt[3]{9x}} = \frac{\sqrt[3]{a}}{\sqrt[3]{9x}} \cdot \frac{\sqrt[3]{3x^2}}{\sqrt[3]{3x^2}} \qquad \text{Multiplying by 1}$$

$$= \frac{\sqrt[3]{3ax^2}}{\sqrt[3]{27x^3}} \longleftarrow \text{This radicand is now a perfect cube.}$$

$$= \frac{\sqrt[3]{3ax^2}}{3x}.$$

c) To change the radicand $2x^2y^3$ into a perfect fifth power, we need four more factors of 2, three more factors of x, and two more factors of y. Thus we multiply by 1, using $\sqrt[5]{2^4x^3y^2}/\sqrt[5]{2^4x^3y^2}$, or $\sqrt[5]{16x^3y^2}/\sqrt[5]{16x^3y^2}$:

$$\frac{3x}{\sqrt[5]{2x^2y^3}} = \frac{3x}{\sqrt[5]{2x^2y^3}} \cdot \frac{\sqrt[5]{16x^3y^2}}{\sqrt[5]{16x^3y^2}} \qquad \text{Multiplying by 1}$$

$$= \frac{3x\sqrt[5]{16x^3y^2}}{\sqrt[5]{32x^5y^5}} \qquad \text{This radicand is now a perfect fifth power.}$$

$$= \frac{3x\sqrt[5]{16x^3y^2}}{2xy} = \frac{3\sqrt[5]{16x^3y^2}}{2y}. \qquad \text{Always simplify if possible.}$$

Sometimes in calculus it is necessary to rationalize a numerator. To do so, we multiply by 1 to make the radicand in the *numerator* a perfect power.

EXAMPLE 6   Rationalize each numerator: **(a)** $\sqrt{\dfrac{7}{5}}$; **(b)** $\dfrac{\sqrt[3]{4a^2}}{\sqrt[3]{5b}}$.

Solution

a) $\sqrt{\dfrac{7}{5}} = \sqrt{\dfrac{7}{5} \cdot \dfrac{7}{7}}$ Multiplying by 1 under the radical. We also could have multiplied by $\sqrt{7}/\sqrt{7}$ outside the radical.

$$= \sqrt{\frac{49}{35}} \qquad \text{The numerator is now a perfect square.}$$

$$= \frac{\sqrt{49}}{\sqrt{35}} \qquad \text{Using the quotient rule for radicals}$$

$$= \frac{7}{\sqrt{35}}$$

b) $\dfrac{\sqrt[3]{4a^2}}{\sqrt[3]{5b}} = \dfrac{\sqrt[3]{4a^2}}{\sqrt[3]{5b}} \cdot \dfrac{\sqrt[3]{2a}}{\sqrt[3]{2a}}$ Multiplying by 1

$$= \frac{\sqrt[3]{8a^3}}{\sqrt[3]{10ba}} \qquad \text{This radicand is now a perfect cube.}$$

$$= \frac{2a}{\sqrt[3]{10ab}}$$

In Section 10.5, we will discuss rationalizing denominators and numerators in which two terms appear.

Exercise Set
10.4

FOR EXTRA HELP

Student's
Solutions
Manual

Digital Video Tutor
CD 5
Videotape 10

AW Math
Tutor Center

MathXL Tutorials
on CD

MathXL   MyMathLab

🍮 *Concept Reinforcement   In each of Exercises 1–8, match the expression with an equivalent expression from the column on the right. Assume $a, b > 0$.*

1. ____ $\sqrt[3]{\dfrac{a^2}{b^6}}$

2. ____ $\dfrac{\sqrt[3]{a^6}}{\sqrt[3]{b^9}}$

3. ____ $\sqrt[5]{\dfrac{a^6}{b^4}}$

4. ____ $\sqrt{\dfrac{a}{b^3}}$

5. ____ $\dfrac{\sqrt[5]{a^2}}{\sqrt[5]{b^2}}$

6. ____ $\dfrac{\sqrt{5a^4}}{\sqrt{5a^3}}$

7. ____ $\dfrac{\sqrt[5]{a^2}}{\sqrt[5]{b^3}}$

8. ____ $\sqrt[4]{\dfrac{16a^6}{a^2}}$

a) $\dfrac{\sqrt[5]{a^2}\sqrt[5]{b^2}}{\sqrt[5]{b^5}}$

b) $\dfrac{a^2}{b^3}$

c) $\sqrt{\dfrac{a \cdot b}{b^3 \cdot b}}$

d) $\sqrt{a}$

e) $\dfrac{\sqrt[3]{a^2}}{b^2}$

f) $\sqrt[5]{\dfrac{a^6 b}{b^4 \cdot b}}$

g) $2a$

h) $\dfrac{\sqrt[5]{a^2 b^3}}{\sqrt[5]{b^5}}$

Divide and, if possible, simplify. Assume all variables represent positive numbers.

27. $\dfrac{\sqrt{35x}}{\sqrt{7x}}$

28. $\dfrac{\sqrt{28y}}{\sqrt{4y}}$

29. $\dfrac{\sqrt[3]{270}}{\sqrt[3]{10}}$

30. $\dfrac{\sqrt[3]{40}}{\sqrt[3]{5}}$

31. $\dfrac{\sqrt{40xy^3}}{\sqrt{8x}}$

32. $\dfrac{\sqrt{56ab^3}}{\sqrt{7a}}$

33. $\dfrac{\sqrt[3]{96a^4b^2}}{\sqrt[3]{12a^2b}}$

34. $\dfrac{\sqrt[3]{189x^5y^7}}{\sqrt[3]{7x^2y^2}}$

35. $\dfrac{\sqrt{100ab}}{5\sqrt{2}}$

36. $\dfrac{\sqrt{75ab}}{3\sqrt{3}}$

37. $\dfrac{\sqrt[4]{48x^9y^{13}}}{\sqrt[4]{3xy^{-2}}}$

38. $\dfrac{\sqrt[5]{64a^{11}b^{28}}}{\sqrt[5]{2ab^{-2}}}$

39. $\dfrac{\sqrt[3]{x^3 - y^3}}{\sqrt[3]{x - y}}$ ← → 40. $\dfrac{\sqrt[3]{r^3 + s^3}}{\sqrt[3]{r + s}}$

> *Hint:* Factor and then simplify.

Simplify by taking the roots of the numerator and the denominator. Assume all variables represent positive numbers.

9. $\sqrt{\dfrac{36}{25}}$

10. $\sqrt{\dfrac{100}{81}}$

11. $\sqrt[3]{\dfrac{64}{27}}$

12. $\sqrt[3]{\dfrac{343}{1000}}$

13. $\sqrt{\dfrac{49}{y^2}}$

14. $\sqrt{\dfrac{121}{x^2}}$

15. $\sqrt{\dfrac{36y^3}{x^4}}$

16. $\sqrt{\dfrac{25a^5}{b^6}}$

17. $\sqrt[3]{\dfrac{27a^4}{8b^3}}$

18. $\sqrt[3]{\dfrac{64x^7}{216y^6}}$

19. $\sqrt[4]{\dfrac{16a^4}{b^4c^8}}$

20. $\sqrt[4]{\dfrac{81x^4}{y^8z^4}}$

21. $\sqrt[4]{\dfrac{a^5b^8}{c^{10}}}$

22. $\sqrt[4]{\dfrac{x^9y^{12}}{z^6}}$

23. $\sqrt[5]{\dfrac{32x^6}{y^{11}}}$

24. $\sqrt[5]{\dfrac{243a^9}{b^{13}}}$

25. $\sqrt[6]{\dfrac{x^6y^8}{z^{15}}}$

26. $\sqrt[6]{\dfrac{a^9b^{12}}{c^{13}}}$

Rationalize each denominator. Assume all variables represent positive numbers.

41. $\sqrt{\dfrac{3}{2}}$

42. $\sqrt{\dfrac{6}{7}}$

43. $\dfrac{2\sqrt{5}}{7\sqrt{3}}$

44. $\dfrac{3\sqrt{5}}{2\sqrt{2}}$

45. $\sqrt[3]{\dfrac{16}{9}}$

46. $\sqrt[3]{\dfrac{2}{9}}$

47. $\dfrac{\sqrt[3]{3a}}{\sqrt[3]{5c}}$

48. $\dfrac{\sqrt[3]{7x}}{\sqrt[3]{3y}}$

49. $\dfrac{\sqrt[3]{5y^4}}{\sqrt[3]{6x^4}}$

50. $\dfrac{\sqrt[3]{3a^4}}{\sqrt[3]{7b^2}}$

51. $\sqrt[3]{\dfrac{2}{x^2y}}$

52. $\sqrt[3]{\dfrac{5}{ab^2}}$

53. $\sqrt{\dfrac{7a}{18}}$

54. $\sqrt{\dfrac{3x}{10}}$

55. $\sqrt{\dfrac{9}{20x^2y}}$

56. $\sqrt{\dfrac{7}{32a^2b}}$ ***Aha!*** 57. $\sqrt{\dfrac{10ab^2}{72a^3b}}$

58. $\sqrt{\dfrac{21x^2y}{75xy^5}}$

Rationalize each numerator. Assume all variables represent positive numbers.

59. $\dfrac{\sqrt{5}}{\sqrt{7x}}$

60. $\dfrac{\sqrt{10}}{\sqrt{3x}}$

61. $\sqrt{\dfrac{14}{21}}$

62. $\sqrt{\dfrac{12}{15}}$

63. $\dfrac{4\sqrt{13}}{3\sqrt{7}}$

64. $\dfrac{5\sqrt{21}}{2\sqrt{5}}$

65. $\dfrac{\sqrt[3]{7}}{\sqrt[3]{2}}$

66. $\dfrac{\sqrt[3]{5}}{\sqrt[3]{4}}$

67. $\sqrt{\dfrac{7x}{3y}}$

68. $\sqrt{\dfrac{7a}{6b}}$

69. $\sqrt[3]{\dfrac{2a^5}{5b}}$

70. $\sqrt[3]{\dfrac{2a^4}{7b}}$

71. $\sqrt{\dfrac{x^3y}{2}}$

72. $\sqrt{\dfrac{ab^5}{3}}$

73. Explain why it is easier to approximate

$$\dfrac{\sqrt{2}}{2} \quad \text{than} \quad \dfrac{1}{\sqrt{2}}$$

if no calculator is available and $\sqrt{2} \approx 1.414213562$.

74. A student *incorrectly* claims that

$$\dfrac{5 + \sqrt{2}}{\sqrt{18}} = \dfrac{5 + \sqrt{1}}{\sqrt{9}} = \dfrac{5 + 1}{3}.$$

How could you convince the student that a mistake has been made? How would you explain the correct way of rationalizing the denominator?

SKILL MAINTENANCE

Multiply. [6.2]

75. $\dfrac{3}{x - 5} \cdot \dfrac{x - 1}{x + 5}$

76. $\dfrac{7}{x + 4} \cdot \dfrac{x - 2}{x - 4}$

Simplify.

77. $\dfrac{a^2 - 8a + 7}{a^2 - 49}$ [6.1]

78. $\dfrac{t^2 + 9t - 22}{t^2 - 4}$ [6.1]

79. $(5a^3b^4)^3$ [4.1]

80. $(3x^4)^2(5xy^3)^2$ [4.1]

SYNTHESIS

81. Is the quotient of two irrational numbers always an irrational number? Why or why not?

82. Is it possible to understand how to rationalize a denominator without knowing how to multiply rational expressions? Why or why not?

83. *Pendulums.* The *period* of a pendulum is the time it takes to complete one cycle, swinging to and fro. For a pendulum that is L centimeters long, the period T is given by the formula

$$T = 2\pi\sqrt{\dfrac{L}{980}},$$

where T is in seconds. Find, to the nearest hundredth of a second, the period of a pendulum of length **(a)** 65 cm; **(b)** 98 cm; **(c)** 120 cm. Use a calculator's $\boxed{\pi}$ key if possible.

Perform the indicated operations.

84. $\dfrac{7\sqrt{a^2b}\,\sqrt{25xy}}{5\sqrt{a^{-4}b^{-1}}\,\sqrt{49x^{-1}y^{-3}}}$

85. $\dfrac{\left(\sqrt[3]{81mn^2}\right)^2}{\left(\sqrt[3]{mn}\right)^2}$

86. $\dfrac{\sqrt{44x^2y^9z}\,\sqrt{22y^9z^6}}{\left(\sqrt{11xy^8z^2}\right)^2}$

87. $\sqrt{a^2 - 3} - \dfrac{a^2}{\sqrt{a^2 - 3}}$

88. $5\sqrt{\dfrac{x}{y}} + 4\sqrt{\dfrac{y}{x}} - \dfrac{3}{\sqrt{xy}}$

89. Provide a reason for each step in the following derivation of the quotient rule:

$$\sqrt[n]{\dfrac{a}{b}} = \left(\dfrac{a}{b}\right)^{1/n} \quad \underline{\hspace{2cm}}$$

$$= \dfrac{a^{1/n}}{b^{1/n}} \quad \underline{\hspace{2cm}}$$

$$= \dfrac{\sqrt[n]{a}}{\sqrt[n]{b}} \quad \underline{\hspace{2cm}}$$

90. Show that $\dfrac{\sqrt[n]{a}}{\sqrt[n]{b}}$ is the nth root of $\dfrac{a}{b}$ by raising it to the nth power and simplifying.

91. Let $f(x) = \sqrt{18x^3}$ and $g(x) = \sqrt{2x}$. Find $(f/g)(x)$ and specify the domain of f/g.

92. Let $f(t) = \sqrt{2t}$ and $g(t) = \sqrt{50t^3}$. Find $(f/g)(t)$ and specify the domain of f/g.

93. Let $f(x) = \sqrt{x^2 - 9}$ and $g(x) = \sqrt{x - 3}$. Find $(f/g)(x)$ and specify the domain of f/g.

Expressions Containing Several Radical Terms

Adding and Subtracting Radical Expressions • Products and Quotients of Two or More Radical Terms • Rationalizing Denominators and Numerators (Part 2) • Terms with Differing Indices

Radical expressions like $6\sqrt{7} + 4\sqrt{7}$ or $\left(\sqrt{a} + \sqrt{b}\right)\left(\sqrt{a} - \sqrt{b}\right)$ contain more than one *radical term* and can sometimes be simplified.

Adding and Subtracting Radical Expressions

When two radical expressions have the same indices and radicands, they are said to be **like radicals**. Like radicals can be combined (added or subtracted) in much the same way that we combined like terms earlier in this text.

EXAMPLE 1   Simplify by combining like radical terms.

a) $6\sqrt{7} + 4\sqrt{7}$

b) $\sqrt[3]{2} - 7x\sqrt[3]{2} + 5\sqrt[3]{2}$

c) $6\sqrt[5]{4x} + 3\sqrt[5]{4x} - \sqrt[3]{4x}$

Solution

a) $6\sqrt{7} + 4\sqrt{7} = (6 + 4)\sqrt{7}$ Using the distributive law (factoring out $\sqrt{7}$)

$\qquad\qquad\quad\, = 10\sqrt{7}$ You can think: 6 square roots of 7 plus 4 square roots of 7 results in 10 square roots of 7.

b) $\sqrt[3]{2} - 7x\sqrt[3]{2} + 5\sqrt[3]{2} = (1 - 7x + 5)\sqrt[3]{2}$ Factoring out $\sqrt[3]{2}$

$\qquad\qquad\qquad\qquad\quad = (6 - 7x)\sqrt[3]{2}$ These parentheses are important!

c) $6\sqrt[5]{4x} + 3\sqrt[5]{4x} - \sqrt[3]{4x} = (6 + 3)\sqrt[5]{4x} - \sqrt[3]{4x}$ Try to do this step mentally.

$\qquad\qquad\qquad\qquad\quad\; = 9\sqrt[5]{4x} - \sqrt[3]{4x}$ Because the indices differ, we are done.

Our ability to simplify radical expressions can help us to find like radicals even when, at first, it may appear that none exists.

EXAMPLE 2   Simplify by combining like radical terms, if possible.

a) $3\sqrt{8} - 5\sqrt{2}$

b) $9\sqrt{5} - 4\sqrt{3}$

c) $\sqrt[3]{2x^6y^4} + 7\sqrt[3]{2y}$

Solution

a) $3\sqrt{8} - 5\sqrt{2} = 3\sqrt{4 \cdot 2} - 5\sqrt{2}$

$\left.\begin{aligned} &= 3\sqrt{4} \cdot \sqrt{2} - 5\sqrt{2} \\ &= 3 \cdot 2 \cdot \sqrt{2} - 5\sqrt{2} \end{aligned}\right\}$ Simplifying $\sqrt{8}$

$= 6\sqrt{2} - 5\sqrt{2}$

$= \sqrt{2}$ Combining like radicals

b) $9\sqrt{5} - 4\sqrt{3}$ cannot be simplified.

c) $\sqrt[3]{2x^6y^4} + 7\sqrt[3]{2y} = \sqrt[3]{x^6y^3 \cdot 2y} + 7\sqrt[3]{2y}$

$\left.\begin{aligned} &= \sqrt[3]{x^6y^3} \cdot \sqrt[3]{2y} + 7\sqrt[3]{2y} \\ &= x^2y \cdot \sqrt[3]{2y} + 7\sqrt[3]{2y} \end{aligned}\right\}$ Simplifying $\sqrt[3]{2x^6y^4}$

$= (x^2y + 7)\sqrt[3]{2y}$ Factoring to combine like radical terms

---

Products and Quotients of Two or More Radical Terms

Radical expressions often contain factors that have more than one term. Multiplying such expressions is similar to finding products of polynomials. Some products will yield like radical terms, which we can now combine.

EXAMPLE 3   Multiply.

a) $\sqrt{3}(x - \sqrt{5})$ **b)** $\sqrt[3]{y}(\sqrt[3]{y^2} + \sqrt[3]{2})$

c) $(4\sqrt{3} + \sqrt{2})(\sqrt{3} - 5\sqrt{2})$ **d)** $(\sqrt{a} + \sqrt{b})(\sqrt{a} - \sqrt{b})$

Solution

a) $\sqrt{3}(x - \sqrt{5}) = \sqrt{3} \cdot x - \sqrt{3} \cdot \sqrt{5}$ Using the distributive law

$= x\sqrt{3} - \sqrt{15}$ Multiplying radicals

b) $\sqrt[3]{y}(\sqrt[3]{y^2} + \sqrt[3]{2}) = \sqrt[3]{y} \cdot \sqrt[3]{y^2} + \sqrt[3]{y} \cdot \sqrt[3]{2}$ Using the distributive law

$= \sqrt[3]{y^3} + \sqrt[3]{2y}$ Multiplying radicals

$= y + \sqrt[3]{2y}$ Simplifying $\sqrt[3]{y^3}$

 F O I L

c) $(4\sqrt{3} + \sqrt{2})(\sqrt{3} - 5\sqrt{2}) = 4(\sqrt{3})^2 - 20\sqrt{3} \cdot \sqrt{2} + \sqrt{2} \cdot \sqrt{3} - 5(\sqrt{2})^2$

$= 4 \cdot 3 - 20\sqrt{6} + \sqrt{6} - 5 \cdot 2$ Multiplying radicals

$= 12 - 20\sqrt{6} + \sqrt{6} - 10$

$= 2 - 19\sqrt{6}$ Combining like terms

d) $(\sqrt{a} + \sqrt{b})(\sqrt{a} - \sqrt{b}) = (\sqrt{a})^2 - \sqrt{a}\,\sqrt{b} + \sqrt{a}\,\sqrt{b} - (\sqrt{b})^2$ Using FOIL

$$= a - b \quad \text{Combining like terms}$$

In Example 3(d) above, you may have noticed that since the outer and inner products in FOIL are opposites, the result, $a - b$, is not itself a radical expression. Pairs of radical terms, like $\sqrt{a} + \sqrt{b}$ and $\sqrt{a} - \sqrt{b}$, are called **conjugates**. In general, the conjugate of $a\sqrt{b} + c\sqrt{d}$ is $a\sqrt{b} - c\sqrt{d}$. The product of conjugates contains no radical expressions.

Rationalizing Denominators and Numerators (Part 2)

The use of conjugates allows us to rationalize denominators or numerators with two terms.

EXAMPLE 4   Rationalize each denominator: **(a)** $\dfrac{4}{\sqrt{3} + x}$;   **(b)** $\dfrac{4 + \sqrt{2}}{\sqrt{5} - \sqrt{2}}$.

Solution

a) $\dfrac{4}{\sqrt{3} + x} = \dfrac{4}{\sqrt{3} + x} \cdot \dfrac{\sqrt{3} - x}{\sqrt{3} - x}$ Multiplying by 1, using the conjugate of $\sqrt{3} + x$, which is $\sqrt{3} - x$

$$= \dfrac{4(\sqrt{3} - x)}{(\sqrt{3} + x)(\sqrt{3} - x)} \quad \begin{array}{l} \text{Multiplying numerators and} \\ \text{denominators} \end{array}$$

$$= \dfrac{4(\sqrt{3} - x)}{(\sqrt{3})^2 - x^2} \quad \text{Using FOIL in the denominator}$$

$$= \dfrac{4\sqrt{3} - 4x}{3 - x^2} \quad \begin{array}{l} \text{Simplifying. No radicals remain in the} \\ \text{denominator.} \end{array}$$

b) $\dfrac{4 + \sqrt{2}}{\sqrt{5} - \sqrt{2}} = \dfrac{4 + \sqrt{2}}{\sqrt{5} - \sqrt{2}} \cdot \dfrac{\sqrt{5} + \sqrt{2}}{\sqrt{5} + \sqrt{2}}$ Multiplying by 1, using the conjugate of $\sqrt{5} - \sqrt{2}$, which is $\sqrt{5} + \sqrt{2}$

$$= \dfrac{(4 + \sqrt{2})(\sqrt{5} + \sqrt{2})}{(\sqrt{5} - \sqrt{2})(\sqrt{5} + \sqrt{2})} \quad \begin{array}{l} \text{Multiplying numerators} \\ \text{and denominators} \end{array}$$

$$= \dfrac{4\sqrt{5} + 4\sqrt{2} + \sqrt{2}\,\sqrt{5} + (\sqrt{2})^2}{(\sqrt{5})^2 - (\sqrt{2})^2} \quad \text{Using FOIL}$$

$$= \dfrac{4\sqrt{5} + 4\sqrt{2} + \sqrt{10} + 2}{5 - 2} \quad \begin{array}{l} \text{Squaring in the} \\ \text{denominator and} \\ \text{the numerator} \end{array}$$

$$= \dfrac{4\sqrt{5} + 4\sqrt{2} + \sqrt{10} + 2}{3} \quad \begin{array}{l} \text{No radicals remain in the} \\ \text{denominator.} \end{array}$$

To rationalize a numerator with more than one term, we use the conjugate of the numerator.

EXAMPLE 5 Rationalize the numerator: $\dfrac{4 + \sqrt{2}}{\sqrt{5} - \sqrt{2}}$.

Solution

$$\frac{4 + \sqrt{2}}{\sqrt{5} - \sqrt{2}} = \frac{4 + \sqrt{2}}{\sqrt{5} - \sqrt{2}} \cdot \frac{4 - \sqrt{2}}{4 - \sqrt{2}} \qquad \text{Multiplying by 1, using the conjugate of } 4 + \sqrt{2}, \text{ which is } 4 - \sqrt{2}$$

$$= \frac{16 - \left(\sqrt{2}\right)^2}{4\sqrt{5} - \sqrt{5}\,\sqrt{2} - 4\sqrt{2} + \left(\sqrt{2}\right)^2}$$

$$= \frac{14}{4\sqrt{5} - \sqrt{10} - 4\sqrt{2} + 2}$$

Terms with Differing Indices

To multiply or divide radical terms with different indices, we can convert to exponential notation, use the rules for exponents, and then convert back to radical notation.

EXAMPLE 6 Divide and, if possible, simplify: $\dfrac{\sqrt[4]{(x + y)^3}}{\sqrt{x + y}}$.

Student Notes _____

Expressions similar to the one in Example 6 are most easily simplified by rewriting the expression using exponents in place of radicals. After simplifying, remember to write your final result in radical notation. In general, if a problem is presented in one form, it is expected that the final result be presented in the same form.

Solution

$$\frac{\sqrt[4]{(x + y)^3}}{\sqrt{x + y}} = \frac{(x + y)^{3/4}}{(x + y)^{1/2}} \qquad \text{Converting to exponential notation}$$

$$= (x + y)^{3/4 - 1/2} \qquad \begin{array}{l}\text{Since the bases are identical, we can} \\ \text{subtract exponents:} \\ \frac{3}{4} - \frac{1}{2} = \frac{3}{4} - \frac{2}{4} = \frac{1}{4}.\end{array}$$

$$\left.\begin{array}{l} = (x + y)^{1/4} \\ = \sqrt[4]{x + y} \end{array}\right\} \qquad \text{Converting back to radical notation}$$

The steps used in Example 6 can be used in a variety of situations.

To Simplify Products or Quotients with Differing Indices

1. Convert all radical expressions to exponential notation.
2. When the bases are identical, subtract exponents to divide and add exponents to multiply. This may require finding a common denominator.
3. Convert back to radical notation and, if possible, simplify.

EXAMPLE 7   Multiply and simplify: $\sqrt{x^3}\,\sqrt[3]{x}$.

Solution

$$\sqrt{x^3}\,\sqrt[3]{x} = x^{3/2} \cdot x^{1/3} \qquad \text{Converting to exponential notation}$$

$$= x^{11/6} \qquad \text{Adding exponents: } \tfrac{3}{2} + \tfrac{1}{3} = \tfrac{9}{6} + \tfrac{2}{6}$$

$$= \sqrt[6]{x^{11}} \qquad \text{Converting back to radical notation}$$

$$\left.\begin{aligned} &= \sqrt[6]{x^6}\,\sqrt[6]{x^5} \\ &= x\sqrt[6]{x^5} \end{aligned}\right\} \quad \text{Simplifying}$$

EXAMPLE 8   If $f(x) = \sqrt[3]{x^2}$ and $g(x) = \sqrt{x} + \sqrt[4]{x}$, find $(f \cdot g)(x)$.

Solution   Recall from Section 7.4 that $(f \cdot g)(x) = f(x) \cdot g(x)$. Thus,

$$(f \cdot g)(x) = \sqrt[3]{x^2}\left(\sqrt{x} + \sqrt[4]{x}\right) \qquad \begin{array}{l} x \text{ is assumed to be} \\ \text{nonnegative.} \end{array}$$

$$= x^{2/3}(x^{1/2} + x^{1/4}) \qquad \begin{array}{l} \text{Converting to exponential} \\ \text{notation} \end{array}$$

$$= x^{2/3} \cdot x^{1/2} + x^{2/3} \cdot x^{1/4} \qquad \text{Using the distributive law}$$

$$= x^{2/3+1/2} + x^{2/3+1/4} \qquad \text{Adding exponents:}$$

$$= x^{7/6} + x^{11/12} \qquad \tfrac{2}{3} + \tfrac{1}{2} = \tfrac{4}{6} + \tfrac{3}{6}; \tfrac{2}{3} + \tfrac{1}{4} = \tfrac{8}{12} + \tfrac{3}{12}$$

$$= \sqrt[6]{x^7} + \sqrt[12]{x^{11}} \qquad \begin{array}{l} \text{Converting back to radical} \\ \text{notation} \end{array}$$

$$\left.\begin{aligned} &= \sqrt[6]{x^6}\,\sqrt[6]{x} + \sqrt[12]{x^{11}} \\ &= x\sqrt[6]{x} + \sqrt[12]{x^{11}} \end{aligned}\right\} \quad \text{Simplifying}$$

If factors are raised to powers that share a common denominator, we can write the final result as a single radical expression.

EXAMPLE 9   Divide and, if possible, simplify: $\dfrac{\sqrt[3]{a^2 b^4}}{\sqrt{ab}}$.

Solution

$$\frac{\sqrt[3]{a^2 b^4}}{\sqrt{ab}} = \frac{(a^2 b^4)^{1/3}}{(ab)^{1/2}} \qquad \text{Converting to exponential notation}$$

$$= \frac{a^{2/3} b^{4/3}}{a^{1/2} b^{1/2}} \qquad \text{Using the product and power rules}$$

$$= a^{2/3-1/2} b^{4/3-1/2} \qquad \text{Subtracting exponents}$$

$$= a^{1/6} b^{5/6}$$

$$= \sqrt[6]{a}\,\sqrt[6]{b^5} \qquad \text{Converting to radical notation}$$

$$= \sqrt[6]{ab^5} \qquad \text{Using the product rule for radicals}$$

Exercise Set

10.5

🦢 *Concept Reinforcement* *For each of Exercises 1–6, fill in the blanks by selecting from the following words (which may be used more than once):*

radicand(s), indices, conjugate(s), base(s), denominator(s), numerator(s).

1. To add radical expressions, the _____ and the _____ must be the same.

2. To multiply radical expressions, the _____ must be the same.

3. To find a product by adding exponents, the _____ must be the same.

4. To add rational expressions, the _____ must be the same.

5. To rationalize the _____ of
$\dfrac{\sqrt{a + 0.1} - \sqrt{a}}{0.1}$, we multiply by a form of 1,
using the _____ of $\sqrt{a + 0.1} - \sqrt{a}$, or
$\sqrt{a + 0.1} + \sqrt{a}$, to write 1.

6. To find a quotient by subtracting exponents, the _____ must be the same.

Add or subtract. Simplify by combining like radical terms, if possible. Assume that all variables and radicands represent positive real numbers.

7. $2\sqrt{5} + 7\sqrt{5}$

8. $4\sqrt{7} + 2\sqrt{7}$

9. $7\sqrt[3]{4} - 5\sqrt[3]{4}$

10. $14\sqrt[5]{2} - 6\sqrt[5]{2}$

11. $\sqrt[3]{y} + 9\sqrt[3]{y}$

12. $9\sqrt[4]{t} - 3\sqrt[4]{t}$

13. $8\sqrt{2} - 6\sqrt{2} + 5\sqrt{2}$

14. $\sqrt{6} + 8\sqrt{6} - 3\sqrt{6}$

15. $9\sqrt[3]{7} - \sqrt{3} + 4\sqrt[3]{7} + 2\sqrt{3}$

16. $5\sqrt{7} - 8\sqrt[4]{11} + \sqrt{7} + 9\sqrt[4]{11}$

17. $4\sqrt{27} - 3\sqrt{3}$

18. $9\sqrt{50} - 4\sqrt{2}$

19. $3\sqrt{45} + 7\sqrt{20}$

20. $5\sqrt{12} + 16\sqrt{27}$

21. $3\sqrt[3]{16} + \sqrt[3]{54}$

22. $\sqrt[3]{27} - 5\sqrt[3]{8}$

23. $\sqrt{5a} + 2\sqrt{45a^3}$

24. $4\sqrt{3x^3} - \sqrt{12x}$

25. $\sqrt[3]{6x^4} + \sqrt[3]{48x}$

26. $\sqrt[3]{54x} - \sqrt[3]{2x^4}$

27. $\sqrt{4a - 4} + \sqrt{a - 1}$

28. $\sqrt{9y + 27} + \sqrt{y + 3}$

29. $\sqrt{x^3 - x^2} + \sqrt{9x - 9}$

30. $\sqrt{4x - 4} - \sqrt{x^3 - x^2}$

Multiply. Assume all variables represent nonnegative real numbers.

31. $\sqrt{3}(4 + \sqrt{3})$

32. $\sqrt{7}(3 - \sqrt{7})$

33. $3\sqrt{5}(\sqrt{5} - \sqrt{2})$

34. $4\sqrt{2}(\sqrt{3} - \sqrt{5})$

35. $\sqrt{2}(3\sqrt{10} - 2\sqrt{2})$

36. $\sqrt{3}(2\sqrt{5} - 3\sqrt{4})$

37. $\sqrt[3]{3}(\sqrt[3]{9} - 4\sqrt[3]{21})$

38. $\sqrt[3]{2}(\sqrt[3]{4} - 2\sqrt[3]{32})$

39. $\sqrt[3]{a}(\sqrt[3]{a^2} + \sqrt[3]{24a^2})$

40. $\sqrt[3]{x}(\sqrt[3]{3x^2} - \sqrt[3]{81x^2})$

41. $(2 + \sqrt{6})(5 - \sqrt{6})$

42. $(4 - \sqrt{5})(2 + \sqrt{5})$

43. $(\sqrt{2} + \sqrt{7})(\sqrt{3} - \sqrt{7})$

44. $(\sqrt{7} - \sqrt{2})(\sqrt{5} + \sqrt{2})$

45. $(3 - \sqrt{5})(3 + \sqrt{5})$

46. $(6 - \sqrt{7})(6 + \sqrt{7})$

47. $(\sqrt{6} + \sqrt{8})(\sqrt{6} - \sqrt{8})$

48. $(\sqrt{5} + \sqrt{3})(\sqrt{5} - \sqrt{3})$

49. $(3\sqrt{7} + 2\sqrt{5})(2\sqrt{7} - 4\sqrt{5})$

50. $(4\sqrt{5} - 3\sqrt{2})(2\sqrt{5} + 4\sqrt{2})$

51. $(2 + \sqrt{3})^2$

52. $(3 + \sqrt{7})^2$

53. $(\sqrt{3} - \sqrt{2})^2$

54. $(\sqrt{5} - \sqrt{3})^2$

55. $(\sqrt{2t} + \sqrt{5})^2$

56. $(\sqrt{3x} - \sqrt{2})^2$

57. $(3 - \sqrt{x+5})^2$

58. $(4 + \sqrt{x-3})^2$

59. $(2\sqrt[4]{7} - \sqrt[4]{6})(3\sqrt[4]{9} + 2\sqrt[4]{5})$

60. $(4\sqrt[3]{3} + \sqrt[3]{10})(2\sqrt[3]{7} + 5\sqrt[3]{6})$

Rationalize each denominator.

61. $\dfrac{5}{4 - \sqrt{3}}$

62. $\dfrac{3}{4 - \sqrt{7}}$

63. $\dfrac{2 + \sqrt{5}}{6 + \sqrt{3}}$

64. $\dfrac{1 + \sqrt{2}}{3 + \sqrt{5}}$

65. $\dfrac{\sqrt{a}}{\sqrt{a} + \sqrt{b}}$

66. $\dfrac{\sqrt{z}}{\sqrt{x} - \sqrt{z}}$

Aha! **67.** $\dfrac{\sqrt{7} - \sqrt{3}}{\sqrt{3} - \sqrt{7}}$

68. $\dfrac{\sqrt{7} + \sqrt{5}}{\sqrt{5} + \sqrt{2}}$

69. $\dfrac{3\sqrt{2} - \sqrt{7}}{4\sqrt{2} + 2\sqrt{5}}$

70. $\dfrac{5\sqrt{3} - \sqrt{11}}{2\sqrt{3} - 5\sqrt{2}}$

Rationalize each numerator. If possible, simplify your result.

71. $\dfrac{\sqrt{7} + 2}{5}$

72. $\dfrac{\sqrt{3} + 1}{4}$

73. $\dfrac{\sqrt{6} - 2}{\sqrt{3} + 7}$

74. $\dfrac{\sqrt{10} + 4}{\sqrt{2} - 3}$

75. $\dfrac{\sqrt{x} - \sqrt{y}}{\sqrt{x} + \sqrt{y}}$

76. $\dfrac{\sqrt{a} + \sqrt{b}}{\sqrt{a} - \sqrt{b}}$

77. $\dfrac{\sqrt{a+h} - \sqrt{a}}{h}$

78. $\dfrac{\sqrt{x-h} - \sqrt{x}}{h}$

Perform the indicated operation and simplify. Assume all variables represent positive real numbers.

79. $\sqrt{a}\,\sqrt[4]{a^3}$

80. $\sqrt[3]{x^2}\,\sqrt[6]{x^5}$

81. $\sqrt[5]{b^2}\,\sqrt{b^3}$

82. $\sqrt[4]{a^3}\,\sqrt[3]{a^2}$

83. $\sqrt{xy^3}\,\sqrt[3]{x^2y}$

84. $\sqrt[5]{a^3b}\,\sqrt{ab}$

85. $\sqrt[4]{9ab^3}\,\sqrt{3a^4b}$

86. $\sqrt{2x^3y^3}\,\sqrt[3]{4xy^2}$

87. $\sqrt{a^4b^3c^4}\,\sqrt[3]{ab^2c}$

88. $\sqrt[3]{xy^2z}\,\sqrt{x^3yz^2}$

89. $\dfrac{\sqrt[3]{a^2}}{\sqrt[4]{a}}$

90. $\dfrac{\sqrt[3]{x^2}}{\sqrt[5]{x}}$

91. $\dfrac{\sqrt[4]{x^2y^3}}{\sqrt[3]{xy}}$

92. $\dfrac{\sqrt[5]{a^4b}}{\sqrt[3]{ab}}$

93. $\dfrac{\sqrt{ab^3}}{\sqrt[5]{a^2b^3}}$

94. $\dfrac{\sqrt[5]{x^3y^4}}{\sqrt{xy}}$

95. $\dfrac{\sqrt[4]{(3x-1)^3}}{\sqrt[5]{(3x-1)^3}}$

96. $\dfrac{\sqrt[3]{(2+5x)^2}}{\sqrt[4]{2+5x}}$

97. $\dfrac{\sqrt[3]{(2x+1)^2}}{\sqrt[5]{(2x+1)^2}}$

98. $\dfrac{\sqrt[4]{(5+3x)^3}}{\sqrt[3]{(5+3x)^2}}$

99. $\sqrt[3]{x^2y}\left(\sqrt{xy} - \sqrt[5]{xy^3}\right)$

100. $\sqrt[4]{a^2b}\left(\sqrt[3]{a^2b} - \sqrt[5]{a^2b^2}\right)$

101. $(m + \sqrt[3]{n^2})(2m + \sqrt[4]{n})$

102. $(r - \sqrt[4]{s^3})(3r - \sqrt[5]{s})$

In Exercises 103–106, f(x) and g(x) are as given. Find $(f \cdot g)(x)$. Assume all variables represent nonnegative real numbers.

103. $f(x) = \sqrt[4]{x}, \; g(x) = \sqrt[4]{2x} - \sqrt[4]{x^{11}}$

104. $f(x) = \sqrt[4]{x^7} + \sqrt[4]{3x^2}, \; g(x) = \sqrt[4]{x}$

105. $f(x) = x + \sqrt{7}, \; g(x) = x - \sqrt{7}$

106. $f(x) = x - \sqrt{2}, \; g(x) = x + \sqrt{6}$

Let $f(x) = x^2$. Find each of the following.

107. $f(5 + \sqrt{2})$

108. $f(7 + \sqrt{3})$

109. $f(\sqrt{3} - \sqrt{5})$

110. $f(\sqrt{6} - \sqrt{3})$

111. In what way(s) is combining like radical terms similar to combining like terms that are monomials?

112. Why do we need to know how to multiply radical expressions before learning how to add them?

SKILL MAINTENANCE

Solve.

113. $\dfrac{12x}{x-4} - \dfrac{3x^2}{x+4} = \dfrac{384}{x^2-16}$ [6.6]

114. $\dfrac{2}{3} + \dfrac{1}{t} = \dfrac{4}{5}$ [6.6]

115. $5x^2 - 6x + 1 = 0$ [5.7]

116. $7t^2 - 8t + 1 = 0$ [5.7]

117. The sum of a number and its square is 20. Find the number. [5.8]

118. The width of a rectangle is one-fourth the length. The area is twice the perimeter. Find the dimensions of the rectangle. [5.8]

SYNTHESIS

119. Ramon *incorrectly* writes
$$\sqrt[5]{x^2} \cdot \sqrt{x^3} = x^{2/5} \cdot x^{3/2} = \sqrt[5]{x^3}.$$
What mistake do you suspect he is making?

120. After examining the expression $\sqrt[4]{25xy^3}\,\sqrt{5x^4y}$, Dyan (correctly) concludes that x and y are both nonnegative. Explain how she could reach this conclusion.

Find a simplified form for $f(x)$. Assume $x \geq 0$.

121. $f(x) = \sqrt{20x^2 + 4x^3} - 3x\sqrt{45 + 9x} + \sqrt{5x^2 + x^3}$

122. $f(x) = \sqrt{x^3 - x^2} + \sqrt{9x^3 - 9x^2} - \sqrt{4x^3 - 4x^2}$

123. $f(x) = \sqrt[4]{x^5 - x^4} + 3\sqrt[4]{x^9 - x^8}$

124. $f(x) = \sqrt[4]{16x^4 + 16x^5} - 2\sqrt[4]{x^8 + x^9}$

Simplify.

125. $\frac{1}{2}\sqrt{36a^5bc^4} - \frac{1}{2}\sqrt[3]{64a^4bc^6} + \frac{1}{6}\sqrt{144a^3bc^6}$

126. $7x\sqrt{(x+y)^3} - 5xy\sqrt{x+y} - 2y\sqrt{(x+y)^3}$

127. $\sqrt{27a^5(b+1)}\,\sqrt[3]{81a(b+1)^4}$

128. $\sqrt{8x(y+z)^5}\,\sqrt[3]{4x^2(y+z)^2}$

129. $\dfrac{\dfrac{1}{\sqrt{w}} - \sqrt{w}}{\dfrac{\sqrt{w}+1}{\sqrt{w}}}$

130. $\dfrac{1}{4+\sqrt{3}} + \dfrac{1}{\sqrt{3}} + \dfrac{1}{\sqrt{3}-4}$

Express each of the following as the product of two radical expressions.

131. $x - 5$

132. $y - 7$

133. $x - a$

Multiply.

134. $\sqrt{9 + 3\sqrt{5}}\,\sqrt{9 - 3\sqrt{5}}$

135. $\left(\sqrt{x+2} - \sqrt{x-2}\right)^2$

136. Use a graphing calculator to check your answers to Exercises 25, 39, and 81.

10.6   Solving Radical Equations

The Principle of Powers   •   Equations with Two Radical Terms

CONNECTING THE CONCEPTS

In Sections 10.1–10.5, we learned how to manipulate radical expressions as well as expressions containing rational exponents. We performed this work to find *equivalent expressions.*

Now that we know how to work with radicals and rational exponents, we can learn how to solve a new type of equation. As in our earlier work with equations, finding *equivalent equations* will be part of our strategy. What is different, however, is that now we will use an equation-solving step that does not always produce equivalent equations. Checking solutions will therefore be more important than ever.

The Principle of Powers

A **radical equation** is an equation in which the variable appears in a radicand. Examples are

$$\sqrt[3]{2x} + 1 = 5, \quad \sqrt{a} + \sqrt{a-2} = 7, \quad \text{and} \quad 4 - \sqrt{3x+1} = \sqrt{6-x}.$$

To solve such equations, we need a new principle. Suppose $a = b$ is true. If we square both sides, we get another true equation: $a^2 = b^2$. This can be generalized.

> **The Principle of Powers**
>
> If $a = b$, then $a^n = b^n$ for any exponent n.

Note that the principle of powers is an "if–then" statement. The statement obtained by interchanging the two parts of the sentence—"if $a^n = b^n$ for some exponent n, then $a = b$"—*is not always true.* For example, "if $x = 3$, then $x^2 = 9$" is true, but the statement "if $x^2 = 9$, then $x = 3$" is *not* true when x is replaced with -3. For this reason, when both sides of an equation are raised to an even exponent, it is essential to check the answer(s) in the *original* equation.

EXAMPLE 1   Solve: $\sqrt{x} - 3 = 4$.

Solution   Before using the principle of powers, we need to isolate the radical term:

$$\sqrt{x} - 3 = 4$$
$$\sqrt{x} = 7 \qquad \text{Isolating the radical by adding 3 to both sides}$$
$$(\sqrt{x})^2 = 7^2 \qquad \text{Using the principle of powers}$$
$$x = 49.$$

Check: $\sqrt{x} - 3 = 4$
$$\frac{\sqrt{49} - 3 \;\big|\; 4}{}$$
$$7 - 3 \;\big|$$
$$4 \overset{?}{=} 4 \quad \text{TRUE}$$

The solution is 49.

EXAMPLE 2   Solve: $\sqrt{x} - 5 = -7$.

Solution

$$\sqrt{x} - 5 = -7$$
$$\sqrt{x} = -2 \qquad \text{Isolating the radical by adding 5 to both sides}$$

> The equation $\sqrt{x} = -2$ has no solution because the principal square root of a number is never negative. We continue as in Example 1 for comparison.

$$(\sqrt{x})^2 = (-2)^2 \qquad \text{Using the principle of powers}$$
$$x = 4$$

Check: $\sqrt{x} - 5 = -7$
$$\frac{\sqrt{4} - 5 \;\big|\; -7}{}$$
$$2 - 5 \;\big|$$
$$-3 \overset{?}{=} -7 \quad \text{FALSE}$$

The number 4 does not check. Thus $\sqrt{x} - 5 = -7$ has no solution.

> *Caution!*   Raising both sides of an equation to an even power may not produce an equivalent equation. In this case, a check is essential.

Note in Example 2 that $x = 4$ has solution 4, but that $\sqrt{x} - 5 = -7$ has *no* solution. Thus the equations $x = 4$ and $\sqrt{x} - 5 = -7$ are *not* equivalent.

> *To Solve an Equation with a Radical Term*
> 1. Isolate the radical term on one side of the equation.
> 2. Use the principle of powers and solve the resulting equation.
> 3. Check any possible solution in the original equation.

EXAMPLE 3

Solve: $x = \sqrt{x + 7} + 5$.

Solution

$$x = \sqrt{x + 7} + 5$$

$$x - 5 = \sqrt{x + 7}$$ Isolating the radical by subtracting 5 from both sides

$$\left.\begin{array}{r} (x - 5)^2 = \left(\sqrt{x + 7}\right)^2 \\ x^2 - 10x + 25 = x + 7 \end{array}\right\}$$ Using the principle of powers; squaring both sides

$$x^2 - 11x + 18 = 0$$ Adding $-x - 7$ to both sides to write the quadratic equation in standard form

$$(x - 9)(x - 2) = 0$$ Factoring

$$x = 9 \quad or \quad x = 2$$ Using the principle of zero products

The possible solutions are 9 and 2. Let's check.

Check: For 9:

$$\begin{array}{c|c} x = \sqrt{x + 7} + 5 \\ \hline 9 & \sqrt{9 + 7} + 5 \\ 9 \overset{?}{=} 9 \end{array}$$ TRUE

For 2:

$$\begin{array}{c|c} x = \sqrt{x + 7} + 5 \\ \hline 2 & \sqrt{2 + 7} + 5 \\ 2 \overset{?}{=} 8 \end{array}$$ FALSE

Since 9 checks but 2 does not, the solution is 9.

technology connection

To solve Example 3, we can graph $y_1 = x$ and $y_2 = (x + 7)^{1/2} + 5$ and then use the INTERSECT option of the CALC menu to find the point of intersection. The intersection occurs at $x = 9$. Note that there is no intersection when $x = 2$, as predicted in the check of Example 3.

$y_1 = x, \ y_2 = (x + 7)^{1/2} + 5$

1. Use a graphing calculator to solve Examples 1, 2, 4, 5, and 6. Compare your answers with those found using the algebraic methods shown.

It is important to isolate a radical term before using the principle of powers. Suppose in Example 3 that both sides of the equation were squared *before* isolating the radical. We then would have had the expression $\left(\sqrt{x + 7} + 5\right)^2$ or $x + 7 + 10\sqrt{x + 7} + 25$ on the right side, and the radical would have remained in the problem.

EXAMPLE 4

Solve: $(2x + 1)^{1/3} + 5 = 0$.

Solution   We need not use radical notation to solve:

$$(2x + 1)^{1/3} + 5 = 0$$

$$(2x + 1)^{1/3} = -5$$ Subtracting 5 from both sides

$$[(2x + 1)^{1/3}]^3 = (-5)^3$$ Cubing both sides

$$(2x + 1)^1 = (-5)^3$$ Multiplying exponents. Try to do this mentally.

$$2x + 1 = -125$$

$$2x = -126$$ Subtracting 1 from both sides

$$x = -63.$$

Because both sides were raised to an *odd* power, it is not *essential* that we check the answer. Students can confirm that -63 checks and is the solution.

Equations with Two Radical Terms

A strategy for solving equations with two or more radical terms is as follows.

To Solve an Equation with Two or More Radical Terms

1. Isolate one of the radical terms.
2. Use the principle of powers.
3. If a radical remains, perform steps (1) and (2) again.
4. Solve the resulting equation.
5. Check possible solutions in the original equation.

EXAMPLE 5   Solve: $\sqrt{2x - 5} = 1 + \sqrt{x - 3}$.

Solution

$$\sqrt{2x - 5} = 1 + \sqrt{x - 3}$$

$$\left(\sqrt{2x - 5}\right)^2 = \left(1 + \sqrt{x - 3}\right)^2 \qquad \text{One radical is already isolated.}$$
$$\text{We square both sides.}$$

This is like squaring a binomial. We square 1, then find twice the product of 1 and $\sqrt{x - 3}$, and then the square of $\sqrt{x - 3}$. Study this carefully.

$$2x - 5 = 1 + 2\sqrt{x - 3} + \left(\sqrt{x - 3}\right)^2$$

$$2x - 5 = 1 + 2\sqrt{x - 3} + (x - 3)$$

$$x - 3 = 2\sqrt{x - 3} \qquad \text{Isolating the remaining radical term}$$

$$(x - 3)^2 = \left(2\sqrt{x - 3}\right)^2 \qquad \text{Squaring both sides}$$

$$x^2 - 6x + 9 = 4(x - 3) \qquad \text{Remember to square both the 2 and the } \sqrt{x - 3} \text{ on the right side.}$$

$$x^2 - 6x + 9 = 4x - 12$$

$$x^2 - 10x + 21 = 0$$

$$(x - 7)(x - 3) = 0 \qquad \text{Factoring}$$

$$x = 7 \quad or \quad x = 3 \qquad \text{Using the principle of zero products}$$

We leave it to the student to show that 7 and 3 both check and are the solutions.

Caution!   A common error in solving equations like

$$\sqrt{2x - 5} = 1 + \sqrt{x - 3}$$

is to obtain $1 + (x - 3)$ as the square of the right side. This is wrong because $(A + B)^2 \neq A^2 + B^2$. For example,

$$(1 + 2)^2 \neq 1^2 + 2^2$$
$$3^2 \neq 1 + 4$$
$$9 \neq 5.$$

See Example 5 for the correct expansion of $\left(1 + \sqrt{x - 3}\right)^2$.

EXAMPLE 6   Let $f(x) = \sqrt{x + 5} - \sqrt{x - 7}$. Find all x-values for which $f(x) = 2$.

Solution   We must have $f(x) = 2$, or

$$\sqrt{x + 5} - \sqrt{x - 7} = 2. \qquad \text{Substituting for } f(x)$$

To solve, we isolate one radical term and square both sides:

$$\sqrt{x + 5} = 2 + \sqrt{x - 7} \qquad \text{Adding } \sqrt{x - 7} \text{ to both sides. This isolates one of the radical terms.}$$

$$\left(\sqrt{x + 5}\right)^2 = \left(2 + \sqrt{x - 7}\right)^2 \qquad \text{Using the principle of powers (squaring both sides)}$$

$$x + 5 = 4 + 4\sqrt{x - 7} + (x - 7) \qquad \text{Using } (A + B)^2 = A^2 + 2AB + B^2$$

$$5 = 4\sqrt{x - 7} - 3 \qquad \text{Adding } -x \text{ to both sides and combining like terms}$$

$$8 = 4\sqrt{x - 7} \qquad \text{Isolating the remaining radical term}$$

$$2 = \sqrt{x - 7}$$

$$2^2 = \left(\sqrt{x - 7}\right)^2 \qquad \text{Squaring both sides}$$

$$4 = x - 7$$

$$11 = x.$$

Student Notes

Be careful when checking answers. You don't want to discard a correct answer because of a careless mistake.

Check: $f(11) = \sqrt{11 + 5} - \sqrt{11 - 7}$
$= \sqrt{16} - \sqrt{4}$
$= 4 - 2 = 2.$

We have $f(x) = 2$ when $x = 11$.

Exercise Set

10.6

FOR EXTRA HELP

 Student's Solutions Manual   Digital Video Tutor CD 5 Videotape 10   Tutor Center AW Math Tutor Center   MathXL Tutorials on CD   MathXL MathXL   MyMathLab MyMathLab

❧ *Concept Reinforcement*   *Classify each of the following as either true or false.*

1. If $x^2 = 25$, then $x = 5$.

2. If $t = 7$, then $t^2 = 49$.

3. If $\sqrt{x} = 3$, then $\left(\sqrt{x}\right)^2 = 3^2$.

4. If $x^2 = 36$, then $x = 6$.

5. $\sqrt{x} - 8 = 7$ is equivalent to $\sqrt{x} = 15$.

6. $\sqrt{t} + 5 = 8$ is equivalent to $\sqrt{t} = 3$.

Solve.

7. $\sqrt{5x - 2} = 7$

8. $\sqrt{3x - 2} = 6$

9. $\sqrt{3x} + 1 = 6$

10. $\sqrt{2x} - 1 = 2$

11. $\sqrt{y+1} - 5 = 8$

12. $\sqrt{x-2} - 7 = -4$

13. $\sqrt{x-7} + 3 = 10$

14. $\sqrt{y+4} + 6 = 7$

15. $\sqrt[3]{x+5} = 2$

16. $\sqrt[3]{x-2} = 3$

17. $\sqrt[4]{y-1} = 3$

18. $\sqrt[4]{x+3} = 2$

19. $3\sqrt{x} = x$

20. $8\sqrt{y} = y$

21. $2y^{1/2} - 7 = 9$

22. $3x^{1/2} + 12 = 9$

23. $\sqrt[3]{x} = -3$

24. $\sqrt[3]{y} = -4$

25. $t^{1/3} - 2 = 3$

26. $x^{1/4} - 2 = 1$

Aha! **27.** $(y-3)^{1/2} = -2$

28. $(x+2)^{1/2} = -4$

29. $\sqrt[4]{3x+1} - 4 = -1$

30. $\sqrt[4]{2x+3} - 5 = -2$

31. $(x+7)^{1/3} = 4$

32. $(y-7)^{1/4} = 3$

33. $\sqrt[3]{3y+6} + 7 = 8$

34. $\sqrt[3]{6x+9} + 5 = 2$

35. $\sqrt{3t+4} = \sqrt{4t+3}$

36. $\sqrt{2t-7} = \sqrt{3t-12}$

37. $3(4-t)^{1/4} = 6^{1/4}$

38. $2(1-x)^{1/3} = 4^{1/3}$

39. $3 + \sqrt{5-x} = x$

40. $x = \sqrt{x-1} + 3$

41. $\sqrt{4x-3} = 2 + \sqrt{2x-5}$

42. $3 + \sqrt{z-6} = \sqrt{z+9}$

43. $\sqrt{20-x} + 8 = \sqrt{9-x} + 11$

44. $4 + \sqrt{10-x} = 6 + \sqrt{4-x}$

45. $\sqrt{x+2} + \sqrt{3x+4} = 2$

46. $\sqrt{6x+7} - \sqrt{3x+3} = 1$

47. If $f(x) = \sqrt{x} + \sqrt{x-9}$, find any x for which $f(x) = 1$.

48. If $g(x) = \sqrt{x} + \sqrt{x-5}$, find any x for which $g(x) = 5$.

49. If $f(t) = \sqrt{t-2} - \sqrt{4t+1}$, find any t for which $f(t) = -3$.

50. If $g(t) = \sqrt{2t+7} - \sqrt{t+15}$, find any t for which $g(t) = -1$.

51. If $f(x) = \sqrt{2x-3}$ and $g(x) = \sqrt{x+7} - 2$, find any x for which $f(x) = g(x)$.

52. If $f(x) = 2\sqrt{3x+6}$ and $g(x) = 5 + \sqrt{4x+9}$, find any x for which $f(x) = g(x)$.

53. If $f(t) = 4 - \sqrt{t-3}$ and $g(t) = (t+5)^{1/2}$, find any t for which $f(t) = g(t)$.

54. If $f(t) = 7 + \sqrt{2t-5}$ and $g(t) = 3(t+1)^{1/2}$, find any t for which $f(t) = g(t)$.

55. Explain in your own words why it is important to check your answers when using the principle of powers.

56. The principle of powers is an "if–then" statement that becomes false when the sentence parts are interchanged. Give an example of another such if–then statement from everyday life (answers will vary).

SKILL MAINTENANCE

57. The base of a triangle is 2 in. longer than the height. The area is $31\frac{1}{2}$ in^2. Find the height and the base. [5.8]

58. During a one-hour television show, there were 12 commercials. Some of the commercials were 30 sec long and the others were 60 sec long. If the number of 30-sec commercials was 6 less than the total number of minutes of commercial time during the show, how many 60-sec commercials were used? [8.3]

Graph.

59. $f(x) = \frac{2}{3}x - 5$ [7.3]

60. $g(x) = 3x + 4$ [7.3]

61. $F(x) < -2x + 4$ [9.4]

62. $G(x) > -3x + 2$ [9.4]

SYNTHESIS

63. Describe a procedure that could be used to create radical equations that have no solution.

64. Is checking essential when the principle of powers is used with an odd power n? Why or why not?

Steel manufacturing. In the production of steel and other metals, the temperature of the molten metal is so great that conventional thermometers melt. Instead, sound is transmitted across the surface of the metal to a receiver on the far side and the speed of the sound is measured. The formula

$$S(t) = 1087.7\sqrt{\frac{9t + 2617}{2457}}$$

gives the speed of sound S(t), in feet per second, at a temperature of t degrees Celsius.

65. Find the temperature of a blast furnace where sound travels 1880 ft/sec.

66. Find the temperature of a blast furnace where sound travels 1502.3 ft/sec.

67. Solve the above equation for t.

Automotive repair.   For an engine with a displacement of 2.8 L, the function given by

$$d(n) = 0.75\sqrt{2.8n}$$

can be used to determine the diameter size of the carburetor's opening, in millimeters. Here n is the number of rpm's at which the engine achieves peak performance.
Source: macdizzy.com

68. If a carburetor's opening is 81 mm, for what number of rpm's will the engine produce peak power?

69. If a carburetor's opening is 84 mm, for what number of rpm's will the engine produce peak power?

Escape velocity.   A formula for the escape velocity v of a satellite is

$$v = \sqrt{2gr}\,\sqrt{\frac{h}{r + h}},$$

where g is the force of gravity, r is the planet or star's radius, and h is the height of the satellite above the planet or star's surface.

70. Solve for h.

71. Solve for r.

Sighting to the horizon.   The function $D(h) = 1.2\sqrt{h}$ can be used to approximate the distance D, in miles, that a person can see to the horizon from a height h, in feet.

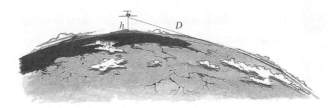

72. How far above sea level must a pilot fly in order to see a horizon that is 180 mi away?

73. How high above sea level must a sailor climb in order to see 10.2 mi out to sea?

Solve.

74. $\left(\dfrac{z}{4} - 5\right)^{2/3} = \dfrac{1}{25}$

75. $\dfrac{x + \sqrt{x + 1}}{x - \sqrt{x + 1}} = \dfrac{5}{11}$

76. $\sqrt{\sqrt{y} + 49} = 7$

77. $(z^2 + 17)^{3/4} = 27$

78. $x^2 - 5x - \sqrt{x^2 - 5x - 2} = 4$
(*Hint*: Let $u = x^2 - 5x - 2$.)

79. $\sqrt{8 - b} = b\sqrt{8 - b}$

Without graphing, determine the x-intercepts of the graphs given by each of the following.

80. $f(x) = \sqrt{x - 2} - \sqrt{x + 2} + 2$

81. $g(x) = 6x^{1/2} + 6x^{-1/2} - 37$

82. $f(x) = (x^2 + 30x)^{1/2} - x - (5x)^{1/2}$

83. Use a graphing calculator to check your answers to Exercises 9, 15, and 31.

84. Saul is trying to solve Exercise 73 using a graphing calculator. Without resorting to trial and error, how can he determine a suitable viewing window for finding the solution?

85. Use a graphing calculator to check your answers to Exercises 27, 35, and 41.

CORNER

Tailgater Alert

Focus: Radical equations and problem solving

Time: 15–25 minutes

Group size: 2–3

Materials: Calculators or square-root tables

The faster a car is traveling, the more distance it needs to stop. Thus it is important for drivers to allow sufficient space between their vehicle and the vehicle in front of them. Police recommend that for each 10 mph of speed, a driver allow 1 car length. Thus a driver going 30 mph should have at least 3 car lengths between his or her vehicle and the one in front.

   In Exercise Set 10.3, the function $r(L) = 2\sqrt{5L}$ was used to find the speed, in miles per hour, that a car was traveling when it left skid marks L feet long.

ACTIVITY

1. Each group member should estimate the length of a car in which he or she frequently travels. (Each should use a different length, if possible.)
2. Using a calculator as needed, each group member should complete the table below.

Column 1 gives a car's speed s, and column 2 lists the minimum amount of space between cars traveling s miles per hour, as recommended by police. Column 3 is the speed that a vehicle *could* travel were it forced to stop in the distance listed in column 2, using the above function.

Column 1 s (in miles per hour)	Column 2 $L(s)$ (in feet)	Column 3 $r(L)$ (in miles per hour)
20		
30		
40		
50		
60		
70		

3. Determine whether there are any speeds at which the "1 car length per 10 mph" guideline might not suffice. On what reasoning do you base your answer? Compare tables to determine how car length affects the results. What recommendations would your group make to a new driver?

10.7   Geometric Applications

Using the Pythagorean Theorem • Two Special Triangles

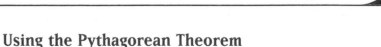

Using the Pythagorean Theorem

There are many kinds of problems that involve powers and roots. Many also involve right triangles and the Pythagorean theorem, which we studied in Section 5.8 and restate here.

Study Skills _____

Making Sketches

One need not be an artist to make highly useful mathematical sketches. That said, it is important to make sure that your sketches are drawn accurately enough to represent the relative sizes within each shape. For example, if one side of a triangle is clearly the longest, make sure your drawing reflects this.

The Pythagorean Theorem*

In any right triangle, if a and b are the lengths of the legs and c is the length of the hypotenuse, then

$$a^2 + b^2 = c^2.$$

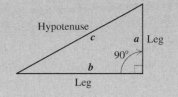

In using the Pythagorean theorem, we often make use of the following principle.

The Principle of Square Roots

For any nonnegative real number n,

If $x^2 = n$, then $x = \sqrt{n}$ or $x = -\sqrt{n}$.

For most real-world applications involving length or distance, $-\sqrt{n}$ is not needed.

EXAMPLE 1

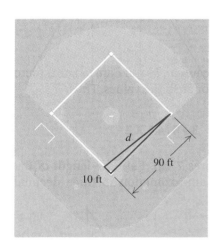

Baseball.   A baseball diamond is actually a square 90 ft on a side. Suppose a catcher fields a ball while standing on the third-base line 10 ft from home plate. How far is the catcher's throw to first base? Give an exact answer and an approximation to three decimal places.

Solution   We make a drawing and let $d =$ the distance, in feet, to first base. Note that a right triangle is formed in which the leg from home plate to first base measures 90 ft and the leg from home plate to where the catcher fields the ball measures 10 ft.

We substitute these values into the Pythagorean theorem to find d:

$$d^2 = 90^2 + 10^2$$
$$d^2 = 8100 + 100$$
$$d^2 = 8200.$$

We now use the principle of square roots: If $d^2 = 8200$, then $d = \sqrt{8200}$ or $d = -\sqrt{8200}$. Since d represents a length, it follows that d is the positive square root of 8200:

$$d = \sqrt{8200} \text{ ft}$$ This is an exact answer.
$$d \approx 90.554 \text{ ft.}$$ Using a calculator for an approximation

---

*The converse of the Pythagorean theorem also holds. That is, if a, b, and c are the lengths of the sides of a triangle and $a^2 + b^2 = c^2$, then the triangle is a right triangle.

Powers of i

Answers to problems involving complex numbers are generally written in the form $a + bi$. In the following discussion, we show why there is no need to use powers of i (other than 1) when writing answers.

Recall that -1 raised to an *even* power is 1, and -1 raised to an *odd* power is -1. Simplifying powers of i can then be done by using the fact that $i^2 = -1$ and expressing the given power of i in terms of i^2. Consider the following:

$$i^2 = -1,$$
$$i^3 = i^2 \cdot i = (-1)i = -i,$$
$$i^4 = (i^2)^2 = (-1)^2 = 1,$$
$$i^5 = i^4 \cdot i = (i^2)^2 \cdot i = (-1)^2 \cdot i = i,$$
$$i^6 = (i^2)^3 = (-1)^3 = -1. \longleftarrow \text{The pattern is now repeating.}$$

The powers of i cycle themselves through the values i, -1, $-i$, and 1. Even powers of i are -1 or 1 whereas odd powers of i are i or $-i$.

EXAMPLE 7   Simplify: **(a)** i^{18}; **(b)** i^{24}.

Solution

a) $i^{18} = (i^2)^9$ Using the power rule

$\quad = (-1)^9 = -1$ Raising -1 to a power

b) $i^{24} = (i^2)^{12}$

$\quad = (-1)^{12} = 1$

To simplify i^n when n is odd, we rewrite i^n as $i^{n-1} \cdot i$.

EXAMPLE 8   Simplify: **(a)** i^{29}; **(b)** i^{75}.

Solution

a) $i^{29} = i^{28}i^1$ Using the product rule. This is a key step when i is raised to an odd power.

$\quad = (i^2)^{14}i$ Using the power rule

$\quad = (-1)^{14}i$

$\quad = 1 \cdot i = i$

b) $i^{75} = i^{74}i^1$ Using the product rule

$\quad = (i^2)^{37}i$ Using the power rule

$\quad = (-1)^{37}i$

$\quad = -1 \cdot i = -i$

Exercise Set

10.8

◞ *Concept Reinforcement* *Classify each statement as either true or false.*

1. Imaginary numbers are so named because they have no real-world applications.

2. Every real number is imaginary, but not every imaginary number is real.

3. Every imaginary number is a complex number, but not every complex number is imaginary.

4. Every real number is a complex number, but not every complex number is real.

5. Addition and subtraction of complex numbers has much in common with addition and subtraction of polynomials.

6. The product of a complex number and its conjugate is always a real number.

7. The square of a complex number is always a real number.

8. The quotient of two complex numbers is always a complex number.

Express in terms of i.

9. $\sqrt{-36}$

10. $\sqrt{-25}$

11. $\sqrt{-13}$

12. $\sqrt{-19}$

13. $\sqrt{-18}$

14. $\sqrt{-98}$

15. $\sqrt{-3}$

16. $\sqrt{-4}$

17. $\sqrt{-81}$

18. $\sqrt{-27}$

19. $-\sqrt{-300}$

20. $-\sqrt{-75}$

21. $6 - \sqrt{-84}$

22. $4 - \sqrt{-60}$

23. $-\sqrt{-76} + \sqrt{-125}$

24. $\sqrt{-4} + \sqrt{-12}$

25. $\sqrt{-18} - \sqrt{-100}$

26. $\sqrt{-72} - \sqrt{-25}$

Perform the indicated operation and simplify. Write each answer in the form a + bi.

27. $(6 + 7i) + (5 + 3i)$

28. $(4 - 5i) + (3 + 9i)$

29. $(9 + 8i) - (5 + 3i)$

30. $(9 + 7i) - (2 + 4i)$

31. $(7 - 4i) - (5 - 3i)$

32. $(5 - 3i) - (9 + 2i)$

33. $(-5 - i) - (7 + 4i)$

34. $(-2 + 6i) - (-7 + i)$

35. $7i \cdot 6i$

36. $6i \cdot 9i$

37. $(-4i)(-6i)$

38. $7i \cdot (-8i)$

39. $\sqrt{-36}\sqrt{-9}$

40. $\sqrt{-49}\sqrt{-25}$

41. $\sqrt{-5}\sqrt{-2}$

42. $\sqrt{-6}\sqrt{-7}$

43. $\sqrt{-6}\sqrt{-21}$

44. $\sqrt{-15}\sqrt{-10}$

45. $5i(2 + 6i)$

46. $2i(7 + 3i)$

47. $-7i(3 - 4i)$

48. $-4i(6 - 5i)$

49. $(1 + i)(3 + 2i)$

50. $(1 + 5i)(4 + 3i)$

51. $(6 - 5i)(3 + 4i)$

52. $(5 - 6i)(2 + 5i)$

53. $(7 - 2i)(2 - 6i)$

54. $(-4 + 5i)(3 - 4i)$

55. $(-2 + 3i)(-2 + 5i)$

56. $(-3 + 6i)(-3 + 4i)$

57. $(-5 - 4i)(3 + 7i)$

58. $(2 + 9i)(-3 - 5i)$

59. $(4 - 2i)^2$

60. $(1 - 2i)^2$

61. $(2 + 3i)^2$

62. $(3 + 2i)^2$

63. $(-2 + 3i)^2$

64. $(-5 - 2i)^2$

65. $\dfrac{7}{4 + i}$

66. $\dfrac{3}{8 + i}$

67. $\dfrac{2}{3 - 2i}$

68. $\dfrac{4}{2 - 3i}$

69. $\dfrac{2i}{5 + 3i}$

70. $\dfrac{3i}{4 + 2i}$

71. $\dfrac{5}{6i}$

72. $\dfrac{4}{7i}$

73. $\dfrac{5 - 3i}{4i}$

74. $\dfrac{2 + 7i}{5i}$

Aha! 75. $\dfrac{7i + 14}{7i}$

76. $\dfrac{6i + 3}{3i}$

696 CHAPTER 10 EXPONENTS AND RADICALS

77. $\dfrac{4 + 5i}{3 - 7i}$

78. $\dfrac{5 + 3i}{7 - 4i}$

79. $\dfrac{2 + 3i}{2 + 5i}$

80. $\dfrac{3 + 2i}{4 + 3i}$

81. $\dfrac{3 - 2i}{4 + 3i}$

82. $\dfrac{5 - 2i}{3 + 6i}$

Simplify.

83. i^7

84. i^{11}

85. i^{24}

86. i^{35}

87. i^{42}

88. i^{64}

89. i^9

90. $(-i)^{71}$

91. $(-i)^6$

92. $(-i)^4$

93. $(5i)^3$

94. $(-3i)^5$

95. $i^2 + i^4$

96. $5i^5 + 4i^3$

97. Is the product of two imaginary numbers always an imaginary number? Why or why not?

98. In what way(s) are conjugates of complex numbers similar to the conjugates used in Section 7.5?

SKILL MAINTENANCE

Graph. [7.3]

99. $f(x) = 3x - 5$

100. $g(x) = -2x + 6$

101. $F(x) = x^2$

102. $G(x) = |x|$

Solve.

103. $28 = 3x^2 - 17x$ [5.7]

104. $|3x + 7| < 22$ [9.3]

SYNTHESIS

105. Is the set of real numbers a subset of the set of complex numbers? Why or why not?

106. Is the union of the set of imaginary numbers and the set of real numbers the set of complex numbers? Why or why not?

A function g is given by
$$g(z) = \dfrac{z^4 - z^2}{z - 1}.$$

107. Find $g(3i)$.

108. Find $g(1 + i)$.

109. Find $g(5i - 1)$.

110. Find $g(2 - 3i)$.

111. Evaluate

$$\dfrac{1}{w - w^2} \quad \text{for} \quad w = \dfrac{1 - i}{10}.$$

Simplify.

112. $\dfrac{i^5 + i^6 + i^7 + i^8}{(1 - i)^4}$

113. $(1 - i)^3(1 + i)^3$

114. $\dfrac{5 - \sqrt{5}i}{\sqrt{5}i}$

115. $\dfrac{6}{1 + \dfrac{3}{i}}$

116. $\left(\dfrac{1}{2} - \dfrac{1}{3}i\right)^2 - \left(\dfrac{1}{2} + \dfrac{1}{3}i\right)^2$

117. $\dfrac{i - i^{38}}{1 + i}$

Study Summary

Radical expressions involve **square roots**, **cube roots**, and, more generally, **nth roots** (pp. 634, 638, and 639):

c is a square root of a if $c^2 = a$;

c is a cube root of a if $c^3 = a$.

The notation $\sqrt{a}$ indicates the **principal** square root of a, the notation $\sqrt[3]{a}$ indicates the cube root of a, and $\sqrt[n]{a}$ indicates the nth root of a (p. 639). For these and other **radical expressions**, we use the following vocabulary (pp. 635, 639):

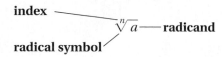

Radical notation can also be written using **rational exponents** (p. 643):

$a^{1/n}$ means $\sqrt[n]{a}$. When a is nonnegative, n can be any natural number greater than 1. When a is negative, n must be odd.

For any natural numbers m and n ($n \neq 1$), and any real number a,

$a^{m/n}$ means $\left(\sqrt[n]{a}\right)^m$ or $\sqrt[n]{a^m}$.

When a is negative, n must be odd.

Radical expressions can be added, subtracted, multiplied, and divided. For multiplication and division, the product and quotient rules, respectively, are used (pp. 651, 658):

The Product Rule for Radicals

For any real numbers $\sqrt[n]{a}$ and $\sqrt[n]{b}$, $\sqrt[n]{a}\,\sqrt[n]{b} = \sqrt[n]{a \cdot b}$.

The Quotient Rule for Radicals

For any real numbers $\sqrt[n]{a}$ and $\sqrt[n]{b}$, $b \neq 0$, $\sqrt[n]{\dfrac{a}{b}} = \dfrac{\sqrt[n]{a}}{\sqrt[n]{b}}$.

When working with radical expressions, it is understood that all results should be written in simplified form. Rational exponents can be especially useful when simplifying certain products or quotients:

Some Ways to Simplify Radical Expressions

1. *Simplifying by factoring.* Factor the radicand and look for factors raised to powers that are divisible by the index.

   Example: $\sqrt[3]{a^6 b} = \sqrt[3]{a^6}\,\sqrt[3]{b} = a^2\sqrt[3]{b}$

2. *Using rational exponents to simplify.* Convert to exponential notation and then use arithmetic and the laws of exponents to simplify the exponents. Then convert back to radical notation as needed.

   Example: $\sqrt[3]{p} \cdot \sqrt[4]{q^3} = p^{1/3} \cdot q^{3/4}$
   $$= p^{4/12} \cdot q^{9/12}$$
   $$= \sqrt[12]{p^4 q^9}$$

3. *Combining like radical terms.*

   Example: $\sqrt{8} + 3\sqrt{2} = \sqrt{4} \cdot \sqrt{2} + 3\sqrt{2}$
   $$= 2\sqrt{2} + 3\sqrt{2} = 5\sqrt{2}$$

There sometimes arises a need to **rationalize** a numerator or a denominator (pp. 660, 662). This is accomplished by multiplying the original expression by a form of 1 that is written using the **conjugate** of the portion of the fraction being rationalized (p. 667):

$$\frac{3}{2 + \sqrt{5}} = \frac{3}{2 + \sqrt{5}} \cdot \frac{2 - \sqrt{5}}{2 - \sqrt{5}} \quad \longleftarrow \quad \text{This is the conjugate of } 2 + \sqrt{5}.$$
$$= \frac{6 - 3\sqrt{5}}{4 - 5} = \frac{6 - 3\sqrt{5}}{-1} = -6 + 3\sqrt{5}.$$

Radical equations are solved using the **principle of powers** (p. 673): If $a = b$, then $a^n = b^n$ for any exponent n. Because the principle of powers does not always produce equivalent equations, it is important that the solutions be checked in the original equation.

To solve an equation with a radical term:

1. Isolate the radical term on one side of the equation.
2. Use the principle of powers and solve the resulting equation.
3. Check any possible solution in the original equation.

To solve an equation with two or more radical terms:

1. Isolate one of the radical terms.
2. Use the principle of powers.
3. If a radical remains, repeat steps (1) and (2).
4. Solve the resulting equation.
5. Check possible solutions in the original equation.

Radical notation arises frequently when we are using the **Pythagorean theorem** and in work with **isosceles** or **30°–60°–90° right triangles** (pp. 681, 684):

The Pythagorean Theorem

For any right triangle with legs of lengths a and b and hypotenuse of length c,

$$a^2 + b^2 = c^2.$$

Special Triangles

The length of the hypotenuse in an isosceles right triangle is the length of a leg times $\sqrt{2}$.

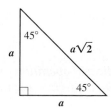

The length of the longer leg in a 30°–60°–90° right triangle is the length of the shorter leg times $\sqrt{3}$. The hypotenuse is twice as long as the shorter leg.

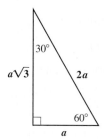

Real numbers and **imaginary** numbers make up the **complex** numbers (pp. 689, 690). Addition, subtraction, multiplication, and division of complex numbers make use of the facts that $i = \sqrt{-1}$ and the product of a complex number and its **conjugate** is a real number (p. 692):

$$(3 + 2i) + (4 - 7i) = 7 - 5i;$$

$$(8 + 6i) - (5 + 2i) = 3 + 4i;$$

$$(2 + 3i)(4 - i) = 8 - 2i + 12i - 3i^2$$
$$= 8 + 10i - 3(-1) = 11 + 10i;$$

$$\frac{1 - 4i}{3 - 2i} = \frac{1 - 4i}{3 - 2i} \cdot \frac{3 + 2i}{3 + 2i} \longleftarrow \text{ The conjugate of } 3 - 2i$$

$$= \frac{3 + 2i - 12i - 8i^2}{9 + 6i - 6i - 4i^2}$$

$$= \frac{3 - 10i - 8(-1)}{9 - 4(-1)} = \frac{11 - 10i}{13} = \frac{11}{13} - \frac{10}{13}i.$$

10 Review Exercises

↪ *Concept Reinforcement*   *Classify each of the following as either true or false.*

1. $\sqrt{ab} = \sqrt{a} \cdot \sqrt{b}$ for any real numbers $\sqrt{a}$ and $\sqrt{b}$. [10.3]

2. $\sqrt{a^2} = a$, for any real number a. [10.1]

3. $\sqrt[3]{a^3} = a$, for any real number a. [10.1]

4. $x^{2/5}$ means $\sqrt[5]{x^2}$ and $(\sqrt[5]{x})^2$. [10.2]

5. A hypotenuse is never shorter than either leg. [10.7]

6. $i^{13} = (i^2)^6 i = i$. [10.8]

7. Some radical equations have no solution. [10.6]

8. If $f(x) = \sqrt{x - 5}$, then the domain of f is the set of all nonnegative real numbers. [10.1]

Simplify. [10.1]

9. $\sqrt{\dfrac{49}{9}}$

10. $-\sqrt{0.25}$

Let $f(x) = \sqrt{2x - 7}$. Find the following. [10.1]

11. $f(16)$

12. The domain of f

Simplify. Assume that each variable can represent any real number.

13. $\sqrt{25t^2}$ [10.1]

14. $\sqrt{(c + 8)^2}$ [10.1]

15. $\sqrt{x^2 - 6x + 9}$ [10.1]

16. $\sqrt{4x^2 + 4x + 1}$ [10.1]

17. $\sqrt[5]{-32}$ [10.1]

18. $\sqrt[3]{-\dfrac{64x^6}{27}}$ [10.4]

19. $\sqrt[4]{x^{12}y^8}$ [10.3]

20. $\sqrt[6]{64x^{12}}$ [10.3]

21. Write an equivalent expression using exponential notation: $(\sqrt[3]{5ab})^4$. [10.2]

22. Write an equivalent expression using radical notation: $(16a^6)^{3/4}$. [10.2]

Use rational exponents to simplify. Assume $x, y \geq 0$. [10.2]

23. $\sqrt{x^6 y^{10}}$

24. $(\sqrt[6]{x^2 y})^2$

Simplify. Do not use negative exponents in the answers. [10.2]

25. $(x^{-2/3})^{3/5}$

26. $\dfrac{7^{-1/3}}{7^{-1/2}}$

27. If $f(x) = \sqrt{25(x - 6)^2}$, find a simplified form for $f(x)$. [10.3]

Perform the indicated operation and, if possible, simplify. Write all answers using radical notation.

28. $\sqrt{2x}\sqrt{3y}$ [10.3]

29. $\sqrt[3]{a^5 b}\,\sqrt[3]{27b}$ [10.3]

30. $\sqrt[3]{-24x^{10}y^8}\,\sqrt[3]{18x^7 y^4}$ [10.3]

31. $\dfrac{\sqrt[3]{60xy^3}}{\sqrt[3]{10x}}$ [10.4]

32. $\dfrac{\sqrt{75x}}{2\sqrt{3}}$ [10.4]

33. $\sqrt[4]{\dfrac{48a^{11}}{c^8}}$ [10.4]

34. $5\sqrt[3]{x} + 2\sqrt[3]{x}$ [10.5]

35. $2\sqrt{75} - 9\sqrt{3}$ [10.5]

36. $\sqrt[3]{8x^4} + \sqrt[3]{xy^6}$ [10.5]

37. $\sqrt{50} + 2\sqrt{18} + \sqrt{32}$ [10.5]

38. $(\sqrt{3} - 3\sqrt{8})(\sqrt{5} + 2\sqrt{8})$ [10.5]

39. $\sqrt[4]{x}\sqrt{x}$ [10.5]

40. $\dfrac{\sqrt[3]{x^2}}{\sqrt[4]{x}}$ [10.5]

41. If $f(x) = x^2$, find $f(a - \sqrt{2})$. [10.5]

42. Rationalize the denominator:
$$\dfrac{4\sqrt{5}}{\sqrt{2} + \sqrt{3}}.$$ [10.5]

43. Rationalize the numerator of the expression in Exercise 42. [10.5]

Solve. [10.6]

44. $\sqrt{y + 6} - 2 = 3$

45. $(x + 1)^{1/3} = -5$

46. $1 + \sqrt{x} = \sqrt{3x - 3}$

47. If $f(x) = \sqrt[4]{x + 2}$, find a such that $f(a) = 2$. [10.6]

Solve. Give an exact answer and, where appropriate, an approximation to three decimal places. [10.7]

48. The diagonal of a square has length 10 cm. Find the length of a side of the square.

49. A skate-park jump has a ramp that is 6 ft long and is 2 ft high. How long is its base?

6 ft   2 ft

?

50. Find the missing lengths. Give exact answers and, where appropriate, an approximation to three decimal places.

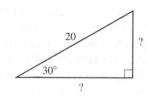

20

?

30°

?

51. Express in terms of i and simplify: $-\sqrt{-8}$. [10.8]

52. Add: $(-4 + 3i) + (2 - 12i)$. [10.8]

53. Subtract: $(9 - 7i) - (3 - 8i)$. [10.8]

Simplify. [10.8]

54. $(2 + 5i)(2 - 5i)$ **55.** i^{18}

56. Solve:
$$\sqrt{11x + \sqrt{6 + x}} = 6. \ [10.6]$$

57. Simplify:
$$\frac{2}{1 - 3i} - \frac{3}{4 + 2i}. \ [10.8]$$

58. Simplify: $(6 - 3i)(2 - i)$. [10.8]

59. Divide and simplify to the form $a + bi$:
$$\frac{7 - 2i}{3 + 4i}. \ [10.8]$$

60. What makes some complex numbers real and others imaginary? [10.8]

SYNTHESIS

61. Explain why $\sqrt[n]{x^n} = |x|$ when n is even, but $\sqrt[n]{x^n} = x$ when n is odd. [10.1]

62. Write a quotient of two imaginary numbers that is a real number (answers may vary). [10.8]

10 Chapter Test

Simplify. Assume that variables can represent any real number.

1. $\sqrt{50}$

2. $\sqrt[3]{-\dfrac{8}{x^6}}$

3. $\sqrt{81a^2}$

4. $\sqrt{x^2 - 8x + 16}$

5. $\sqrt[5]{x^{12}y^8}$

6. $\sqrt{\dfrac{25x^2}{36y^4}}$

7. $\sqrt[3]{3z}\,\sqrt[3]{5y^2}$

8. $\dfrac{\sqrt[5]{x^3y^4}}{\sqrt[5]{xy^2}}$

9. $\sqrt[4]{x^3y^2}\,\sqrt{xy}$

10. $\dfrac{\sqrt[5]{a^2}}{\sqrt[4]{a}}$

11. $8\sqrt{2} - 2\sqrt{2}$

12. $\sqrt{x^4y} + \sqrt{9y^3}$

13. $\left(7 + \sqrt{x}\right)\left(2 - 3\sqrt{x}\right)$

14. Write an equivalent expression using exponential notation: $\sqrt{7xy}$.

15. Write an equivalent expression using radical notation: $(4a^3b)^{5/6}$.

16. If $f(x) = \sqrt{2x - 10}$, determine the domain of f.

17. If $f(x) = x^2$, find $f\left(5 + \sqrt{2}\right)$.

18. Rationalize the denominator:

$$\dfrac{\sqrt{3}}{5 + \sqrt{2}}.$$

Solve.

19. $x = \sqrt{2x - 5} + 4$

20. $\sqrt{x} = \sqrt{x + 1} - 5$

Solve. Give exact answers and approximations to three decimal places.

21. One leg of a 30°–60°–90° right triangle is 7 cm long. Find the possible lengths of the other leg.

22. A referee jogs diagonally from one corner of a 50-ft by 90-ft basketball court to the far corner. How far does she jog?

23. Express in terms of i and simplify: $\sqrt{-50}$.

24. Subtract: $(9 + 8i) - (-3 + 6i)$.

25. Multiply: $\sqrt{-16}\,\sqrt{-36}$.

26. Multiply. Write the answer in the form $a + bi$.
$$(4 - i)^2$$

27. Divide and simplify to the form $a + bi$:
$$\dfrac{-2 + i}{3 - 5i}.$$

28. Simplify: i^{37}.

SYNTHESIS

29. Solve:
$$\sqrt{2x - 2} + \sqrt{7x + 4} = \sqrt{13x + 10}.$$

30. Simplify:
$$\dfrac{1 - 4i}{4i(1 + 4i)^{-1}}.$$

31. Drake's Discount Shoe Center has two locations. The sign at the original location is shaped like an isosceles right triangle. The sign at the newer location is shaped like a 30°–60°–90° triangle. The hypotenuse of each sign measures 6 ft. Which sign has the greater area and by how much? (Round to three decimal places.)

11

Quadratic Functions and Equations

AN APPLICATION

An athlete's hang time T, in seconds, is related to vertical leap V, in inches, by the formula $V = 48T^2$. The NBA's Steve Francis reportedly has a vertical leap of 45 in. What is his hang time?

This problem appears as Exercise 37 in Section 11.3.

Elizabeth Bluebird
PHYSICAL THERAPIST
Oklahoma City, Oklahoma

A treadmill test helps me to set up an exercise program for people with heart disease. I use an algebraic formula to figure a single-stage treadmill test using variables such as age, heart rate and speed. I also use math every day when measuring a person's range of motion—the arc or angle through which a body part moves. Knowing this angle, I can help make a diagnosis and show progress in my patient's therapy.

*I*n translating problem situations to mathematics, we often obtain a function or equation containing a second-degree polynomial in one variable. Such functions or equations are said to be quadratic. *In this chapter, we examine a variety of equations, inequalities, and applications for which we will need to solve quadratic equations or graph quadratic functions.*

11.1   Quadratic Equations

The Principle of Square Roots   •   Completing the Square   •
Problem Solving

 ALGEBRAIC–GRAPHICAL CONNECTION

Let's reexamine the graphical connections to the algebraic equation-solving concepts we have studied before.

In Chapter 7, we introduced the graph of a quadratic function given by

$$f(x) = ax^2 + bx + c, \quad a \neq 0.$$

For example, the graphs of $f(x) = x^2 + 6x + 8$ and $g(x) = 0$ are shown below.

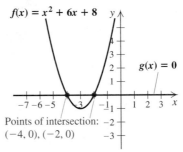

$f(x) = x^2 + 6x + 8$

$g(x) = 0$

Points of intersection: $(-4, 0), (-2, 0)$

Note that $(-4, 0)$ and $(-2, 0)$ are the points of intersection of the graphs of $f(x) = x^2 + 6x + 8$ and $g(x) = 0$ (the x-axis). In Sections 11.6 and 11.7, we will develop efficient ways to graph quadratic functions. For now, the graphs simply aid in visualizing solutions.

In Chapter 5, we solved equations like $x^2 + 6x + 8 = 0$ by factoring:

$$x^2 + 6x + 8 = 0$$

$$(x + 4)(x + 2) = 0 \qquad \text{Factoring}$$

$$x + 4 = 0 \quad or \quad x + 2 = 0 \qquad \text{Using the principle of zero products}$$

$$x = -4 \quad or \quad x = -2.$$

Note that -4 and -2 are the first coordinates of the points of intersection (or the x-intercepts) above.

In this section and the next, we develop algebraic methods for solving *any* quadratic equation, whether it is factorable or not.

EXAMPLE 1   Solve: $x^2 = 25$.

Solution   We have

$$x^2 = 25$$
$$x^2 - 25 = 0 \qquad \text{Writing in standard form}$$
$$(x - 5)(x + 5) = 0 \qquad \text{Factoring}$$
$$x - 5 = 0 \quad or \quad x + 5 = 0 \qquad \text{Using the principle of zero products}$$
$$x = 5 \quad or \qquad x = -5.$$

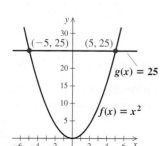

A visualization of Example 1

The solutions are 5 and −5. A graph in which $f(x) = x^2$ represents the left side of the original equation and $g(x) = 25$ represents the right side provides a check (see the figure at left). Of course, we can also check by substituting 5 and −5 into the original equation.

The Principle of Square Roots

Let's reconsider $x^2 = 25$. We know from Chapter 10 that the number 25 has two real-number square roots, 5 and −5, the solutions of the equation in Example 1. Thus we see that square roots can provide quick solutions for equations of the type $x^2 = k$.

> **The Principle of Square Roots**
> For any real number k, if $x^2 = k$, then $x = \sqrt{k}$ or $x = -\sqrt{k}$.

EXAMPLE 2   Solve: $3x^2 = 6$. Give exact solutions and approximations to three decimal places.

Solution   We have

$$3x^2 = 6$$
$$x^2 = 2 \qquad \text{Isolating } x^2$$
$$x = \sqrt{2} \quad or \quad x = -\sqrt{2}. \qquad \text{Using the principle of square roots}$$

We often use the symbol $\pm\sqrt{2}$ to represent both of the solutions.

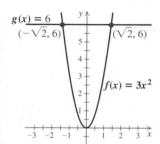

A visualization of Example 2

Check: For $\sqrt{2}$:

$$\frac{3x^2 = 6}{3(\sqrt{2})^2 \mid 6}$$
$$3 \cdot 2 \mid$$
$$6 \overset{?}{=} 6 \quad \text{TRUE}$$

For $-\sqrt{2}$:

$$\frac{3x^2 = 6}{3(-\sqrt{2})^2 \mid 6}$$
$$3 \cdot 2 \mid$$
$$6 \overset{?}{=} 6 \quad \text{TRUE}$$

The solutions are $\sqrt{2}$ and $-\sqrt{2}$, or $\pm\sqrt{2}$, which round to 1.414 and −1.414.

EXAMPLE 3   Solve: $-5x^2 + 2 = 0$.

Solution   We have

$$-5x^2 + 2 = 0$$

$$x^2 = \frac{2}{5}$$ Isolating x^2

$$x = \sqrt{\frac{2}{5}} \quad or \quad x = -\sqrt{\frac{2}{5}}.$$ Using the principle of square roots

The solutions are $\sqrt{\frac{2}{5}}$ and $-\sqrt{\frac{2}{5}}$. This can also be written as $\pm\sqrt{\frac{2}{5}}$. In the days before calculators, it was standard practice to rationalize denominators when simplifying answers. If we rationalize the denominator, the solutions are $\pm\dfrac{\sqrt{10}}{5}$. The checks are left to the student.

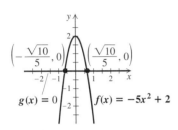

A visualization of Example 3

Sometimes we get solutions that are imaginary numbers.

EXAMPLE 4   Solve: $4x^2 + 9 = 0$.

Solution   We have

$$4x^2 + 9 = 0$$

$$x^2 = -\tfrac{9}{4}$$ Isolating x^2

$$x = \sqrt{-\tfrac{9}{4}} \quad or \quad x = -\sqrt{-\tfrac{9}{4}}$$ Using the principle of square roots

$$x = \sqrt{\tfrac{9}{4}}\sqrt{-1} \quad or \quad x = -\sqrt{\tfrac{9}{4}}\sqrt{-1}$$

$$x = \tfrac{3}{2}i \quad or \quad x = -\tfrac{3}{2}i.$$ Recall that $\sqrt{-1} = i$.

Check: For $\tfrac{3}{2}i$:

$$\begin{array}{c|c} 4x^2 + 9 = 0 & \\ \hline 4\left(\tfrac{3}{2}i\right)^2 + 9 & 0 \\ 4 \cdot \tfrac{9}{4} \cdot i^2 + 9 & \\ 9(-1) + 9 & \\ & 0 \overset{?}{=} 0 \quad \text{TRUE} \end{array}$$

For $-\tfrac{3}{2}i$:

$$\begin{array}{c|c} 4x^2 + 9 = 0 & \\ \hline 4\left(-\tfrac{3}{2}i\right)^2 + 9 & 0 \\ 4 \cdot \tfrac{9}{4} \cdot i^2 + 9 & \\ 9(-1) + 9 & \\ & 0 \overset{?}{=} 0 \quad \text{TRUE} \end{array}$$

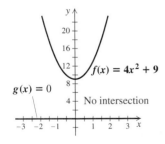

A visualization of Example 4

The solutions are $\tfrac{3}{2}i$ and $-\tfrac{3}{2}i$, or $\pm\tfrac{3}{2}i$. The graph at left confirms that there are no real-number solutions.

The principle of square roots can be restated in a more general form that pertains to more complicated algebraic expressions than just x.

> **The Principle of Square Roots (Generalized Form)**
> For any real number k and any algebraic expression X,
> $$\text{If } X^2 = k, \quad \text{then} \quad X = \sqrt{k} \quad \text{or} \quad X = -\sqrt{k}.$$

EXAMPLE 5

Let $f(x) = (x - 2)^2$. Find all x-values for which $f(x) = 7$.

Solution   We are asked to find all x-values for which

$$f(x) = 7,$$

or

$$(x - 2)^2 = 7. \qquad \text{Substituting } (x - 2)^2 \text{ for } f(x)$$

The generalized principle of square roots gives us

$$x - 2 = \sqrt{7} \qquad or \quad x - 2 = -\sqrt{7} \qquad \text{Using the principle of square roots}$$

$$x = 2 + \sqrt{7} \quad or \qquad x = 2 - \sqrt{7}.$$

Check: $f\left(2 + \sqrt{7}\right) = \left(2 + \sqrt{7} - 2\right)^2 = \left(\sqrt{7}\right)^2 = 7.$

Similarly,

$$f\left(2 - \sqrt{7}\right) = \left(2 - \sqrt{7} - 2\right)^2 = \left(-\sqrt{7}\right)^2 = 7.$$

The solutions are $2 + \sqrt{7}$ and $2 - \sqrt{7}$, or simply $2 \pm \sqrt{7}$.

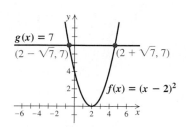

A visualization of Example 5

Example 5 is of the form $(x - a)^2 = c$, where a and c are constants. Sometimes we must factor in order to obtain this form.

EXAMPLE 6

Solve: $x^2 + 6x + 9 = 2$.

Solution   We have

$$x^2 + 6x + 9 = 2 \qquad \text{The left side is the square of a binomial.}$$
$$(x + 3)^2 = 2 \qquad \text{Factoring}$$
$$x + 3 = \sqrt{2} \qquad or \quad x + 3 = -\sqrt{2} \qquad \text{Using the principle of square roots}$$
$$x = -3 + \sqrt{2} \quad or \qquad x = -3 - \sqrt{2}. \qquad \text{Adding } -3 \text{ to both sides}$$

The solutions are $-3 + \sqrt{2}$ and $-3 - \sqrt{2}$, or $-3 \pm \sqrt{2}$. The checks are left to the student.

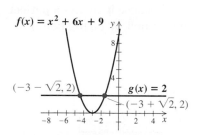

A visualization of Example 6

Completing the Square

Not all quadratic equations can be solved as we did Examples 1–6. By using a method called *completing the square*, we can use the principle of square roots to solve *any* quadratic equation.

EXAMPLE 7   Solve: $x^2 + 6x + 4 = 0$.

Solution   We have

$$x^2 + 6x + 4 = 0$$

$$x^2 + 6x = -4 \qquad \text{Subtracting 4 from both sides}$$

$$x^2 + 6x + 9 = -4 + 9 \qquad \text{Adding 9 to both sides. We explain this shortly.}$$

$$(x + 3)^2 = 5 \qquad \text{Factoring the perfect-square trinomial}$$

$$x + 3 = \pm\sqrt{5} \qquad \text{Using the principle of square roots. Remember that } \pm\sqrt{5} \text{ represents two numbers.}$$

$$x = -3 \pm \sqrt{5}. \qquad \text{Adding } -3 \text{ to both sides}$$

Check: For $-3 + \sqrt{5}$:

$$\dfrac{x^2 + 6x + 4 = 0}{}$$

$\left(-3 + \sqrt{5}\right)^2 + 6\left(-3 + \sqrt{5}\right) + 4$	0
$9 - 6\sqrt{5} + 5 - 18 + 6\sqrt{5} + 4$	
$9 + 5 - 18 + 4 - 6\sqrt{5} + 6\sqrt{5}$	

$$0 \overset{?}{=} 0 \quad \text{TRUE}$$

For $-3 - \sqrt{5}$:

$$\dfrac{x^2 + 6x + 4 = 0}{}$$

$\left(-3 - \sqrt{5}\right)^2 + 6\left(-3 - \sqrt{5}\right) + 4$	0
$9 + 6\sqrt{5} + 5 - 18 - 6\sqrt{5} + 4$	
$9 + 5 - 18 + 4 + 6\sqrt{5} - 6\sqrt{5}$	

$$0 \overset{?}{=} 0 \quad \text{TRUE}$$

The solutions are $-3 + \sqrt{5}$ and $-3 - \sqrt{5}$, or $-3 \pm \sqrt{5}$.

technology connection

One way to check Example 7 is to store $-3 + \sqrt{5}$ as x using the **STO▸** key. We can then evaluate $x^2 + 6x + 4$ by entering $x^2 + 6x + 4$ and pressing **ENTER**.

1. Check Example 7 using the method described above.

In Example 7, we chose to add 9 to both sides because it creates a perfect-square trinomial on the left side. The 9 was determined by taking half of the coefficient of x and squaring it—that is,

$$\left(\tfrac{1}{2} \cdot 6\right)^2 = 3^2, \quad \text{or} \quad 9.$$

To help see why this procedure works, examine the following drawings.

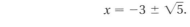
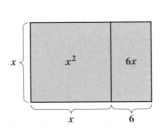
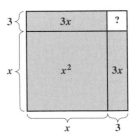

Note that the shaded areas in both figures represent the same area, $x^2 + 6x$. However, only the figure on the right, in which the $6x$ is halved, can be converted into a square with the addition of a constant term. The constant 9 is the "missing" piece that *completes* the square.

To complete the square for $x^2 + bx$, we add $(b/2)^2$.

Example 8, which follows, provides practice in finding numbers that complete the square. We will then use this skill to solve equations.

EXAMPLE 8   Replace the blanks in each equation with constants to form a true equation.

a) $x^2 + 14x +$ ____ $= (x +$ ____$)^2$
b) $x^2 - 5x +$ ____ $= (x -$ ____$)^2$
c) $x^2 + \frac{3}{4}x +$ ____ $= (x +$ ____$)^2$

Solution   We take half of the coefficient of x and square it.

a) Half of 14 is 7, and $7^2 = 49$. Thus, $x^2 + 14x + 49$ is a perfect-square trinomial and is equivalent to $(x + 7)^2$. We have

$$x^2 + 14x + 49 = (x + 7)^2.$$

b) Half of -5 is $-\frac{5}{2}$, and $\left(-\frac{5}{2}\right)^2 = \frac{25}{4}$. Thus, $x^2 - 5x + \frac{25}{4}$ is a perfect-square trinomial and is equivalent to $\left(x - \frac{5}{2}\right)^2$. We have

$$x^2 - 5x + \frac{25}{4} = \left(x - \frac{5}{2}\right)^2.$$

c) Half of $\frac{3}{4}$ is $\frac{3}{8}$, and $\left(\frac{3}{8}\right)^2 = \frac{9}{64}$. Thus, $x^2 + \frac{3}{4}x + \frac{9}{64}$ is a perfect-square trinomial and is equivalent to $\left(x + \frac{3}{8}\right)^2$. We have

$$x^2 + \frac{3}{4}x + \frac{9}{64} = \left(x + \frac{3}{8}\right)^2.$$

Student Notes _____

In problems like Examples 8(b) and (c), it is best to avoid decimal notation. Most students have an easier time recognizing $\frac{9}{64}$ as $\left(\frac{3}{8}\right)^2$ than regarding 0.140625 as 0.375^2.

We can now use the method of completing the square to solve equations similar to Example 7.

EXAMPLE 9   Solve: **(a)** $x^2 - 8x - 7 = 0$; **(b)** $x^2 + 5x - 3 = 0$.

Solution

a) $x^2 - 8x - 7 = 0$

$x^2 - 8x \quad\quad = 7$ Adding 7 to both sides. We can now complete the square on the left side.

$x^2 - 8x + 16 = 7 + 16$ Adding 16 to both sides to complete the square: $\frac{1}{2}(-8) = -4$, and $(-4)^2 = 16$

$(x - 4)^2 = 23$ Factoring and simplifying

$x - 4 = \pm\sqrt{23}$ Using the principle of square roots

$x = 4 \pm \sqrt{23}$ Adding 4 to both sides

The solutions are $4 - \sqrt{23}$ and $4 + \sqrt{23}$, or $4 \pm \sqrt{23}$. The checks are left to the student.

b)

$$x^2 + 5x - 3 = 0$$

$$x^2 + 5x = 3 \qquad \text{Adding 3 to both sides}$$

$$x^2 + 5x + \frac{25}{4} = 3 + \frac{25}{4} \qquad \text{Completing the square: } \frac{1}{2} \cdot 5 = \frac{5}{2}, \text{ and } \left(\frac{5}{2}\right)^2 = \frac{25}{4}$$

$$\left(x + \frac{5}{2}\right)^2 = \frac{37}{4} \qquad \text{Factoring and simplifying}$$

$$x + \frac{5}{2} = \pm\frac{\sqrt{37}}{2} \qquad \text{Using the principle of square roots and the quotient rule for radicals}$$

$$x = -\frac{5}{2} \pm \frac{\sqrt{37}}{2}, \quad \text{or} \quad \frac{-5 \pm \sqrt{37}}{2} \qquad \text{Adding } -\frac{5}{2} \text{ to both sides}$$

The checks are left to the student. The solutions are $-\frac{5}{2} \pm \frac{\sqrt{37}}{2}$, or $\frac{-5 \pm \sqrt{37}}{2}$. This can be written as $-\frac{5}{2} - \frac{\sqrt{37}}{2}$ and $-\frac{5}{2} + \frac{\sqrt{37}}{2}$, or $\frac{-5 - \sqrt{37}}{2}$ and $\frac{-5 + \sqrt{37}}{2}$.

Before we complete the square, the x^2-coefficient must be 1. When it is not 1, we divide both sides of the equation by whatever that coefficient may be.

EXAMPLE 10   Find the x-intercepts of the function given by $f(x) = 3x^2 + 7x - 2$.

Solution   The value of $f(x)$ must be 0 at any x-intercepts. Thus,

$$f(x) = 0 \qquad \text{We set } f(x) \text{ equal to 0.}$$

$$3x^2 + 7x - 2 = 0 \qquad \text{Substituting}$$

$$3x^2 + 7x = 2 \qquad \text{Adding 2 to both sides}$$

$$x^2 + \frac{7}{3}x = \frac{2}{3} \qquad \text{Dividing both sides by 3}$$

$$x^2 + \frac{7}{3}x + \frac{49}{36} = \frac{2}{3} + \frac{49}{36} \qquad \text{Completing the square: } \left(\frac{1}{2} \cdot \frac{7}{3}\right)^2 = \frac{49}{36}$$

$$\left(x + \frac{7}{6}\right)^2 = \frac{73}{36} \qquad \text{Factoring and simplifying}$$

$$x + \frac{7}{6} = \pm\frac{\sqrt{73}}{6} \qquad \text{Using the principle of square roots and the quotient rule for radicals}$$

$$x = -\frac{7}{6} \pm \frac{\sqrt{73}}{6}, \quad \text{or} \quad \frac{-7 \pm \sqrt{73}}{6}. \qquad \text{Adding } -\frac{7}{6} \text{ to both sides}$$

The x-intercepts are

$$\left(-\frac{7}{6} - \frac{\sqrt{73}}{6}, 0\right) \quad \text{and} \quad \left(-\frac{7}{6} + \frac{\sqrt{73}}{6}, 0\right), \quad \text{or}$$

$$\left(\frac{-7 - \sqrt{73}}{6}, 0\right) \quad \text{and} \quad \left(\frac{-7 + \sqrt{73}}{6}, 0\right).$$

The checks are left to the student.

A visualization of Example 10

The procedure used in Example 10 is important because it can be used to solve *any* quadratic equation.

To Solve a Quadratic Equation in x by Completing the Square

1. Isolate the terms with variables on one side of the equation, and arrange them in descending order.
2. Divide both sides by the coefficient of x^2 if that coefficient is not 1.
3. Complete the square by taking half of the coefficient of x and adding its square to both sides.
4. Express the trinomial as the square of a binomial (factor the trinomial) and simplify the other side.
5. Use the principle of square roots (find the square roots of both sides).
6. Solve for x by adding or subtracting on both sides.

Problem Solving

After one year, an amount of money P, invested at 4% per year, is worth 104% of P, or $P(1.04)$. If that amount continues to earn 4% interest per year, after the second year the investment will be worth 104% of $P(1.04)$, or $P(1.04)^2$. This is called **compounding interest** since after the first time period, interest is earned on both the initial investment *and* the interest from the first time period. Continuing the above pattern, we see that after the third year, the investment will be worth 104% of $P(1.04)^2$. Generalizing, we have the following.

The Compound-Interest Formula

If an amount of money P is invested at interest rate r, compounded annually, then in t years, it will grow to the amount A given by

$$A = P(1 + r)^t. \qquad (r \text{ is written in decimal notation.})$$

We can use quadratic equations to solve certain interest problems.

EXAMPLE 11   **Investment growth.**   Rosa invested $4000 at interest rate r, compounded annually. In 2 yr, it grew to $4410. What was the interest rate?

Solution

1. **Familiarize.**   We are already familiar with the compound-interest formula. If we were not, we would need to consult an outside source.

2. **Translate.**   The translation consists of substituting into the formula:

$$A = P(1 + r)^t$$
$$4410 = 4000(1 + r)^2. \qquad \text{Substituting}$$

3. **Carry out.** We solve for r:

$$4410 = 4000(1 + r)^2$$

$$\frac{4410}{4000} = (1 + r)^2 \qquad \text{Dividing both sides by 4000}$$

$$\frac{441}{400} = (1 + r)^2 \qquad \text{Simplifying}$$

$$\pm\sqrt{\frac{441}{400}} = 1 + r \qquad \text{Using the principle of square roots}$$

$$\pm\frac{21}{20} = 1 + r \qquad \text{Simplifying}$$

$$-\frac{20}{20} \pm \frac{21}{20} = r \qquad \text{Adding } -1, \text{ or } -\frac{20}{20}, \text{ to both sides}$$

$$\frac{1}{20} = r \quad or \quad -\frac{41}{20} = r.$$

4. **Check.** Since the interest rate cannot be negative, we need only check $\frac{1}{20}$, or 5%. If \$4000 were invested at 5% interest, compounded annually, then in 2 yr it would grow to $4000(1.05)^2$, or \$4410. The number 5% checks.

5. **State.** The interest rate was 5%.

EXAMPLE 12

Free-falling objects. The formula $s = 16t^2$ is used to approximate the distance s, in feet, that an object falls freely from rest in t seconds. Ireland's Cliffs of Moher are 702 ft tall (*Source*: Based on data from 4windstravel.com). How long will it take a stone to fall from the top? Round to the nearest tenth of a second.

Solution

1. **Familiarize.** We make a drawing to help visualize the problem and agree to disregard air resistance.

2. **Translate.** We substitute into the formula:

$$s = 16t^2$$
$$702 = 16t^2.$$

3. **Carry out.** We solve for t:

$$702 = 16t^2$$

$$\frac{702}{16} = t^2$$

$$43.875 = t^2$$

$$\sqrt{43.875} = t \qquad \text{Using the principle of square roots;}$$
$$\text{rejecting the negative square root since } t$$
$$\text{cannot be negative in this problem}$$

$$6.6 \approx t. \qquad \text{Using a calculator and rounding to}$$
$$\text{the nearest tenth}$$

4. **Check.** Since $16(6.6)^2 \approx 697 \approx 702$, our answer checks.

5. **State.** It takes about 6.6 sec for a stone to fall freely from the Cliffs of Moher.

---

technology connection

As we saw in Section 5.7, a graphing calculator can be used to find approximate solutions of any quadratic equation that has real-number solutions.

To check Example 9(a), we graph $y = x^2 - 8x - 7$ and use the ZERO or ROOT option of the CALC menu. When asked for a Left and Right Bound, we enter cursor positions to the left of and to the right of the root. A Guess between the bounds is entered and a value for the root then appears.

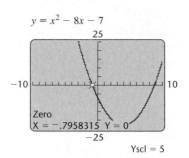

1. Use a graphing calculator to check the second solution of Example 9(a).
2. Use a graphing calculator to confirm the solutions in Examples 7 and 9(b).
3. Can a graphing calculator be used to find *exact* solutions in Example 10? Why or why not?
4. Use a graphing calculator to confirm that there are no real-number solutions of $x^2 - 6x + 11 = 0$.

 Exercise Set **11.1**

 Concept Reinforcement   Complete each of the following to form true statements.

1. The principle of square roots states that if $x^2 = k$, then $x = $ ____ or $x = $ ____.
2. If $(x + 5)^2 = 49$, then $x + 5 = $ ____ or $x + 5 = $ ____.
3. If $t^2 + 6t + 9 = 17$, then (____)$^2 = 17$ and ____ $= \pm\sqrt{17}$.
4. The equations $x^2 + 8x + $ ____ $= 23$ and $x^2 + 8x = 7$ are equivalent.
5. The expressions $t^2 + 10t + $ ____ and $(t + $ ____$)^2$ are equivalent.
6. The expressions $x^2 - 6x + $ ____ and $(x - $ ____$)^2$ are equivalent.

Solve.
7. $4x^2 = 20$
8. $7x^2 = 21$
9. $9x^2 + 16 = 0$
10. $25x^2 + 4 = 0$
11. $5t^2 - 7 = 0$
12. $3t^2 - 2 = 0$
13. $(x - 1)^2 = 49$
14. $(x + 2)^2 = 25$
15. $(a - 13)^2 = 18$
16. $(a + 5)^2 = 8$
17. $(x + 1)^2 = -9$
18. $(x - 1)^2 = -49$
19. $\left(y + \frac{3}{4}\right)^2 = \frac{17}{16}$
20. $\left(t + \frac{3}{2}\right)^2 = \frac{7}{2}$
21. $x^2 - 10x + 25 = 64$
22. $x^2 - 6x + 9 = 100$
23. Let $f(x) = (x - 5)^2$. Find x such that $f(x) = 16$.
24. Let $g(x) = (x - 2)^2$. Find x such that $g(x) = 25$.
25. Let $F(t) = (t + 4)^2$. Find t such that $F(t) = 13$.
26. Let $f(t) = (t + 6)^2$. Find t such that $f(t) = 15$.
Aha! 27. Let $g(x) = x^2 + 14x + 49$. Find x such that $g(x) = 49$.
28. Let $F(x) = x^2 + 8x + 16$. Find x such that $F(x) = 9$.

Replace the blanks in each equation with constants to complete the square and form a true equation.

29. $x^2 + 16x + \underline{\quad} = (x + \underline{\quad})^2$

30. $x^2 + 8x + \underline{\quad} = (x + \underline{\quad})^2$

31. $t^2 - 10t + \underline{\quad} = (t - \underline{\quad})^2$

32. $t^2 - 6t + \underline{\quad} = (t - \underline{\quad})^2$

33. $x^2 + 3x + \underline{\quad} = (x + \underline{\quad})^2$

34. $x^2 + 7x + \underline{\quad} = (x + \underline{\quad})^2$

35. $t^2 - 9t + \underline{\quad} = (t - \underline{\quad})^2$

36. $t^2 - 3t + \underline{\quad} = (t - \underline{\quad})^2$

37. $x^2 + \frac{2}{5}x + \underline{\quad} = (x + \underline{\quad})^2$

38. $x^2 + \frac{2}{3}x + \underline{\quad} = (x + \underline{\quad})^2$

39. $t^2 - \frac{5}{6}t + \underline{\quad} = (t - \underline{\quad})^2$

40. $t^2 - \frac{5}{3}t + \underline{\quad} = (t - \underline{\quad})^2$

Solve by completing the square. Show your work.

41. $x^2 + 6x = 7$ **42.** $x^2 + 8x = 9$

43. $t^2 - 10t = -24$ **44.** $t^2 - 10t = -21$

45. $x^2 + 10x + 9 = 0$ **46.** $x^2 + 8x + 7 = 0$

47. $t^2 + 8t - 3 = 0$ **48.** $t^2 + 6t - 5 = 0$

Complete the square to find the x-intercepts of each function given by the equation listed.

49. $f(x) = x^2 + 6x + 7$ **50.** $f(x) = x^2 + 5x + 3$

51. $g(x) = x^2 + 12x + 25$ **52.** $g(x) = x^2 + 4x + 2$

53. $f(x) = x^2 - 10x - 22$ **54.** $f(x) = x^2 - 8x - 10$

Solve by completing the square. Remember to first divide, as in Example 10, to make sure that the coefficient of x^2 is 1.

55. $9x^2 + 18x = -8$ **56.** $4x^2 + 8x = -3$

57. $3x^2 - 5x - 2 = 0$ **58.** $2x^2 - 5x - 3 = 0$

59. $5x^2 + 4x - 3 = 0$ **60.** $4x^2 + 3x - 5 = 0$

61. Find the x-intercepts of the function given by $f(x) = 4x^2 + 2x - 3$.

62. Find the x-intercepts of the function given by $f(x) = 3x^2 + x - 5$.

63. Find the x-intercepts of the function given by $g(x) = 2x^2 - 3x - 1$.

64. Find the x-intercepts of the function given by $g(x) = 3x^2 - 5x - 1$.

Interest.   Use $A = P(1 + r)^t$ to find the interest rate in Exercises 65–70. Refer to Example 11.

65. $2000 grows to $2420 in 2 yr

66. $2560 grows to $2890 in 2 yr

67. $1280 grows to $1805 in 2 yr

68. $1000 grows to $1440 in 2 yr

69. $6250 grows to $6760 in 2 yr

70. $6250 grows to $7290 in 2 yr

Free-falling objects.   Use $s = 16t^2$ for Exercises 71–74. Refer to Example 12 and neglect air resistance.

71. Suspended 1053 ft above the water, the bridge over Colorado's Royal Gorge is the world's highest bridge. How long would it take an object to fall freely from the bridge?
Source: *The Guinness Book of Records*

72. The CN Tower in Toronto, at 1815 ft, is the world's tallest self-supporting tower (no guy wires). How long would it take an object to fall freely from the top?
Source: *The Guinness Book of Records*

73. The Sears Tower in Chicago is 1454 ft tall. How long would it take an object to fall freely from the top?

74. The Gateway Arch in St. Louis is 630 ft high. How long would it take an object to fall freely from the top?
Source: www.icivilengineer.com

75. Explain in your own words a sequence of steps that can be used to solve any quadratic equation in the quickest way.

76. Write an interest-rate problem for a classmate to solve. Devise the problem so that the solution is "The loan was made at 7% interest."

SKILL MAINTENANCE

Evaluate. [1.8]

77. $at^2 - bt$, for $a = 3$, $b = 5$, and $t = 4$

78. $mn^2 - mp$, for $m = -2$, $n = 7$, and $p = 3$

Simplify. [10.3]

79. $\sqrt[3]{270}$ **80.** $\sqrt{80}$

Let $f(x) = \sqrt{3x - 5}$. [10.1]

81. Find $f(10)$.   **82.** Find $f(18)$.

SYNTHESIS

83. What would be better: to receive 3% interest every 6 months, or to receive 6% interest every 12 months? Why?

84. Write a problem involving a free-falling object for a classmate to solve (see Example 12). Devise the problem so that the solution is "The object takes about 4.5 sec to fall freely from the top of the structure."

Find b such that each trinomial is a square.

85. $x^2 + bx + 81$ **86.** $x^2 + bx + 49$

87. If $f(x) = 2x^5 - 9x^4 - 66x^3 + 45x^2 + 280x$ and $x^2 - 5$ is a factor of $f(x)$, find all a for which $f(a) = 0$.

88. If $f(x) = \left(x - \frac{1}{3}\right)(x^2 + 6)$ and $g(x) = \left(x - \frac{1}{3}\right)\left(x^2 - \frac{2}{3}\right)$, find all a for which $(f + g)(a) = 0$.

89. *Boating.*   A barge and a fishing boat leave a dock at the same time, traveling at a right angle to each other. The barge travels 7 km/h slower than the fishing boat. After 4 hr, the boats are 68 km apart. Find the speed of each boat.

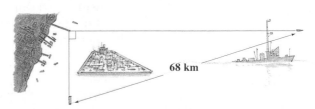

68 km

90. Find three consecutive integers such that the square of the first plus the product of the other two is 67.

91. Exercises 15, 23, and 43 can be solved on a graphing calculator without first rewriting in standard form. Simply let y_1 represent the left side of the equation and y_2 the right side. Then use a graphing calculator to determine the x-coordinate of any point of intersection. Use a graphing calculator to solve Exercises 15, 23, and 43 in this manner.

92. Use a graphing calculator to check your answers to Exercises 5, 11, 61, and 63.

93. Example 11 can be solved with a graphing calculator by graphing each side of

$$4410 = 4000(1 + r)^2.$$

How could you determine, from a reading of the problem, a suitable viewing window? What might that window be?

11.2   # The Quadratic Formula

Solving Using the Quadratic Formula   •   Approximating Solutions

There are at least two reasons for learning to complete the square. One is to help graph certain equations that appear in this and other chapters. Another is to develop a general formula for solving quadratic equations.

Solving Using the Quadratic Formula

Each time we solve by completing the square, the procedure is the same. In mathematics, when a procedure is repeated many times, a formula can often be developed to speed up our work.

We begin with a quadratic equation in standard form,

$$ax^2 + bx + c = 0,$$

with $a > 0$. For $a < 0$, a slightly different derivation is needed (see Exercise 58), but the result is the same. Let's solve by completing the square. As the steps are performed, compare them with Example 10 on p. 710.

$$ax^2 + bx = -c \qquad \text{Adding } -c \text{ to both sides}$$

$$x^2 + \frac{b}{a}x = -\frac{c}{a} \qquad \text{Dividing both sides by } a$$

Half of $\dfrac{b}{a}$ is $\dfrac{b}{2a}$ and $\left(\dfrac{b}{2a}\right)^2$ is $\dfrac{b^2}{4a^2}$. We add $\dfrac{b^2}{4a^2}$ to both sides:

$$x^2 + \frac{b}{a}x + \frac{b^2}{4a^2} = -\frac{c}{a} + \frac{b^2}{4a^2} \qquad \text{Adding } \dfrac{b^2}{4a^2} \text{ to complete the square}$$

$$\left(x + \frac{b}{2a}\right)^2 = -\frac{4ac}{4a^2} + \frac{b^2}{4a^2} \qquad \begin{array}{l}\text{Factoring on the left side;}\\\text{finding a common denomi-}\\\text{nator on the right side}\end{array}$$

$$\left(x + \frac{b}{2a}\right)^2 = \frac{b^2 - 4ac}{4a^2}$$

$$x + \frac{b}{2a} = \pm\frac{\sqrt{b^2 - 4ac}}{2a} \qquad \begin{array}{l}\text{Using the principle of}\\\text{square roots and the quo-}\\\text{tient rule for radicals; since}\\a > 0, \sqrt{4a^2} = 2a\end{array}$$

$$x = \frac{-b \pm \sqrt{b^2 - 4ac}}{2a}. \qquad \text{Adding } -\dfrac{b}{2a} \text{ to both sides}$$

It is important to remember the quadratic formula and know how to use it.

The Quadratic Formula

The solutions of $ax^2 + bx + c = 0$, $a \neq 0$, are given by

$$x = \frac{-b \pm \sqrt{b^2 - 4ac}}{2a}.$$

EXAMPLE 1   Solve $5x^2 + 8x = -3$ using the quadratic formula.

Solution   We first find standard form and determine a, b, and c:

$$5x^2 + 8x + 3 = 0; \qquad \text{Adding 3 to both sides to get 0 on one side}$$

$$a = 5, \quad b = 8, \quad c = 3.$$

Next, we use the quadratic formula:

$$x = \frac{-b \pm \sqrt{b^2 - 4ac}}{2a}$$

$$x = \frac{-8 \pm \sqrt{8^2 - 4 \cdot 5 \cdot 3}}{2 \cdot 5} \qquad \text{Substituting}$$

$$x = \frac{-8 \pm \sqrt{64 - 60}}{10}$$

Be sure to write the fraction bar all the way across.

$$x = \frac{-8 \pm \sqrt{4}}{10} = \frac{-8 \pm 2}{10}$$

$$x = \frac{-8 + 2}{10} \quad or \quad x = \frac{-8 - 2}{10}$$

$$x = \frac{-6}{10} \qquad or \quad x = \frac{-10}{10}$$

$$x = -\frac{3}{5} \qquad or \quad x = -1.$$

The solutions are $-\frac{3}{5}$ and -1. The checks are left to the student.

Study Skills

Know It "By Heart"

When memorizing something like the quadratic formula, try to first understand and write out the derivation. Doing this two or three times will help you remember the formula.

Because $5x^2 + 8x + 3$ can be factored, the quadratic formula may not have been the fastest way of solving Example 1. However, because the quadratic formula works for *any* quadratic equation, we need not spend too much time struggling to solve a quadratic equation by factoring.

To Solve a Quadratic Equation

1. If the equation can be easily written in the form $ax^2 = p$ or $(x + k)^2 = d$, use the principle of square roots as in Section 11.1.
2. If step (1) does not apply, write the equation in the form $ax^2 + bx + c = 0$.
3. Try factoring and using the principle of zero products.
4. If factoring seems difficult or impossible, use the quadratic formula. Completing the square can also be used, but is slower.

The solutions of a quadratic equation can always be found using the quadratic formula. They cannot always be found by factoring.

Recall that a second-degree polynomial in one variable is said to be quadratic. Similarly, a second-degree polynomial function in one variable is said to be a **quadratic function.**

EXAMPLE 2

For the quadratic function given by $f(x) = 3x^2 - 6x - 4$, find all x for which $f(x) = 0$.

Solution   We substitute and solve for x:

$$f(x) = 0$$

$$3x^2 - 6x - 4 = 0 \qquad \text{Substituting. You can try to solve this by factoring.}$$

$$a = 3; \quad b = -6; \quad c = -4.$$

We then substitute into the quadratic formula:

$$x = \frac{-(-6) \pm \sqrt{(-6)^2 - 4 \cdot 3 \cdot (-4)}}{2 \cdot 3}$$

$$= \frac{6 \pm \sqrt{36 + 48}}{6}$$

$$= \frac{6 \pm \sqrt{84}}{6} \qquad \text{Note that 4 is a perfect-square factor of 84.}$$

$$= \frac{6}{6} \pm \frac{\sqrt{84}}{6}$$

$$= 1 \pm \frac{\sqrt{4}\sqrt{21}}{6} \qquad 84 = 4 \cdot 21$$

$$\left. \begin{array}{l} = 1 \pm \dfrac{2\sqrt{21}}{6} \\[2mm] = 1 \pm \dfrac{\sqrt{21}}{3}. \end{array} \right\} \quad \text{Simplifying}$$

The solutions are $1 - \dfrac{\sqrt{21}}{3}$ and $1 + \dfrac{\sqrt{21}}{3}$. The checks are left to the student.

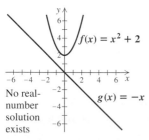

technology connection

To check Example 2 by graphing $y_1 = 3x^2 - 6x - 4$, press (TRACE) and enter $1 + \sqrt{21}/3$. A rational approximation and the y-value 0 should appear.

$y = 3x^2 - 6x - 4$

X = 2.5275252   Y = 0

Use this approach to check the other solution of Example 2.

Some quadratic equations have solutions that are imaginary numbers.

EXAMPLE 3

Solve: $x^2 + 2 = -x$.

Solution   We first find standard form:

$$x^2 + x + 2 = 0. \qquad \text{Adding } x \text{ to both sides}$$

Since we cannot factor $x^2 + x + 2$, we use the quadratic formula with $a = 1$, $b = 1$, and $c = 2$:

$$x = \frac{-1 \pm \sqrt{1^2 - 4 \cdot 1 \cdot 2}}{2 \cdot 1} \qquad \text{Substituting}$$

$$= \frac{-1 \pm \sqrt{1 - 8}}{2}$$

$$= \frac{-1 \pm \sqrt{-7}}{2}$$

$$= \frac{-1 \pm i\sqrt{7}}{2}, \text{ or } -\frac{1}{2} \pm \frac{\sqrt{7}}{2}i.$$

$f(x) = x^2 + 2$

$g(x) = -x$

No real-number solution exists

A visualization of Example 3

The solutions are $-\frac{1}{2} - \frac{\sqrt{7}}{2}i$ and $-\frac{1}{2} + \frac{\sqrt{7}}{2}i$. The checks are left to the student.

The quadratic formula can be used to solve certain rational equations.

EXAMPLE 4   If $f(x) = 2 + \frac{7}{x}$ and $g(x) = \frac{4}{x^2}$, find all x for which $f(x) = g(x)$.

Solution   We set $f(x)$ equal to $g(x)$ and solve:

$$f(x) = g(x)$$

$$2 + \frac{7}{x} = \frac{4}{x^2}.$$ Substituting. Note that $x \neq 0$.

This is a rational equation similar to those in Section 6.6. To solve, we multiply both sides by the LCD, x^2:

$$x^2\left(2 + \frac{7}{x}\right) = x^2 \cdot \frac{4}{x^2}$$

$$2x^2 + 7x = 4$$ Simplifying

$$2x^2 + 7x - 4 = 0.$$ Subtracting 4 from both sides

We have

$$a = 2, \quad b = 7, \quad \text{and} \quad c = -4.$$

Substituting then gives us

$$x = \frac{-7 \pm \sqrt{7^2 - 4 \cdot 2 \cdot (-4)}}{2 \cdot 2}$$

$$= \frac{-7 \pm \sqrt{49 + 32}}{4}$$

$$= \frac{-7 \pm \sqrt{81}}{4}$$

$$= \frac{-7 \pm 9}{4}$$

$$x = \frac{2}{4} = \frac{1}{2} \; \text{ or } \; x = \frac{-16}{4} = -4. \qquad \begin{array}{l}\text{Both answers should check}\\\text{since } x \neq 0.\end{array}$$

You can confirm that $f\left(\frac{1}{2}\right) = g\left(\frac{1}{2}\right)$ and $f(-4) = g(-4)$. The solutions are $\frac{1}{2}$ and -4.

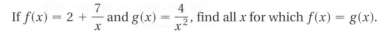

technology connection

We saw in Sections 5.7 and 11.1 how graphing calculators can solve quadratic equations. To determine whether quadratic equations are solved more quickly on a graphing calculator or by using the quadratic formula, solve Examples 2 and 4 both ways. Which method is faster? Which method is more precise? Why?

Approximating Solutions

When the solution of an equation is irrational, a rational-number approximation is often useful. This is often the case in real-world applications similar to those found in Section 11.3.

EXAMPLE 5   Use a calculator to approximate the solutions of Example 2.

Student Notes _____

It is important that you understand both the rules for order of operations *and* the manner in which your calculator applies those rules.

Solution   On most calculators, one of the following sequences of keystrokes can be used to approximate $1 + \sqrt{21}/3$:

 or

Similar keystrokes can be used to approximate $1 - \sqrt{21}/3$.
     The solutions are approximately 2.527525232 and -0.5275252317.

11.2 Exercise Set

FOR EXTRA HELP

Student's Solutions Manual   Digital Video Tutor CD 6 Videotape 11   Tutor Center AW Math Tutor Center   MathXL Tutorials on CD   MathXL   MyMathLab

🍂 *Concept Reinforcement*   *Classify each of the following as either true or false.*

1. The quadratic formula can be used to solve *any* quadratic equation.

2. The quadratic formula does not work if solutions are imaginary numbers.

3. Solving by factoring is always slower than using the quadratic formula.

4. The steps used to derive the quadratic formula are the same as those used when solving by completing the square.

5. A quadratic equation can have as many as four solutions.

6. It is possible for a quadratic equation to have no real-number solutions.

Solve.

7. $x^2 + 7x - 3 = 0$ **8.** $x^2 - 7x + 4 = 0$

9. $3p^2 = 18p - 6$ **10.** $3u^2 = 8u - 5$

11. $x^2 + x + 1 = 0$ **12.** $x^2 + x + 2 = 0$

13. $x^2 + 13 = 4x$ **14.** $x^2 + 13 = 6x$

15. $h^2 + 4 = 6h$ **16.** $r^2 + 3r = 8$

17. $\dfrac{1}{x^2} - 3 = \dfrac{8}{x}$ **18.** $\dfrac{9}{x} - 2 = \dfrac{5}{x^2}$

19. $3x + x(x - 2) = 4$ **20.** $4x + x(x - 3) = 5$

21. $12t^2 + 9t = 1$ **22.** $15t^2 + 7t = 2$

23. $25x^2 - 20x + 4 = 0$ **24.** $36x^2 + 84x + 49 = 0$

25. $7x(x + 2) + 5 = 3x(x + 1)$

26. $5x(x - 1) - 7 = 4x(x - 2)$

27. $14(x - 4) - (x + 2) = (x + 2)(x - 4)$

28. $11(x - 2) + (x - 5) = (x + 2)(x - 6)$

29. $5x^2 = 13x + 17$

30. $25x = 3x^2 + 28$

31. $x^2 + 9 = 4x$

32. $x^2 + 7 = 3x$

33. $x^3 - 8 = 0$ (*Hint*: Factor the difference of cubes. Then use the quadratic formula.)

34. $x^3 + 1 = 0$

35. Let $f(x) = 3x^2 - 5x + 2$. Find x such that $f(x) = 0$.

36. Let $g(x) = 4x^2 - 2x - 3$. Find x such that $g(x) = 0$.

37. Let
$$f(x) = \frac{7}{x} + \frac{7}{x+4}.$$
Find all x for which $f(x) = 1$.

38. Let
$$g(x) = \frac{2}{x} + \frac{2}{x+3}.$$
Find all x for which $g(x) = 1$.

39. Let
$$F(x) = \frac{x+3}{x} \quad \text{and} \quad G(x) = \frac{x-4}{3}.$$
Find all x for which $F(x) = G(x)$.

40. Let
$$f(x) = \frac{3-x}{4} \quad \text{and} \quad g(x) = \frac{1}{4x}.$$
Find all x for which $f(x) = g(x)$.

41. Let
$$f(x) = \frac{15 - 2x}{6} \quad \text{and} \quad g(x) = \frac{3}{x}.$$
Find all x for which $f(x) = g(x)$.

42. Let
$$f(x) = x + 5 \quad \text{and} \quad g(x) = \frac{3}{x-5}.$$
Find all x for which $f(x) = g(x)$.

Solve. Use a calculator to approximate, as precisely as possible, the solutions as rational numbers.

43. $x^2 + 4x - 7 = 0$

44. $x^2 + 6x + 4 = 0$

45. $x^2 - 6x + 4 = 0$

46. $x^2 - 4x + 1 = 0$

47. $2x^2 - 3x - 7 = 0$

48. $3x^2 - 3x - 2 = 0$

49. Are there any equations that can be solved by the quadratic formula but not by completing the square? Why or why not?

50. If you had to choose between remembering the method of completing the square and remembering the quadratic formula, which would you choose? Why?

SKILL MAINTENANCE

51. *Coffee beans.*   Twin Cities Roasters has Kenyan coffee for which they pay $6.75 a pound and Kona coffee for which they pay $11.25 a pound. How much of each kind should be mixed in order to obtain a 50-lb mixture that costs them $8.55 a pound? [8.3]

52. *Donuts.*   South Street Bakers charges $1.10 for a cream-filled donut and 85¢ for a glazed donut. On a recent Sunday, a total of 90 glazed and cream-filled donuts were sold for $88.00. How many of each type were sold? [8.3]

Simplify.

53. $\sqrt{27a^2b^5} \cdot \sqrt{6a^3b}$ [10.3]

54. $\sqrt{8a^3b} \cdot \sqrt{12ab^5}$ [10.3]

55. $\dfrac{\dfrac{3}{x-1}}{\dfrac{1}{x+1} + \dfrac{2}{x-1}}$ [6.5]

56. $\dfrac{\dfrac{4}{a^2b}}{\dfrac{3}{a} - \dfrac{4}{b^2}}$ [6.5]

SYNTHESIS

57. Suppose you had a large number of quadratic equations to solve and none of the equations had a constant term. Would you use factoring or the quadratic formula to solve these equations? Why?

58. If $a < 0$ and $ax^2 + bx + c = 0$, then $-a$ is positive and the equivalent equation, $-ax^2 - bx - c = 0$, can be solved using the quadratic formula.

   a) Find this solution, replacing a, b, and c in the formula with $-a$, $-b$, and $-c$ from the equation.

   b) How does the result of part (a) indicate that the quadratic formula "works" regardless of the sign of a?

For Exercises 59–61, let

$$f(x) = \frac{x^2}{x-2} + 1 \quad and \quad g(x) = \frac{4x-2}{x-2} + \frac{x+4}{2}.$$

59. Find the x-intercepts of the graph of f.

60. Find the x-intercepts of the graph of g.

61. Find all x for which $f(x) = g(x)$.

Solve.

62. $x^2 - 0.75x - 0.5 = 0$

63. $z^2 + 0.84z - 0.4 = 0$

64. $\left(1 + \sqrt{3}\right)x^2 - \left(3 + 2\sqrt{3}\right)x + 3 = 0$

65. $\sqrt{2}x^2 + 5x + \sqrt{2} = 0$

66. $ix^2 - 2x + 1 = 0$

67. One solution of $kx^2 + 3x - k = 0$ is -2. Find the other.

68. Use a graphing calculator to solve Exercises 9, 23, and 39.

69. Use a graphing calculator to solve Exercises 15, 31, and 37. Use the method of graphing each side of the equation.

70. Can a graphing calculator be used to solve *any* quadratic equation? Why or why not?

11.3 Applications Involving Quadratic Equations

Solving Problems • Solving Formulas

Solving Problems

As we found in Section 6.7, some problems translate to rational equations. The solution of such rational equations can involve quadratic equations.

EXAMPLE 1   Motorcycle travel.   Makita rode her motorcycle 300 mi at a certain average speed. Had she averaged 10 mph more, the trip would have taken 1 hr less. Find the average speed of the motorcycle.

Solution

1. Familiarize.   We make a drawing, labeling it with the information provided. As in Section 6.7, we can create a table. We let r represent the rate, in miles per hour, and t the time, in hours, for Makita's trip.

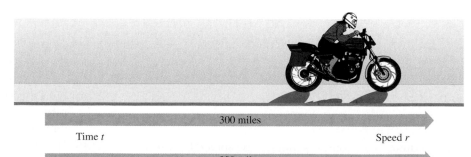

Distance	Speed	Time
300	r	t
300	$r + 10$	$t - 1$

$\longrightarrow r = \dfrac{300}{t}$

$\longrightarrow r + 10 = \dfrac{300}{t - 1}$

Recall that the definition of speed, $r = d/t$, relates the three quantities.

2. Translate.   From the table, we obtain

$$r = \frac{300}{t} \quad \text{and} \quad r + 10 = \frac{300}{t - 1}.$$

3. Carry out.   A system of equations has been formed. We substitute for r from the first equation into the second and solve the resulting equation:

$$\frac{300}{t} + 10 = \frac{300}{t - 1} \qquad \text{Substituting } 300/t \text{ for } r$$

$$t(t - 1) \cdot \left[\frac{300}{t} + 10\right] = t(t - 1) \cdot \frac{300}{t - 1} \qquad \text{Multiplying by the LCD}$$

$$\cancel{t}(t - 1) \cdot \frac{300}{\cancel{t}} + t(t - 1) \cdot 10 = t\cancel{(t - 1)} \cdot \frac{300}{\cancel{t - 1}}$$

Using the distributive law and removing factors that equal 1: $\dfrac{t}{t} = 1$; $\dfrac{t - 1}{t - 1} = 1$

$$\left.\begin{aligned} 300(t - 1) + 10(t^2 - t) &= 300t \\ 300t - 300 + 10t^2 - 10t &= 300t \\ 10t^2 - 10t - 300 &= 0 \end{aligned}\right\} \quad \text{Rewriting in standard form}$$

$$t^2 - t - 30 = 0 \qquad \text{Multiplying by } \tfrac{1}{10} \text{ or dividing by 10}$$

$$(t - 6)(t + 5) = 0 \qquad \text{Factoring}$$

$$t = 6 \quad or \quad t = -5. \qquad \text{Principle of zero products}$$

4. Check.   Note that we have solved for t, not r as required. Since negative time has no meaning here, we disregard the -5 and use 6 hr to find r:

$$r = \frac{300 \text{ mi}}{6 \text{ hr}} = 50 \text{ mph.}$$

> *Caution!*   Always make sure that you find the quantity asked for in the problem.

To see if 50 mph checks, we increase the speed 10 mph to 60 mph and see how long the trip would have taken at that speed:

$$t = \frac{d}{r} = \frac{300 \text{ mi}}{60 \text{ mph}} = 5 \text{ hr}.$$

Note that $\text{mi/mph} = \text{mi} \div \frac{\text{mi}}{\text{hr}} = $

$$\text{mi} \cdot \frac{\text{hr}}{\text{mi}} = \text{hr}.$$

This is 1 hr less than the trip actually took, so the answer checks.

5. State. Makita's motorcycle traveled at an average speed of 50 mph.

Solving Formulas

Recall that to solve a formula for a certain letter, we use the principles for solving equations to get that letter alone on one side.

EXAMPLE 2

Period of a pendulum. The time T required for a pendulum of length l to swing back and forth (complete one period) is given by the formula $T = 2\pi\sqrt{l/g}$, where g is the earth's gravitational constant. Solve for l.

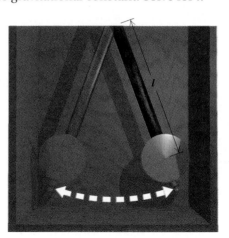

Solution We have

$$T = 2\pi\sqrt{\frac{l}{g}}$$

This is a radical equation (see Section 10.6).

$$T^2 = \left(2\pi\sqrt{\frac{l}{g}}\right)^2$$

Principle of powers (squaring both sides)

$$T^2 = 2^2\pi^2\frac{l}{g}$$

$$gT^2 = 4\pi^2 l$$

Multiplying both sides by g to clear fractions

$$\frac{gT^2}{4\pi^2} = l.$$

Dividing both sides by $4\pi^2$

We now have l alone on one side and l does not appear on the other side, so the formula is solved for l.

In formulas for which variables represent only nonnegative numbers, there is no need for absolute-value signs when taking square roots.

EXAMPLE 3   Hang time.* An athlete's *hang time* is the amount of time that the athlete can remain airborne when jumping. A formula relating an athlete's vertical leap V, in inches, to hang time T, in seconds, is $V = 48T^2$. Solve for T.

Solution   We have

$$48T^2 = V$$

$$T^2 = \frac{V}{48} \qquad \text{Dividing by 48 to isolate } T^2$$

$$T = \frac{\sqrt{V}}{\sqrt{48}} \qquad \begin{array}{l} \text{Using the principle of square roots} \\ \text{and the quotient rule for radicals.} \\ \text{We assume } V, T \geq 0. \end{array}$$

$$\left. \begin{array}{l} = \dfrac{\sqrt{V}}{\sqrt{16}\,\sqrt{3}} = \dfrac{\sqrt{V}}{4\sqrt{3}} \\[2ex] = \dfrac{\sqrt{V}}{4\sqrt{3}} \cdot \dfrac{\sqrt{3}}{\sqrt{3}} = \dfrac{\sqrt{3V}}{12}. \end{array} \right\} \quad \text{Rationalizing the denominator}$$

EXAMPLE 4   Falling distance.   An object tossed downward with an initial speed (velocity) of v_0 will travel a distance of s meters, where $s = 4.9t^2 + v_0 t$ and t is measured in seconds. Solve for t.

Solution   Since t is squared in one term and raised to the first power in the other term, the equation is quadratic in t.

$$4.9t^2 + v_0 t = s$$

$$4.9t^2 + v_0 t - s = 0 \qquad \text{Writing standard form}$$

$$a = 4.9, \quad b = v_0, \quad c = -s$$

$$t = \frac{-v_0 \pm \sqrt{v_0^2 - 4(4.9)(-s)}}{2(4.9)} \qquad \text{Using the quadratic formula}$$

---

*This formula is taken from an article by Peter Brancazio, "The Mechanics of a Slam Dunk," *Popular Mechanics*, November 1991. Courtesy of Professor Peter Brancazio, Brooklyn College.

Since the negative square root would yield a negative value for t, we use only the positive root:

$$t = \frac{-v_0 + \sqrt{v_0^2 + 19.6s}}{9.8}.$$

The following list of steps should help you when solving formulas for a given letter. Try to remember that when solving a formula, you use the same approach that you would to solve an equation.

Student Notes _____

After identifying which numbers to use as a, b, and c, be careful to replace only the *letters* in the quadratic formula.

To Solve a Formula for a Letter—Say, b

1. Clear fractions and use the principle of powers, as needed. Perform these steps until radicals containing b are gone and b is not in any denominator.
2. Combine all like terms.
3. If the only power of b is b^1, the equation can be solved as in Sections 2.3 and 7.5.
4. If b^2 appears but b does not, solve for b^2 and use the principle of square roots to solve for b.
5. If there are terms containing both b and b^2, put the equation in standard form and use the quadratic formula.

Exercise Set

11.3

Solve.

1. *Car trips.*   During the first part of a trip, Trudy's Honda traveled 120 mi at a certain speed. Trudy then drove another 100 mi at a speed that was 10 mph slower. If the total time of Trudy's trip was 4 hr, what was her speed on each part of the trip?

2. *Canoeing.*   During the first part of a canoe trip, Tim covered 60 km at a certain speed. He then traveled 24 km at a speed that was 4 km/h slower. If the total time for the trip was 8 hr, what was the speed on each part of the trip?

3. *Car trips.*   Petra's Plymouth travels 200 mi averaging a certain speed. If the car had gone 10 mph faster, the trip would have taken 1 hr less. Find Petra's average speed.

4. *Car trips.*   Sandi's Subaru travels 280 mi averaging a certain speed. If the car had gone 5 mph faster, the trip would have taken 1 hr less. Find Sandi's average speed.

5. *Air travel.*   A Cessna flies 600 mi at a certain speed. A Beechcraft flies 1000 mi at a speed that is 50 mph faster, but takes 1 hr longer. Find the speed of each plane.

6. *Air travel.*   A turbo-jet flies 50 mph faster than a super-prop plane. If a turbo-jet goes 2000 mi in 3 hr less time than it takes the super-prop to go 2800 mi, find the speed of each plane.

7. *Bicycling.*   Naoki bikes the 40 mi to Hillsboro averaging a certain speed. The return trip is made at a speed that is 6 mph slower. Total time for the round trip is 14 hr. Find Naoki's average speed on each part of the trip.

8. *Car speed.*   On a sales trip, Gail drives the 600 mi to Richmond averaging a certain speed. The return trip is made at an average speed that is 10 mph slower. Total time for the round trip is 22 hr. Find Gail's average speed on each part of the trip.

9. *Navigation.*   The Hudson River flows at a rate of 3 mph. A patrol boat travels 60 mi upriver and returns in a total time of 9 hr. What is the speed of the boat in still water?

10. *Navigation.*   The current in a typical Mississippi River shipping route flows at a rate of 4 mph. In order for a barge to travel 24 mi upriver and then return in a total of 5 hr, approximately how fast must the barge be able to travel in still water?

11. *Filling a pool.*   A well and a spring are filling a swimming pool. Together, they can fill the pool in 4 hr. The well, working alone, can fill the pool in 6 hr less time than the spring. How long would the spring take, working alone, to fill the pool?

12. *Filling a tank.*   Two pipes are connected to the same tank. Working together, they can fill the tank in 2 hr. The larger pipe, working alone, can fill the tank in 3 hr less time than the smaller one. How long would the smaller one take, working alone, to fill the tank?

13. *Paddleboats.*   Ellen paddles 1 mi upstream and 1 mi back in a total time of 1 hr. The speed of the river is 2 mph. Find the speed of Ellen's paddleboat in still water.

14. *Rowing.*   Dan rows 10 km upstream and 10 km back in a total time of 3 hr. The speed of the river is 5 km/h. Find Dan's speed in still water.

Solve each formula for the indicated letter. Assume that all variables represent nonnegative numbers.

15. $A = 4\pi r^2$, for r
(Surface area of a sphere of radius r)

16. $A = 6s^2$, for s
(Surface area of a cube with sides of length s)

17. $A = 2\pi r^2 + 2\pi rh$, for r
(Surface area of a right cylindrical solid with radius r and height h)

18. $F = \dfrac{Gm_1m_2}{r^2}$, for r
(Law of gravity)

19. $N = \dfrac{kQ_1Q_2}{s^2}$, for s
(Number of phone calls between two cities)

20. $A = \pi r^2$, for r
(Area of a circle)

21. $T = 2\pi\sqrt{\dfrac{l}{g}}$, for g
(A pendulum formula)

22. $a^2 + b^2 = c^2$, for b
(Pythagorean formula in two dimensions)

23. $a^2 + b^2 + c^2 = d^2$, for c
(Pythagorean formula in three dimensions)

24. $N = \dfrac{k^2 - 3k}{2}$, for k
(Number of diagonals of a polygon with k sides)

25. $s = v_0t + \dfrac{gt^2}{2}$, for t
(A motion formula)

26. $A = \pi r^2 + \pi rs$, for r
(Surface area of a cone)

27. $N = \frac{1}{2}(n^2 - n)$, for n
(Number of games if n teams play each other once)

28. $A = A_0(1 - r)^2$, for r
(A business formula)

29. $V = 3.5\sqrt{h}$, for h
(Distance to horizon from a height)

30. $W = \sqrt{\dfrac{1}{LC}}$, for L
(An electricity formula)

Aha! **31.** $at^2 + bt + c = 0$, for t
(An algebraic formula)

32. $A = P_1(1 + r)^2 + P_2(1 + r)$, for r
(Amount in an account when P_1 is invested for 2 yr and P_2 for 1 yr at interest rate r)

Solve.

33. *Falling distance.* (Use $4.9t^2 + v_0t = s$.)

   a) A bolt falls off an airplane at an altitude of 500 m. Approximately how long does it take the bolt to reach the ground?

   b) A ball is thrown downward at a speed of 30 m/sec from an altitude of 500 m. Approximately how long does it take the ball to reach the ground?

   c) Approximately how far will an object fall in 5 sec, when thrown downward at an initial velocity of 30 m/sec from a plane?

34. *Falling distance.* (Use $4.9t^2 + v_0t = s$.)

   a) A ring is dropped from a helicopter at an altitude of 75 m. Approximately how long does it take the ring to reach the ground?

   b) A coin is tossed downward with an initial velocity of 30 m/sec from an altitude of 75 m. Approximately how long does it take the coin to reach the ground?

   c) Approximately how far will an object fall in 2 sec, if thrown downward at an initial velocity of 20 m/sec from a helicopter?

35. *Bungee jumping.* Jesse is tied to one end of a 40-m elasticized (bungee) cord. The other end of the cord is tied to the middle of a bridge. If Jesse jumps off the bridge, for how long will he fall before the cord begins to stretch? (Use $4.9t^2 = s$.)

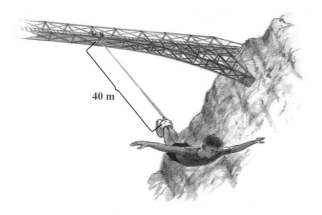

40 m

36. *Bungee jumping.* Sheila is tied to a bungee cord (see Exercise 35) and falls for 2.5 sec before her cord begins to stretch. How long is the bungee cord?

37. *Hang time.* The NBA's Steve Francis reportedly has a vertical leap of 45 in. What is his hang time? (Use $V = 48T^2$.)
Source: www.maximonline.com

38. *League schedules.* In a bowling league, each team plays each of the other teams once. If a total of 66 games is played, how many teams are in the league? (See Exercise 27.)

For Exercises 39 and 40, use $4.9t^2 + v_0t = s$.

39. *Downward speed.* An object thrown downward from a 100-m cliff travels 51.6 m in 3 sec. What was the initial velocity of the object?

40. *Downward speed.* An object thrown downward from a 200-m cliff travels 91.2 m in 4 sec. What was the initial velocity of the object?

For Exercises 41 and 42, use
$A = P_1(1 + r)^2 + P_2(1 + r)$. *(See Exercise 32.)*

41. *Compound interest.* A firm invests $3000 in a savings account for 2 yr. At the beginning of the second year, an additional $1700 is invested. If a total of $5253.70 is in the account at the end of the second year, what is the annual interest rate?

42. *Compound interest.* A business invests $10,000 in a savings account for 2 yr. At the beginning of the second year, an additional $3500 is invested. If a total of $15,569.75 is in the account at the end of the second year, what is the annual interest rate?

43. Marti is tied to a bungee cord that is twice as long as the cord tied to Pedro. Will Marti's fall take twice as long as Pedro's before their cords begin to stretch? Why or why not? (See Exercises 35 and 36.)

44. Under what circumstances would a negative value for t, time, have meaning?

SKILL MAINTENANCE

Evaluate.

45. $b^2 - 4ac$, for $a = 5$, $b = 6$, and $c = 7$ [1.8]

46. $\sqrt{b^2 - 4ac}$, for $a = 3$, $b = 4$, and $c = 5$ [10.8]

Simplify.

47. $\dfrac{x^2 + xy}{2x}$ [6.1]

48. $\dfrac{a^3 - ab^2}{ab}$ [6.1]

49. $\dfrac{3 + \sqrt{45}}{6}$ [10.3]

50. $\dfrac{2 - \sqrt{28}}{10}$ [10.3]

SYNTHESIS

51. Write a problem for a classmate to solve. Devise the problem so that **(a)** the solution is found after solving a rational equation and **(b)** the solution is "The express train travels 90 mph."

52. In what ways do the motion problems of this section (like Example 1) differ from the motion problems in Chapter 6 (see p. 423)?

53. *Biochemistry.*   The equation

$$A = 6.5 - \frac{20.4t}{t^2 + 36}$$

is used to calculate the acid level A in a person's blood t minutes after sugar is consumed. Solve for t.

54. *Special relativity.*   Einstein found that an object with initial mass m_0 and traveling velocity v has mass

$$m = \frac{m_0}{\sqrt{1 - \dfrac{v^2}{c^2}}},$$

where c is the speed of light. Solve the formula for c.

55. Find a number for which the reciprocal of 1 less than the number is the same as 1 more than the number.

56. *Purchasing.*   A discount store bought a quantity of beach towels for $250 and sold all but 15 at a profit of $3.50 per towel. With the total amount received, the manager could buy 4 more than twice as many as were bought before. Find the cost per towel.

57. *Art and aesthetics.*   For over 2000 yr, artists, sculptors, and architects have regarded the proportions of a "golden" rectangle as visually appealing. A rectangle of width w and length l is considered "golden" if

$$\frac{w}{l} = \frac{l}{w + l}.$$

Solve for l.

58. *Diagonal of a cube.*   Find a formula that expresses the length of the three-dimensional diagonal of a cube as a function of the cube's surface area.

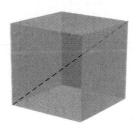

59. Solve for n:
$$mn^4 - r^2pm^3 - r^2n^2 + p = 0.$$

60. *Surface area.*   Find a formula that expresses the diameter of a right cylindrical solid as a function of its surface area and its height. (See Exercise 17.)

61. A sphere is inscribed in a cube as shown in the figure below. Express the surface area of the sphere as a function of the surface area S of the cube. (See Exercise 15.)

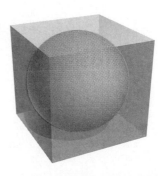

11.4 Studying Solutions of Quadratic Equations

The Discriminant • Writing Equations from Solutions

The Discriminant

It is sometimes enough to know what *type* of number a solution will be, without actually solving the equation. Suppose we want to know if $4x^2 - 5x - 2 = 0$ has rational solutions (and thus can be solved by factoring). Using the quadratic formula, we would have

$$x = \frac{-b \pm \sqrt{b^2 - 4ac}}{2a}$$

$$= \frac{-(-5) \pm \sqrt{(-5)^2 - 4 \cdot 4(-2)}}{2 \cdot 4}.$$

Note that the radicand, $(-5)^2 - 4 \cdot 4 \cdot (-2)$, determines what type of number the solutions will be. Since $(-5)^2 - 4 \cdot 4 \cdot (-2) = 25 - 16(-2) = 25 + 32 = 57$ and since 57 is not a perfect square, we know that the solutions of the equation are not rational numbers. This means that $4x^2 - 5x - 2 = 0$ *cannot* be solved by factoring.

It is $b^2 - 4ac$, known as the **discriminant**, that determines what type of number the solutions of a quadratic equation are. If *a*, *b*, and *c* are rational, then:

- When $b^2 - 4ac$ simplifies to 0, it doesn't matter if we use $+\sqrt{b^2 - 4ac}$ or $-\sqrt{b^2 - 4ac}$; we get the same solution twice. Thus, when the discriminant is 0, there is one *repeated* solution and it is rational.

  Example: $9x^2 + 6x + 1 = 0 \rightarrow b^2 - 4ac = 6^2 - 4 \cdot 9 \cdot 1 = 0.$

- When $b^2 - 4ac$ is positive, there are two different real-number solutions: If $b^2 - 4ac$ is a perfect square, these solutions are rational numbers.

  Example: $6x^2 + 5x + 1 = 0 \rightarrow b^2 - 4ac = 5^2 - 4 \cdot 6 \cdot 1 = 1.$

- When $b^2 - 4ac$ is positive but not a perfect square, there are two irrational solutions and they are conjugates of each other (see p. 469).

  Example: $2x^2 + 4x + 1 = 0 \rightarrow b^2 - 4ac = 4^2 - 4 \cdot 2 \cdot 1 = 8.$

- When the discriminant is negative, there are two imaginary-number solutions and they are complex conjugates of each other.

  Example: $3x^2 + 2x + 1 = 0 \rightarrow b^2 - 4ac = 2^2 - 4 \cdot 3 \cdot 1 = -8.$

Note that any equation for which $b^2 - 4ac$ is a perfect square can be solved by factoring.

Discriminant $b^2 - 4ac$	Nature of Solutions
0	One solution; a rational number

Positive
   Perfect square
   Not a perfect square
	Two different real-number solutions
	   Solutions are rational.
	   Solutions are irrational conjugates.

Negative	Two different imaginary-number solutions (complex conjugates)

EXAMPLE 1

For each equation, determine what type of number the solutions are and how many solutions exist.

a) $9x^2 - 12x + 4 = 0$

b) $x^2 + 5x + 8 = 0$

c) $2x^2 + 7x - 3 = 0$

Solution

a) For $9x^2 - 12x + 4 = 0$, we have

$$a = 9, \quad b = -12, \quad c = 4.$$

We substitute and compute the discriminant:

$$b^2 - 4ac = (-12)^2 - 4 \cdot 9 \cdot 4$$
$$= 144 - 144 = 0.$$

There is exactly one solution, and it is rational. This indicates that $9x^2 - 12x + 4 = 0$ can be solved by factoring.

b) For $x^2 + 5x + 8 = 0$, we have

$$a = 1, \quad b = 5, \quad c = 8.$$

We substitute and compute the discriminant:

$$b^2 - 4ac = 5^2 - 4 \cdot 1 \cdot 8$$
$$= 25 - 32 = -7.$$

Since the discriminant is negative, there are two imaginary-number solutions that are complex conjugates of each other.

c) For $2x^2 + 7x - 3 = 0$, we have

$$a = 2, \quad b = 7, \quad c = -3;$$
$$b^2 - 4ac = 7^2 - 4 \cdot 2(-3)$$
$$= 49 - (-24) = 73.$$

The discriminant is a positive number that is not a perfect square. Thus there are two irrational solutions that are conjugates of each other.

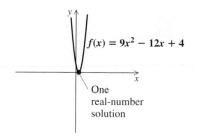

$f(x) = 9x^2 - 12x + 4$

One real-number solution

A visualization of part (a)

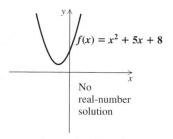

$f(x) = x^2 + 5x + 8$

No real-number solution

A visualization of part (b)

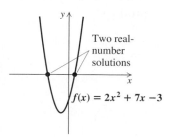

Two real-number solutions

$f(x) = 2x^2 + 7x - 3$

A visualization of part (c)

Discriminants can also be used to determine the number of real-number solutions of $ax^2 + bx + c = 0$. This can be used as an aid in graphing.

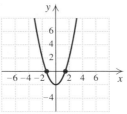

$y = ax^2 + bx + c$
$b^2 - 4ac > 0$
Two real solutions
of $ax^2 + bx + c = 0$
Two x-intercepts

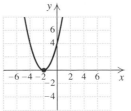

$y = ax^2 + bx + c$
$b^2 - 4ac = 0$
One real solution
of $ax^2 + bx + c = 0$
One x-intercept

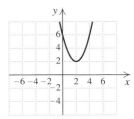

$y = ax^2 + bx + c$
$b^2 - 4ac < 0$
No real solutions
of $ax^2 + bx + c = 0$
No x-intercept

Writing Equations from Solutions

We know by the principle of zero products that $(x - 2)(x + 3) = 0$ has solutions 2 and -3. If we know the solutions of an equation, we can write an equation, using the principle in reverse.

EXAMPLE 2   Find an equation for which the given numbers are solutions.

a) 3 and $-\frac{2}{5}$

b) $2i$ and $-2i$

c) $5\sqrt{7}$ and $-5\sqrt{7}$

d) $-4, 0,$ and 1

Solution

a)
$$x = 3 \quad or \quad x = -\frac{2}{5}$$
$$x - 3 = 0 \quad or \quad x + \frac{2}{5} = 0 \qquad \text{Getting 0's on one side}$$
$$(x - 3)\left(x + \frac{2}{5}\right) = 0 \qquad \text{Using the principle of zero products (multiplying)}$$
$$x^2 + \frac{2}{5}x - 3x - 3 \cdot \frac{2}{5} = 0 \qquad \text{Multiplying}$$
$$x^2 - \frac{13}{5}x - \frac{6}{5} = 0 \qquad \text{Combining like terms}$$
$$5x^2 - 13x - 6 = 0 \qquad \text{Multiplying both sides by 5 to clear fractions}$$

Note that multiplying both sides by the LCD, 5, clears the equation of fractions. Had we preferred, we could have multiplied $x + \frac{2}{5} = 0$ by 5, thus clearing fractions *before* using the principle of zero products.

b)
$$x = 2i \quad or \quad x = -2i$$
$$x - 2i = 0 \quad or \quad x + 2i = 0 \qquad \text{Getting 0's on one side}$$
$$(x - 2i)(x + 2i) = 0 \qquad \text{Using the principle of zero products (multiplying)}$$
$$x^2 - (2i)^2 = 0 \qquad \text{Finding the product of a sum and difference}$$
$$x^2 - 4i^2 = 0$$
$$x^2 + 4 = 0 \qquad i^2 = -1$$

c) $\qquad x = 5\sqrt{7} \quad$ *or* $\qquad x = -5\sqrt{7}$

$x - 5\sqrt{7} = 0 \qquad$ *or* $\quad x + 5\sqrt{7} = 0 \qquad$ Getting 0's on one side

$\left(x - 5\sqrt{7}\right)\left(x + 5\sqrt{7}\right) = 0 \qquad$ Using the principle of zero products

$x^2 - \left(5\sqrt{7}\right)^2 = 0 \qquad$ Finding the product of a sum and difference

$x^2 - 25 \cdot 7 = 0$

$x^2 - 175 = 0$

d) $\qquad x = -4 \quad$ *or* $\quad x = 0 \quad$ *or* $\qquad x = 1$

$x + 4 = 0 \qquad$ *or* $\quad x = 0 \quad$ *or* $\quad x - 1 = 0 \qquad$ Getting 0's on one side

$(x + 4)x(x - 1) = 0 \qquad$ Using the principle of zero products

$x(x^2 + 3x - 4) = 0 \qquad$ Multiplying

$x^3 + 3x^2 - 4x = 0$

To check any of these equations, we can simply substitute one or more of the given solutions. For example, in Example 2(d) above,

$$(-4)^3 + 3(-4)^2 - 4(-4) = -64 + 3 \cdot 16 + 16$$
$$= -64 + 48 + 16 = 0.$$

The other checks are left to the student.

Exercise Set

11.4

FOR EXTRA HELP

 Student's Solutions Manual   Digital Video Tutor CD 6 Videotape 11   AW Math Tutor Center   MathXL Tutorials on CD   *Math* XL MathXL   *MyMathLab* MyMathLab

⤸ *Concept Reinforcement* *Complete each of the following.*

1. In the quadratic formula, the expression $b^2 - 4ac$ is called the _____.

2. When $b^2 - 4ac$ is 0, there is/are _____ solution(s).

3. When $b^2 - 4ac$ is positive, there is/are _____ solution(s).

4. When $b^2 - 4ac$ is negative, there is/are _____ solution(s).

5. When $b^2 - 4ac$ is a perfect square, the answers are _____ numbers.

6. When $b^2 - 4ac$ is negative, the answer(s) is/are _____ numbers.

For each equation, determine what type of number the solutions are and how many solutions exist.

7. $x^2 - 7x + 5 = 0$

8. $x^2 - 5x + 3 = 0$

9. $x^2 + 3 = 0$

10. $x^2 + 5 = 0$

11. $x^2 - 5 = 0$

12. $x^2 - 3 = 0$

13. $4x^2 + 8x - 5 = 0$

14. $4x^2 - 12x + 9 = 0$

15. $x^2 + 4x + 6 = 0$

16. $x^2 - 2x + 4 = 0$

17. $9t^2 - 48t + 64 = 0$

18. $6t^2 - 19t - 20 = 0$

19. $10x^2 - x - 2 = 0$

20. $6x^2 + 5x - 4 = 0$

Aha! **21.** $9t^2 - 3t = 0$

22. $4m^2 + 7m = 0$

23. $x^2 + 4x = 8$

24. $x^2 + 5x = 9$

25. $2a^2 - 3a = -5$

26. $3a^2 + 5 = 7a$

27. $y^2 + \frac{9}{4} = 4y$

28. $x^2 = \frac{1}{2}x - \frac{3}{5}$

Write a quadratic equation having the given numbers as solutions.

29. $-7, 3$

30. $-6, 4$

31. 3, only solution
(*Hint*: It must be a repeated solution.)

32. -5, only solution

33. $-1, -3$

34. $-2, -5$

35. $5, \frac{3}{4}$

36. $4, \frac{2}{3}$

37. $-\frac{1}{4}, -\frac{1}{2}$

38. $\frac{1}{2}, \frac{1}{3}$

39. $2.4, -0.4$

40. $-0.6, 1.4$

41. $-\sqrt{3}, \sqrt{3}$

42. $-\sqrt{7}, \sqrt{7}$

43. $2\sqrt{5}, -2\sqrt{5}$

44. $3\sqrt{2}, -3\sqrt{2}$

45. $4i, -4i$

46. $3i, -3i$

47. $2 - 7i, 2 + 7i$

48. $5 - 2i, 5 + 2i$

49. $3 - \sqrt{14}, 3 + \sqrt{14}$

50. $2 - \sqrt{10}, 2 + \sqrt{10}$

51. $1 - \dfrac{\sqrt{21}}{3}, 1 + \dfrac{\sqrt{21}}{3}$

52. $\dfrac{5}{4} - \dfrac{\sqrt{33}}{4}, \dfrac{5}{4} + \dfrac{\sqrt{33}}{4}$

Write a third-degree equation having the given numbers as solutions.

53. $-2, 1, 5$

54. $-5, 0, 2$

55. $-1, 0, 3$

56. $-2, 2, 3$

57. Under what condition(s) is the discriminant *not* the fastest way to determine how many and what type of solutions exist?

58. Describe a procedure that could be used to write an equation having the first 7 natural numbers as solutions.

SKILL MAINTENANCE

Simplify. [4.1]

59. $(3a^2)^4$

60. $(4x^3)^2$

Find the x-intercepts of the graph of f. [11.1]

61. $f(x) = x^2 - 7x - 8$

62. $f(x) = x^2 - 6x + 8$

63. During a one-hour television show, there were 12 commercials. Some of the commercials were 30 sec long and the others were 60 sec long. The amount of time for 30-sec commercials was 6 min less than the total number of minutes of commercial time during the show. How many 30-sec commercials were used? [8.3]

64. Graph: $y = -\frac{3}{7}x + 4$. [7.3]

SYNTHESIS

65. If we assume that a quadratic equation has integers for coefficients, will the product of the solutions always be a real number? Why or why not?

66. Can a fourth-degree equation have exactly three irrational solutions? Why or why not?

67. The graph of an equation of the form
$$y = ax^2 + bx + c$$
is a curve similar to the one shown below. Determine *a*, *b*, and *c* from the information given.

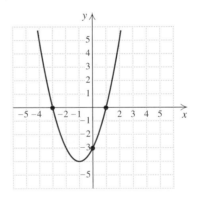

68. Show that the product of the solutions of $ax^2 + bx + c = 0$ is c/a.

For each equation under the given condition, (**a**) *find k and* (**b**) *find the other solution.*

69. $kx^2 - 2x + k = 0$; one solution is -3

70. $x^2 - kx + 2 = 0$; one solution is $1 + i$

71. $x^2 - (6 + 3i)x + k = 0$; one solution is 3

72. Show that the sum of the solutions of $ax^2 + bx + c = 0$ is $-b/a$.

73. Show that whenever there is just one solution of $ax^2 + bx + c = 0$, that solution is of the form $-b/2a$.

74. Find h and k, where $3x^2 - hx + 4k = 0$, the sum of the solutions is -12, and the product of the solutions is 20. (*Hint*: See Exercises 68 and 72.)

75. Suppose that $f(x) = ax^2 + bx + c$, with $f(-3) = 0$, $f\left(\frac{1}{2}\right) = 0$, and $f(0) = -12$. Find a, b, and c.

76. Find an equation for which $2 - \sqrt{3}$, $2 + \sqrt{3}$, $5 - 2i$, and $5 + 2i$ are solutions.

Aha! **77.** Find an equation with integer coefficients for which $1 - \sqrt{5}$ and $3 + 2i$ are two of the solutions.

 78. A discriminant that is a perfect square indicates that factoring can be used to solve the quadratic equation. Why?

 79. While solving a quadratic equation of the form $ax^2 + bx + c = 0$ with a graphing calculator, Shawn-Marie gets the following screen. How could the sign of the discriminant help her check the graph?

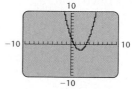

11.5 Equations Reducible to Quadratic

Recognizing Equations in Quadratic Form   •   Radical and Rational Equations

Recognizing Equations in Quadratic Form

Certain equations that are not really quadratic can be thought of in such a way that they can be solved as quadratic. For example, because the square of x^2 is x^4, the equation $x^4 - 9x^2 + 8 = 0$ is said to be "quadratic in x^2":

$$x^4 - 9x^2 + 8 = 0$$
$$\downarrow \quad\quad \downarrow \quad\quad \downarrow \quad \downarrow$$
$$(x^2)^2 - 9(x^2) + 8 = 0 \qquad \text{Thinking of } x^4 \text{ as } (x^2)^2$$
$$\downarrow \quad\quad \downarrow \quad\quad \downarrow \quad \downarrow$$
$$u^2 - 9u + 8 = 0. \qquad \text{To make this clearer, write } u \text{ instead of } x^2.$$

The equation $u^2 - 9u + 8 = 0$ can be solved by factoring or by the quadratic formula. Then, remembering that $u = x^2$, we can solve for x. Equations that can be solved like this are *reducible to quadratic*, or *in quadratic form*.

EXAMPLE 1   Solve: $x^4 - 9x^2 + 8 = 0$.

Solution   Let $u = x^2$. Then we solve by substituting u for x^2 and u^2 for x^4:

$$u^2 - 9u + 8 = 0$$
$$(u - 8)(u - 1) = 0 \qquad\qquad \text{Factoring}$$
$$u - 8 = 0 \quad or \quad u - 1 = 0 \qquad \text{Principle of zero products}$$
$$u = 8 \quad or \qquad u = 1.$$

Student Notes _____

To recognize an equation in quadratic form, note that there will be two terms with variables. The exponent of the first term is twice the exponent of the second term. It is the variable expression in the *second* term that is written as u.

We replace u with x^2 and solve these equations:

$$x^2 = 8 \quad \text{or} \quad x^2 = 1$$
$$x = \pm\sqrt{8} \quad \text{or} \quad x = \pm 1$$
$$x = \pm 2\sqrt{2} \quad \text{or} \quad x = \pm 1.$$

To check, note that for both $x = 2\sqrt{2}$ and $-2\sqrt{2}$, we have $x^2 = 8$ and $x^4 = 64$. Similarly, for both $x = 1$ and -1, we have $x^2 = 1$ and $x^4 = 1$. Thus instead of making four checks, we need make only two.

Check:

For $\pm 2\sqrt{2}$:

$$\begin{array}{c|c} x^4 - 9x^2 + 8 = 0 & \\ \hline (\pm 2\sqrt{2})^4 - 9(\pm 2\sqrt{2})^2 + 8 & 0 \\ 64 - 9 \cdot 8 + 8 & \\ & 0 \overset{?}{=} 0 \quad \text{TRUE} \end{array}$$

For ± 1:

$$\begin{array}{c|c} x^4 - 9x^2 + 8 = 0 & \\ \hline (\pm 1)^4 - 9(\pm 1)^2 + 8 & 0 \\ 1 - 9 + 8 & \\ & 0 \overset{?}{=} 0 \quad \text{TRUE} \end{array}$$

The solutions are $1, -1, 2\sqrt{2}$, and $-2\sqrt{2}$.

> *Caution!* A common error on problems like Example 1 is to solve for u but forget to solve for x. Remember to solve for the *original* variable!

Example 1 can be solved directly by factoring:

$$x^4 - 9x^2 + 8 = 0$$
$$(x^2 - 1)(x^2 - 8) = 0$$
$$x^2 - 1 = 0 \quad \text{or} \quad x^2 - 8 = 0$$
$$x^2 = 1 \quad \text{or} \quad x^2 = 8$$
$$x = \pm 1 \quad \text{or} \quad x = \pm 2\sqrt{2}.$$

There is nothing wrong with this approach. However, in the examples that follow, you will note that it becomes increasingly difficult to solve the equation without first making a substitution.

Radical and Rational Equations

Sometimes rational equations, radical equations, or equations containing exponents that are fractions are reducible to quadratic. It is especially important that answers to these equations be checked in the original equation.

EXAMPLE 2   Solve: $x - 3\sqrt{x} - 4 = 0$.

Solution   This radical equation could be solved using the method discussed in Section 10.6. However, if we note that the square of $\sqrt{x}$ is x, we can regard the equation as "quadratic in $\sqrt{x}$."

We let $u = \sqrt{x}$ and consequently $u^2 = x$:

$$x - 3\sqrt{x} - 4 = 0$$
$$u^2 - 3u - 4 = 0 \qquad \text{Substituting}$$
$$(u - 4)(u + 1) = 0$$
$$u = 4 \quad or \quad u = -1. \qquad \text{Using the principle of zero products}$$

Next, we replace u with $\sqrt{x}$ and solve these equations:

$$\sqrt{x} = 4 \quad or \quad \sqrt{x} = -1.$$

Squaring gives us $x = 16$ or $x = 1$ and also makes checking essential.

Check: For 16:   For 1:

$$\begin{array}{c|c} x - 3\sqrt{x} - 4 = 0 & \\ \hline 16 - 3\sqrt{16} - 4 & 0 \\ 16 - 3 \cdot 4 - 4 & \\ & 0 \overset{?}{=} 0 \quad \text{TRUE} \end{array} \qquad \begin{array}{c|c} x - 3\sqrt{x} - 4 = 0 & \\ \hline 1 - 3\sqrt{1} - 4 & 0 \\ 1 - 3 \cdot 1 - 4 & \\ & -6 \overset{?}{=} 0 \quad \text{FALSE} \end{array}$$

The number 16 checks, but 1 does not. Had we noticed that $\sqrt{x} = -1$ has no solution (since principal roots are never negative), we could have solved only the equation $\sqrt{x} = 4$. The solution is 16.

EXAMPLE 3

technology connection

Check Example 3 with a graphing calculator. Use the ZERO, ROOT, or INTERSECT option, if possible.

Find the *x*-intercepts of the graph of $f(x) = (x^2 - 1)^2 - (x^2 - 1) - 2$.

Solution   The *x*-intercepts occur where $f(x) = 0$ so we must have

$$(x^2 - 1)^2 - (x^2 - 1) - 2 = 0. \qquad \text{Setting } f(x) \text{ equal to 0}$$

This equation is quadratic in $x^2 - 1$, so we let $u = x^2 - 1$ and $u^2 = (x^2 - 1)^2$:

$$u^2 - u - 2 = 0 \qquad \begin{array}{l} \text{Substituting in} \\ (x^2 - 1)^2 - (x^2 - 1) - 2 = 0 \end{array}$$
$$(u - 2)(u + 1) = 0$$
$$u = 2 \quad or \quad u = -1. \qquad \text{Using the principle of zero products}$$

Next, we replace u with $x^2 - 1$ and solve these equations:

$$x^2 - 1 = 2 \qquad or \quad x^2 - 1 = -1$$
$$x^2 = 3 \qquad or \qquad x^2 = 0 \qquad \text{Adding 1 to both sides}$$
$$x = \pm\sqrt{3} \quad or \qquad x = 0. \qquad \begin{array}{l} \text{Using the principle of} \\ \text{square roots} \end{array}$$

The *x*-intercepts occur at $\left(-\sqrt{3}, 0\right)$, $(0, 0)$, and $\left(\sqrt{3}, 0\right)$.

Sometimes great care must be taken in deciding what substitution to make.

EXAMPLE 4   Solve: $m^{-2} - 6m^{-1} + 4 = 0$.

Solution   Note that the square of m^{-1} is $(m^{-1})^2$, or m^{-2}. This allows us to regard the equation as quadratic in m^{-1}.

We let $u = m^{-1}$ and $u^2 = m^{-2}$:

$$u^2 - 6u + 4 = 0 \qquad \text{Substituting}$$

$$u = \frac{-(-6) \pm \sqrt{(-6)^2 - 4 \cdot 1 \cdot 4}}{2 \cdot 1} \qquad \begin{array}{l}\text{Using the quadratic}\\\text{formula}\end{array}$$

$$\left.\begin{array}{l} u = \dfrac{6 \pm \sqrt{20}}{2} = \dfrac{2 \cdot 3 \pm 2\sqrt{5}}{2} \\[2mm] u = 3 \pm \sqrt{5}. \end{array}\right\} \qquad \text{Simplifying}$$

Next, we replace u with m^{-1} and solve:

$$m^{-1} = 3 \pm \sqrt{5}$$

$$\frac{1}{m} = 3 \pm \sqrt{5} \qquad \text{Recall that } m^{-1} = \frac{1}{m}.$$

$$1 = m(3 \pm \sqrt{5}) \qquad \text{Multiplying both sides by } m$$

$$\frac{1}{3 \pm \sqrt{5}} = m. \qquad \text{Dividing both sides by } 3 \pm \sqrt{5}$$

We can check both solutions as follows.

Check:

For $1/(3 - \sqrt{5})$:

$$\begin{array}{c|c} m^{-2} - 6m^{-1} + 4 = 0 & \\ \hline \left(\dfrac{1}{3 - \sqrt{5}}\right)^{-2} - 6\left(\dfrac{1}{3 - \sqrt{5}}\right)^{-1} + 4 & 0 \\ (3 - \sqrt{5})^2 - 6(3 - \sqrt{5}) + 4 & \\ 9 - 6\sqrt{5} + 5 - 18 + 6\sqrt{5} + 4 & \\ & 0 \overset{?}{=} 0 \quad \text{TRUE} \end{array}$$

For $1/(3 + \sqrt{5})$:

$$\begin{array}{c|c} m^{-2} - 6m^{-1} + 4 = 0 & \\ \hline \left(\dfrac{1}{3 + \sqrt{5}}\right)^{-2} - 6\left(\dfrac{1}{3 + \sqrt{5}}\right)^{-1} + 4 & 0 \\ (3 + \sqrt{5})^2 - 6(3 + \sqrt{5}) + 4 & \\ 9 + 6\sqrt{5} + 5 - 18 - 6\sqrt{5} + 4 & \\ & 0 \overset{?}{=} 0 \quad \text{TRUE} \end{array}$$

Both numbers check. The solutions are $1/(3 - \sqrt{5})$ and $1/(3 + \sqrt{5})$, or approximately 1.309016994 and 0.1909830056.

EXAMPLE 5   Solve: $t^{2/5} - t^{1/5} - 2 = 0$.

Solution   Note that the square of $t^{1/5}$ is $(t^{1/5})^2$, or $t^{2/5}$. The equation is therefore quadratic in $t^{1/5}$, so we let $u = t^{1/5}$ and $u^2 = t^{2/5}$:

$$u^2 - u - 2 = 0 \qquad \text{Substituting}$$

$$(u - 2)(u + 1) = 0$$

$$u = 2 \quad or \quad u = -1. \qquad \text{Using the principle of zero products}$$

Now we replace u with $t^{1/5}$ and solve:

$$t^{1/5} = 2 \quad or \quad t^{1/5} = -1$$

$$t = 32 \quad or \quad t = -1. \qquad \begin{array}{l}\text{Principle of powers; raising to the}\\\text{5th power}\end{array}$$

Check:

For 32:

$$t^{2/5} - t^{1/5} - 2 = 0$$

$32^{2/5} - 32^{1/5} - 2$	0
$(32^{1/5})^2 - 32^{1/5} - 2$	
$2^2 - 2 - 2$	

$$0 \overset{?}{=} 0 \quad \text{TRUE}$$

For -1:

$$t^{2/5} - t^{1/5} - 2 = 0$$

$(-1)^{2/5} - (-1)^{1/5} - 2$	0
$[(-1)^{1/5}]^2 - (-1)^{1/5} - 2$	
$(-1)^2 - (-1) - 2$	

$$0 \overset{?}{=} 0 \quad \text{TRUE}$$

Both numbers check. The solutions are 32 and -1.

The following tips may prove useful.

To Solve an Equation That Is Reducible to Quadratic

1. The equation is quadratic in form if the variable factor in one term is the square of the variable factor in the other variable term.
2. Write down any substitutions that you are making.
3. Whenever you make a substitution, remember to solve for the variable that is used in the original equation.
4. Check possible answers in the original equation.

Exercise Set

11.5

 Concept Reinforcement   In each of Exercises 1–8, match the equation with an appropriate substitution from the column on the right that could be used to reduce the equation to quadratic form.

1. ___ $4x^6 - 2x^3 + 1 = 0$

2. ___ $3x^4 + 4x^2 - 7 = 0$

3. ___ $5x^8 + 2x^4 - 3 = 0$

4. ___ $2x^{2/3} - 5x^{1/3} + 4 = 0$

5. ___ $3x^{4/3} + 4x^{2/3} - 7 = 0$

6. ___ $2x^{-2/3} + x^{-1/3} + 6 = 0$

7. ___ $4x^{-4/3} - 2x^{-2/3} + 3 = 0$

8. ___ $3x^{-4} + 4x^{-2} - 2 = 0$

a) $u = x^{-1/3}$

b) $u = x^{1/3}$

c) $u = x^{-2}$

d) $u = x^2$

e) $u = x^{-2/3}$

f) $u = x^3$

g) $u = x^{2/3}$

h) $u = x^4$

Solve.

9. $x^4 - 5x^2 + 4 = 0$

10. $x^4 - 10x^2 + 9 = 0$

11. $x^4 - 9x^2 + 20 = 0$

12. $x^4 - 12x^2 + 27 = 0$

13. $4t^4 - 19t^2 + 12 = 0$

14. $9t^4 - 14t^2 + 5 = 0$

15. $r - 2\sqrt{r} - 6 = 0$

16. $s - 4\sqrt{s} - 1 = 0$

17. $(x^2 - 7)^2 - 3(x^2 - 7) + 2 = 0$

18. $(x^2 - 1)^2 - 5(x^2 - 1) + 6 = 0$

19. $(1 + \sqrt{x})^2 + 5(1 + \sqrt{x}) + 6 = 0$

20. $(3 + \sqrt{x})^2 + 3(3 + \sqrt{x}) - 10 = 0$

21. $x^{-2} - x^{-1} - 6 = 0$

22. $2x^{-2} - x^{-1} - 1 = 0$

23. $4x^{-2} + x^{-1} - 5 = 0$

24. $m^{-2} + 9m^{-1} - 10 = 0$

25. $t^{2/3} + t^{1/3} - 6 = 0$

26. $w^{2/3} - 2w^{1/3} - 8 = 0$

27. $y^{1/3} - y^{1/6} - 6 = 0$

28. $t^{1/2} + 3t^{1/4} + 2 = 0$

29. $t^{1/3} + 2t^{1/6} = 3$

30. $m^{1/2} + 6 = 5m^{1/4}$

31. $(3 - \sqrt{x})^2 - 10(3 - \sqrt{x}) + 23 = 0$

32. $(5 + \sqrt{x})^2 - 12(5 + \sqrt{x}) + 33 = 0$

33. $16\left(\dfrac{x-1}{x-8}\right)^2 + 8\left(\dfrac{x-1}{x-8}\right) + 1 = 0$

34. $9\left(\dfrac{x+2}{x+3}\right)^2 - 6\left(\dfrac{x+2}{x+3}\right) + 1 = 0$

Find all x-intercepts of the given function f. If none exist, state this.

35. $f(x) = 5x + 13\sqrt{x} - 6$

36. $f(x) = 3x + 10\sqrt{x} - 8$

37. $f(x) = (x^2 - 3x)^2 - 10(x^2 - 3x) + 24$

38. $f(x) = (x^2 - 6x)^2 - 2(x^2 - 6x) - 35$

39. $f(x) = x^{2/5} + x^{1/5} - 6$

40. $f(x) = x^{1/2} - x^{1/4} - 6$

Aha! 41. $f(x) = \left(\dfrac{x^2+2}{x}\right)^4 + 7\left(\dfrac{x^2+2}{x}\right)^2 + 5$

42. $f(x) = \left(\dfrac{x^2+1}{x}\right)^4 + 4\left(\dfrac{x^2+1}{x}\right)^2 + 12$

43. To solve $25x^6 - 10x^3 + 1 = 0$, Don lets $u = 5x^3$ and Robin lets $u = x^3$. Can they both be correct? Why or why not?

44. Can the examples and exercises of this section be understood without knowing the rules for exponents? Why or why not?

SKILL MAINTENANCE

Graph. [7.3]

45. $f(x) = \frac{3}{2}x$

46. $f(x) = -\frac{2}{3}x$

47. $f(x) = \dfrac{2}{x}$

48. $f(x) = \dfrac{3}{x}$

49. Hiker's Mix is 18% peanuts and Trail Snax is 45% peanuts. How much of each should be mixed together in order to get 12 lb of a mixture that is 36% peanuts? [8.3]

50. If $g(x) = x^2 - x$, find $g(a + 1)$. [7.1]

SYNTHESIS

51. Describe a procedure that could be used to solve any equation of the form $ax^4 + bx^2 + c = 0$.

52. Describe a procedure that could be used to write an equation that is quadratic in $3x^2 - 1$. Then explain how the procedure could be adjusted to write equations that are quadratic in $3x^2 - 1$ and have no real-number solution.

Solve.

53. $5x^4 - 7x^2 + 1 = 0$

54. $3x^4 + 5x^2 - 1 = 0$

55. $(x^2 - 4x - 2)^2 - 13(x^2 - 4x - 2) + 30 = 0$

56. $(x^2 - 5x - 1)^2 - 18(x^2 - 5x - 1) + 65 = 0$

57. $\dfrac{x}{x-1} - 6\sqrt{\dfrac{x}{x-1}} - 40 = 0$

58. $\left(\sqrt{\dfrac{x}{x-3}}\right)^2 - 24 = 10\sqrt{\dfrac{x}{x-3}}$

59. $a^5(a^2 - 25) + 13a^3(25 - a^2) + 36a(a^2 - 25) = 0$

60. $a^3 - 26a^{3/2} - 27 = 0$

61. $x^6 - 28x^3 + 27 = 0$

62. $x^6 + 7x^3 - 8 = 0$

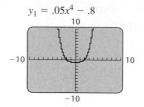 **63.** Use a graphing calculator to check your answers to Exercises 9, 11, 37, and 55.

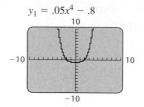 **64.** Use a graphing calculator to solve
$$x^4 - x^3 - 13x^2 + x + 12 = 0.$$

65. While trying to solve $0.05x^4 - 0.8 = 0$ with a graphing calculator, Murray gets the following screen. Can Murray solve this equation with a graphing calculator? Why or why not?

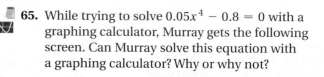

$$y_1 = .05x^4 - .8$$

11.6 Quadratic Functions and Their Graphs

The Graph of $f(x) = ax^2$ • The Graph of $f(x) = a(x - h)^2$ •
The Graph of $f(x) = a(x - h)^2 + k$

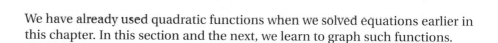

We have already used quadratic functions when we solved equations earlier in this chapter. In this section and the next, we learn to graph such functions.

The Graph of $f(x) = ax^2$

The most basic quadratic function is $f(x) = x^2$.

EXAMPLE 1   Graph: $f(x) = x^2$.

*Study Skills*_____

A Quick Review

Take the time, later the same day if possible, to briefly review the material from the day's class. Highlight important notes, fill in any sketchy details, and mark any areas you know will require extra study.

Solution   We choose some values for x and compute $f(x)$ for each. Then we plot the ordered pairs and connect them with a smooth curve.

x	$f(x) = x^2$	$(x, f(x))$
-3	9	$(-3, 9)$
-2	4	$(-2, 4)$
-1	1	$(-1, 1)$
0	0	$(0, 0)$
1	1	$(1, 1)$
2	4	$(2, 4)$
3	9	$(3, 9)$

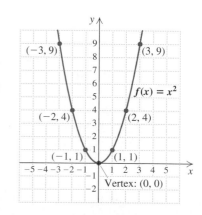

Student Notes

By paying attention to the symmetry of each parabola and the location of the vertex, you save yourself considerable work. Note too that if the x^2-coefficient is a, the x-values 1 unit to the right or left of the vertex are paired with the y-value a units above the vertex. Thus the graph of $y = \frac{3}{2}x^2$ includes the points $\left(-1, \frac{3}{2}\right)$ and $\left(1, \frac{3}{2}\right)$.

technology connection

To explore the effect of a on the graph of $y = ax^2$, let $y_1 = x^2$, $y_2 = 3x^2$, and $y_3 = \frac{1}{3}x^2$. Graph the equations and use TRACE to see how the y-values compare, using ⌃ or ⌄ to hop the cursor from one curve to the next.

On many graphing calculators, the APPS key will access the Transfrm application. If you run that application and let $y_1 = Ax^2$, the graph becomes interactive and allows for A to be changed while viewing the graph. Selecting the SETTINGS option, after pressing WINDOW, permits us to adjust the step by which A can be changed.

1. Compare the graphs of $y_1 = \frac{1}{5}x^2$, $y_2 = x^2$, $y_3 = \frac{5}{2}x^2$, $y_4 = -\frac{1}{5}x^2$, $y_5 = -x^2$, and $y_6 = -\frac{5}{2}x^2$.
2. Describe the effect that A has on each graph.

All quadratic functions have graphs similar to the one in Example 1. Such curves are called *parabolas*. They are U-shaped and symmetric with respect to a vertical line known as the parabola's *axis of symmetry*. For the graph of $f(x) = x^2$, the y-axis (the vertical line $x = 0$) is the axis of symmetry. Were the paper folded on this line, the two halves of the curve would match. The point $(0, 0)$ is known as the *vertex* of this parabola.

By plotting points, we can compare the graphs of $g(x) = \frac{1}{2}x^2$ and $h(x) = 2x^2$ with the graph of $f(x) = x^2$.

x	$g(x) = \frac{1}{2}x^2$
-3	$\frac{9}{2}$
-2	2
-1	$\frac{1}{2}$
0	0
1	$\frac{1}{2}$
2	2
3	$\frac{9}{2}$

x	$h(x) = 2x^2$
-3	18
-2	8
-1	2
0	0
1	2
2	8
3	18

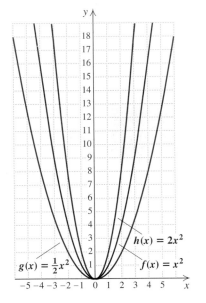

Note that the graph of $g(x) = \frac{1}{2}x^2$ is "wider" than the graph of $f(x) = x^2$, and the graph of $h(x) = 2x^2$ is "narrower." The vertex and the axis of symmetry, however, remain $(0, 0)$ and the line $x = 0$, respectively.

When we consider the graph of $k(x) = -\frac{1}{2}x^2$, we see that the parabola is the same shape as the graph of $g(x) = \frac{1}{2}x^2$, but opens downward. We say that the graphs of k and g are *reflections* of each other across the x-axis.

x	$k(x) = -\frac{1}{2}x^2$
-3	$-\frac{9}{2}$
-2	-2
-1	$-\frac{1}{2}$
0	0
1	$-\frac{1}{2}$
2	-2
3	$-\frac{9}{2}$

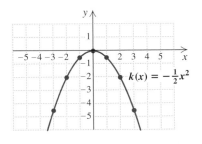

> *Graphing $f(x) = ax^2$*
>
> The graph of $f(x) = ax^2$ is a parabola with $x = 0$ as its axis of symmetry. Its vertex is the origin.
>
> For $a > 0$, the parabola opens upward. For $a < 0$, the parabola opens downward.
>
> If $|a|$ is greater than 1, the parabola is narrower than $y = x^2$.
>
> If $|a|$ is between 0 and 1, the parabola is wider than $y = x^2$.

The Graph of $f(x) = a(x - h)^2$

We *could* next consider graphs of

$$f(x) = ax^2 + bx + c,$$

where b and c are not both 0. In effect, we will do that, but in a disguised form. It turns out to be convenient to first graph $f(x) = a(x - h)^2$, where h is some constant. This allows us to observe similarities to the graphs drawn above.

EXAMPLE 2   Graph: $f(x) = (x - 3)^2$.

Solution   We choose some values for x and compute $f(x)$. It is important to note that when an input here is 3 more than an input for Example 1, the outputs match. We plot the points and draw the curve.

x	$f(x) = (x - 3)^2$	
-1	16	
0	9	
1	4	
2	1	
3	0	← Vertex
4	1	
5	4	
6	9	

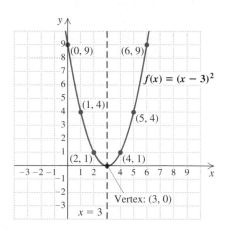

Note that $f(x)$ is smallest when $x - 3$ is 0, that is, for $x = 3$. Thus the line $x = 3$ is now the axis of symmetry and the point $(3, 0)$ is the vertex. Had we recognized earlier that $x = 3$ is the axis of symmetry, we could have computed some values on one side, such as $(4, 1)$, $(5, 4)$, and $(6, 9)$, and then used symmetry to get their mirror images $(2, 1)$, $(1, 4)$, and $(0, 9)$ without further computation.

EXAMPLE 3   Graph: $g(x) = -2(x + 4)^2$.

Solution   We choose some values for x and compute $g(x)$. Note that $g(x)$ is greatest when $x + 4$ is 0, that is, for $x = -4$. Thus the line given by $x = -4$ is the axis of symmetry and the point $(-4, 0)$ is the vertex. We plot some points and draw the curve.

To explore the effect of h on the graph of $f(x) = a(x - h)^2$, let $y_1 = 7x^2$ and $y_2 = 7(x - 1)^2$. Graph both y_1 and y_2 and compare y-values, beginning at $x = 1$ and increasing x by one unit at a time. The G-T or HORIZ **MODE** can be used to view a split screen showing both the graph and a table.

Next, let $y_3 = 7(x - 2)^2$ and compare its graph and y-values with those of y_1 and y_2. Then let $y_4 = 7(x + 1)^2$ and $y_5 = 7(x + 2)^2$.

1. Compare graphs and y-values and describe the effect of h on the graph of $f(x) = a(x - h)^2$.
2. If the Transfrm application is available, let $y_1 = A(x - B)^2$ and describe the effect that A and B have on each graph.

x	$g(x) = -2(x + 4)^2$
-6	-8
-5	-2
-4	0
-3	-2
-2	-8

$\leftarrow$ Vertex

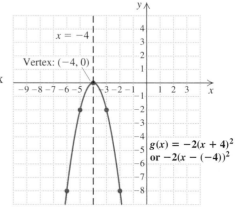

In Example 2, the graph of $f(x) = (x - 3)^2$ looks just like the graph of $y = x^2$, except that it is moved, or *translated*, 3 units to the right. In Example 3, the graph of $g(x) = -2(x + 4)^2$ looks like the graph of $y = -2x^2$, except that it is shifted 4 units to the left. These results are generalized as follows.

Graphing $f(x) = a(x - h)^2$

The graph of $f(x) = a(x - h)^2$ has the same shape as the graph of $y = ax^2$.

If h is positive, the graph of $y = ax^2$ is shifted h units to the right.

If h is negative, the graph of $y = ax^2$ is shifted $|h|$ units to the left.

The vertex is $(h, 0)$ and the axis of symmetry is $x = h$.

The Graph of $f(x) = a(x - h)^2 + k$

Given a graph of $f(x) = a(x - h)^2$, what happens if we add a constant k? Suppose that we add 2. This increases $f(x)$ by 2, so the curve is moved up. If k is negative, the curve is moved down. The axis of symmetry for the parabola remains $x = h$, but the vertex will be at (h, k), or, equivalently, $(h, f(h))$.

Note that if a parabola opens upward $(a > 0)$, the function value, or y-value, at the vertex is a least, or *minimum*, value. That is, it is less than the y-value at any other point on the graph. If the parabola opens downward $(a < 0)$, the function value at the vertex is a greatest, or *maximum*, value.

technology connection

To study the effect of k on the graph of $f(x) = a(x - h)^2 + k$, let $y_1 = 7(x - 1)^2$ and $y_2 = 7(x - 1)^2 + 2$. Graph both y_1 and y_2 in the window $[-5, 5, -5, 5]$ and use TRACE or a TABLE to compare the y-values for any given x-value.

1. Let $y_3 = 7(x - 1)^2 - 4$ and compare its graph and y-values with those of y_1 and y_2.

2. Try other values of k, including decimals and fractions. Describe the effect of k on the graph of $f(x) = a(x - h)^2$.

3. If the Transfrm application is available, let $y_1 = A(x - B)^2 + C$ and describe the effect that A, B, and C have on each graph.

Graphs of $f(x) = a(x - h)^2 + k$

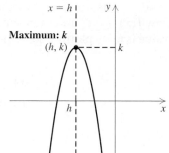

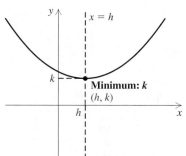

Graphing $f(x) = a(x - h)^2 + k$

The graph of $f(x) = a(x - h)^2 + k$ has the same shape as the graph of $y = a(x - h)^2$.

If k is positive, the graph of $y = a(x - h)^2$ is shifted k units up.

If k is negative, the graph of $y = a(x - h)^2$ is shifted $|k|$ units down.

The vertex is (h, k), and the axis of symmetry is $x = h$.

For $a > 0$, k is the minimum function value. For $a < 0$, k is the maximum function value.

EXAMPLE 4   Graph $g(x) = (x - 3)^2 - 5$, and find the minimum function value.

Solution   The graph will look like that of $f(x) = (x - 3)^2$ (see Example 2) but shifted 5 units down. You can confirm this by plotting some points. For instance, $g(4) = (4 - 3)^2 - 5 = -4$, whereas in Example 2, $f(4) = (4 - 3)^2 = 1$. The vertex is now $(3, -5)$, and the minimum function value is -5.

x	$g(x) = (x - 3)^2 - 5$
0	4
1	-1
2	-4
3	-5 ←—Vertex
4	-4
5	-1
6	4

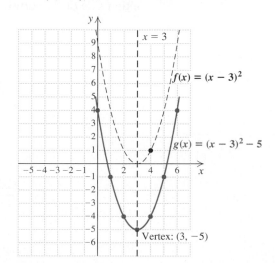

EXAMPLE 5   Graph $h(x) = \frac{1}{2}(x - 3)^2 + 6$, and find the minimum function value.

Solution   The graph looks just like that of $f(x) = \frac{1}{2}x^2$ but moved 3 units to the right and 6 units up. The vertex is (3, 6), and the axis of symmetry is $x = 3$. We draw $f(x) = \frac{1}{2}x^2$ and then shift the curve over and up. The minimum function value is 6. By plotting some points, we have a check.

x	$h(x) = \frac{1}{2}(x - 3)^2 + 6$
0	$10\frac{1}{2}$
1	8
3	6
5	8
6	$10\frac{1}{2}$

←—Vertex

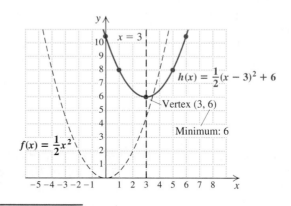

EXAMPLE 6   Graph $y = -2(x + 3)^2 + 5$. Find the vertex, the axis of symmetry, and the maximum or minimum value.

Solution   We first express the equation in the equivalent form

$$y = -2[x - (-3)]^2 + 5.$$

The graph looks like that of $y = -2x^2$ translated 3 units to the left and 5 units up. The vertex is $(-3, 5)$, and the axis of symmetry is $x = -3$. Since -2 is negative, we know that 5, the second coordinate of the vertex, is the maximum y-value.

We compute a few points as needed, selecting convenient x-values on either side of the vertex. The graph is shown here.

x	$y = -2(x + 3)^2 + 5$
-4	3
-3	5
-2	3

←—Vertex

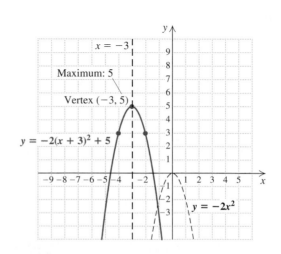

CONNECTING THE CONCEPTS

The ability to graph a function is an important skill. Later in this chapter, as well as in future courses, you will find that graphs of polynomial functions can be used as a tool for solving equations, inequalities, and real-world applications. In the process of learning how to graph quadratic functions, we have developed the ability to reflect or shift (translate) a graph. This skill will prove useful not only in future courses, but in Chapters 12 and 13 as well.

11.6 Exercise Set

FOR EXTRA HELP

Student's Solutions Manual · Digital Video Tutor CD 6 Videotape 11 · AW Math Tutor Center · MathXL Tutorials on CD · MathXL · MyMathLab

↪ *Concept Reinforcement*   *In each of Exercises 1–8, match the equation with the corresponding graph from those shown.*

1. _____ $f(x) = 2(x - 1)^2 + 3$

2. _____ $f(x) = -2(x - 1)^2 + 3$

3. _____ $f(x) = 2(x + 1)^2 + 3$

4. _____ $f(x) = 2(x - 1)^2 - 3$

5. _____ $f(x) = -2(x + 1)^2 + 3$

6. _____ $f(x) = -2(x + 1)^2 - 3$

7. _____ $f(x) = 2(x + 1)^2 - 3$

8. _____ $f(x) = -2(x - 1)^2 - 3$

c)
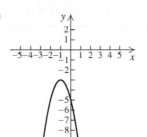

d)
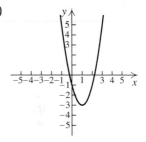

e)
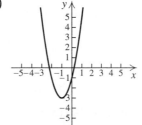

f)
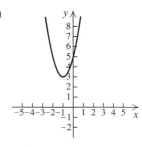

a)
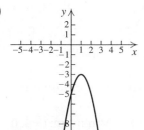

b)
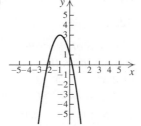

g)
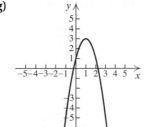

h)
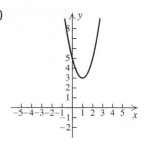

Graph.

9. $f(x) = x^2$

10. $f(x) = -x^2$

11. $f(x) = -2x^2$

12. $f(x) = -3x^2$

13. $g(x) = \frac{1}{3}x^2$

14. $g(x) = \frac{1}{4}x^2$

Aha! **15.** $h(x) = -\frac{1}{3}x^2$

16. $h(x) = -\frac{1}{4}x^2$

17. $f(x) = \frac{5}{2}x^2$

18. $f(x) = \frac{3}{2}x^2$

For each of the following, graph the function, label the vertex, and draw the axis of symmetry.

19. $g(x) = (x + 1)^2$

20. $g(x) = (x + 4)^2$

21. $f(x) = (x - 2)^2$

22. $f(x) = (x - 1)^2$

23. $h(x) = (x - 3)^2$

24. $h(x) = (x - 4)^2$

25. $f(x) = -(x + 1)^2$

26. $f(x) = -(x - 1)^2$

27. $g(x) = -(x - 2)^2$

28. $g(x) = -(x + 4)^2$

29. $f(x) = 2(x + 1)^2$

30. $f(x) = 2(x + 4)^2$

31. $h(x) = -\frac{1}{2}(x - 4)^2$

32. $h(x) = -\frac{3}{2}(x - 2)^2$

33. $f(x) = \frac{1}{2}(x - 1)^2$

34. $f(x) = \frac{1}{3}(x + 2)^2$

35. $f(x) = -2(x + 5)^2$

36. $f(x) = 2(x + 7)^2$

37. $h(x) = -3(x - \frac{1}{2})^2$

38. $h(x) = -2(x + \frac{1}{2})^2$

For each of the following, graph the function and find the vertex, the axis of symmetry, and the maximum value or the minimum value.

39. $f(x) = (x - 5)^2 + 2$

40. $f(x) = (x + 3)^2 - 2$

41. $f(x) = (x + 1)^2 - 3$

42. $f(x) = (x - 1)^2 + 2$

43. $g(x) = (x + 4)^2 + 1$

44. $g(x) = -(x - 2)^2 - 4$

45. $h(x) = -2(x - 1)^2 - 3$

46. $h(x) = -2(x + 1)^2 + 4$

47. $f(x) = 2(x + 4)^2 + 1$

48. $f(x) = 2(x - 5)^2 - 3$

49. $g(x) = -\frac{3}{2}(x - 1)^2 + 4$

50. $g(x) = \frac{3}{2}(x + 2)^2 - 3$

Without graphing, find the vertex, the axis of symmetry, and the maximum value or the minimum value.

51. $f(x) = 6(x - 8)^2 + 7$

52. $f(x) = 4(x + 5)^2 - 6$

53. $h(x) = -\frac{2}{7}(x + 6)^2 + 11$

54. $h(x) = -\frac{3}{11}(x - 7)^2 - 9$

55. $f(x) = 7(x + \frac{1}{4})^2 - 13$

56. $f(x) = 6(x - \frac{1}{4})^2 + 15$

57. $f(x) = \sqrt{2}(x + 4.58)^2 + 65\pi$

58. $f(x) = 4\pi(x - 38.2)^2 - \sqrt{34}$

59. Explain, without plotting points, why the graph of $y = x^2 - 4$ looks like the graph of $y = x^2$ translated 4 units down.

60. Explain, without plotting points, why the graph of $y = (x + 2)^2$ looks like the graph of $y = x^2$ translated 2 units to the left.

SKILL MAINTENANCE

Graph using intercepts. [3.3]

61. $2x - 7y = 28$

62. $6x - 3y = 36$

Solve each system. [8.2]

63. $3x + 4y = -19,$
$7x - 6y = -29$

64. $5x + 7y = 9,$
$3x - 4y = -11$

Replace the blanks with constants to form a true equation. [11.1]

65. $x^2 + 5x + \underline{\quad} = (x + \underline{\quad})^2$

66. $x^2 - 9x + \underline{\quad} = (x - \underline{\quad})^2$

SYNTHESIS

67. Before graphing a quadratic function, Sophie always plots five points. First, she calculates and plots the coordinates of the vertex. Then she plots *four* more points after calculating *two* more ordered pairs. How is this possible?

68. If the graphs of $f(x) = a_1(x - h_1)^2 + k_1$ and $g(x) = a_2(x - h_2)^2 + k_2$ have the same shape, what, if anything, can you conclude about the a's, the h's, and the k's? Why?

Write an equation for a function having a graph with the same shape as the graph of $f(x) = \frac{3}{5}x^2$, but with the given point as the vertex.

69. $(4, 1)$

70. $(2, 6)$

71. $(3, -1)$

72. $(5, -6)$

73. $(-2, -5)$

74. $(-4, -2)$

For each of the following, write the equation of the parabola that has the shape of $f(x) = 2x^2$ or $g(x) = -2x^2$ and has a maximum or minimum value at the specified point.

75. Minimum: $(2, 0)$

76. Minimum: $(-4, 0)$

77. Maximum: $(0, 3)$

78. Maximum: $(3, 8)$

Find an equation for a quadratic function F that satisfies the following conditions.

79. The graph of F is the same shape as the graph of f, where $f(x) = 3(x + 2)^2 + 7$, and $F(x)$ is a minimum at the same point that $g(x) = -2(x - 5)^2 + 1$ is a maximum.

80. The graph of F is the same shape as the graph of f, where $f(x) = -\frac{1}{3}(x - 2)^2 + 7$, and $F(x)$ is a maximum at the same point that $g(x) = 2(x + 4)^2 - 6$ is a minimum.

Functions other than parabolas can be translated. When calculating $f(x)$, if we replace x with $x - h$, where h is a constant, the graph will be moved horizontally. If we replace $f(x)$ with $f(x) + k$, the graph will be moved vertically. Use the graph below for Exercises 81–86.

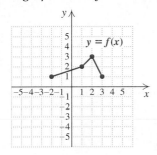

Draw a graph of each of the following.

81. $y = f(x - 1)$

82. $y = f(x + 2)$

83. $y = f(x) + 2$

84. $y = f(x) - 3$

85. $y = f(x + 3) - 2$

86. $y = f(x - 3) + 1$

 87. Use the TRACE and/or TABLE features of a graphing calculator to confirm the maximum and minimum values given as answers to Exercises 51, 53, and 55. Be sure to adjust the window appropriately. On many graphing calculators, a maximum or minimum option may be available by using a CALC key.

 88. Use a graphing calculator to check your graphs for Exercises 18, 28, and 48.

89. While trying to graph $y = -\frac{1}{2}x^2 + 3x + 1$, Omar gets the following screen. How can Omar tell at a glance that a mistake has been made?

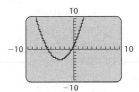

CORNER

Match the Graph

Focus: Graphing quadratic functions

Time: 15–20 minutes

Group size: 6

Materials: Index cards

ACTIVITY

1. On each of six index cards, write one of the following equations:

$y = \frac{1}{2}(x - 3)^2 + 1;$ $\quad y = \frac{1}{2}(x - 1)^2 + 3;$

$y = \frac{1}{2}(x + 1)^2 - 3;$ $\quad y = \frac{1}{2}(x + 3)^2 + 1;$

$y = \frac{1}{2}(x + 3)^2 - 1;$ $\quad y = \frac{1}{2}(x + 1)^2 + 3.$

2. Fold each index card and mix up the six cards in a hat or bag. Then, one by one, each group member should select one of the equations. Do not let anyone see your equation.

3. Each group member should carefully graph the equation selected. Make the graph large enough so that when it is finished, it can be easily viewed by the rest of the group. Be sure to scale the axes and label the vertex, but **do not label the graph with the equation used.**

4. When all group members have drawn a graph, place the graphs in a pile. The group should then match and agree on the correct equation for each graph *with no help from the person who drew the graph*. If a mistake has been made and a graph has no match, determine what its equation *should* be.

5. Compare your group's labeled graphs with those of other groups to reach consensus within the class on the correct label for each graph.

COLLABORATIVE

11.7 More About Graphing Quadratic Functions

Completing the Square • Finding Intercepts

Completing the Square

By *completing the square* (see Section 11.1), we can rewrite any polynomial $ax^2 + bx + c$ in the form $a(x - h)^2 + k$. Once that has been done, the procedures discussed in Section 11.6 will enable us to graph any quadratic function.

EXAMPLE 1 Graph: $g(x) = x^2 - 6x + 4$.

Solution We have

$$g(x) = x^2 - 6x + 4$$
$$= (x^2 - 6x) + 4.$$

To complete the square inside the parentheses, we take half the x-coefficient, $\frac{1}{2} \cdot (-6) = -3$, and square it to get $(-3)^2 = 9$. Then we add $9 - 9$ inside the parentheses:

$$g(x) = (x^2 - 6x + 9 - 9) + 4 \qquad \text{The effect is of adding 0.}$$
$$= (x^2 - 6x + 9) + (-9 + 4) \qquad \text{Using the associative law of addition to regroup}$$
$$= (x - 3)^2 - 5. \qquad \text{Factoring and simplifying}$$

This equation appeared as Example 4 of Section 11.6. The graph is that of $f(x) = x^2$ translated right 3 units and down 5 units. The vertex is $(3, -5)$.

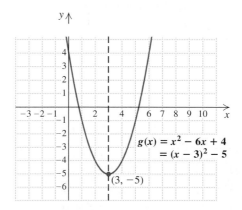

When the leading coefficient is not 1, we factor out that number from the first two terms. Then we complete the square and use the distributive law.

EXAMPLE 2   Graph: $f(x) = 3x^2 + 12x + 13$.

Solution   Since the coefficient of x^2 is not 1, we need to factor out that number—in this case, 3—from the first two terms. Remember that we want the form $f(x) = a(x - h)^2 + k$:

$$f(x) = 3x^2 + 12x + 13$$
$$= 3(x^2 + 4x) + 13.$$

Now we complete the square as before. We take half of the x-coefficient, $\frac{1}{2} \cdot 4 = 2$, and square it: $2^2 = 4$. Then we add $4 - 4$ inside the parentheses:

$$f(x) = 3(x^2 + 4x + 4 - 4) + 13. \qquad \text{Adding } 4 - 4, \text{ or } 0, \text{ inside the parentheses}$$

The distributive law allows us to separate the -4 from the perfect-square trinomial so long as it is multiplied by 3. *This step is critical*:

$$f(x) = 3(x^2 + 4x + 4) + 3(-4) + 13 \qquad \begin{array}{l}\text{This leaves a perfect-square} \\ \text{trinomial inside the} \\ \text{parentheses.}\end{array}$$

$$= 3(x + 2)^2 + 1. \qquad \text{Factoring and simplifying}$$

The vertex is $(-2, 1)$, and the axis of symmetry is $x = -2$. The coefficient of x^2 is 3, so the graph is narrow and opens upward. We choose a few x-values on either side of the vertex, compute y-values, and then graph the parabola.

x	$f(x) = 3(x + 2)^2 + 1$
-2	1
-3	4
-1	4

←——Vertex

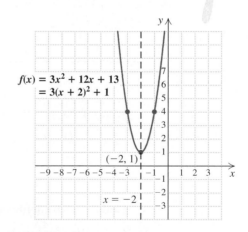

EXAMPLE 3   Graph: $f(x) = -2x^2 + 10x - 7$.

Solution   We first find the vertex by completing the square. To do so, we factor out -2 from the first two terms of the expression. This makes the coefficient of x^2 inside the parentheses 1:

$$f(x) = -2x^2 + 10x - 7$$
$$= -2(x^2 - 5x) - 7.$$

Now we complete the square as before. We take half of the x-coefficient and square it to get $\frac{25}{4}$. Then we add $\frac{25}{4} - \frac{25}{4}$ inside the parentheses:

$$f(x) = -2\left(x^2 - 5x + \frac{25}{4} - \frac{25}{4}\right) - 7$$

$$= -2\left(x^2 - 5x + \frac{25}{4}\right) + (-2)\left(-\frac{25}{4}\right) - 7 \qquad \text{Multiplying by } -2,\ \text{using the distributive law, and regrouping}$$

$$= -2\left(x - \frac{5}{2}\right)^2 + \frac{11}{2}. \qquad \text{Factoring and simplifying}$$

The vertex is $\left(\frac{5}{2}, \frac{11}{2}\right)$, and the axis of symmetry is $x = \frac{5}{2}$. The coefficient of x^2, -2, is negative, so the graph opens downward. We plot a few points on either side of the vertex, including the y-intercept, $f(0)$, and graph the parabola.

x	$f(x)$	
$\frac{5}{2}$	$\frac{11}{2}$	← Vertex
0	-7	← y-intercept
1	1	
4	1	

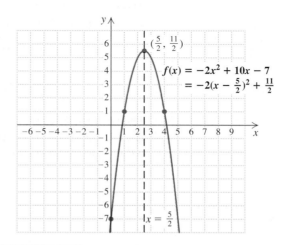

The method used in Examples 1–3 can be generalized to find a formula for locating the vertex. We complete the square as follows:

$$f(x) = ax^2 + bx + c$$

$$= a\left(x^2 + \frac{b}{a}x\right) + c. \qquad \text{Factoring } a \text{ out of the first two terms. Check by multiplying.}$$

Half of the x-coefficient, $\frac{b}{a}$, is $\frac{b}{2a}$. We square it to get $\frac{b^2}{4a^2}$ and add $\frac{b^2}{4a^2} - \frac{b^2}{4a^2}$ inside the parentheses. Then we distribute the a and regroup terms:

$$f(x) = a\left(x^2 + \frac{b}{a}x + \frac{b^2}{4a^2} - \frac{b^2}{4a^2}\right) + c$$

$$= a\left(x^2 + \frac{b}{a}x + \frac{b^2}{4a^2}\right) + a\left(-\frac{b^2}{4a^2}\right) + c \qquad \text{Using the distributive law}$$

$$= a\left(x + \frac{b}{2a}\right)^2 + \frac{-b^2}{4a} + \frac{4ac}{4a} \qquad \text{Factoring and finding a common denominator}$$

$$= a\left[x - \left(-\frac{b}{2a}\right)\right]^2 + \frac{4ac - b^2}{4a}.$$

Student Notes _____

The easiest way to remember a formula is to understand its derivation. Check with your instructor to determine what, if any, formulas you will be expected to remember.

Thus we have the following.

The Vertex of a Parabola

The vertex of the parabola given by $f(x) = ax^2 + bx + c$ is

$$\left(-\frac{b}{2a}, f\left(-\frac{b}{2a}\right)\right) \quad \text{or} \quad \left(-\frac{b}{2a}, \frac{4ac - b^2}{4a}\right).$$

The x-coordinate of the vertex is $-b/(2a)$. The axis of symmetry is $x = -b/(2a)$. The second coordinate of the vertex is most commonly found by computing $f\left(-\frac{b}{2a}\right)$.

Let's reexamine Example 3 to see how we could have found the vertex directly. From the formula above,

$$\text{the } x\text{-coordinate of the vertex is } -\frac{b}{2a} = -\frac{10}{2(-2)} = \frac{5}{2}.$$

Substituting $\frac{5}{2}$ into $f(x) = -2x^2 + 10x - 7$, we find the second coordinate of the vertex:

$$\begin{aligned}
f\left(\tfrac{5}{2}\right) &= -2\left(\tfrac{5}{2}\right)^2 + 10\left(\tfrac{5}{2}\right) - 7 \\
&= -2\left(\tfrac{25}{4}\right) + 25 - 7 \\
&= -\tfrac{25}{2} + 18 \\
&= -\tfrac{25}{2} + \tfrac{36}{2} = \tfrac{11}{2}.
\end{aligned}$$

The vertex is $\left(\frac{5}{2}, \frac{11}{2}\right)$. The axis of symmetry is $x = \frac{5}{2}$.

We have actually developed two methods for finding the vertex. One is by completing the square and the other is by using a formula. You should check to see if your instructor prefers one method over the other or wants you to use both.

Finding Intercepts

For any function f, the y-intercept occurs at $f(0)$. Thus, for $f(x) = ax^2 + bx + c$, the y-intercept is simply $(0, c)$. To find x-intercepts, we look for points where $y = 0$ or $f(x) = 0$. Thus, for $f(x) = ax^2 + bx + c$, the x-intercepts occur at those x-values for which

$$ax^2 + bx + c = 0.$$

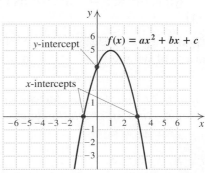

EXAMPLE 4   Find the x- and y-intercepts of the graph of $f(x) = x^2 - 2x - 2$.

Solution   The y-intercept is simply $(0, f(0))$, or $(0, -2)$. To find the x-intercepts, we solve the equation

$$0 = x^2 - 2x - 2.$$

We are unable to factor $x^2 - 2x - 2$, so we use the quadratic formula and get $x = 1 \pm \sqrt{3}$. Thus the x-intercepts are $\left(1 - \sqrt{3}, 0\right)$ and $\left(1 + \sqrt{3}, 0\right)$. If graphing, we would approximate, to get $(-0.7, 0)$ and $(2.7, 0)$.

Exercise Set

11.7

FOR EXTRA HELP

 Student's Solutions Manual

Digital Video Tutor CD 6 Videotape 11

 Tutor Center AW Math Tutor Center

 MathXL Tutorials on CD

 Math XL MathXL

MyMathLab MyMathLab

↪ *Concept Reinforcement*   *Complete each of the following.*

1. The expressions $x^2 + 6x + 5$ and $(x^2 + 6x + 9) - \underline{\quad} + 5$ are equivalent.

2. The expressions $x^2 + 8x + 3$ and $(x^2 + 8x + \underline{\quad}) - 16 + 3$ are equivalent.

3. The functions given by $f(x) = 2x^2 + 12x - 7$ and $f(x) = 2(x^2 + 6x + \underline{\quad}) - 18 - 7$ are equivalent.

4. The functions given by $g(x) = 3x^2 - 6x - 5$ and $g(x) = 3(x^2 - 2x + \underline{\quad}) - 3 - 5$ are equivalent.

5. The graph of $f(x) = -2(x - \underline{\quad})^2 + 7$ has its vertex at $(3, 7)$.

6. The graph of $g(x) = -3(x - 4)^2 + \underline{\quad}$ has its vertex at $(4, 1)$.

7. The graph of $f(x) = 2(x - \underline{\quad})^2 + \underline{\quad}$ has its axis of symmetry at $x = \frac{5}{2}$ and has its vertex at $\left(\frac{5}{2}, -4\right)$.

8. The graph of $g(x) = \frac{1}{2}(x - \underline{\quad})^2 + \frac{7}{2}$ has $x = -2$ as its axis of symmetry and $\underline{\quad}$ as its vertex.

For each quadratic function, **(a)** *find the vertex and the axis of symmetry and* **(b)** *graph the function.*

9. $f(x) = x^2 + 4x + 5$

10. $f(x) = x^2 + 2x - 5$

11. $g(x) = x^2 - 6x + 13$

12. $g(x) = x^2 - 4x + 5$

13. $f(x) = x^2 + 8x + 20$

14. $f(x) = x^2 - 10x + 21$

15. $h(x) = 2x^2 - 16x + 25$

16. $h(x) = 2x^2 + 16x + 23$

17. $f(x) = -x^2 + 2x + 5$

18. $f(x) = -x^2 - 2x + 7$

19. $g(x) = x^2 + 3x - 10$

20. $g(x) = x^2 + 5x + 4$

21. $f(x) = 3x^2 - 24x + 50$

22. $f(x) = 4x^2 + 8x - 3$

23. $h(x) = x^2 + 7x$

24. $h(x) = x^2 - 5x$

25. $f(x) = -2x^2 - 4x - 6$

26. $f(x) = -3x^2 + 6x + 2$

27. $g(x) = 2x^2 - 8x + 3$

28. $g(x) = 2x^2 + 5x - 1$

29. $f(x) = -3x^2 + 5x - 2$

30. $f(x) = -3x^2 - 7x + 2$

31. $h(x) = \frac{1}{2}x^2 + 4x + \frac{19}{3}$

32. $h(x) = \frac{1}{2}x^2 - 3x + 2$

Find the x- and y-intercepts. If no x-intercepts exist, state this.

33. $f(x) = x^2 - 6x + 3$ **34.** $f(x) = x^2 + 5x + 2$

35. $g(x) = -x^2 + 2x + 3$ **36.** $g(x) = x^2 - 6x + 9$

Aha! **37.** $f(x) = x^2 - 9x$ **38.** $f(x) = x^2 - 7x$

39. $h(x) = -x^2 + 4x - 4$ **40.** $h(x) = 4x^2 - 12x + 3$

41. $f(x) = 2x^2 - 4x + 6$ **42.** $f(x) = x^2 - x + 2$

43. Does the graph of every quadratic function have a y-intercept? Why or why not?

44. Is it possible for the graph of a quadratic function to have only one x-intercept if the vertex is off the x-axis? Why or why not?

SKILL MAINTENANCE

Solve each system.

45. $5x - 3y = 16$,
$4x + 2y = 4$ [8.2]

46. $2x - 5y = 9$,
$5x - 15y = 20$ [8.2]

47. $4a - 5b + c = 3$,
$3a - 4b + 2c = 3$,
$a + b - 7c = -2$
[8.4]

48. $2a - 7b + c = 25$,
$a + 5b - 2c = -18$,
$3a - b + 4c = 14$
[8.4]

Solve. [10.6]

49. $\sqrt{4x - 4} = \sqrt{x + 4} + 1$

50. $\sqrt{5x - 4} + \sqrt{13 - x} = 7$

SYNTHESIS

51. If the graphs of two quadratic functions have the same x-intercepts, will they also have the same vertex? Why or why not?

52. Suppose that the graph of $f(x) = ax^2 + bx + c$ has $(x_1, 0)$ and $(x_2, 0)$ as x-intercepts. Explain why the graph of $g(x) = -ax^2 - bx - c$ will also have $(x_1, 0)$ and $(x_2, 0)$ as x-intercepts.

For each quadratic function, find **(a)** *the maximum or minimum value and* **(b)** *the x- and y-intercepts.*

53. $f(x) = 2.31x^2 - 3.135x - 5.89$

54. $f(x) = -18.8x^2 + 7.92x + 6.18$

55. Graph the function
$$f(x) = x^2 - x - 6.$$
Then use the graph to approximate solutions to each of the following equations.
a) $x^2 - x - 6 = 2$
b) $x^2 - x - 6 = -3$

56. Graph the function
$$f(x) = \frac{x^2}{2} + x - \frac{3}{2}.$$
Then use the graph to approximate solutions to each of the following equations.

a) $\frac{x^2}{2} + x - \frac{3}{2} = 0$

b) $\frac{x^2}{2} + x - \frac{3}{2} = 1$

c) $\frac{x^2}{2} + x - \frac{3}{2} = 2$

Find an equivalent equation of the type
$$f(x) = a(x - h)^2 + k.$$

57. $f(x) = mx^2 - nx + p$

58. $f(x) = 3x^2 + mx + m^2$

59. A quadratic function has $(-1, 0)$ as one of its intercepts and $(3, -5)$ as its vertex. Find an equation for the function.

60. A quadratic function has $(4, 0)$ as one of its intercepts and $(-1, 7)$ as its vertex. Find an equation for the function.

Graph.

61. $f(x) = |x^2 - 1|$

62. $f(x) = |x^2 - 3x - 4|$

63. $f(x) = |2(x - 3)^2 - 5|$

64. Use a graphing calculator to check your answers to Exercises 17, 31, 41, 53, and 55.

11.8 Problem Solving and Quadratic Functions

Maximum and Minimum Problems • Fitting Quadratic Functions to Data

Let's look now at some of the many situations in which quadratic functions are used for problem solving.

Maximum and Minimum Problems

We have seen that for any quadratic function f, the value of $f(x)$ at the vertex is either a maximum or a minimum. Thus problems in which a quantity must be maximized or minimized can be solved by finding the coordinates of a vertex, assuming the problem can be modeled with a quadratic function.

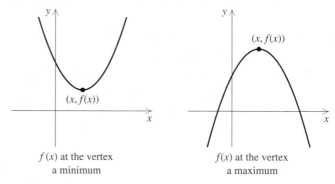

$f(x)$ at the vertex $f(x)$ at the vertex
a minimum   a maximum

EXAMPLE 1 **Newborn calves.** The number of pounds of milk per day recommended for a calf that is x weeks old can be approximated by $p(x)$, where $p(x) = -0.2x^2 + 1.3x + 6.2$ (*Source*: C. Chaloux, University of Vermont, 1998). When is a calf's milk consumption greatest and how much milk does it consume at that time?

Solution

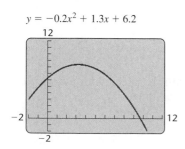

$y = -0.2x^2 + 1.3x + 6.2$

A visualization for Example 1

1., 2. Familiarize and **Translate.** We are given the function for milk consumption by a calf. Note that it is a quadratic function of x, the calf's age in weeks. Since the coefficient of x^2 is negative, it appears that milk consumption increases and then decreases. The calculator-generated graph at left confirms this.

3. Carry out. We can either complete the square,

$$p(x) = -0.2x^2 + 1.3x + 6.2$$
$$= -0.2(x^2 - 6.5x) + 6.2$$
$$= -0.2(x^2 - 6.5x + 3.25^2 - 3.25^2) + 6.2 \qquad \text{Completing the square; } 6.5/2 = 3.25$$
$$= -0.2(x^2 - 6.5x + 3.25^2) + (-0.2)(-3.25^2) + 6.2$$
$$= -0.2(x - 3.25)^2 + 8.3125, \qquad \text{Factoring and simplifying}$$

or we can use $-b/(2a) = -1.3/(-0.4) = 3.25$. Using a calculator, we find that

$$p(3.25) = -0.2(3.25)^2 + 1.3(3.25) + 6.2 = 8.3125.$$

4. **Check.**   Both of the approaches in step (3) indicate that a maximum occurs when $x = 3.25$, or $3\frac{1}{4}$. The graph also serves as a check.

5. **State.**   A calf's milk consumption is greatest when the calf is $3\frac{1}{4}$ weeks old. At that time, it drinks about 8.3 lb of milk per day.

EXAMPLE 2

Swimming area.   A lifeguard has 100 m of roped-together flotation devices with which to cordon off a rectangular swimming area at Lakeside Beach. If the shoreline forms one side of the rectangle, what dimensions will maximize the size of the area for swimming?

Solution

1. **Familiarize.**   We make a drawing and label it, letting $w =$ the width of the rectangle, in meters, and $l =$ the length of the rectangle, in meters.

   Recall that Area $= l \cdot w$ and Perimeter $= 2w + 2l$. Since the beach forms one length of the rectangle, the flotation devices comprise three sides. Thus

   $$2w + l = 100.$$

   To get a better feel for the problem, we can look at some possible dimensions for a rectangular area that can be enclosed with 100 m of flotation devices. All possibilities are chosen so that $2w + l = 100$.

l	w	Rope Length	Area
40 m	30 m	100 m	1200 m^2
30 m	35 m	100 m	1050 m^2
20 m	40 m	100 m	800 m^2
⋮	⋮	⋮	⋮

What choice of l and w will maximize A?

2. **Translate.**   We have two equations: One guarantees that all 100 m of flotation devices are used; the other expresses area in terms of length and width.

   $$2w + l = 100,$$
   $$A = l \cdot w$$

3. **Carry out.**   We need to express A as a function of l or w but not both. To do so, we solve for l in the first equation to obtain $l = 100 - 2w$. Substituting for l in the second equation, we get a quadratic function:

   $$A = (100 - 2w)w \qquad \text{Substituting for } l$$
   $$= 100w - 2w^2. \qquad \text{This represents a parabola opening downward, so a maximum exists.}$$

Factoring and completing the square, we get

$$A = -2(w^2 - 50w + 625 - 625)$$ We could also use the vertex formula.

$$= -2(w - 25)^2 + 1250.$$ This suggests a maximum of 1250 m² when $w = 25$ m.

The maximum area, 1250 m², occurs when $w = 25$ m and $l = 100 - 2(25)$, or 50 m.

4. **Check.** Note that 1250 m² is greater than any of the values for A found in the *Familiarize* step. To be more certain, we could check values other than those used in that step. For example, if $w = 26$ m, then $l = 100 - 2 \cdot 26 = 48$ m, and $A = 26 \cdot 48 = 1248$ m². Since 1250 m² is greater than 1248 m², it appears that we have a maximum.

5. **State.** The largest rectangular area for swimming that can be enclosed is 25 m by 50 m.

Fitting Quadratic Functions to Data

Whenever a certain quadratic function fits a situation, that function can be determined if three inputs and their outputs are known. Each of the given ordered pairs is called a *data point*.

EXAMPLE 3   The decline of teen smoking. Deadly and less fashionable than ever, teen smoking has declined since 1997. According to the Centers for Disease Control and Prevention, the percentage of high-school students who reported having smoked a cigarette in the preceding 30 days increased from 30.5% in 1993 to 36.4% in 1997, but has declined since then to 21.9% in 2003.

Years After 1993	Percentage of High-School Students Who Smoked a Cigarette in the Preceding 30 Days
0	30.5
4	36.4
10	21.9

Source: Centers for Disease Control and Prevention, *Morbidity and Mortality Weekly Report* 6/18/04

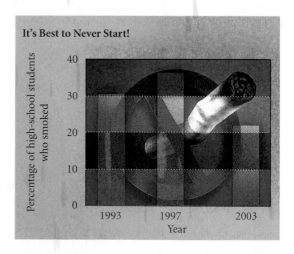

The rise and fall in the percentage of teen smokers suggests that the situation can be modeled by a quadratic function.

a) Use the data points (0, 30.5), (4, 36.4), and (10, 21.9) to find a quadratic function that fits the data.

b) Use the function from part (a) to estimate the percentage of high-school students in 2005 who smoked a cigarette in the preceding 30 days.

Solution

a) We are looking for a function of the form $T(x) = ax^2 + bx + c$, given that $T(0) = 30.5$, $T(4) = 36.4$, and $T(10) = 21.9$. Thus,

$$30.5 = a \cdot 0^2 + b \cdot 0 + c, \qquad \text{Using the data point (0, 30.5)}$$
$$36.4 = a \cdot 4^2 + b \cdot 4 + c, \qquad \text{Using the data point (4, 36.4)}$$
$$21.9 = a \cdot 10^2 + b \cdot 10 + c. \qquad \text{Using the data point (10, 21.9)}$$

After simplifying, we see that we need to solve the system

$$30.5 = c, \qquad\qquad\qquad \textbf{(1)}$$
$$36.4 = 16a + 4b + c, \qquad \textbf{(2)}$$
$$21.9 = 100a + 10b + c. \quad \textbf{(3)}$$

We know from equation (1) that $c = 30.5$. Substituting that value into equations (2) and (3), we have

$$36.4 = 16a + 4b + 30.5,$$
$$21.9 = 100a + 10b + 30.5.$$

Subtracting 30.5 from both sides of each equation, we have

$$5.9 = 16a + 4b,$$
$$-8.6 = 100a + 10b$$

or

$$59 = 160a + 40b, \qquad \textbf{(4)} \left.\right\} \text{ Multiplying both sides}$$
$$-86 = 1000a + 100b. \quad \textbf{(5)} \left.\right\} \text{ by 10 to clear decimals}$$

To solve, we multiply equation (4) by 5 and equation (5) by -2. We then add to eliminate b:

$$295 = 800a + 200b$$
$$\underline{172 = -2000a - 200b}$$
$$467 = -1200a$$
$$-\frac{467}{1200} = a, \quad \text{or} \quad a \approx -0.39. \qquad \text{Converting to decimal notation}$$

Next, we solve for b, using equation (5) above:

$$-86 = 1000\left(-\frac{467}{1200}\right) + 100b$$
$$-86 = -\frac{2335}{6} + 100b$$
$$\frac{1819}{6} = 100b \qquad\qquad\qquad \text{Adding } \frac{2335}{6} \text{ to both sides and}$$
$$\text{simplifying}$$
$$\frac{1819}{600} = b, \quad \text{or} \quad b \approx 3.03. \qquad \text{Dividing both sides by 100 and}$$
$$\text{converting to decimal notation}$$

We can now write $T(x) = ax^2 + bx + c$ as

$$T(x) = -\frac{467}{1200}x^2 + \frac{1819}{600}x + 30.5 \quad \text{or} \quad T(x) = -0.39x^2 + 3.03x + 30.5.$$

Student Notes

Try to keep the "big picture" in mind on problems like Example 3. Solving a system of three equations is but one part of the solution.

b) To find the percentage of high-school students who will have smoked at least once during 30 days in 2005, we evaluate the function. Note that 2005 is 12 yr after 1993. Thus,

$$T(12) = -\frac{467}{1200} \cdot 12^2 + \frac{1819}{600} \cdot 12 + 30.5$$

$$= 10.84.$$

In 2005, an estimated 10.8% of all high-schoolers smoked at least 1 cigarette during the 30 days preceding the survey in 2005.

---

technology connection

To use a graphing calculator to fit a quadratic function to the data in Example 3, we first select the EDIT option of the **STAT** key's menu and enter the given data.

Next, we press (**Y=**), (∧), and **ENTER** to turn on the plot feature. Using ZoomStat, we obtain the following.

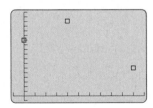

To fit a quadratic function to the data, we press **STAT** (▷) (**5**) **VARS** (▷) (**1**) (**1**) **ENTER**. The first three keystrokes select QuadReg from the STAT CALC menu and display the coefficients a, b, and c of the regression equation $y = ax^2 + bx + c$. The keystrokes **VARS** (▷) (**1**) (**1**) copy the regression equation to the equation-editor screen as y_1. We see that the regression equation is $y = -.38916666666668x^2 + 3.0316666666668x + 30.5$. Pressing (**ZOOM**) (**9**), we see the regression equation graphed with the data points.

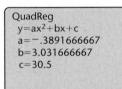

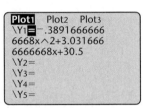

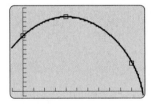

To check Example 3(b), we press (**ZOOM**) (**3**) **ENTER** and then (**TRACE**) (∧) (**1**) (**2**) **ENTER**. The result, 10.84, confirms our earlier answer.

1. Use the above approach to estimate the percentage of high-school students who smoked in 2000.

Exercise Set

11.8

🌱 *Concept Reinforcement* *In each of Exercises 1–6, match the description with the graph that displays that characteristic.*

1. ____ A minimum value of $f(x)$ exists.

2. ____ A maximum value of $f(x)$ exists.

3. ____ No maximum or minimum value of $f(x)$ exists.

4. ____ The data points appear to suggest a linear model.

5. ____ The data points appear to suggest a quadratic model with a maximum.

6. ____ The data points appear to suggest a quadratic model with a minimum.

a)

b)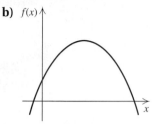

c)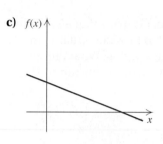

d)

e)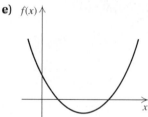

f)

Solve.

7. *Ticket sales.*   The number of tickets sold each day for an upcoming Los Lobos show can be approximated by

$$N(x) = -0.4x^2 + 9x + 11,$$

where x is the number of days since the concert was first announced. When will daily ticket sales peak and how many tickets will be sold that day?

8. *Stock prices.*   The value of a share of I. J. Solar can be represented by $V(x) = x^2 - 6x + 13$, where x is the number of months after January 2004. What is the lowest value $V(x)$ will reach, and when did that occur?

9. *Minimizing cost.*   Sweet Harmony Crafts has determined that when x hundred Dobros are built, the average cost per Dobro can be estimated by

$$C(x) = 0.1x^2 - 0.7x + 2.425,$$

where $C(x)$ is in hundreds of dollars. What is the minimum average cost per Dobro and how many Dobros should be built to achieve that minimum?

10. *Maximizing profit.*   Recall that total profit P is the difference between total revenue R and total cost C. Given $R(x) = 1000x - x^2$ and $C(x) = 3000 + 20x$, find the total profit, the maximum value of the total profit, and the value of x at which it occurs.

11. *Furniture design.* A furniture builder is designing a rectangular end table with a perimeter of 128 in. What dimensions will yield the maximum area?

12. *Architecture.* An architect is designing an atrium for a hotel. The atrium is to be rectangular with a perimeter of 720 ft of brass piping. What dimensions will maximize the area of the atrium?

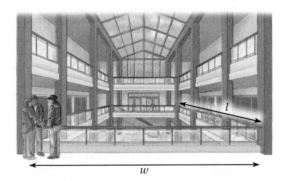

13. *Patio design.* A stone mason has enough stones to enclose a rectangular patio with 60 ft of perimeter, assuming that the attached house forms one side of the rectangle. What is the maximum area that the mason can enclose? What should the dimensions of the patio be in order to yield this area?

14. *Garden design.* Ginger is fencing in a rectangular garden, using the side of her house as one side of the rectangle. What is the maximum area that she can enclose with 40 ft of fence? What should the dimensions of the garden be in order to yield this area?

15. *Molding plastics.* Economite Plastics plans to produce a one-compartment vertical file by bending the long side of an 8-in. by 14-in. sheet of plastic along two lines to form a U shape. How tall should the file be in order to maximize the volume that the file can hold?

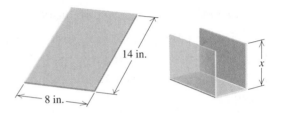

16. *Composting.* A rectangular compost container is to be formed in a corner of a fenced yard, with 8 ft of chicken wire completing the other two sides of the rectangle. If the chicken wire is 3 ft high, what dimensions of the base will maximize the container's volume?

17. What is the maximum product of two numbers that add to 18? What numbers yield this product?

18. What is the maximum product of two numbers that add to 26? What numbers yield this product?

19. What is the minimum product of two numbers that differ by 8? What are the numbers?

20. What is the minimum product of two numbers that differ by 7? What are the numbers?

Aha! **21.** What is the maximum product of two numbers that add to -10? What numbers yield this product?

22. What is the maximum product of two numbers that add to -12? What numbers yield this product?

Choosing models. *For the scatterplots and graphs in Exercises 23–34, determine which, if any, of the following functions might be used as a model for the data: Linear, with $f(x) = mx + b$; quadratic, with $f(x) = ax^2 + bx + c, a > 0$; quadratic, with $f(x) = ax^2 + bx + c, a < 0$; neither quadratic nor linear.*

23.

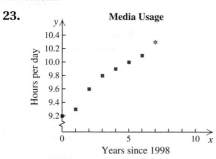

Media Usage

*Estimated
Source: Statistical Abstract of the United States, 2003

24.

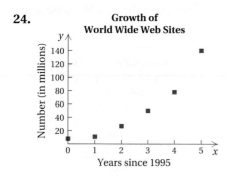

Growth of World Wide Web Sites

25.

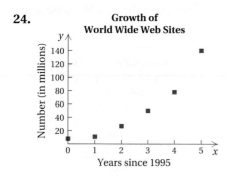

Valley Community College

26.

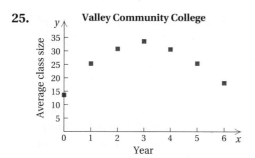

Valley Community College

27.

Driver Fatalities by Age

Source: National Highway Traffic Administration

28.

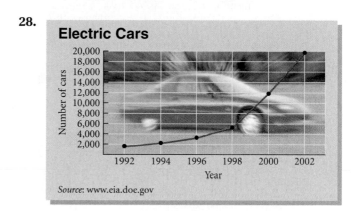

Electric Cars

Source: www.eia.doe.gov

29.

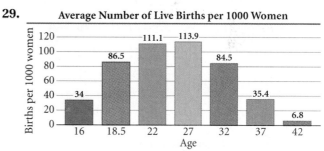

Average Number of Live Births per 1000 Women

Source: U.S. Centers for Disease Control

30.

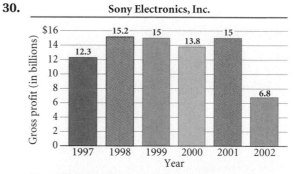

Sony Electronics, Inc.

Source: The New York Stock Exchange

31.

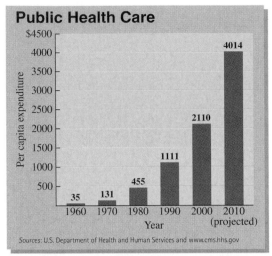

Public Health Care

Sources: U.S. Department of Health and Human Services and www.cms.hhs.gov

32.

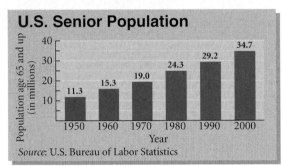

U.S. Senior Population

Source: U.S. Bureau of Labor Statistics

33.

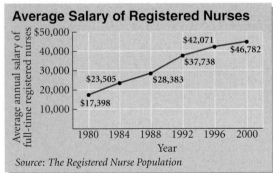

Average Salary of Registered Nurses

Source: The Registered Nurse Population

34.

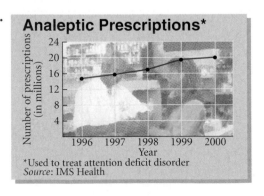

Analeptic Prescriptions*

*Used to treat attention deficit disorder
Source: IMS Health

Find a quadratic function that fits the set of data points.

35. $(1, 4), (-1, -2), (2, 13)$ **36.** $(1, 4), (-1, 6), (-2, 16)$

37. $(2, 0), (4, 3), (12, -5)$ **38.** $(-3, -30), (3, 0), (6, 6)$

39. a) Find a quadratic function that fits the following data.

Travel Speed (in kilometers per hour)	Number of Nighttime Accidents (for every 200 million kilometers driven)
60	400
80	250
100	250

b) Use the function to estimate the number of nighttime accidents that occur at 50 km/h.

40. a) Find a quadratic function that fits the following data.

Travel Speed (in kilometers per hour)	Number of Daytime Accidents (for every 200 million kilometers driven)
60	100
80	130
100	200

b) Use the function to estimate the number of daytime accidents that occur at 50 km/h.

41. *Archery.* The Olympic flame tower at the 1992 Summer Olympics was lit at a height of about 27 m by a flaming arrow that was launched about 63 m from the base of the tower. If the arrow landed about 63 m beyond the tower, find a quadratic function that expresses the height h of the arrow as a function of the distance d that it traveled horizontally.

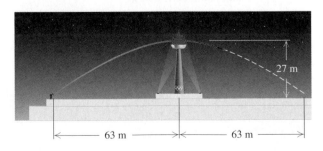

42. *Pizza prices.*   Pizza Unlimited has the following prices for pizzas.

Diameter	Price
8 in.	$ 6.00
12 in.	$ 8.50
16 in.	$11.50

Is price a quadratic function of diameter? It probably should be, because the price should be proportional to the area, and the area is a quadratic function of the diameter. (The area of a circular region is given by $A = \pi r^2$ or $(\pi/4) \cdot d^2$.)

a) Express price as a quadratic function of diameter using the data points (8, 6), (12, 8.50), and (16, 11.50).

b) Use the function to find the price of a 14-in. pizza.

43. Does every nonlinear function have a minimum or maximum value? Why or why not?

44. Explain how the leading coefficient of a quadratic function can be used to determine if a maximum or a minimum function value exists.

SKILL MAINTENANCE

Simplify.

45. $\dfrac{x}{x^2 + 17x + 72} - \dfrac{8}{x^2 + 15x + 56}$ [6.4]

46. $\dfrac{x^2 - 9}{x^2 - 8x + 7} \div \dfrac{x^2 + 6x + 9}{x^2 - 1}$ [6.2]

47. $\dfrac{t^2 - 4}{t^2 - 7t - 8} \cdot \dfrac{t^2 - 64}{t^2 - 5t + 6}$ [6.2]

48. $\dfrac{t}{t^2 - 10t + 21} + \dfrac{t}{t^2 - 49}$ [6.4]

Solve. [9.1]

49. $5x - 9 < 31$

50. $3x - 8 \geq 22$

SYNTHESIS

51. Write a problem for a classmate to solve. Design the problem so that its solution requires finding the minimum or maximum value.

52. Explain what restrictions should be placed on the quadratic functions developed in Exercises 39 and 42 and why such restrictions are needed.

53. *Bridge design.*   The cables supporting a straight-line suspension bridge are nearly parabolic in shape. Suppose that a suspension bridge is being designed with concrete supports 160 ft apart and with vertical cables 30 ft above road level at the midpoint of the bridge and 80 ft above road level at a point 50 ft from the midpoint of the bridge. How long are the longest vertical cables?

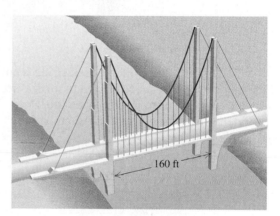

160 ft

54. *Trajectory of a launched object.*   The height above the ground of a launched object is a quadratic function of the time that it is in the air. Suppose that a flare is launched from a cliff 64 ft above sea level. If 3 sec after being launched the flare is again level with the cliff, and if 2 sec after that it lands in the sea, what is the maximum height that the flare will reach?

55. *Cover charges.*   When the owner of Sweet Sounds charges a $10 cover charge, an average of 80 people will attend a show. For each 25¢ increase in admission price, the average number attending decreases by 1. What should the owner charge in order to make the most money?

56. *Crop yield.*   An orange grower finds that she gets an average yield of 40 bushels (bu) per tree when she plants 20 trees on an acre of ground. Each time she adds a tree to an acre, the yield per tree decreases by 1 bu, due to congestion. How many trees per acre should she plant for maximum yield?

57. *Norman window.* A *Norman window* is a rectangle with a semicircle on top. Big Sky Windows is designing a Norman window that will require 24 ft of trim. What dimensions will allow the maximum amount of light to enter a house?

58. *Minimizing area.* A 36-in. piece of string is cut into two pieces. One piece is used to form a circle while the other is used to form a square. How should the string be cut so that the sum of the areas is a minimum?

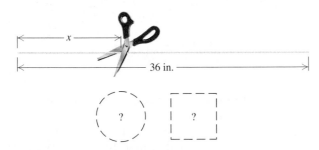

Regression can be used to find the "best"-fitting quadratic function when more than three data points are provided. In Exercises 59 and 60, six data points are given, but the approach used in the Technology Connection on p. 760 still applies.

59. *Alternative fueled vehicles.* The number of cars fueled by electricity in the United States during several years is shown in the table below.

Year	Number of Cars
1992	1,607
1994	2,224
1996	3,280
1998	5,243
2000	11,834
2002	19,755

Source: www.eia.doe.gov

a) Use regression to find a quadratic function that can be used to estimate the number of cars c that are fueled by electricity x years after 1992.
b) Use the function found in part (a) to predict the number of cars fueled by electricity in 2008.

60. *Hydrology.* The drawing below shows the cross section of a river. Typically rivers are deepest in the middle, with the depth decreasing to 0 at the edges. A hydrologist measures the depths D, in feet, of a river at distances x, in feet, from one bank. The results are listed in the table below.

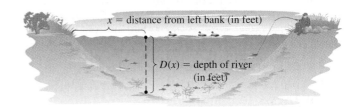

Distance x, from the Left Bank (in feet)	Depth, D, of the River (in feet)
0	0
15	10.2
25	17
50	20
90	7.2
100	0

a) Use regression to find a quadratic function that fits the data.
b) Use the function to estimate the depth of the river 70 ft from the left bank.

CORNER

Quadratic Counter Settings

Focus: Modeling quadratic functions
Time: 20–30 minutes
Group size: 3 or 4
Materials: Graphing calculators are optional.

The Panasonic Portable Stereo System RX-DT680® has a counter for finding locations on an audio cassette. When a fully wound cassette with 45 min of music on a side begins to play, the counter is at 0. After 15 min of music has played, the counter reads 250 and after 35 min, it reads 487. When the 45-min side is finished playing, the counter reads 590.

ACTIVITY

1. The paragraph above describes four ordered pairs of the form (counter number, minutes played). Three pairs are enough to find a function of the form

$$T(n) = an^2 + bn + c,$$

where $T(n)$ represents the time, in minutes, that the tape has run at counter reading n hundred. Each group member should select a different set of three points from the four given and then fit a quadratic function to the data.

2. Of the 3 or 4 functions found in part (1) above, which fits the data "best"? One way to answer this is to see how well each function predicts other pairs. The same counter used above reads 432 after a 45-min tape has played for 30 min. Which function comes closest to predicting this?

3. If a graphing calculator is available with a QUADREG option (see Exercise 59), what function does it fit to the four pairs originally listed?

4. If a class member has access to a Panasonic System RX-DT680, see how well the functions developed above predict the counter readings for a tape that has played for 5 or 10 min.

11.9 Polynomial and Rational Inequalities

> Quadratic and Other Polynomial Inequalities •
> Rational Inequalities

Quadratic and Other Polynomial Inequalities

Inequalities like the following are called *polynomial inequalities*:

$$x^3 - 5x > x^2 + 7, \qquad 4x - 3 < 9, \qquad 5x^2 - 3x + 2 \geq 0.$$

Second-degree polynomial inequalities in one variable are called *quadratic inequalities*. To solve polynomial inequalities, we often focus attention on where the outputs of a polynomial function are positive and where they are negative.

EXAMPLE 1 Solve: $x^2 + 3x - 10 > 0$.

Study Skills

Map Out Your Day

As the semester winds down and term papers are due, it becomes more critical than ever that you manage your time wisely. If you aren't already doing so, consider writing out an hour-by-hour schedule for each day and then abide by it as much as possible.

Solution Consider the "related" function $f(x) = x^2 + 3x - 10$ and its graph. Its graph opens upward since the leading coefficient is positive. Thus y-values are positive outside the interval formed by the x-intercepts. To find the intercepts, we set the polynomial equal to 0 and solve:

$$x^2 + 3x - 10 = 0$$
$$(x + 5)(x - 2) = 0$$
$$x + 5 = 0 \quad or \quad x - 2 = 0$$
$$x = -5 \quad or \quad x = 2.$$

Test values can be used to confirm that $f(x)$ is positive outside the interval $[-5, 2]$:

$$f(3) = 3^2 + 3 \cdot 3 - 10 = 9 + 9 - 10 = 8; \quad \text{Positive}$$
$$f(-6) = (-6)^2 + 3(-6) - 10 = 36 - 18 - 10 = 8.$$

Thus the solution set of the inequality is

$$\{x \mid x < -5 \text{ or } x > 2\}, \quad \text{or} \quad (-\infty, -5) \cup (2, \infty).$$

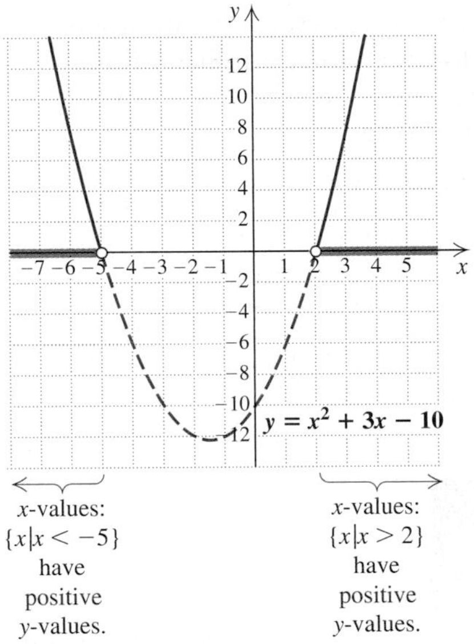

Any inequality with 0 on one side can be solved by considering a graph of the related function and finding intercepts as in Example 1. Sometimes the quadratic formula is needed to find the intercepts.

EXAMPLE 2 Solve: $x^2 - 2x \le 2$.

Solution We first write the quadratic inequality in standard form, with 0 on one side:

$$x^2 - 2x - 2 \le 0. \qquad \text{This is equivalent to the original inequality.}$$

The graph of $f(x) = x^2 - 2x - 2$ is a parabola opening upward. Values of $f(x)$ are negative for x-values between the x-intercepts. We find the x-intercepts by solving $f(x) = 0$:

$$x = \frac{-b \pm \sqrt{b^2 - 4ac}}{2a}$$

$$= \frac{-(-2) \pm \sqrt{(-2)^2 - 4 \cdot 1(-2)}}{2 \cdot 1}$$

$$= \frac{2 \pm \sqrt{12}}{2} = \frac{2}{2} \pm \frac{2\sqrt{3}}{2} = 1 \pm \sqrt{3}.$$

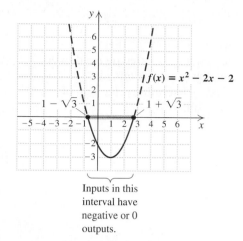

Inputs in this interval have negative or 0 outputs.

At the x-intercepts, $1 - \sqrt{3}$ and $1 + \sqrt{3}$, the value of $f(x)$ is 0. Thus the solution set of the inequality is

$$\left[1 - \sqrt{3}, 1 + \sqrt{3}\right], \quad \text{or} \quad \left\{x \mid 1 - \sqrt{3} \le x \le 1 + \sqrt{3}\right\}.$$

In Example 2, it was not essential to draw the graph. The important information came from finding the x-intercepts and the sign of $f(x)$ on each side of those intercepts. We now solve a third-degree polynomial inequality, without graphing, by locating the x-intercepts, or **zeros**, of f and then using *test points* to determine the sign of $f(x)$ over each interval of the x-axis.

EXAMPLE 3   For $f(x) = 5x^3 + 10x^2 - 15x$, find all x-values for which $f(x) > 0$.

Solution   We first solve the related equation:

$$f(x) = 0$$
$$5x^3 + 10x^2 - 15x = 0 \qquad \text{Substituting}$$
$$5x(x^2 + 2x - 3) = 0$$
$$5x(x + 3)(x - 1) = 0$$
$$5x = 0 \quad or \quad x + 3 = 0 \quad or \quad x - 1 = 0$$
$$x = 0 \quad or \qquad x = -3 \quad or \qquad x = 1.$$

The zeros of f are $-3, 0,$ and 1. These zeros divide the number line, or x-axis, into four intervals: A, B, C, and D.

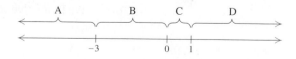

Next, selecting one convenient test value from each interval, we determine the sign of $f(x)$ for that interval. We know that, within each interval, the sign of $f(x)$ cannot change. If it did, there would need to be another zero in that interval.

Student Notes _____

When we are evaluating test values, there is often no need to do lengthy computations since all we need to determine is the sign of the result.

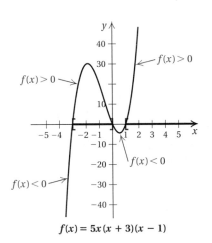

$f(x) = 5x(x + 3)(x - 1)$

A visualization of Example 3

Using the factored form of $f(x)$ eases the computations:

$$f(x) = 5x(x + 3)(x - 1).$$

For interval A,

$$f(-4) = 5(-4)((-4) + 3)((-4) - 1)$$

-4 is a convenient value in interval A.

$$= -20(-1)(-5)$$
$$= -100.$$

$f(-4)$ is negative.

For interval B,

$$f(-1) = 5(-1)((-1) + 3)((-1) - 1)$$

-1 is a convenient value in interval B.

$$= -5(2)(-2)$$
$$= 20.$$

$f(-1)$ is positive.

For interval C,

$$f(\tfrac{1}{2}) = 5 \cdot \tfrac{1}{2} \cdot (\tfrac{1}{2} + 3) \cdot (\tfrac{1}{2} - 1).$$

$\tfrac{1}{2}$ is a convenient value in interval C.

Positive   Positive   Negative

Negative

Only the sign is important. The product is negative, so $f(\tfrac{1}{2})$ is negative.

For interval D,

$$f(2) = 5 \cdot 2 \cdot (2 + 3) \cdot (2 - 1).$$

Positive   Positive   Positive

2 is a convenient value in interval D.

$f(2)$ is positive.

Recall that we are looking for all x for which $5x^3 + 10x^2 - 15x > 0$. The calculations above indicate that $f(x)$ is positive for any number in intervals B and D. The solution set of the original inequality is

$$(-3, 0) \cup (1, \infty), \quad \text{or} \quad \{x \mid -3 < x < 0 \text{ or } x > 1\}.$$

The calculations in Example 3 were made simpler by using a factored form of the polynomial. This process was simplified further when, for intervals C and D, we concentrated on only the *sign* of $f(x)$. In the next example, we determine the sign of a polynomial function over each interval by tracking the sign of each factor. By looking at how many positive or negative factors are being multiplied, we will be able to determine the sign of the polynomial function.

EXAMPLE 4   For $f(x) = 4x^3 - 4x$, find all x-values for which $f(x) \le 0$.

Solution   We first solve the related equation:

$$f(x) = 0$$
$$4x^3 - 4x = 0$$
$$4x(x^2 - 1) = 0$$
$$4x(x + 1)(x - 1) = 0$$
$$4x = 0 \quad or \quad x + 1 = 0 \quad or \quad x - 1 = 0$$
$$x = 0 \quad or \quad x = -1 \quad or \quad x = 1.$$

To solve $2.3x^2 \le 9.11 - 2.94x$, we first rewrite the inequality in the form $2.3x^2 + 2.94x - 9.11 \le 0$ and graph the function $f(x) = 2.3x^2 + 2.94x - 9.11$.

$y = 2.3x^2 + 2.94x - 9.11$

To find the values of x for which $f(x) \le 0$, we focus on the region in which the graph lies *on or below* the x-axis. It appears that this region begins somewhere between -3 and -2, and continues to somewhere between 1 and 2. Using the ZERO or ROOT option of CALC, we can find the endpoints of this region. To two decimal places, the endpoints are -2.73 and 1.45. The solution set is approximately $\{x | -2.73 \le x \le 1.45\}$.

Had the inequality been $2.3x^2 > 9.11 - 2.94x$, we would look for portions of the graph that lie *above* the x-axis. An approximate solution set of such an inequality would be $\{x | x < -2.73 \text{ or } x > 1.45\}$.

Use a graphing calculator to solve each inequality. Round the values of the endpoints to the nearest hundredth.

1. $4.32x^2 - 3.54x - 5.34 \le 0$
2. $7.34x^2 - 16.55x - 3.89 \ge 0$
3. $10.85x^2 + 4.28x + 4.44 > 7.91x^2 + 7.43x + 13.03$
4. $5.79x^3 - 5.68x^2 + 10.68x > 2.11x^3 + 16.90x - 11.69$

The function f has zeros at $-1, 0,$ and 1. Rather than use test values, as in Example 3, let's use the factorization $f(x) = 4x(x + 1)(x - 1)$. The product $4x(x + 1)(x - 1)$ is positive or negative, depending on the signs of $4x$, $x + 1$, and $x - 1$. This is easily determined using a chart.

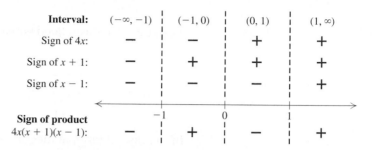

Interval:	$(-\infty, -1)$	$(-1, 0)$	$(0, 1)$	$(1, \infty)$
Sign of $4x$:	$-$	$-$	$+$	$+$
Sign of $x + 1$:	$-$	$+$	$+$	$+$
Sign of $x - 1$:	$-$	$-$	$-$	$+$
Sign of product $4x(x + 1)(x - 1)$:	$-$	$+$	$-$	$+$

A product is negative when it has an odd number of negative factors. Since the $\le$ sign allows for equality, the endpoints $-1, 0,$ and 1 are solutions. From the chart, we see that the solution set is

$$(-\infty, -1] \cup [0, 1], \text{ or } \{x | x \le -1 \text{ or } 0 \le x \le 1\}.$$

To Solve a Polynomial Inequality Using Factors

1. Add or subtract to get 0 on one side and solve the related polynomial equation by factoring.
2. Use the numbers found in step (1) to divide the number line into intervals.
3. Using a test value from each interval, determine the sign of each factor over that interval.
4. Determine the sign of the product of the factors over each interval. Remember that the product of an odd number of negative numbers is negative.
5. Select the interval(s) for which the inequality is satisfied and write set-builder notation or interval notation for the solution set. Include the endpoints of the intervals when $\le$ or $\ge$ is used.

Rational Inequalities

Inequalities involving rational expressions are called **rational inequalities**. Like polynomial inequalities, rational inequalities can be solved using test values. Unlike polynomials, however, rational expressions often have values for which the expression is undefined.

EXAMPLE 5   Solve: $\dfrac{x-3}{x+4} \geq 2$.

Solution   We write the related equation by changing the $\geq$ symbol to $=$:

$$\frac{x-3}{x+4} = 2. \qquad \text{Note that } x \neq -4.$$

Next, we solve this related equation:

$$(x+4) \cdot \frac{x-3}{x+4} = (x+4) \cdot 2 \qquad \begin{array}{l}\text{Multiplying both sides}\\ \text{by the LCD, } x+4\end{array}$$

$$x - 3 = 2x + 8$$

$$-11 = x. \qquad\qquad\qquad \text{Solving for } x$$

In the case of rational inequalities, we must always find any values that make the denominator 0. As noted at the beginning of this example, $x \neq -4$.

Now we use -11 and -4 to divide the number line into intervals:

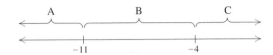

We test a number in each interval to see where the original inequality is satisfied:

$$\frac{x-3}{x+4} \geq 2.$$

A: Test -15, $\dfrac{-15-3}{-15+4} = \dfrac{-18}{-11}$

$$= \frac{18}{11} \not\geq 2 \qquad \begin{array}{l}-15 \text{ } is \text{ } not \text{ a solution, so interval A is}\\ \text{not part of the solution set.}\end{array}$$

B: Test -8, $\dfrac{-8-3}{-8+4} = \dfrac{-11}{-4}$

$$= \frac{11}{4} \geq 2 \qquad \begin{array}{l}-8 \text{ } is \text{ a solution, so interval B is part of}\\ \text{the solution set.}\end{array}$$

C: Test 1, $\dfrac{1-3}{1+4} = \dfrac{-2}{5}$

$$= -\frac{2}{5} \not\geq 2 \qquad \begin{array}{l}1 \text{ } is \text{ } not \text{ a solution, so interval C is not}\\ \text{part of the solution set.}\end{array}$$

The solution set includes interval B. The endpoint -11 is included because the inequality symbol is $\geq$ and -11 is a solution of the related equation. The number -4 is *not* included because $(x-3)/(x+4)$ is undefined for $x = -4$. Thus the solution set of the original inequality is

$$[-11, -4), \quad \text{or} \quad \{x \mid -11 \leq x < -4\}.$$

ALGEBRAIC—GRAPHICAL CONNECTION

Let's compare the algebraic solution of Example 5 to a graphical solution. By graphing $f(x) = (x - 3)/(x + 4)$, we can find the solutions of $(x - 3)/(x + 4) \geq 2$ by sketching the line $y = 2$ and locating all x-values for which $f(x) \geq 2$.

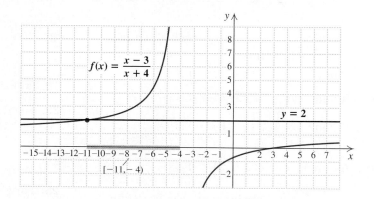

Because graphing rational functions can be very time-consuming, we generally just use test values.

To Solve a Rational Inequality

1. Change the inequality symbol to an equals sign and solve the related equation.
2. Find any replacements for which the rational expression is undefined.
3. Use the numbers found in steps (1) and (2) to divide the number line into intervals.
4. Substitute a test value from each interval into the inequality. If the number is a solution, then the interval to which it belongs is part of the solution set.
5. Select the interval(s) and any endpoints for which the inequality is satisfied and write set-builder or interval notation for the solution set. If the inequality symbol is $\leq$ or $\geq$, then the solutions from step (1) are also included in the solution set. Those numbers found in step (2) should be excluded from the solution set, even if they are solutions from step (1).

Exercise Set

11.9

↳ *Concept Reinforcement* *Classify each of the following as either true or false.*

1. The solution of $(x - 3)(x + 2) \le 0$ is $[-2, 3]$.

2. The solution of $(x + 5)(x - 4) \ge 0$ is $[-5, 4]$.

3. The solution of $(x - 1)(x - 6) > 0$ is $\{x \mid x < 1 \text{ or } x > 6\}$.

4. The solution of $(x + 4)(x + 2) < 0$ is $(-4, -2)$.

5. To solve $\dfrac{x - 5}{x + 4} \ge 0$ using intervals, we divide the number line into the intervals $(-\infty, -4)$, $(-4, 5)$, and $(5, \infty)$.

6. To solve $\dfrac{x + 2}{x - 3} < 0$ using intervals, we divide the number line into the intervals $(-\infty, -2)$, $(-2, 3)$, and $(3, \infty)$.

7. The solution of $\dfrac{3}{x - 5} \le 0$ is $[5, \infty)$.

8. The solution of $\dfrac{-2}{x + 3} \ge 0$ is $(-\infty, -3]$.

Solve.

9. $(x + 4)(x - 3) < 0$

10. $(x - 5)(x + 2) > 0$

11. $(x + 7)(x - 2) \ge 0$

12. $(x - 1)(x + 4) \le 0$

13. $x^2 - x - 2 > 0$

14. $x^2 + x - 2 < 0$

Aha! **15.** $x^2 + 4x + 4 < 0$

16. $x^2 + 6x + 9 < 0$

17. $x^2 - 4x < 12$

18. $x^2 + 6x > -8$

19. $3x(x + 2)(x - 2) < 0$

20. $5x(x + 1)(x - 1) > 0$

21. $(x - 1)(x + 2)(x - 4) \ge 0$

22. $(x + 3)(x + 2)(x - 1) < 0$

23. For $f(x) = x^2 - 1$, find all x-values for which $f(x) \le 3$.

24. For $f(x) = x^2 - 20$, find all x-values for which $f(x) > 5$.

25. For $g(x) = (x - 2)(x - 3)(x + 1)$, find all x-values for which $g(x) > 0$.

26. For $g(x) = (x + 3)(x - 2)(x + 1)$, find all x-values for which $g(x) < 0$.

27. For $F(x) = x^3 - 7x^2 + 10x$, find all x-values for which $F(x) \le 0$.

28. For $G(x) = x^3 - 8x^2 + 12x$, find all x-values for which $G(x) \ge 0$.

Solve.

29. $\dfrac{1}{x + 5} < 0$

30. $\dfrac{1}{x + 4} > 0$

31. $\dfrac{x + 1}{x - 3} \ge 0$

32. $\dfrac{x - 2}{x + 4} \le 0$

33. $\dfrac{x + 1}{x + 6} \ge 1$

34. $\dfrac{x - 1}{x - 2} \le 1$

35. $\dfrac{(x - 2)(x + 1)}{x - 5} \le 0$

36. $\dfrac{(x + 4)(x - 1)}{x + 3} \ge 0$

37. $\dfrac{x}{x + 3} \ge 0$

38. $\dfrac{x - 2}{x} \le 0$

39. $\dfrac{x - 5}{x} < 1$

40. $\dfrac{x}{x - 1} > 2$

41. $\dfrac{x - 1}{(x - 3)(x + 4)} \le 0$

42. $\dfrac{x + 2}{(x - 2)(x + 7)} \ge 0$

43. For $f(x) = \dfrac{5 - 2x}{4x + 3}$, find all x-values for which $f(x) \ge 0$.

44. For $g(x) = \dfrac{2 + 3x}{2x - 4}$, find all x-values for which

$g(x) \geq 0$.

45. For $G(x) = \dfrac{1}{x - 2}$, find all x-values for which

$G(x) \leq 1$.

46. For $F(x) = \dfrac{1}{x - 3}$, find all x-values for which

$F(x) \leq 2$.

47. Explain how any quadratic inequality can be solved by examining a parabola.

48. Describe a method for creating a quadratic inequality for which there is no solution.

SKILL MAINTENANCE

Simplify.

49. $(2a^3b^2c^4)^3$ [4.1]

50. $(5a^4b^7)^2$ [4.1]

51. 2^{-5} [4.8]

52. 3^{-4} [4.8]

53. If $f(x) = 3x^2$, find $f(a + 1)$. [7.1]

54. If $g(x) = 5x - 3$, find $g(a + 2)$. [7.1]

SYNTHESIS

55. Step (5) on p. 773 states that even when the inequality symbol is $\leq$ or $\geq$, the solutions from step (1) are not always part of the solution set. Why?

56. Describe a method that could be used to create quadratic inequalities that have $(-\infty, a] \cup [b, \infty)$ as the solution set. Assume $a < b$.

Find each solution set.

57. $x^2 + 2x < 5$

58. $x^4 + 2x^2 \geq 0$

59. $x^4 + 3x^2 \leq 0$

60. $\left| \dfrac{x + 2}{x - 1} \right| \leq 3$

61. *Total profit.*   Derex, Inc., determines that its total-profit function is given by

$$P(x) = -3x^2 + 630x - 6000.$$

a) Find all values of x for which Derex makes a profit.

b) Find all values of x for which Derex loses money.

62. *Height of a thrown object.*   The function

$$S(t) = -16t^2 + 32t + 1920$$

gives the height S, in feet, of an object thrown from a cliff that is 1920 ft high. Here t is the time, in seconds, that the object is in the air.

a) For what times does the height exceed 1920 ft?

b) For what times is the height less than 640 ft?

63. *Number of handshakes.*   There are n people in a room. The number N of possible handshakes by the people is given by the function

$$N(n) = \dfrac{n(n - 1)}{2}.$$

For what number of people n is $66 \leq N \leq 300$?

64. *Number of diagonals.*   A polygon with n sides has D diagonals, where D is given by the function

$$D(n) = \dfrac{n(n - 3)}{2}.$$

Find the number of sides n if

$27 \leq D \leq 230$.

Use a graphing calculator to graph each function and find solutions of $f(x) = 0$. Then solve the inequalities $f(x) < 0$ and $f(x) > 0$.

65. $f(x) = x^3 - 2x^2 - 5x + 6$

66. $f(x) = \dfrac{1}{3}x^3 - x + \dfrac{2}{3}$

67. $f(x) = x + \dfrac{1}{x}$

68. $f(x) = x - \sqrt{x},\ x \geq 0$

69. $f(x) = \dfrac{x^3 - x^2 - 2x}{x^2 + x - 6}$

70. $f(x) = x^4 - 4x^3 - x^2 + 16x - 12$

71. Use a graphing calculator to solve Exercises 39 and 45 by drawing two curves, one for each side of the inequality.

Study Summary

Any equation that can be written in the form $ax^2 + bx + c = 0$, with a, b, and c constant, is said to be **quadratic** (p. 704). There are several methods for solving quadratic equations:

Factoring (p. 704)

Easiest method to use *if* you can factor the polynomial.

$$x^2 - 3x - 10 = 0$$
$$(x + 2)(x - 5) = 0$$
$$x + 2 = 0 \quad or \quad x - 5 = 0$$
$$x = -2 \quad or \quad x = 5$$

Principle of Square Roots (p. 705)

Works only if a perfect-square trinomial is on one side and a constant is on the other side.

$$x^2 - 8x + 16 = 25$$
$$(x - 4)^2 = 25$$
$$x - 4 = -5 \quad or \quad x - 4 = 5$$
$$x = -1 \quad or \quad x = 9$$

Completing the Square (p. 707)

Can be used to solve *any* quadratic equation, but calculations can be lengthy.

$$x^2 + 6x = 1$$
$$x^2 + 6x + \left(\tfrac{6}{2}\right)^2 = 1 + \left(\tfrac{6}{2}\right)^2$$
$$x^2 + 6x + 9 = 1 + 9$$
$$(x + 3)^2 = 10$$
$$x + 3 = \pm\sqrt{10}$$
$$x = -3 \pm \sqrt{10}$$

Quadratic Formula (p. 716)

> If $ax^2 + bx + c = 0$,
> then $x = \dfrac{-b \pm \sqrt{b^2 - 4ac}}{2a}$.

Is based on completing the square but is quicker to use. Can be used to solve *any* quadratic equation.

$$3x^2 - 2x - 5 = 0$$
$$x = \frac{-(-2) \pm \sqrt{(-2)^2 - 4 \cdot 3(-5)}}{2 \cdot 3}$$
$$x = \frac{2 \pm \sqrt{4 + 60}}{6}$$
$$x = \frac{2 \pm \sqrt{64}}{6}$$
$$x = \frac{2 \pm 8}{6}$$
$$x = \frac{10}{6} = \frac{5}{3} \quad or \quad x = \frac{-6}{6} = -1$$

The **discriminant** of the quadratic formula can be used to find the nature of the solution(s) of a quadratic equation (p. 730):

$b^2 - 4ac = 0 \;\rightarrow\;$ One solution; a rational number.

$b^2 - 4ac > 0 \;\rightarrow\;$ Two real solutions, both rational if $b^2 - 4ac$ is a perfect square.

$b^2 - 4ac < 0 \;\rightarrow\;$ Two imaginary-number solutions.

The methods for solving quadratic equations can be applied to equations that are not quadratic but are in **quadratic form** (p. 735):

$$x^4 - 10x^2 + 9 = 0 \qquad \text{Think of } x^2 \text{ as } u \text{ and } x^4 \text{ as } u^2.$$
$$u^2 - 10u + 9 = 0$$
$$(u - 9)(u - 1) = 0$$
$$u - 9 = 0 \quad or \quad u - 1 = 0$$
$$u = 9 \quad or \quad u = 1$$
$$x^2 = 9 \quad or \quad x^2 = 1$$
$$x = \pm 3 \quad or \quad x = \pm 1.$$

The graph of a quadratic function is a **parabola** (p. 742). The graph of $f(x) = ax^2 + bx + c$ opens upward for $a > 0$ and downward for $a < 0$. The graph of an equation of the form $f(x) = a(x - h)^2 + k$ looks like the graph of $y = ax^2$ **translated** $|h|$ units to the right (for $h > 0$) or left (for $h < 0$) and $|k|$ units up (for $k > 0$) or down (for $k < 0$).

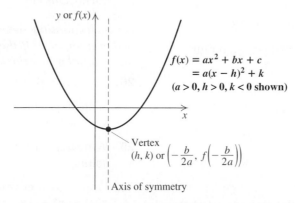

Every parabola has an **axis of symmetry** and **vertex** as shown above (p. 742). For a quadratic function, the second coordinate of the vertex is a **minimum** (for $a > 0$) or **maximum** (for $a < 0$) function value (p. 744).

The x-intercepts, or **zeros**, of a function are used to divide the x-axis into intervals when solving **polynomial** or **rational inequalities** (pp. 767, 771). Rational inequalities also require forming intervals on either side of any x-value(s) for which the denominator is 0. We then use test values from each interval to identify the solution set.

11 Review Exercises

Classify each statement as either true or false.

1. Every quadratic equation has two different solutions. [11.4]

2. Every quadratic equation has at least one solution. [11.4]

3. If an equation cannot be solved by completing the square, it cannot be solved by the quadratic formula. [11.2]

4. A negative discriminant indicates two imaginary-number solutions of a quadratic equation. [11.4]

5. Certain radical or rational equations can be written in quadratic form. [11.5]

6. The graph of $f(x) = 2(x + 3)^2 - 4$ has its vertex at $(3, -4)$. [11.6]

7. The graph of $g(x) = 5x^2$ has $x = 0$ as its axis of symmetry. [11.6]

8. The graph of $f(x) = -2x^2 + 1$ has no minimum value. [11.6]

9. The zeros of $g(x) = x^2 - 9$ are -3 and 3. [11.6]

10. To solve a polynomial inequality, we often must solve a polynomial equation. [11.9]

Solve.

11. $4x^2 - 9 = 0$ [11.1]

12. $8x^2 + 6x = 0$ [11.1]

13. $x^2 - 12x + 36 = 9$ [11.1]

14. $x^2 - 4x + 8 = 0$ [11.2]

15. $x(3x + 4) = 4x(x - 1) + 15$ [11.2]

16. $x^2 + 9x = 1$ [11.2]

17. $x^2 - 5x - 2 = 0$. Use a calculator to approximate the solutions with rational numbers. [11.2]

18. Let $f(x) = 4x^2 - 3x - 1$. Find x such that $f(x) = 0$. [11.2]

Replace the blanks with constants to form a true equation. [11.1]

19. $x^2 - 12x + \underline{\quad} = (x - \underline{\quad})^2$

20. $x^2 + \frac{3}{5}x + \underline{\quad} = (x + \underline{\quad})^2$

21. Solve by completing the square. Show your work.
$x^2 - 6x + 1 = 0$ [11.1]

22. \$2500 grows to \$3025 in 2 yr. Use the formula $A = P(1 + r)^t$ to find the interest rate. [11.1]

23. The Peachtree Center Plaza in Atlanta, Georgia, is 723 ft tall. Use $s = 16t^2$ to approximate how long it would take an object to fall from the top. [11.1]

Solve. [11.3]

24. A corporate pilot must fly from company headquarters to a manufacturing plant and back in 4 hr. The distance between headquarters and the plant is 300 mi. If there is a 20-mph headwind going and a 20-mph tailwind returning, how fast must the plane be able to travel in still air?

25. Working together, Erica and Shawna can answer a day's worth of customer-service e-mails in 4 hr. Working alone, Erica takes 6 hr longer than Shawna. How long would it take Shawna to answer the e-mails alone?

For each equation, determine whether the solutions are real or imaginary. If they are real, specify whether they are rational or irrational. [11.4]

26. $x^2 + 3x - 6 = 0$

27. $x^2 + 2x + 5 = 0$

28. Write a quadratic equation having the solutions $\sqrt{5}$ and $-\sqrt{5}$. [11.4]

29. Write a quadratic equation having -4 as its only solution. [11.4]

30. Find all x-intercepts of the graph of $f(x) = x^4 - 13x^2 + 36$. [11.5]

Solve. [11.5]

31. $15x^{-2} - 2x^{-1} - 1 = 0$

32. $(x^2 - 4)^2 - (x^2 - 4) - 6 = 0$

33. **a)** Graph: $f(x) = -3(x + 2)^2 + 4$. [11.6]
    b) Label the vertex.
    c) Draw the axis of symmetry.
    d) Find the maximum or the minimum value.

34. For the function given by $f(x) = 2x^2 - 12x + 23$: [11.7]

   a) find the vertex and the axis of symmetry;
   b) graph the function.

35. Find the x- and y-intercepts of
$$f(x) = x^2 - 9x + 14.\ [11.7]$$

36. Solve $N = 3\pi\sqrt{1/p}$ for p. [11.3]

37. Solve $2A + T = 3T^2$ for T. [11.3]

State whether each graph appears to represent a quadratic or linear function. [11.8]

38.

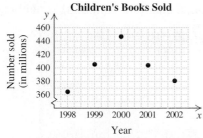

Children's Books Sold

Source: Statistical Abstract of the United States, 2003

39.

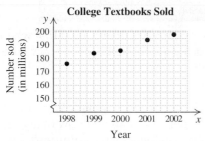

College Textbooks Sold

Source: Statistical Abstract of the United States, 2003

40. Eastgate Consignments wants to build a rectangular area in a corner for children to play in while their parents shop. They have 30 ft of low fencing. What is the maximum area they can enclose? What dimensions will yield this area? [11.8]

41. The following table lists the number of children's books sold (in millions) x years after 1998. (See Exercise 38.) [11.8]

Years Since 1998	Number of Children's Books Sold (in millions)
1	406
2	447
3	404

   a) Find the quadratic function that fits the data.
   b) Use the function to estimate the number of children's books sold in 2002.

Solve. [11.9]

42. $x^3 - 3x > 2x^2$

43. $\dfrac{x - 5}{x + 3} \le 0$

SYNTHESIS

44. Explain how the x-intercepts of a quadratic function can be used to help find the maximum or minimum value of the function. [11.7], [11.8]

45. Suppose that the quadratic formula is used to solve a quadratic equation. If the discriminant is a perfect square, could factoring have been used to solve the equation? Why or why not? [11.2], [11.4]

46. What is the greatest number of solutions that an equation of the form $ax^4 + bx^2 + c = 0$ can have? Why? [11.5]

47. Discuss two ways in which completing the square was used in this chapter. [11.1], [11.2], [11.7]

48. A quadratic function has x-intercepts at -3 and 5. If the y-intercept is at -7, find an equation for the function. [11.7]

49. Find h and k if, for $3x^2 - hx + 4k = 0$, the sum of the solutions is 20 and the product of the solutions is 80. [11.4]

50. The average of two positive integers is 171. One of the numbers is the square root of the other. Find the integers. [11.5]

11 Chapter Test

Solve.

1. $4x^2 - 11 = 0$

2. $4x(x - 2) - 3x(x + 1) = -18$

3. $x^2 + 2x + 3 = 0$

4. $2x + 5 = x^2$ 5. $x^{-2} - x^{-1} = \frac{3}{4}$

6. $x^2 + 3x = 5$. Use a calculator to approximate the solutions with rational numbers.

7. Let $f(x) = 12x^2 - 19x - 21$. Find x such that $f(x) = 0$.

Replace the blanks with constants to form a true equation.

8. $x^2 - 16x + \underline{\quad} = (x - \underline{\quad})^2$

9. $x^2 + \frac{2}{7}x + \underline{\quad} = \left(x + \underline{\quad}\right)^2$

10. Solve by completing the square. Show your work.
    $$x^2 + 10x + 15 = 0$$

Solve.

11. The Connecticut River flows at a rate of 4 km/h for the length of a popular scenic route. In order for a cruiser to travel 60 km upriver and then return in a total of 8 hr, how fast must the boat be able to travel in still water?

12. Brock and Ian can assemble a swing set in $1\frac{1}{2}$ hr. Working alone, it takes Ian 4 hr longer than Brock to assemble the swing set. How long would it take Brock, working alone, to assemble the swing set?

13. Determine the type of number that the solutions of $x^2 + 5x + 13 = 0$ will be.

14. Write a quadratic equation having solutions -2 and $\frac{1}{3}$.

15. Find all x-intercepts of the graph of
    $$f(x) = x^4 - 15x^2 - 16.$$

16. a) Graph: $f(x) = 4(x - 3)^2 + 5$.
    b) Label the vertex.
    c) Draw the axis of symmetry.
    d) Find the maximum or the minimum function value.

17. For the function $f(x) = 2x^2 + 4x - 6$:
    a) find the vertex and the axis of symmetry;
    b) graph the function.

18. Find the x- and y-intercepts of
    $$f(x) = x^2 - x - 6.$$

19. Solve $V = \frac{1}{3}\pi(R^2 + r^2)$ for r. Assume all variables are positive.

20. State whether the graph appears to represent a linear function, a quadratic function, or neither.

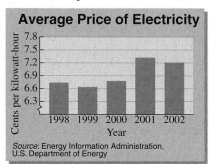

Average Price of Electricity

Source: Energy Information Administration, U.S. Department of Energy

21. Jay's Custom Pickups has determined that when x hundred truck caps are built, the average cost per cap is given by
    $$C(x) = 0.2x^2 - 1.3x + 3.4025,$$
    where $C(x)$ is in hundreds of dollars. What is the minimum cost per truck cap and how many caps should be built to achieve that minimum?

22. Find the quadratic function that fits the data points $(0, 0)$, $(3, 0)$, and $(5, 2)$.

Solve.

23. $x^2 + 5x < 6$

24. $x - \dfrac{1}{x} \geq 0$

SYNTHESIS

25. One solution of $kx^2 + 3x - k = 0$ is -2. Find the other solution.

26. Find a fourth-degree polynomial equation, with integer coefficients, for which $2 - \sqrt{3}$ and $5 - i$ are solutions.

27. Find a polynomial equation, with integer coefficients, for which 5 is a repeated root and $\sqrt{2}$ and $\sqrt{3}$ are solutions.

12

Exponential and Logarithmic Functions

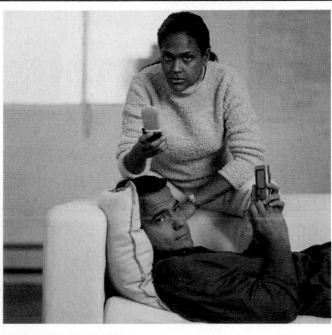

AN APPLICATION

As more Americans make cell phones their *only* phones, the percentage of phone lines that are land lines is shrinking and can be estimated by

$$P(t) = 63.03(0.95)^t,$$

where t is the number of years since 2000. In what year will the percentage of phones that are land lines drop below 25%?

This problem appears as Exercise 7 in Section 12.7.

Teresa Matos
ENGINEER
Falls Church, Virginia

We use math with everything. Without math, we could not have technology. We use math to quantify cost as well. With knowledge of math, people can do anything.

*T*he functions that we consider in this chapter are interesting not only from a purely intellectual point of view, but also for their rich applications to many fields. We will look at applications such as spread of a disease and population growth, to name just two.

The theory centers on functions with variable exponents (exponential functions). Results follow from those functions, their properties, and the inverses of those functions.

12.1 Composite and Inverse Functions

Composite Functions • Inverses and One-to-One Functions • Finding Formulas for Inverses • Graphing Functions and Their Inverses • Inverse Functions and Composition

Composite Functions

In the real world, functions frequently occur in which some quantity depends on a variable that, in turn, depends on another variable. For instance, a firm's profits may depend on the number of items the firm produces, which may in turn depend on the number of employees hired. Functions like this are called **composite functions**.

For example, the function g that gives a correspondence between women's shoe sizes in the United States and those in Italy is given by $g(x) = 2x + 24$, where x is the U.S. size and $g(x)$ is the Italian size. Thus a U.S. size 4 corresponds to a shoe size of $g(4) = 2 \cdot 4 + 24$, or 32, in Italy.

A different function gives a correspondence between women's shoe sizes in Italy and those in Britain. This particular function is given by $f(x) = \frac{1}{2}x - 14$, where x is the Italian size and $f(x)$ is the corresponding British size. Thus an Italian size 32 corresponds to a British size $f(32) = \frac{1}{2} \cdot 32 - 14$, or 2.

It seems reasonable to conclude that a U.S. size 4 corresponds to a British size 2 and that some function h describes this correspondence. Can we find a formula for h? If we look at the following tables, we might guess that such a formula is $h(x) = x - 2$, and that is indeed correct. But, for more complicated formulas, we would need to use algebra.

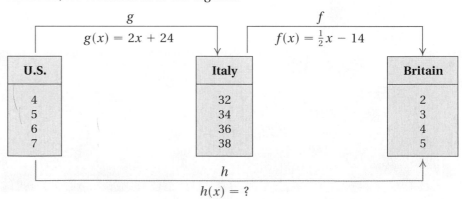

Size x shoes in the United States correspond to size $g(x)$ shoes in Italy, where

$$g(x) = 2x + 24.$$

Size n shoes in Italy correspond to size $f(n)$ shoes in Britain. Similarly, size $g(x)$ shoes in Italy correspond to size $f(g(x))$ shoes in Britain. Since the x in the expression $f(g(x))$ represents a U.S. shoe size, we can find the British shoe size that corresponds to a U.S. size x as follows:

$$f(g(x)) = f(2x + 24) = \tfrac{1}{2} \cdot (2x + 24) - 14 \qquad \text{Using } g(x) \text{ as an input}$$
$$= x + 12 - 14 = x - 2.$$

This gives a formula for h: $h(x) = x - 2$. Thus U.S. size 4 corresponds to British size $h(4) = 4 - 2$, or 2. The function h is the *composition* of f and g and is denoted $f \circ g$ (read "the composition of f and g," "f composed with g," or "f circle g").

Composition of Functions

The *composite function* $f \circ g$, the *composition* of f and g, is defined as

$$(f \circ g)(x) = f(g(x)).$$

We can visualize the composition of functions as follows.

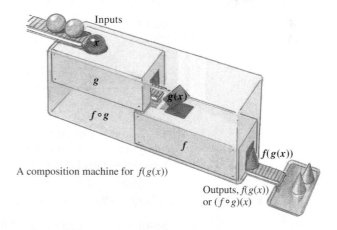

A composition machine for $f(g(x))$

EXAMPLE 1   Given $f(x) = 3x$ and $g(x) = 1 + x^2$:

a) Find $(f \circ g)(5)$ and $(g \circ f)(5)$.   **b)** Find $(f \circ g)(x)$ and $(g \circ f)(x)$.

Solution   Consider each function separately:

$$f(x) = 3x \qquad \text{This function multiplies each input by 3.}$$

and

$$g(x) = 1 + x^2. \qquad \text{This function adds 1 to the square of each input.}$$

In Example 3, we see that if $g(x) = 7x + 3$ and $f(x) = x^2$, then $f(g(x)) = (7x + 3)^2$. One way to show this is to let $y_1 = 7x + 3$ and $y_2 = (y_1)^2$ (this is accomplished by using the Y-VARS option of the VARS key's menu). We then let $y_3 = (7x + 3)^2$ and use graphs or a table to show that $y_2 = y_3$.

   Another approach is to let $y_1 = 7x + 3$ and $y_2 = x^2$ and have $y_4 = y_2(y_1)$. If we again let $y_3 = (7x + 3)^2$, we complete the check by showing that $y_3 = y_4$.

1. Check Example 2 by using one of the above approaches.

a) To find $(f \circ g)(5)$, we find $g(5)$ and then use that as an input for f:

$$(f \circ g)(5) = f(g(5)) = f(1 + 5^2) \qquad \text{Using } g(x) = 1 + x^2$$
$$= f(26) = 3 \cdot 26 = 78. \qquad \text{Using } f(x) = 3x$$

To find $(g \circ f)(5)$, we find $f(5)$ and then use that as an input for g:

$$(g \circ f)(5) = g(f(5)) = g(3 \cdot 5) \qquad \text{Note that } f(5) = 3 \cdot 5 = 15.$$
$$= g(15) = 1 + 15^2 = 1 + 225 = 226.$$

b) We find $(f \circ g)(x)$ by substituting $g(x)$ for x in the equation for $f(x)$:

$$(f \circ g)(x) = f(g(x)) = f(1 + x^2) \qquad \text{Using } g(x) = 1 + x^2$$
$$= 3 \cdot (1 + x^2) = 3 + 3x^2. \qquad \text{Using } f(x) = 3x$$

To find $(g \circ f)(x)$, we substitute $f(x)$ for x in the equation for $g(x)$:

$$(g \circ f)(x) = g(f(x)) = g(3x) \qquad \text{Substituting } 3x \text{ for } f(x)$$
$$= 1 + (3x)^2 = 1 + 9x^2.$$

As a check, note that $(g \circ f)(5) = 1 + 9 \cdot 5^2 = 1 + 9 \cdot 25 = 226$, as expected from part (a) above.

Example 1 shows that, in general, $(f \circ g)(5) \neq (g \circ f)(5)$ and $(f \circ g)(x) \neq (g \circ f)(x)$.

EXAMPLE 2   Given $f(x) = \sqrt{x}$ and $g(x) = x - 1$, find $(f \circ g)(x)$ and $(g \circ f)(x)$.

Solution

$$(f \circ g)(x) = f(g(x)) = f(x - 1) = \sqrt{x - 1} \qquad \text{Using } g(x) = x - 1$$
$$(g \circ f)(x) = g(f(x)) = g(\sqrt{x}) = \sqrt{x} - 1 \qquad \text{Using } f(x) = \sqrt{x}$$

In fields ranging from chemistry to geology and economics, one needs to recognize how a function can be regarded as the composition of two "simpler" functions. This is sometimes called *de*composition.

EXAMPLE 3   If $h(x) = (7x + 3)^2$, find f and g such that $h(x) = (f \circ g)(x)$.

Solution   We can think of $h(x)$ as the result of first finding $7x + 3$ and then squaring that. This suggests that $g(x) = 7x + 3$ and $f(x) = x^2$. We check by forming the composition:

$$(f \circ g)(x) = f(g(x))$$
$$= f(7x + 3) = (7x + 3)^2 = h(x), \text{ as desired.}$$

This is probably the most "obvious" answer to the question. There are other less obvious answers. For example, if

$$f(x) = (x - 1)^2 \quad \text{and} \quad g(x) = 7x + 4,$$

Student Notes

Throughout this chapter, keep in mind that functions are defined using dummy variables that represent an arbitrary member of the domain. Thus, $f(x) = x^2 - 3x$ and $f(t) = t^2 - 3t$ describe the same function f.

then

$$(f \circ g)(x) = f(g(x)) = f(7x + 4)$$
$$= (7x + 4 - 1)^2 = (7x + 3)^2 = h(x).$$

Inverses and One-to-One Functions

Let's view the following two functions as relations, or correspondences.

Selected Professions and Their Median Yearly Salary in 2003*

Domain (Set of Inputs)	Range (Set of Outputs)
Registered nurse	→ $49,550
Film and video editor	→ $40,600
Firefighter	→ $37,060
Computer programmer	→ $61,340
Secondary-school teacher	→ $44,580
Architect	→ $57,950

U.S. Senators and Their States

Domain (Set of Inputs)	Range (Set of Outputs)
Feinstein	→ California
Boxer	
Obama	→ Illinois
Durban	
Clinton	→ New York
Schumer	

Suppose we reverse the arrows. We obtain what is called the **inverse relation**. Are these inverse relations functions?

Selected Professions and Their Median Yearly Salary in 2003

Range (Set of Outputs)	Domain (Set of Inputs)
Registered nurse ←	$49,550
Film and video editor ←	$40,600
Firefighter ←	$37,060
Computer programmer ←	$61,340
Secondary-school teacher ←	$44,580
Architect ←	$57,950

U.S. Senators and Their States

Range (Set of Outputs)	Domain (Set of Inputs)
Feinstein ←	California
Boxer ←	
Obama ←	Illinois
Durban ←	
Clinton ←	New York
Schumer ←	

Recall that for each input, a function provides exactly one output. However, a function can have the same output for two or more different inputs. Thus it is possible for different inputs to correspond to the same output. Only when this possibility is *excluded* will the inverse be a function. For the functions listed above, this means the inverse of the "Selected Professions" correspondence is a function, but the inverse of the "U.S. Senator" correspondence is not.

*Source: U.S. Bureau of Labor Statistics, May 2003, Occupational Employment and Wage Estimates

In the Selected Professions function, different inputs have different outputs, so it is a **one-to-one function**. In the U.S. Senator function, *Clinton* and *Schumer* are both paired with *New York*. Thus the U.S. Senator function is not one-to-one.

One-To-One Function

A function f is *one-to-one* if different inputs have different outputs. That is, if for a and b in the domain of f with $a \neq b$, we have $f(a) \neq f(b)$, then the function f is one-to-one. If a function is one-to-one, then its inverse correspondence is also a function.

How can we tell graphically whether a function is one-to-one?

EXAMPLE 4

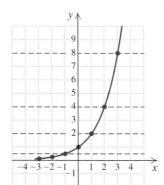

At left is the graph of a function similar to those we will study in Section 9.2. Determine whether the function is one-to-one and thus has an inverse that is a function.

Solution   A function is one-to-one if different inputs have different outputs—that is, if no two x-values have the same y-value. For this function, we cannot find two x-values that have the same y-value. Note that this means that no horizontal line can be drawn so that it crosses the graph more than once. The function is one-to-one so its inverse is a function.

The graph of every function must pass the vertical-line test. In order for a function to have an inverse that is a function, it must pass the *horizontal-line test* as well.

The Horizontal-Line Test

If it is impossible to draw a horizontal line that intersects a function's graph more than once, then the function is one-to-one. For every one-to-one function, an inverse function exists.

EXAMPLE 5

Determine whether the function $f(x) = x^2$ is one-to-one and thus has an inverse that is a function.

Solution   The graph of $f(x) = x^2$ is shown here. Many horizontal lines cross the graph more than once. For example, the line $y = 4$ crosses where the first coordinates are -2 and 2. Although these are different inputs, they have the same output. That is, $-2 \neq 2$, but

$$f(-2) = (-2)^2 = 4 = 2^2 = f(2).$$

Thus the function is not one-to-one and no inverse function exists.

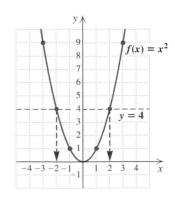

Finding Formulas for Inverses

When the inverse of f is also a function, it is denoted f^{-1} (read "f-inverse").

> *Caution!* The -1 in f^{-1} is *not* an exponent!

Suppose a function is described by a formula. If its inverse is a function, how do we find a formula for that inverse? For any equation in two variables, if we interchange the variables, we form an equation of the inverse correspondence. If it is a function, we proceed as follows to find a formula for f^{-1}.

> *To Find a Formula for f^{-1}*
>
> First make sure that f is one-to-one. Then:
>
> **1.** Replace $f(x)$ with y.
> **2.** Interchange x and y. (This gives the inverse function.)
> **3.** Solve for y.
> **4.** Replace y with $f^{-1}(x)$. (This is inverse function notation.)

EXAMPLE 6   Determine whether each function is one-to-one and if it is, find a formula for $f^{-1}(x)$.

a) $f(x) = x + 2$ b) $f(x) = 2x - 3$

Solution

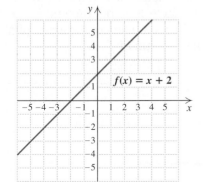

$f(x) = x + 2$

a) The graph of $f(x) = x + 2$ is shown at left. It passes the horizontal-line test, so it is one-to-one. Thus its inverse is a function.

1. Replace $f(x)$ with y: $y = x + 2$.
2. Interchange x and y: $x = y + 2$.   This gives the inverse function.
3. Solve for y: $x - 2 = y$.
4. Replace y with $f^{-1}(x)$: $f^{-1}(x) = x - 2$.   We also "reversed" the equation.

In this case, the function f adds 2 to all inputs. Thus, to "undo" f, the function f^{-1} must subtract 2 from its inputs.

b) The function $f(x) = 2x - 3$ is also linear. Any linear function that is not constant will pass the horizontal-line test. Thus, f is one-to-one.

1. Replace $f(x)$ with y: $y = 2x - 3$.
2. Interchange x and y: $x = 2y - 3$.
3. Solve for y: $x + 3 = 2y$
     $$\frac{x + 3}{2} = y.$$

4. Replace y with $f^{-1}(x)$: $f^{-1}(x) = \dfrac{x + 3}{2}$.

In this case, the function f doubles all inputs and then subtracts 3. Thus, to "undo" f, the function f^{-1} adds 3 to each input and then divides by 2.

Graphing Functions and Their Inverses

How do the graphs of a function and its inverse compare?

EXAMPLE 7   Graph $f(x) = 2x - 3$ and $f^{-1}(x) = (x + 3)/2$ on the same set of axes. Then compare.

Solution   The graph of each function follows. Note that the graph of f^{-1} can be drawn by reflecting the graph of f across the line $y = x$. That is, if we graph $f(x) = 2x - 3$ in wet ink and fold the paper along the line $y = x$, the graph of $f^{-1}(x) = (x + 3)/2$ will appear as the impression made by f.

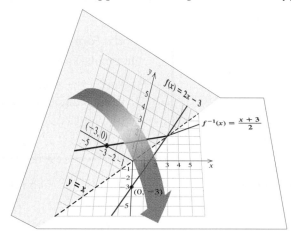

When x and y are interchanged to find a formula for the inverse, we are, in effect, reflecting or flipping the graph of $f(x) = 2x - 3$ across the line $y = x$. For example, when $(0, -3)$, the coordinates of the y-intercept of the graph of f, are reversed, we get $(-3, 0)$, the x-intercept of the graph of f^{-1}.

> *Visualizing Inverses*
>
> The graph of f^{-1} is a reflection of the graph of f across the line $y = x$.

EXAMPLE 8   Consider $g(x) = x^3 + 2$.

a) Determine whether the function is one-to-one.

b) If it is one-to-one, find a formula for its inverse.

c) Graph the inverse, if it exists.

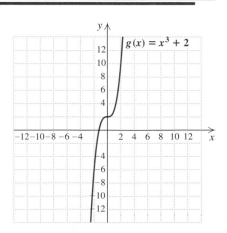

Solution

a) The graph of $g(x) = x^3 + 2$ is shown at right. It passes the horizontal-line test and thus has an inverse.

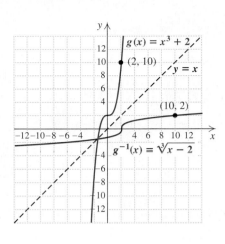

b) 1. Replace $g(x)$ with y: $y = x^3 + 2.$ Using $g(x) = x^3 + 2$
2. Interchange x and y: $x = y^3 + 2.$
3. Solve for y: $x - 2 = y^3$
     $\sqrt[3]{x - 2} = y.$ Each real number has
     only one cube root, so
     we can solve for y.

4. Replace y with $g^{-1}(x)$: $g^{-1}(x) = \sqrt[3]{x - 2}.$

c) To find the graph, we reflect the graph of $g(x) = x^3 + 2$ across the line $y = x$, as we did in Example 7. We can also substitute into $g^{-1}(x) = \sqrt[3]{x - 2}$ and plot points. Note that $(2, 10)$ is on the graph of g, whereas $(10, 2)$ is on the graph of g^{-1}. The graphs of g and g^{-1} are shown together at left.

Inverse Functions and Composition

Let's consider inverses of functions in terms of function machines. Suppose that a one-to-one function f is programmed into a machine. If the machine has a reverse switch, when the switch is thrown, the machine performs the inverse function f^{-1}. Inputs then enter at the opposite end, and the entire process is reversed.

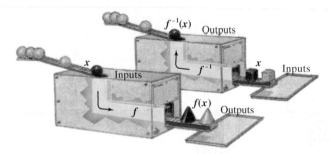

Consider $f(x) = x^3 + 2$ and $f^{-1}(x) = \sqrt[3]{x - 2}$ from Example 8. For the input 3,

$$f(3) = 3^3 + 2 = 27 + 2 = 29.$$

The output is 29. Now we use 29 for the input in the inverse:

$$f^{-1}(29) = \sqrt[3]{29 - 2} = \sqrt[3]{27} = 3.$$

The function f takes 3 to 29. The inverse function f^{-1} takes the number 29 back to 3.

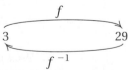

In general, for any output $f(x)$, the function f^{-1} takes that output back to x. Similarly, for any output $f^{-1}(x)$, the function f takes that output back to x.

Composition and Inverses

If a function f is one-to-one, then f^{-1} is the unique function for which

$$(f^{-1} \circ f)(x) = f^{-1}(f(x)) = x \quad \text{and} \quad (f \circ f^{-1})(x) = f(f^{-1}(x)) = x.$$

EXAMPLE 9   Let $f(x) = 2x + 1$. Show that

$$f^{-1}(x) = \frac{x-1}{2}.$$

Solution   We find $(f^{-1} \circ f)(x)$ and $(f \circ f^{-1})(x)$ and check to see that each is x.

$$(f^{-1} \circ f)(x) = f^{-1}(f(x)) = f^{-1}(2x + 1)$$

$$= \frac{(2x + 1) - 1}{2}$$

$$= \frac{2x}{2} = x$$

$$(f \circ f^{-1})(x) = f(f^{-1}(x)) = f\left(\frac{x-1}{2}\right)$$

$$= 2 \cdot \frac{x-1}{2} + 1$$

$$= x - 1 + 1 = x$$

---

technology connection

To determine whether $y_1 = 2x + 6$ and $y_2 = \frac{1}{2}x - 3$ are inverses of each other, we can graph both functions, along with the line $y = x$, on a "squared" set of axes. It *appears* that y_1 and y_2 are inverses of each other. A more precise check is achieved by selecting the DRAWINV option of the (DRAW) menu. The resulting graph of the inverse of y_1 should coincide with y_2.

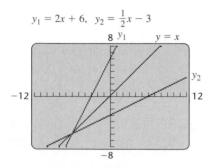

For a more dependable check, examine a TABLE in which $y_1 = 2x + 6$ and $y_2 = \frac{1}{2} \cdot y_1 - 3$. Note that y_2 "undoes" what y_1 does.

TBL MIN = -3 ΔTBL = 1 $y_2 = \frac{1}{2}y_1 - 3$

X	Y1	Y2
-3	0	-3
-2	2	-2
-1	4	-1
0	6	0
1	8	1
2	10	2
3	12	3
X = 3		

1. Use a graphing calculator to check Examples 7, 8, and 9.
2. Will DRAWINV work for *any* choice of y_1? Why or why not?

12.1

Exercise Set

FOR EXTRA HELP

Student's Solutions Manual | Digital Video Tutor CD 6 Videotape 12 | AW Math Tutor Center | MathXL Tutorials on CD | Math*XL* MathXL | MyMathLab MyMathLab

🔖 **Concept Reinforcement**   *Classify each statement as either true or false.*

1. The composition of two functions f and g is written $f \circ g$.

2. The notation $(f \circ g)(x)$ means $f(g(x))$.

3. If $f(x) = x^2$ and $g(x) = x + 3$, then $(g \circ f)(x) = (x + 3)^2$.

4. If $f(2) = 15$ and $g(15) = 25$, then $(g \circ f)(2) = 25$.

5. The function f is one-to-one if $f(1) = 1$.

6. For f^{-1} to be a function, f cannot be one-to-one.

7. The function f is the inverse of f^{-1}.

8. If g and h are inverses of each other, then $(g \circ h)(x) = x$.

Find $(f \circ g)(1), (g \circ f)(1), (f \circ g)(x),$ *and* $(g \circ f)(x)$.

9. $f(x) = x^2 + 1; \ g(x) = 2x - 3$

10. $f(x) = 2x + 1; \ g(x) = x^2 - 5$

11. $f(x) = x - 3; \ g(x) = 2x^2 - 7$

12. $f(x) = 3x^2 + 4; \ g(x) = 4x - 1$

13. $f(x) = x + 7; \ g(x) = 1/x^2$

14. $f(x) = 1/x^2; \ g(x) = x + 2$

15. $f(x) = \sqrt{x}; \ g(x) = x + 3$

16. $f(x) = 10 - x; \ g(x) = \sqrt{x}$

17. $f(x) = \sqrt{4x}; \ g(x) = 1/x$

18. $f(x) = \sqrt{x + 3}; \ g(x) = 13/x$

19. $f(x) = x^2 + 4; \ g(x) = \sqrt{x - 1}$

20. $f(x) = x^2 + 8; \ g(x) = \sqrt{x + 17}$

Find $f(x)$ *and* $g(x)$ *such that* $h(x) = (f \circ g)(x)$. *Answers may vary.*

21. $h(x) = (7 + 5x)^2$

22. $h(x) = (3x - 1)^2$

23. $h(x) = \sqrt{2x + 7}$

24. $h(x) = \sqrt{5x + 2}$

25. $h(x) = \dfrac{2}{x - 3}$

26. $h(x) = \dfrac{3}{x} + 4$

Determine whether each function is one-to-one.

27. $f(x) = x - 5$

28. $f(x) = 5 - 2x$

Aha! **29.** $f(x) = x^2 + 1$

30. $f(x) = 1 - x^2$

31.

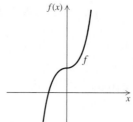

32.

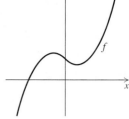

33.

34.

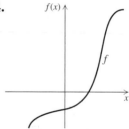

For each function, **(a)** *determine whether it is one-to-one;* **(b)** *if it is one-to-one, find a formula for the inverse.*

35. $f(x) = x + 4$

36. $f(x) = x + 2$

37. $f(x) = 2x$

38. $f(x) = 3x$

39. $g(x) = 3x - 1$

40. $g(x) = 2x - 3$

41. $f(x) = \dfrac{1}{2}x + 1$

42. $f(x) = \dfrac{1}{3}x + 2$

43. $g(x) = x^2 + 5$

44. $g(x) = x^2 - 4$

45. $h(x) = -2x + 4$

46. $h(x) = -3x + 1$

Aha! **47.** $f(x) = \dfrac{1}{x}$

48. $f(x) = \dfrac{3}{x}$

49. $G(x) = 4$

50. $H(x) = 2$

51. $f(x) = \dfrac{2x + 1}{3}$

52. $f(x) = \dfrac{3x + 2}{5}$

53. $f(x) = x^3 - 5$

54. $f(x) = x^3 + 2$

55. $g(x) = (x - 2)^3$

56. $g(x) = (x + 7)^3$

57. $f(x) = \sqrt{x}$ **58.** $f(x) = \sqrt{x-1}$

Graph each function and its inverse using the same set of axes.

59. $f(x) = \dfrac{2}{3}x + 4$ **60.** $g(x) = \dfrac{1}{4}x + 2$

61. $f(x) = x^3 + 1$ **62.** $f(x) = x^3 - 1$

63. $g(x) = \dfrac{1}{2}x^3$ **64.** $g(x) = \dfrac{1}{3}x^3$

65. $F(x) = -\sqrt{x}$ **66.** $f(x) = \sqrt{x}$

67. $f(x) = -x^2, x \geq 0$ **68.** $f(x) = x^2 - 1, x \leq 0$

69. Let $f(x) = \sqrt[3]{x - 4}$. Show that
$$f^{-1}(x) = x^3 + 4.$$

70. Let $f(x) = 3/(x + 2)$. Show that
$$f^{-1}(x) = \frac{3}{x} - 2.$$

71. Let $f(x) = (1 - x)/x$. Show that
$$f^{-1}(x) = \frac{1}{x + 1}.$$

72. Let $f(x) = x^3 - 5$. Show that
$$f^{-1}(x) = \sqrt[3]{x + 5}.$$

73. *Dress sizes in the United States and Italy.* A size-6 dress in the United States is size 36 in Italy. A function that converts dress sizes in the United States to those in Italy is
$$f(x) = 2(x + 12).$$
   a) Find the dress sizes in Italy that correspond to sizes 8, 10, 14, and 18 in the United States.
   b) Determine whether this function has an inverse that is a function. If so, find a formula for the inverse.
   c) Use the inverse function to find dress sizes in the United States that correspond to sizes 40, 44, 52, and 60 in Italy.

74. *Dress sizes in the United States and France.* A size-6 dress in the United States is size 38 in France. A function that converts dress sizes in the United States to those in France is
$$f(x) = x + 32.$$
   a) Find the dress sizes in France that correspond to sizes 8, 10, 14, and 18 in the United States.
   b) Determine whether this function has an inverse that is a function. If so, find a formula for the inverse.
   c) Use the inverse function to find dress sizes in the United States that correspond to sizes 40, 42, 46, and 50 in France.

75. Is there a one-to-one relationship between the letters and the numbers on the keypad of a telephone? Why or why not?

76. Mathematicians usually try to select "logical" words when forming definitions. Does the term "one-to-one" seem logical? Why or why not?

SKILL MAINTENANCE

Simplify.

77. $(a^5 b^4)^2 (a^3 b^5)$ [4.1]

78. $(x^3 y^5)^2 (x^4 y^2)$ [4.1]

79. $27^{4/3}$ [10.2]

80. $25^{3/2}$ [10.2]

Solve. [2.3]

81. $x = \frac{2}{3}y - 7$, for y

82. $x = 10 - 3y$, for y

SYNTHESIS

83. The function $V(t) = 750(1.2)^t$ is used to predict the value, $V(t)$, of a certain rare stamp t years from 2001. Do not calculate $V^{-1}(t)$, but explain how V^{-1} could be used.

84. An organization determines that the cost per person of chartering a bus is given by the function
$$C(x) = \frac{100 + 5x}{x},$$
where x is the number of people in the group and $C(x)$ is in dollars. Determine $C^{-1}(x)$ and explain how this inverse function could be used.

For Exercises 85 and 86, graph the inverse of f.

85.

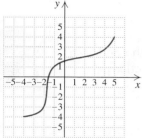

86.

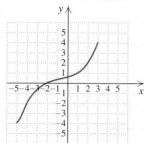

87. *Dress sizes in France and Italy.* Use the information in Exercises 73 and 74 to find a function for the French dress size that corresponds to a size x dress in Italy.

88. *Dress sizes in Italy and France.* Use the information in Exercises 73 and 74 to find a function for the Italian dress size that corresponds to a size x dress in France.

89. What relationship exists between the answers to Exercises 87 and 88? Explain how you determined this.

90. Show that function composition is associative by showing that $((f \circ g) \circ h)(x) = (f \circ (g \circ h))(x)$.

91. Show that if $h(x) = (f \circ g)(x)$, then $h^{-1}(x) = (g^{-1} \circ f^{-1})(x)$. (*Hint*: Use Exercise 90.)

Determine whether or not the given pairs of functions are inverses of each other.

92. $f(x) = 0.75x^2 + 2$; $g(x) = \sqrt{\dfrac{4(x-2)}{3}}$

93. $f(x) = 1.4x^3 + 3.2$; $g(x) = \sqrt[3]{\dfrac{x-3.2}{1.4}}$

94. $f(x) = \sqrt{2.5x + 9.25}$; $g(x) = 0.4x^2 - 3.7, \ x \geq 0$

95. $f(x) = 0.8x^{1/2} + 5.23$; $g(x) = 1.25(x^2 - 5.23), \ x \geq 0$

96. $f(x) = 2.5(x^3 - 7.1)$; $g(x) = \sqrt[3]{0.4x + 7.1}$

97. Match each function in Column A with its inverse from Column B.

Column A	Column B
(1) $y = 5x^3 + 10$	**A.** $y = \dfrac{\sqrt[3]{x} - 10}{5}$
(2) $y = (5x + 10)^3$	**B.** $y = \sqrt[3]{\dfrac{x}{5}} - 10$
(3) $y = 5(x + 10)^3$	**C.** $y = \sqrt[3]{\dfrac{x - 10}{5}}$
(4) $y = (5x)^3 + 10$	**D.** $y = \dfrac{\sqrt[3]{x - 10}}{5}$

98. Examine the following table. Is it possible that f and g are inverses of each other? Why or why not?

x	$f(x)$	$g(x)$
6	6	6
7	6.5	8
8	7	10
9	7.5	12
10	8	14
11	8.5	16
12	9	18

99. The following window appears on a graphing calculator.

X	Y1	Y2
0	1	−2
1	1.5	0
2	2	2
3	2.5	4
4	3	6
5	3.5	8
6	4	10
X = 0		

a) What evidence is there that the functions Y1 and Y2 are inverses of each other?

b) Find equations for Y1 and Y2, assuming that both are linear functions.

c) On the basis of your answer to part (b), are Y1 and Y2 inverses of each other?

12.2 Exponential Functions

Graphing Exponential Functions • Equations with x and y Interchanged • Applications of Exponential Functions

CONNECTING THE CONCEPTS

Composite and inverse functions, as shown in Section 12.1, are very useful in and of themselves. The reason they are included in this chapter, however, is that they are needed in order to understand the logarithmic functions that appear in Section 12.3. Here in Section 12.2, we make no reference to composite or inverse functions. Instead, we introduce a new type of function, the *exponential function*, so that we can study both it and its inverse in Sections 12.3–12.7.

Study Skills

Know Your Machine

Whether you use a scientific or a graphing calculator, it is a wise investment of time to study the user's manual. If you cannot find a paper manual to consult, an electronic version can usually be found, online, at the manufacturer's website. Experimenting by pressing various combinations of keystrokes is also useful.

Consider the graph below. The rapidly rising curve approximates the graph of an *exponential function*. We now consider such functions and some of their applications.

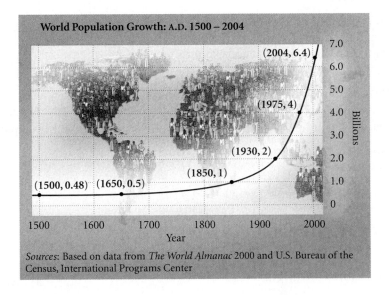

World Population Growth: A.D. 1500 – 2004

(2004, 6.4)
(1975, 4)
(1930, 2)
(1850, 1)
(1500, 0.48) (1650, 0.5)

Sources: Based on data from *The World Almanac* 2000 and U.S. Bureau of the Census, International Programs Center

Graphing Exponential Functions

In Chapter 10, we studied exponential expressions with rational-number exponents, such as

$$5^{1/4}, \qquad 3^{-3/4}, \qquad 7^{2.34}, \qquad 5^{1.73}.$$

For example, $5^{1.73}$, or $5^{173/100}$, represents the 100th root of 5 raised to the 173rd power. What about expressions with irrational exponents, such as $5^{\sqrt{3}}$ or $7^{-\pi}$?

To attach meaning to $5^{\sqrt{3}}$, consider a rational approximation, r, of $\sqrt{3}$. As r gets closer to $\sqrt{3}$, the value of 5^r gets closer to some real number p.

$\underbrace{r \text{ closes in on } \sqrt{3}.}$	$\underbrace{5^r \text{ closes in on some real number } p.}$
$1.7 < r < 1.8$	$15.426 \approx 5^{1.7} < p < 5^{1.8} \approx 18.119$
$1.73 < r < 1.74$	$16.189 \approx 5^{1.73} < p < 5^{1.74} \approx 16.452$
$1.732 < r < 1.733$	$16.241 \approx 5^{1.732} < p < 5^{1.733} \approx 16.267$

We define $5^{\sqrt{3}}$ to be the number p. To eight decimal places,

$$5^{\sqrt{3}} \approx 16.24245082.$$

Any positive irrational exponent can be interpreted in a similar way. Negative irrational exponents are then defined using reciprocals. Thus, so long as a is positive, a^x has meaning for *any* real number x. All of the laws of exponents still hold, but we will not prove that here. We now define an *exponential function.*

Exponential Function

The function $f(x) = a^x$, where a is a positive constant, $a \neq 1$, is called the *exponential function*, base a.

We require the base a to be positive to avoid imaginary numbers that would result from taking even roots of negative numbers. The restriction $a \neq 1$ is made to exclude the constant function $f(x) = 1^x$, or $f(x) = 1$.

The following are examples of exponential functions:

$$f(x) = 2^x, \qquad f(x) = \left(\tfrac{1}{3}\right)^x, \qquad f(x) = 5^{-3x}. \qquad \text{Note that } 5^{-3x} = (5^{-3})^x.$$

Like polynomial functions, the domain of an exponential function is the set of all real numbers. Unlike polynomial functions, exponential functions have a variable exponent. Because of this, graphs of exponential functions either rise or fall dramatically.

EXAMPLE 1   Graph the exponential function given by $y = f(x) = 2^x$.

Solution   We compute some function values, thinking of y as $f(x)$, and list the results in a table. It is a good idea to start by letting $x = 0$.

$$f(0) = 2^0 = 1; \qquad\qquad f(-1) = 2^{-1} = \frac{1}{2^1} = \frac{1}{2};$$
$$f(1) = 2^1 = 2;$$
$$f(2) = 2^2 = 4; \qquad\qquad f(-2) = 2^{-2} = \frac{1}{2^2} = \frac{1}{4};$$
$$f(3) = 2^3 = 8;$$
$$f(-3) = 2^{-3} = \frac{1}{2^3} = \frac{1}{8}$$

Next, we plot these points and connect them with a smooth curve.

x	y, or $f(x)$
0	1
1	2
2	4
3	8
−1	$\frac{1}{2}$
−2	$\frac{1}{4}$
−3	$\frac{1}{8}$

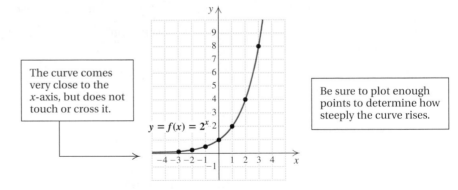

The curve comes very close to the x-axis, but does not touch or cross it.

Be sure to plot enough points to determine how steeply the curve rises.

$y = f(x) = 2^x$

Note that as x increases, the function values increase without bound. As x decreases, the function values decrease, getting very close to 0. The x-axis, or the line $y = 0$, is a horizontal *asymptote*, meaning that the curve gets closer and closer to this line the further we move to the left.

EXAMPLE 2

Graph: $y = f(x) = \left(\frac{1}{2}\right)^x$.

Solution   We compute some function values, thinking of y as $f(x)$, and list the results in a table. Before we do this, note that

$$y = f(x) = \left(\tfrac{1}{2}\right)^x = (2^{-1})^x = 2^{-x}.$$

Then we have

$$f(0) = 2^{-0} = 1;$$

$$f(1) = 2^{-1} = \frac{1}{2^1} = \frac{1}{2};$$

$$f(2) = 2^{-2} = \frac{1}{2^2} = \frac{1}{4};$$

$$f(3) = 2^{-3} = \frac{1}{2^3} = \frac{1}{8};$$

$$f(-1) = 2^{-(-1)} = 2^1 = 2;$$

$$f(-2) = 2^{-(-2)} = 2^2 = 4;$$

$$f(-3) = 2^{-(-3)} = 2^3 = 8.$$

x	y, or $f(x)$
0	1
1	$\frac{1}{2}$
2	$\frac{1}{4}$
3	$\frac{1}{8}$
−1	2
−2	4
−3	8

Next, we plot these points and connect them with a smooth curve. This curve is a mirror image, or *reflection*, of the graph of $y = 2^x$ (see Example 1) across the y-axis. The line $y = 0$ is again the asymptote.

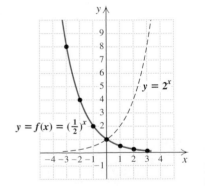

$y = f(x) = \left(\frac{1}{2}\right)^x$

$y = 2^x$

From Examples 1 and 2, we can make the following observations.

A. For $a > 1$, the graph of $f(x) = a^x$ increases from left to right. The greater the value of a, the steeper the curve. (See the figure on the left below.)

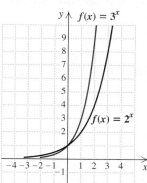

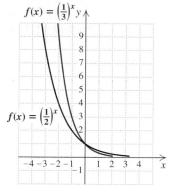

B. For $0 < a < 1$, the graph of $f(x) = a^x$ decreases from left to right. For smaller values of a, the curve becomes steeper. (See the figure on the right above.)
C. All graphs of $f(x) = a^x$ go through the y-intercept $(0, 1)$.
D. All graphs of $f(x) = a^x$ have the x-axis as the asymptote.
E. If $f(x) = a^x$, with $a > 0$, $a \neq 1$, the domain of f is all real numbers, and the range of f is all positive real numbers.
F. For $a > 0$, $a \neq 1$, the function given by $f(x) = a^x$ is one-to-one. Its graph passes the horizontal-line test.

EXAMPLE 3

Graph: $y = f(x) = 2^{x-2}$.

Student Notes

When using translations, make sure that you are shifting in the correct direction. When in doubt, substitute a value for x and make some calculations.

Solution   We construct a table of values. Then we plot the points and connect them with a smooth curve. Here $x - 2$ is the *exponent*.

$$f(0) = 2^{0-2} = 2^{-2} = \frac{1}{4};$$ $$f(-1) = 2^{-1-2} = 2^{-3} = \frac{1}{8};$$

$$f(1) = 2^{1-2} = 2^{-1} = \frac{1}{2};$$ $$f(-2) = 2^{-2-2} = 2^{-4} = \frac{1}{16}$$

$$f(2) = 2^{2-2} = 2^0 = 1;$$
$$f(3) = 2^{3-2} = 2^1 = 2;$$
$$f(4) = 2^{4-2} = 2^2 = 4;$$

technology connection

To practice graphing equations that are translations of each other, use **MODE** SIMUL and **FORMAT** ExprOff to graph $y_1 = 2^x$, $y_2 = 2^{x+1}$, $y_3 = 2^{x-1}$, $y_4 = 2^x + 1$, and $y_5 = 2^x - 1$. Use a bold curve for y_1 and then predict which curve represents which equation. Use **TRACE** to confirm your predictions. Switching **FORMAT** to ExprOn and using **TRACE** provides a definitive check (see also Exercise 75).

x	y, or $f(x)$
0	$\frac{1}{4}$
1	$\frac{1}{2}$
2	1
3	2
4	4
-1	$\frac{1}{8}$
-2	$\frac{1}{16}$

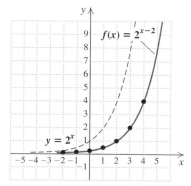

The graph looks just like the graph of $y = 2^x$, but it is translated 2 units to the right. The y-intercept of $y = 2^x$ is $(0, 1)$. The y-intercept of $y = 2^{x-2}$ is $\left(0, \frac{1}{4}\right)$. The line $y = 0$ is again the asymptote.

Equations with x and y Interchanged

It will be helpful in later work to be able to graph an equation in which the x and the y in $y = a^x$ are interchanged.

EXAMPLE 4   Graph: $x = 2^y$.

Solution   Note that x is alone on one side of the equation. To find ordered pairs that are solutions, we choose values for y and then compute values for x:

For $y = 0,$ $x = 2^0 = 1.$

For $y = 1,$ $x = 2^1 = 2.$

For $y = 2,$ $x = 2^2 = 4.$

For $y = 3,$ $x = 2^3 = 8.$

For $y = -1,$ $x = 2^{-1} = \dfrac{1}{2}.$

For $y = -2,$ $x = 2^{-2} = \dfrac{1}{4}.$

For $y = -3,$ $x = 2^{-3} = \dfrac{1}{8}.$

x	y
1	0
2	1
4	2
8	3
$\frac{1}{2}$	-1
$\frac{1}{4}$	-2
$\frac{1}{8}$	-3

(1) Choose values for y.
(2) Compute values for x.

We plot the points and connect them with a smooth curve.

This curve does not touch or cross the y-axis, which serves as a vertical asymptote.

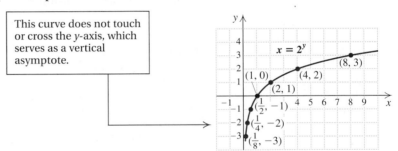

Note too that this curve looks just like the graph of $y = 2^x$, except that it is reflected across the line $y = x$, as shown here.

We have graphed $y = 2^x$ and its inverse, $x = 2^y$.

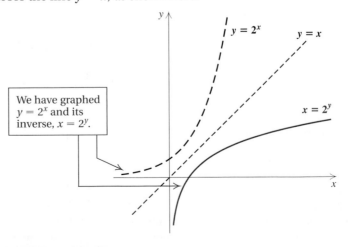

Applications of Exponential Functions

EXAMPLE 5   Interest compounded annually.   The amount of money A that a principal P will be worth after t years at interest rate i, compounded annually, is given by the formula

$$A = P(1 + i)^t.$$ You might review Example 11 in Section 11.1.

Suppose that \$100,000 is invested at 8% interest, compounded annually.

a) Find a function for the amount in the account after t years.

b) Find the amount of money in the account at $t = 0$, $t = 4$, $t = 8$, and $t = 10$.

c) Graph the function.

Solution

a) If $P =$ \$100,000 and $i = 8\% = 0.08$, we can substitute these values and form the following function:

$$A(t) = \$100{,}000(1 + 0.08)^t \quad \text{Using } A = P(1 + i)^t$$
$$= \$100{,}000(1.08)^t.$$

technology connection

Graphing calculators can quickly find many function values at the touch of a few keys. To see this, let $y_1 = 100{,}000(1.08)^x$. Then use the TABLE feature to check Example 5(b).

b) To find the function values, a calculator with a power key is helpful.

$$A(0) = \$100{,}000(1.08)^0 \qquad\qquad A(8) = \$100{,}000(1.08)^8$$
$$= \$100{,}000(1) \qquad\qquad\qquad\;\; \approx \$100{,}000(1.85093021)$$
$$= \$100{,}000 \qquad\qquad\qquad\quad\;\; \approx \$185{,}093.02$$

$$A(4) = \$100{,}000(1.08)^4 \qquad\qquad A(10) = \$100{,}000(1.08)^{10}$$
$$= \$100{,}000(1.36048896) \qquad\quad \approx \$100{,}000(2.158924997)$$
$$\approx \$136{,}048.90 \qquad\qquad\qquad\quad \approx \$215{,}892.50$$

c) We use the function values computed in part (b), and others if we wish, to draw the graph as follows. Note that the axes are scaled differently because of the large numbers.

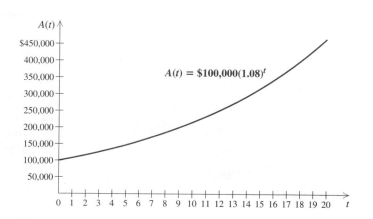

Exercise Set

12.2

↩ *Concept Reinforcement* *Classify each of the following as either true or false.*

1. The graph of $f(x) = a^x$ always passes through the point $(0, 1)$.

2. The graph of $g(x) = \left(\frac{1}{2}\right)^x$ gets closer and closer to the x-axis as x gets larger and larger.

3. The graph of $f(x) = 2^{x-3}$ looks just like the graph of $y = 2^x$, but it is translated 3 units to the right.

4. The graph of $g(x) = 2^x - 3$ looks just like the graph of $y = 2^x$, but it is translated 3 units up.

5. The graph of $y = 3^x$ gets close to, but never touches, the y-axis.

6. The graph of $x = 3^y$ gets close to, but never touches, the y-axis.

Graph.

7. $y = f(x) = 3^x$

8. $y = f(x) = 2^x$

9. $y = 6^x$

10. $y = 5^x$

11. $y = 2^x + 1$

12. $y = 2^x + 3$

13. $y = 3^x - 2$

14. $y = 3^x - 1$

15. $y = 2^x - 5$

16. $y = 2^x - 4$

17. $y = 2^{x-2}$

18. $y = 2^{x-1}$

19. $y = 2^{x+1}$

20. $y = 2^{x+3}$

21. $y = \left(\frac{1}{4}\right)^x$

22. $y = \left(\frac{1}{5}\right)^x$

23. $y = \left(\frac{1}{3}\right)^x$

24. $y = \left(\frac{1}{2}\right)^x$

25. $y = 2^{x+1} - 3$

26. $y = 2^{x-3} - 1$

27. $x = 6^y$

28. $x = 3^y$

29. $x = 3^{-y}$

30. $x = 2^{-y}$

31. $x = 4^y$

32. $x = 5^y$

33. $x = \left(\frac{4}{3}\right)^y$

34. $x = \left(\frac{3}{2}\right)^y$

Graph each pair of equations on the same set of axes.

35. $y = 3^x,\ x = 3^y$

36. $y = 2^x,\ x = 2^y$

37. $y = \left(\frac{1}{2}\right)^x,\ x = \left(\frac{1}{2}\right)^y$

38. $y = \left(\frac{1}{4}\right)^x,\ x = \left(\frac{1}{4}\right)^y$

Solve.

39. *Population growth.* The world population $P(t)$, in billions, t years after 1980, can be approximated by
$$P(t) = 4.495(1.015)^t.$$
Source: Based on data from U.S. Bureau of the Census, International Data Base

a) Predict the world population in 2008, 2012, and 2016.

b) Graph the function.

40. *Growth of bacteria.* The bacteria *Escherichia coli* are commonly found in the human bladder. Suppose that 3000 of the bacteria are present at time $t = 0$. Then t minutes later, the number of bacteria present can be approximated by
$$N(t) = 3000(2)^{t/20}.$$

a) How many bacteria will be present after 10 min? 20 min? 30 min? 40 min? 60 min?

b) Graph the function.

41. *Smoking cessation.* The percentage of smokers P who receive telephone counseling to quit smoking and are still successful t months later can be approximated by
$$P(t) = 21.4(0.914)^t.$$
Sources: *New England Journal of Medicine*; data from California's Smokers' Hotline

a) Estimate the percentage of smokers receiving telephone counseling who are successful in quitting for 1 month, 3 months, and 1 year.

b) Graph the function.

42. *Smoking cessation.* The percentage of smokers P who, without telephone counseling, have successfully quit smoking for t months (see Exercise 41) can be approximated by
$$P(t) = 9.02(0.93)^t.$$
Sources: *New England Journal of Medicine*; data from California's Smokers' Hotline

a) Estimate the percentage of smokers not receiving telephone counseling who are successful in quitting for 1 month, 3 months, and 1 year.

b) Graph the function.

43. *Marine biology.*   Due to excessive whaling prior to the mid 1970s, the humpback whale is considered an endangered species. The worldwide population of humpbacks, $P(t)$, in thousands, t years after 1900 ($t < 70$) can be approximated by*

$$P(t) = 150(0.960)^t.$$

a) How many humpback whales were alive in 1930? in 1960?

b) Graph the function.

44. *Salvage value.*   A photocopier is purchased for $5200. Its value each year is about 80% of the value of the preceding year. Its value, in dollars, after t years is given by the exponential function

$$V(t) = 5200(0.8)^t.$$

a) Find the value of the machine after 0 yr, 1 yr, 2 yr, 5 yr, and 10 yr.

b) Graph the function.

45. *Marine biology.*   As a result of preservation efforts in most countries in which whaling was common, the humpback whale population has grown since the 1970s. The worldwide population of humpbacks, $P(t)$, in thousands, t years after 1982 can be approximated by*

$$P(t) = 5.5(1.047)^t.$$

a) How many humpback whales were alive in 1992? in 2004?

b) Graph the function.

46. *Recycling aluminum cans.*   It is estimated that $\frac{1}{2}$ of all aluminum cans distributed will be recycled each year. A beverage company distributes 250,000 cans. The number still in use after time t, in years, is given by the exponential function

$$N(t) = 250{,}000\left(\tfrac{1}{2}\right)^t.$$

Source: The Aluminum Association, Inc., May 2004

a) How many cans are still in use after 0 yr? 1 yr? 4 yr? 10 yr?

b) Graph the function.

47. *Spread of zebra mussels.*   Beginning in 1988, infestations of zebra mussels started spreading throughout North American waters.† These mussels spread with such speed that water treatment facilities, power plants, and entire

*Based on information from the American Cetacean Society, 2001, and the ASK Archive, 1998.

†Many thanks to Dr. Gerald Mackie of the Department of Zoology at the University of Guelph in Ontario for the background information for this exercise.

ecosystems can become threatened. The function

$$A(t) = 10 \cdot 34^t$$

can be used to estimate the number of square centimeters of lake bottom that will be covered with mussels t years after an infestation covering 10 cm^2 first occurs.

a) How many square centimeters of lake bottom will be covered with mussels 5 years after an infestation covering 10 cm^2 first appears? 7 years after the infestation first appears?

b) Graph the function.

48. *Cell phones.*   The number of cell phones in use in the United States is increasing exponentially. The number N, in millions, in use can be estimated by

$$N(t) = 7.12(1.3)^t,$$

where t is the number of years after 1990.

Source: Cellular Telecommunications and Internet Association

a) Estimate the number of cell phones in use in 1995, 2005, and 2010.

b) Graph the function.

49. Without using a calculator, explain why 2^π must be greater than 8 but less than 16.

50. Suppose that $1000 is invested for 5 yr at 7% interest, compounded annually. In what year will the most interest be earned? Why?

SKILL MAINTENANCE

Simplify.

51. 5^{-2} [4.8]

52. 2^{-5} [4.8]

53. $1000^{2/3}$ [10.2]

54. $25^{-3/2}$ [10.2]

55. $\dfrac{10a^8b^7}{2a^2b^4}$ [4.1]

56. $\dfrac{24x^6y^4}{4x^2y^3}$ [4.1]

SYNTHESIS

57. Examine Exercise 48. Do you believe that the equation for the number of cell phones in use in the United States will be accurate 20 yr from now? Why or why not?

58. Why was it necessary to discuss irrational exponents before graphing exponential functions?

Determine which of the two numbers is larger. Do not use a calculator.

59. $\pi^{1.3}$ or $\pi^{2.4}$

60. $\sqrt{8^3}$ or $8^{\sqrt{3}}$

Graph.

61. $f(x) = 3.8^x$

62. $f(x) = 2.3^x$

63. $y = 2^x + 2^{-x}$

64. $y = \left|\left(\frac{1}{2}\right)^x - 1\right|$

65. $y = |2^x - 2|$

66. $y = 2^{-(x-1)^2}$

67. $y = |2^{x^2} - 1|$

68. $y = 3^x + 3^{-x}$

Graph both equations using the same set of axes.

69. $y = 3^{-(x-1)}$, $x = 3^{-(y-1)}$ **70.** $y = 1^x$, $x = 1^y$

71. *Sales of DVD players.* As prices of DVD players continue to drop, sales have grown from $171 million in 1997 to $1099 million in 1999 and $2697 million in 2001. After pressing **STAT**, use the ExpReg option in the CALC menu to find an exponential function that models the total sales of DVD players t years after 1997. Then use that function to predict the total sales in 2008.
Source: *Statistical Abstract of the United States*, 2003

72. *Keyboarding speed.* Ali is studying keyboarding. After he has studied for t hours, Ali's speed, in words per minute, is given by the exponential function
$$S(t) = 200[1 - (0.99)^t].$$

Use a graph and/or table of values to predict Ali's speed after studying for 10 hr, 40 hr, and 80 hr.

73. *Spread of AIDS.*   In 2000, a total of 40,282 cases of AIDS was reported in the United States; in 2001, a total of 41,450 cases; and in 2002, a total of 42,745 cases.

   a) Graph the data points, letting t represent the number of years since 2000.
   b) Which function best fits the data: linear, exponential, or quadratic? Why?

74. Consider any exponential function of the form $f(x) = a^x$ with $a > 1$. Will it always follow that $f(3) - f(2) > f(2) - f(1)$, and, in general, $f(n + 2) - f(n + 1) > f(n + 1) - f(n)$? Why or why not? (*Hint:* Think graphically.)

75. On many graphing calculators, it is possible to enter and graph $y_1 = A \wedge (X - B) + C$ after first pressing **APPS** Transfrm. Use this application to graph $f(x) = 2.5^{x-3} + 2$, $g(x) = 2.5^{x+3} + 2$, $h(x) = 2.5^{x-3} - 2$, and $k(x) = 2.5^{x+3} - 2$.

CORNER

COLLABORATIVE

The True Cost of a New Car

Focus: Car loans and exponential functions

Time: 30 minutes

Group size: 2

Materials: Calculators with exponentiation keys

The formula
$$M = \frac{Pr}{1 - (1 + r)^{-n}}$$
is used to determine the payment size, M, when a loan of P dollars is to be repaid in n equally sized monthly payments. Here r represents the monthly interest rate. Loans repaid in this fashion are said to be *amortized* (spread out equally) over a period of n months.

ACTIVITY

1. Suppose one group member is selling the other a car for $2600, financed at 1% interest per month for 24 months. What should be the size of each monthly payment?

2. Suppose both group members are shopping for the same model new car. To save time, each group member visits a different dealer. One dealer offers the car for $13,000 at 10.5% interest (0.00875 monthly interest) for 60 months (no down payment). The other dealer offers the same car for $12,000, but at 12% interest (0.01 monthly interest) for 48 months (no down payment).

   a) Determine the monthly payment size for each offer. Then determine the total amount paid for the car under each offer. How much of each total is interest?
   b) Work together to find the annual interest rate for which the total cost of 60 monthly payments for the $13,000 car would equal the total amount paid for the $12,000 car (as found in part a above).

12.3 Logarithmic Functions

Graphs of Logarithmic Functions • Equivalent Equations • Solving Certain Logarithmic Equations

We are now ready to study inverses of exponential functions. These functions have many applications and are called *logarithm*, or *logarithmic, functions.*

Graphs of Logarithmic Functions

Consider the exponential function $f(x) = 2^x$. Like all exponential functions, f is one-to-one. Can a formula for f^{-1} be found? To answer this, we use the method of Section 12.1:

1. Replace $f(x)$ with y: $y = 2^x$.
2. Interchange x and y: $x = 2^y$.
3. Solve for y: $y =$ the exponent to which we raise 2 to get x.
4. Replace y with $f^{-1}(x)$: $f^{-1}(x) =$ the exponent to which we raise 2 to get x.

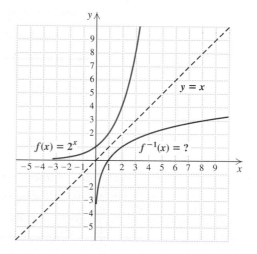

We now define a new symbol to replace the words "the exponent to which we raise 2 to get x":

$\log_2 x$, read "the logarithm, base 2, of x," or "log, base 2, of x," means "the exponent to which we raise 2 to get x."

Thus if $f(x) = 2^x$, then $f^{-1}(x) = \log_2 x$. Note that $f^{-1}(8) = \log_2 8 = 3$, because 3 is *the exponent to which we raise* 2 *to get* 8.

EXAMPLE 1 Simplify: **(a)** $\log_2 32$; **(b)** $\log_2 1$; **(c)** $\log_2 \frac{1}{8}$.

Solution

a) Think of $\log_2 32$ as the exponent to which we raise 2 to get 32. That exponent is 5. Therefore, $\log_2 32 = 5$.

b) We ask ourselves: "To what exponent do we raise 2 in order to get 1?" That exponent is 0 (recall that $2^0 = 1$). Thus, $\log_2 1 = 0$.

c) To what exponent do we raise 2 in order to get $\frac{1}{8}$? Since $2^{-3} = \frac{1}{8}$, we have $\log_2 \frac{1}{8} = -3$.

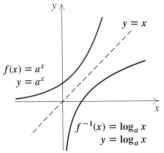

Although numbers like $\log_2 13$ can only be approximated, we must remember that $\log_2 13$ represents *the exponent to which we raise* 2 *to get* 13. That is, $2^{\log_2 13} = 13$. A calculator can be used to show that $\log_2 13 \approx 3.7$ and $2^{3.7} \approx 13$. Later in this chapter, we will use a calculator to find such approximations.

For any exponential function $f(x) = a^x$, the inverse is called a **logarithmic function, base a.** The graph of the inverse can be drawn by reflecting the graph of $f(x) = a^x$ across the line $y = x$. It will be helpful to remember that the inverse of $f(x) = a^x$ is given by $f^{-1}(x) = \log_a x$.

Student Notes

As an aid in remembering what $\log_a x$ means, note that a is called the *base*, just as it is the base in $a^y = x$.

The Meaning of $\log_a x$

For $x > 0$ and a a positive constant other than 1, $\log_a x$ is the exponent to which a must be raised in order to get x. Thus,

$$\log_a x = m \text{ means } a^m = x$$

or equivalently,

$$\log_a x \text{ is that unique exponent for which } a^{\log_a x} = x.$$

It is important to remember that *a logarithm is an exponent.* It might help to repeat several times: "The logarithm, base a, of a number x is the exponent to which a must be raised in order to get x."

EXAMPLE 2 Simplify: $7^{\log_7 85}$.

Solution Remember that $\log_7 85$ is the exponent to which 7 is raised to get 85. Raising 7 to that exponent, we have

$$7^{\log_7 85} = 85.$$

Because logarithmic and exponential functions are inverses of each other, the result in Example 2 should come as no surprise: If $f(x) = \log_7 x$, then

$$\text{for} \quad f(x) = \log_7 x, \text{ we have } f^{-1}(x) = 7^x$$
$$\text{and} \quad f^{-1}(f(x)) = f^{-1}(\log_7 x) = 7^{\log_7 x} = x.$$

Thus, $f^{-1}(f(85)) = 7^{\log_7 85} = 85$.

The following is a comparison of exponential and logarithmic functions.

Exponential Function	Logarithmic Function
$y = a^x$	$x = a^y$
$f(x) = a^x$	$g(x) = \log_a x$
$a > 0, a \neq 1$	$a > 0, a \neq 1$
The domain is $\mathbb{R}$.	The range is $\mathbb{R}$.
$y > 0$ (Outputs are positive.)	$x > 0$ (Inputs are positive.)
$f^{-1}(x) = \log_a x$	$g^{-1}(x) = a^x$

EXAMPLE 3

technology connection

To see that $f(x) = 10^x$ and $g(x) = \log_{10} x$ are inverses of each other, let $y_1 = 10^x$ and $y_2 = \log_{10} x = \log x$. Then, using a squared window, compare both graphs. If possible, select DrawInv from the (DRAW) menu and then press (VARS)()(1)(1)(ENTER) to see another representation of f^{-1}. Finally, let $y_3 = y_1(y_2)$ and $y_4 = y_2(y_1)$ to show, using a table or graphs, that, for $x > 0$, $y_3 = y_4 = x$.

Graph: $y = f(x) = \log_5 x$.

Solution   If $y = \log_5 x$, then $5^y = x$. We can find ordered pairs that are solutions by choosing values for y and computing the x-values.

For $y = 0, x = 5^0 = 1.$
For $y = 1, x = 5^1 = 5.$
For $y = 2, x = 5^2 = 25.$
For $y = -1, x = 5^{-1} = \frac{1}{5}.$
For $y = -2, x = 5^{-2} = \frac{1}{25}.$

(1) Select y.
(2) Compute x.

x, or 5^y	y
1	0
5	1
25	2
$\frac{1}{5}$	-1
$\frac{1}{25}$	-2

This table shows the following:

$\left.\begin{array}{l} \log_5 1 = 0; \\ \log_5 5 = 1; \\ \log_5 25 = 2; \\ \log_5 \frac{1}{5} = -1; \\ \log_5 \frac{1}{25} = -2. \end{array}\right\}$

These can all be checked using the equations above.

We plot the set of ordered pairs and connect the points with a smooth curve. The graphs of $y = 5^x$ and $y = x$ are shown only for reference.

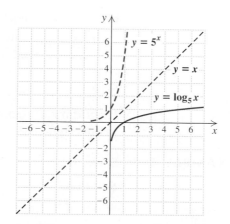

Equivalent Equations

We use the definition of logarithm to rewrite a *logarithmic equation* as an equivalent *exponential equation* or the other way around:

$$m = \log_a x \quad \text{is equivalent to} \quad a^m = x.$$

> *Caution!* **Do not forget this relationship!** It is probably the most important definition in the chapter. Many times this definition will be used to justify a property we are considering.

EXAMPLE 4   Rewrite each as an equivalent exponential equation: **(a)** $y = \log_3 5$; **(b)** $-2 = \log_a 7$; **(c)** $a = \log_b d$.

Solution

a) $y = \log_3 5$ is equivalent to $3^y = 5$ The logarithm is the exponent.

The base remains the base.

b) $-2 = \log_a 7$ is equivalent to $a^{-2} = 7$

c) $a = \log_b d$ is equivalent to $b^a = d$

We also use the definition of logarithm to rewrite an exponential equation as an equivalent logarithmic equation.

EXAMPLE 5   Rewrite each as an equivalent logarithmic equation: **(a)** $8 = 2^x$; **(b)** $y^{-1} = 4$; **(c)** $a^b = c$.

Solution

a) $8 = 2^x$ is equivalent to $x = \log_2 8$ The exponent is the logarithm.

The base remains the base.

b) $y^{-1} = 4$ is equivalent to $-1 = \log_y 4$

c) $a^b = c$ is equivalent to $b = \log_a c$

Solving Certain Logarithmic Equations

Logarithmic equations are often solved by rewriting them as equivalent exponential equations.

EXAMPLE 6   Solve: **(a)** $\log_2 x = -3$; **(b)** $\log_x 16 = 2$.

Solution

a) $\log_2 x = -3$

$2^{-3} = x$ Rewriting as an exponential equation

$\frac{1}{8} = x$ Computing 2^{-3}

Check: $\log_2 \frac{1}{8}$ is the exponent to which 2 is raised to get $\frac{1}{8}$. Since that exponent is -3, we have a check. The solution is $\frac{1}{8}$.

b) $\log_x 16 = 2$

$$x^2 = 16 \qquad \text{Rewriting as an exponential equation}$$

$$x = 4 \quad or \quad x = -4 \qquad \text{Principle of square roots}$$

Check: $\log_4 16 = 2$ because $4^2 = 16$. Thus, 4 is a solution of $\log_x 16 = 2$. Because all logarithmic bases must be positive, -4 cannot be a solution. Logarithmic bases must be positive because logarithms are defined using exponential functions that require positive bases. The solution is 4.

One method for solving certain logarithmic and exponential equations relies on the following property, which results from the fact that exponential functions are one-to-one.

The Principle of Exponential Equality

For any real number b, where $b \neq -1, 0,$ or $1,$

$$b^{x_1} = b^{x_2} \quad \text{is equivalent to} \quad x_1 = x_2.$$

(Powers of the same base are equal if and only if the exponents are equal.)

EXAMPLE 7

Solve: **(a)** $\log_{10} 1000 = x;$ **(b)** $\log_4 1 = t.$

Solution

a) We rewrite $\log_{10} 1000 = x$ in exponential form and solve:

$$10^x = 1000 \qquad \text{Rewriting as an exponential equation}$$

$$10^x = 10^3 \qquad \text{Writing 1000 as a power of 10}$$

$$x = 3. \qquad \text{Equating exponents}$$

Check: This equation can also be solved directly by determining the exponent to which we raise 10 in order to get 1000. In both cases we find that $\log_{10} 1000 = 3$, so we have a check. The solution is 3.

b) We rewrite $\log_4 1 = t$ in exponential form and solve:

$$4^t = 1 \qquad \text{Rewriting as an exponential equation}$$

$$4^t = 4^0 \qquad \text{Writing 1 as a power of 4. This can be done mentally.}$$

$$t = 0. \qquad \text{Equating exponents}$$

Check: As in part (a), this equation can be solved directly by determining the exponent to which we raise 4 in order to get 1. In both cases we find that $\log_4 1 = 0$, so we have a check. The solution is 0.

Example 7 illustrates an important property of logarithms.

$\log_a 1$

The logarithm, base a, of 1 is always 0: $\log_a 1 = 0$.

This follows from the fact that $a^0 = 1$ is equivalent to the logarithmic equation $\log_a 1 = 0$. Thus, $\log_{10} 1 = 0$, $\log_7 1 = 0$, and so on.

Another property results from the fact that $a^1 = a$. This is equivalent to the equation $\log_a a = 1$.

$\log_a a$

The logarithm, base a, of a is always 1: $\log_a a = 1$.

Thus, $\log_{10} 10 = 1$, $\log_8 8 = 1$, and so on.

Exercise Set

12.3

FOR EXTRA HELP

Student's Solutions Manual | Digital Video Tutor CD 6 Videotape 12 | AW Math Tutor Center | MathXL Tutorials on CD | MathXL | MyMathLab

 Concept Reinforcement *In each of Exercises 1–8, match the expression or equation with an equivalent expression or equation from the column on the right.*

1. _____ $\log_5 25$

2. _____ $2^5 = x$

3. _____ $\log_5 5$

4. _____ $\log_2 1$

5. _____ $\log_5 5^x$

6. _____ $\log_x 27 = 5$

7. _____ $8 = 2^x$

8. _____ $x^{-2} = 5$

a) 1

b) x

c) $x^5 = 27$

d) $\log_2 x = 5$

e) $\log_2 8 = x$

f) $\log_x 5 = -2$

g) 2

h) 0

Simplify.

9. $\log_{10} 1000$

10. $\log_{10} 100$

11. $\log_2 16$

12. $\log_2 8$

13. $\log_3 81$

14. $\log_3 27$

15. $\log_4 \frac{1}{16}$

16. $\log_4 \frac{1}{4}$

17. $\log_7 \frac{1}{7}$

18. $\log_7 \frac{1}{49}$

19. $\log_5 625$

20. $\log_5 125$

21. $\log_8 8$

22. $\log_7 1$

23. $\log_8 1$

24. $\log_8 8$

25. $\log_9 9^5$

26. $\log_9 9^{10}$

27. $\log_{10} 0.01$

28. $\log_{10} 0.1$

29. $\log_9 3$

30. $\log_{16} 4$

31. $\log_9 27$

32. $\log_{16} 64$

33. $\log_{1000} 100$

34. $\log_{27} 9$

35. $5^{\log_5 7}$

36. $6^{\log_6 13}$

Graph.

37. $y = \log_{10} x$

38. $y = \log_2 x$

39. $y = \log_3 x$

40. $y = \log_7 x$

41. $f(x) = \log_6 x$ **42.** $f(x) = \log_4 x$

43. $f(x) = \log_{2.5} x$ **44.** $f(x) = \log_{1/2} x$

Graph both functions using the same set of axes.

45. $f(x) = 3^x$, $f^{-1}(x) = \log_3 x$

46. $f(x) = 4^x$, $f^{-1}(x) = \log_4 x$

Rewrite each of the following as an equivalent exponential equation. Do not solve.

47. $t = \log_5 9$ **48.** $h = \log_7 10$

49. $\log_5 25 = 2$ **50.** $\log_6 6 = 1$

51. $\log_{10} 0.1 = -1$ **52.** $\log_{10} 0.01 = -2$

53. $\log_{10} 7 = 0.845$ **54.** $\log_{10} 3 = 0.4771$

55. $\log_c m = 8$ **56.** $\log_b n = 23$

57. $\log_t Q = r$ **58.** $\log_m P = a$

59. $\log_e 0.25 = -1.3863$ **60.** $\log_e 0.989 = -0.0111$

61. $\log_r T = -x$ **62.** $\log_c M = -w$

Rewrite each of the following as an equivalent logarithmic equation. Do not solve.

63. $10^2 = 100$ **64.** $10^4 = 10,000$

65. $4^{-5} = \frac{1}{1024}$ **66.** $5^{-3} = \frac{1}{125}$

67. $16^{3/4} = 8$ **68.** $8^{1/3} = 2$

69. $10^{0.4771} = 3$ **70.** $10^{0.3010} = 2$

71. $z^m = 6$ **72.** $m^n = r$

73. $p^m = V$ **74.** $Q^t = x$

75. $e^3 = 20.0855$ **76.** $e^2 = 7.3891$

77. $e^{-4} = 0.0183$ **78.** $e^{-2} = 0.1353$

Solve.

79. $\log_3 x = 2$ **80.** $\log_4 x = 3$

81. $\log_5 125 = x$ **82.** $\log_4 64 = x$

83. $\log_2 16 = x$ **84.** $\log_3 27 = x$

85. $\log_x 7 = 1$ **86.** $\log_x 8 = 1$

87. $\log_3 x = -2$ **88.** $\log_2 x = -1$

89. $\log_{32} x = \frac{2}{5}$ **90.** $\log_8 x = \frac{2}{3}$

91. Express in words what number is represented by $\log_b c$.

92. Is it true that $2 = b^{\log_b 2}$? Why or why not?

SKILL MAINTENANCE

Simplify.

93. $\dfrac{x^{12}}{x^4}$ [4.1] **94.** $\dfrac{a^{15}}{a^3}$ [4.1]

95. $(a^4 b^6)(a^3 b^2)$ [4.1] **96.** $(x^3 y^5)(x^2 y^7)$ [4.1]

97. $\dfrac{\dfrac{3}{x} - \dfrac{2}{xy}}{\dfrac{2}{x^2} + \dfrac{1}{xy}}$ [6.5] **98.** $\dfrac{\dfrac{4 + x}{x^2 + 2x + 1}}{\dfrac{3}{x + 1} - \dfrac{2}{x + 2}}$ [6.5]

SYNTHESIS

99. Would a manufacturer be pleased or unhappy if sales of a product grew logarithmically? Why?

100. Explain why the number $\log_2 13$ must be between 3 and 4.

101. Graph both equations using the same set of axes:
$$y = \left(\tfrac{3}{2}\right)^x, \qquad y = \log_{3/2} x.$$

Graph.

102. $y = \log_2(x - 1)$

103. $y = \log_3 |x + 1|$

Solve.

104. $|\log_3 x| = 2$

105. $\log_4 (3x - 2) = 2$

106. $\log_8 (2x + 1) = -1$

107. $\log_{10} (x^2 + 21x) = 2$

Simplify.

108. $\log_{1/4} \frac{1}{64}$

109. $\log_{1/5} 25$

110. $\log_{81} 3 \cdot \log_3 81$

111. $\log_{10} (\log_4 (\log_3 81))$

112. $\log_2 (\log_2 (\log_4 256))$

113. Show that $b^{x_1} = b^{x_2}$ is *not* equivalent to $x_1 = x_2$ for $b = 0$ or $b = 1$.

114. If $\log_b a = x$, does it follow that $\log_a b = 1/x$? Why or why not?

12.4 Properties of Logarithmic Functions

Logarithms of Products • Logarithms of Powers •
Logarithms of Quotients • Using the Properties Together

Logarithmic functions are important in many applications and in more advanced mathematics. We now establish some basic properties that are useful in manipulating expressions involving logarithms. As their proofs reveal, the properties of logarithms are related to the properties of exponents.

Logarithms of Products

The first property we discuss is related to the product rule for exponents: $a^m \cdot a^n = a^{m+n}$. Its proof appears immediately after Example 2.

> **The Product Rule for Logarithms**
>
> For any positive numbers M, N, and a ($a \neq 1$),
>
> $$\log_a (MN) = \log_a M + \log_a N.$$
>
> (The logarithm of a product is the sum of the logarithms of the factors.)

EXAMPLE 1   Express as an equivalent expression that is a sum of logarithms: $\log_2 (4 \cdot 16)$.

Solution   We have

$$\log_2 (4 \cdot 16) = \log_2 4 + \log_2 16. \qquad \text{Using the product rule for logarithms}$$

As a check, note that

$$\log_2 (4 \cdot 16) = \log_2 64 = 6 \qquad 2^6 = 64$$

and that

$$\log_2 4 + \log_2 16 = 2 + 4 = 6. \qquad 2^2 = 4 \text{ and } 2^4 = 16$$

EXAMPLE 2   Express as an equivalent expression that is a single logarithm: $\log_b 7 + \log_b 5$.

Solution   We have

$$\log_b 7 + \log_b 5 = \log_b (7 \cdot 5) \qquad \text{Using the product rule for logarithms}$$

$$= \log_b 35.$$

A Proof of the Product Rule.   Let $\log_a M = x$ and $\log_a N = y$. Converting to exponential equations, we have $a^x = M$ and $a^y = N$.

Now we multiply the left side of the first exponential equation by the left side of the second equation and similarly multiply the right sides to obtain

$$MN = a^x \cdot a^y, \text{ or } MN = a^{x+y}.$$

Converting back to a logarithmic equation, we get

$$\log_a (MN) = x + y.$$

Recalling what x and y represent, we have

$$\log_a (MN) = \log_a M + \log_a N.$$

Logarithms of Powers

The second basic property is related to the power rule for exponents: $(a^m)^n = a^{mn}$. Its proof follows Example 3.

The Power Rule for Logarithms

For any positive numbers M and a ($a \neq 1$), and any real number p,

$$\log_a M^p = p \cdot \log_a M.$$

(The logarithm of a power of M is the exponent times the logarithm of M.)

To better understand the power rule, note that

$$\log_a M^3 = \log_a (M \cdot M \cdot M) = \log_a M + \log_a M + \log_a M = 3 \log_a M.$$

EXAMPLE 3   Use the power rule for logarithms to write an equivalent expression that is a product: **(a)** $\log_a 9^{-5}$;   **(b)** $\log_7 \sqrt[3]{x}$.

Solution

a) $\log_a 9^{-5} = -5 \log_a 9$ Using the power rule for logarithms

b) $\log_7 \sqrt[3]{x} = \log_7 x^{1/3}$ Writing exponential notation

$\qquad\qquad = \frac{1}{3} \log_7 x$ Using the power rule for logarithms

---

A Proof of the Power Rule.   Let $x = \log_a M$. We then write the equivalent exponential equation, $a^x = M$. Raising both sides to the pth power, we get

$$(a^x)^p = M^p, \text{ or } a^{xp} = M^p.$$ Multiplying exponents

Converting back to a logarithmic equation gives us

$$\log_a M^p = xp.$$

But $x = \log_a M$, so substituting, we have

$$\log_a M^p = (\log_a M)p = p \cdot \log_a M.$$

Student Notes _____

Without understanding and *remembering* the rules of this section, it will be extremely difficult to solve the equations of Section 12.6.

Logarithms of Quotients

The third property that we study is similar to the quotient rule for exponents: $a^m/a^n = a^{m-n}$.

The Quotient Rule for Logarithms

For any positive numbers M, N, and a ($a \neq 1$),

$$\log_a \frac{M}{N} = \log_a M - \log_a N.$$

(The logarithm of a quotient is the logarithm of the dividend minus the logarithm of the divisor.)

To better understand the quotient rule, note that

$$\log_a \left(\frac{b^5}{b^3} \right) = \log_a b^2 = 2 \log_a b = 5 \log_a b - 3 \log_a b$$

$$= \log_a b^5 - \log_a b^3.$$

EXAMPLE 4   Express as an equivalent expression that is a difference of logarithms: $\log_t (6/U)$.

Solution

$$\log_t \frac{6}{U} = \log_t 6 - \log_t U \qquad \text{Using the quotient rule for logarithms}$$

EXAMPLE 5   Express as an equivalent expression that is a single logarithm: $\log_b 17 - \log_b 27$.

Solution

$$\log_b 17 - \log_b 27 = \log_b \frac{17}{27} \qquad \begin{array}{l}\text{Using the quotient rule for} \\ \text{logarithms "in reverse"}\end{array}$$

A Proof of the Quotient Rule.   Our proof uses both the product and power rules:

$$\log_a \frac{M}{N} = \log_a MN^{-1} \qquad \text{Rewriting } \frac{M}{N} \text{ as } MN^{-1}$$

$$= \log_a M + \log_a N^{-1} \qquad \begin{array}{l}\text{Using the product rule for} \\ \text{logarithms}\end{array}$$

$$= \log_a M + (-1)\log_a N \qquad \begin{array}{l}\text{Using the power rule for} \\ \text{logarithms}\end{array}$$

$$= \log_a M - \log_a N.$$

Using the Properties Together

EXAMPLE 6   Express as an equivalent expression, using the individual logarithms of x, y, and z.

a) $\log_b \dfrac{x^3}{yz}$

b) $\log_a \sqrt[4]{\dfrac{xy}{z^3}}$

Solution

a) $\log_b \dfrac{x^3}{yz} = \log_b x^3 - \log_b yz$ Using the quotient rule for logarithms

$\qquad = 3 \log_b x - \log_b yz$ Using the power rule for logarithms

$\qquad = 3 \log_b x - (\log_b y + \log_b z)$ Using the product rule for logarithms. Because of the subtraction, parentheses are essential.

$\qquad = 3 \log_b x - \log_b y - \log_b z$ Using the distributive law

b) $\log_a \sqrt[4]{\dfrac{xy}{z^3}} = \log_a \left(\dfrac{xy}{z^3}\right)^{1/4}$ Writing exponential notation

$\qquad = \dfrac{1}{4} \cdot \log_a \dfrac{xy}{z^3}$ Using the power rule for logarithms

$\qquad = \dfrac{1}{4}\left(\log_a xy - \log_a z^3\right)$ Using the quotient rule for logarithms. Parentheses are important.

$\qquad = \dfrac{1}{4}\left(\log_a x + \log_a y - 3 \log_a z\right)$ Using the product and power rules for logarithms

---

> *Caution!*   Because the product and quotient rules replace one term with two, it is often best to use the rules within parentheses, as in Example 6.

EXAMPLE 7   Express as an equivalent expression that is a single logarithm.

a) $\dfrac{1}{2} \log_a x - 7 \log_a y + \log_a z$

b) $\log_a \dfrac{b}{\sqrt{x}} + \log_a \sqrt{bx}$

Solution

a) $\dfrac{1}{2} \log_a x - 7 \log_a y + \log_a z$

$\qquad = \log_a x^{1/2} - \log_a y^7 + \log_a z$ Using the power rule for logarithms

$\qquad = \left(\log_a \sqrt{x} - \log_a y^7\right) + \log_a z$ Using parentheses to emphasize the order of operations; $x^{1/2} = \sqrt{x}$

$\qquad = \log_a \dfrac{\sqrt{x}}{y^7} + \log_a z$ Using the quotient rule for logarithms

$\qquad = \log_a \dfrac{z\sqrt{x}}{y^7}$ Using the product rule for logarithms

b) $\log_a \dfrac{b}{\sqrt{x}} + \log_a \sqrt{bx} = \log_a \dfrac{b \cdot \sqrt{bx}}{\sqrt{x}}$ Using the product rule for logarithms

$\qquad\qquad\qquad\qquad\quad = \log_a b\sqrt{b}$ Removing a factor equal to 1: $\dfrac{\sqrt{x}}{\sqrt{x}} = 1$

$\qquad\qquad\qquad\qquad\quad = \log_a b^{3/2}$, or $\dfrac{3}{2}\log_a b$ Since $b\sqrt{b} = b^1 \cdot b^{1/2}$

If we know the logarithms of two different numbers (to the same base), the properties allow us to calculate other logarithms.

EXAMPLE 8   Given $\log_a 2 = 0.431$ and $\log_a 3 = 0.683$, calculate a numerical value for each of the following.

a) $\log_a 6$ **b)** $\log_a \frac{2}{3}$ **c)** $\log_a 81$
d) $\log_a \frac{1}{3}$ **e)** $\log_a 2a$ **f)** $\log_a 5$

Solution

a) $\log_a 6 = \log_a(2 \cdot 3) = \log_a 2 + \log_a 3$ Using the product rule for logarithms

$\qquad\quad = 0.431 + 0.683 = 1.114$

   Check: $a^{1.114} = a^{0.431} \cdot a^{0.683} = 2 \cdot 3 = 6$

b) $\log_a \frac{2}{3} = \log_a 2 - \log_a 3$ Using the quotient rule for logarithms

$\qquad\quad = 0.431 - 0.683 = -0.252$

c) $\log_a 81 = \log_a 3^4 = 4\log_a 3$ Using the power rule for logarithms

$\qquad\quad = 4(0.683) = 2.732$

d) $\log_a \frac{1}{3} = \log_a 1 - \log_a 3$ Using the quotient rule for logarithms

$\qquad\quad = 0 - 0.683 = -0.683$

e) $\log_a 2a = \log_a 2 + \log_a a$ Using the product rule for logarithms

$\qquad\quad = 0.431 + 1 = 1.431$

f) $\log_a 5$ *cannot be found using these properties.* ($\log_a 5 \neq \log_a 2 + \log_a 3$)

A final property follows from the product rule: Since $\log_a a^k = k\log_a a$, and $\log_a a = 1$, we have $\log_a a^k = k$.

The Logarithm of the Base to an Exponent

For any base a,

$$\log_a a^k = k.$$

(The logarithm, base a, of a to an exponent is the exponent.

This property also follows from the definition of logarithm: k is the exponent to which you raise a in order to get a^k.

EXAMPLE 9 Simplify: **(a)** $\log_3 3^7$; **(b)** $\log_{10} 10^{-5.2}$.

Solution

a) $\log_3 3^7 = 7$ 7 is the exponent to which you raise 3 in order to get 3^7.

b) $\log_{10} 10^{-5.2} = -5.2$

We summarize the properties of logarithms as follows.

> For any positive numbers M, N, and a ($a \neq 1$):
>
> $$\log_a MN = \log_a M + \log_a N; \qquad \log_a M^p = p \cdot \log_a M;$$
>
> $$\log_a \frac{M}{N} = \log_a M - \log_a N; \qquad \log_a a^k = k.$$

> *Caution!*   Keep in mind that, in general,
>
> $$\log_a (M + N) \neq \log_a M + \log_a N, \qquad \log_a MN \neq (\log_a M)(\log_a N),$$
>
> $$\log_a (M - N) \neq \log_a M - \log_a N, \qquad \log_a \frac{M}{N} \neq \frac{\log_a M}{\log_a N}.$$

Exercise Set

12.4

FOR EXTRA HELP

Student's
Solutions
Manual

Digital Video Tutor
CD 6
Videotape 12

Tutor
Center
AW Math
Tutor Center

MathXL Tutorials
on CD

Math*XL*
MathXL

MyMathLab
MyMathLab

🖐 *Concept Reinforcement* *In each of Exercises 1–6, match the expression with an equivalent expression from the column on the right.*

1. ___ $\log_7 20$

2. ___ $\log_7 5^4$

3. ___ $\log_7 \frac{5}{4}$

4. ___ $\log_7 7$

5. ___ $\log_7 1$

6. ___ $\log_7 5 + \log_7 6$

a) $\log_7 5 - \log_7 4$

b) 1

c) 0

d) $\log_7 30$

e) $\log_7 5 + \log_7 4$

f) $4 \log_7 5$

Express as an equivalent expression that is a sum of logarithms.

7. $\log_3 (81 \cdot 27)$

8. $\log_2 (16 \cdot 32)$

9. $\log_4 (64 \cdot 16)$

10. $\log_5 (25 \cdot 125)$

11. $\log_c (rst)$

12. $\log_t (3ab)$

Express as an equivalent expression that is a single logarithm.

13. $\log_a 5 + \log_a 14$

14. $\log_b 65 + \log_b 2$

15. $\log_c t + \log_c y$

16. $\log_t H + \log_t M$

Express as an equivalent expression that is a product.

17. $\log_a r^8$

18. $\log_b t^5$

19. $\log_c y^6$

20. $\log_{10} y^7$

21. $\log_b C^{-3}$

22. $\log_c M^{-5}$

Express as an equivalent expression that is a difference of two logarithms.

23. $\log_2 \frac{25}{13}$

24. $\log_3 \frac{23}{9}$

25. $\log_b \dfrac{m}{n}$

26. $\log_a \dfrac{y}{x}$

Express as an equivalent expression that is a single logarithm.

27. $\log_a 17 - \log_a 6$

28. $\log_b 32 - \log_b 7$

29. $\log_b 36 - \log_b 4$

30. $\log_a 26 - \log_a 2$

31. $\log_a 7 - \log_a 18$

32. $\log_b 5 - \log_b 13$

Express as an equivalent expression, using the individual logarithms of w, x, y, and z.

33. $\log_a (xyz)$

34. $\log_a (wxy)$

35. $\log_a (x^3 z^4)$

36. $\log_a (x^2 y^5)$

37. $\log_a (x^2 y^{-2} z)$

38. $\log_a (xy^2 z^{-3})$

39. $\log_a \dfrac{x^4}{y^3 z}$

40. $\log_a \dfrac{x^4}{yz^2}$

41. $\log_b \dfrac{xy^2}{wz^3}$

42. $\log_b \dfrac{w^2 x}{y^3 z}$

43. $\log_a \sqrt{\dfrac{x^7}{y^5 z^8}}$

44. $\log_c \sqrt[3]{\dfrac{x^4}{y^3 z^2}}$

45. $\log_a \sqrt[3]{\dfrac{x^6 y^3}{a^2 z^7}}$

46. $\log_a \sqrt[4]{\dfrac{x^8 y^{12}}{a^3 z^5}}$

Express as an equivalent expression that is a single logarithm and, if possible, simplify.

47. $8 \log_a x + 3 \log_a z$

48. $2 \log_b m + \frac{1}{2} \log_b n$

49. $\log_a x^2 - 2 \log_a \sqrt{x}$

50. $\log_a \dfrac{a}{\sqrt{x}} - \log_a \sqrt{ax}$

51. $\frac{1}{2} \log_a x + 5 \log_a y - 2 \log_a x$

52. $\log_a 2x + 3(\log_a x - \log_a y)$

53. $\log_a (x^2 - 4) - \log_a (x + 2)$

54. $\log_a (2x + 10) - \log_a (x^2 - 25)$

Given $\log_b 3 = 0.792$ and $\log_b 5 = 1.161$. If possible, calculate numerical values for each of the following.

55. $\log_b 15$

56. $\log_b \frac{5}{3}$

57. $\log_b \frac{3}{5}$

58. $\log_b \frac{1}{3}$

59. $\log_b \frac{1}{5}$

60. $\log_b \sqrt{b}$

61. $\log_b \sqrt{b^3}$

62. $\log_b 3b$

63. $\log_b 8$

64. $\log_b 45$

Simplify.

Aha! **65.** $\log_t t^7$

66. $\log_p p^4$

67. $\log_e e^m$

68. $\log_Q Q^{-2}$

69. A student *incorrectly* reasons that

$$\log_b \frac{1}{x} = \log_b \frac{x}{xx}$$
$$= \log_b x - \log_b x + \log_b x = \log_b x.$$

What mistake has the student made?

70. How could you convince someone that
$$\log_a c \neq \log_c a?$$

SKILL MAINTENANCE

Graph. [10.1]

71. $f(x) = \sqrt{x} - 3$

72. $g(x) = \sqrt{x} + 2$

73. $g(x) = \sqrt[3]{x} + 1$

74. $f(x) = \sqrt[3]{x} - 1$

Simplify. [4.1]

75. $(a^3 b^2)^5 (a^2 b^7)$

76. $(x^5 y^3 z^2)(x^2 yz^2)^3$

SYNTHESIS

77. Is it possible to express $\log_b \dfrac{x}{5}$ as an equivalent expression that is a difference of two logarithms without using the quotient rule? Why or why not?

78. Is it true that $\log_a x + \log_b x = \log_{ab} x$? Why or why not?

Express as an equivalent expression that is a single logarithm and, if possible, simplify.

79. $\log_a (x^8 - y^8) - \log_a (x^2 + y^2)$

80. $\log_a (x + y) + \log_a (x^2 - xy + y^2)$

Express as an equivalent expression that is a sum or difference of logarithms and, if possible, simplify.

81. $\log_a \sqrt{1 - s^2}$

82. $\log_a \dfrac{c - d}{\sqrt{c^2 - d^2}}$

83. If $\log_a x = 2$, $\log_a y = 3$, and $\log_a z = 4$, what is
$\log_a \dfrac{\sqrt[3]{x^2 z}}{\sqrt[3]{y^2 z^{-2}}}$?

84. If $\log_a x = 2$, what is $\log_a (1/x)$?

85. If $\log_a x = 2$, what is $\log_{1/a} x$?

Classify each of the following as true or false. Assume a, x, P, and Q > 0, a ≠ 1.

86. $\log_a \left(\dfrac{P}{Q} \right)^x = x \log_a P - \log_a Q$

87. $\log_a (Q + Q^2) = \log_a Q + \log_a (Q + 1)$

 88. Use graphs to show that
$$\log x^2 \neq \log x \cdot \log x.$$
(*Note*: log means $\log_{10}$.)

12.5   Common and Natural Logarithms

Common Logarithms on a Calculator   •   The Base *e* and Natural Logarithms on a Calculator   •   Changing Logarithmic Bases   •   Graphs of Exponential and Logarithmic Functions, Base *e*

Study Skills

Is Your Answer Reasonable?

It is always a good idea—especially when using a calculator—to check that your answer is reasonable. It is easy for an incorrect calculation or keystroke to result in an answer that is clearly too big or too small.

Any positive number other than 1 can serve as the base of a logarithmic function. However, some numbers are easier to use than others, and there are logarithmic bases that fit into certain applications more naturally than others.

Base-10 logarithms, called **common logarithms**, are useful because they have the same base as our "commonly" used decimal system. Before calculators became widely available, common logarithms helped with tedious calculations. In fact, that is why logarithms were devised.

The logarithmic base most widely used today is an irrational number named *e*. We will consider *e* and base *e*, or *natural*, logarithms later in this section. First we examine common logarithms.

Common Logarithms on a Calculator

Before the advent of scientific calculators, tables were developed to list common logarithms. Today we find common logarithms using calculators.

Here, and in most books, the abbreviation **log**, with no base written, is understood to mean logarithm base 10, or a common logarithm. Thus,

log 17   means $\log_{10} 17$.   It is important to remember this abbreviation.

On most calculators, the key for common logarithms is marked **LOG**. To find the common logarithm of a number, we key in that number and press **LOG**. On most graphing calculators, we press **LOG**, the number, and then **ENTER**.

EXAMPLE 1

Use a scientific calculator to approximate each number to four decimal places.

a) $\log 53{,}128$

b) $\dfrac{\log 6500}{\log 0.007}$

Solution

a) We enter 53,128 and then press **LOG**. We find that

$$\log 53{,}128 \approx 4.7253. \qquad \text{Rounded to four decimal places}$$

b) We enter 6500 and then press **LOG**. Next, we press (÷), enter 0.007, and then press **LOG** =. Be careful not to round until the end:

$$\frac{\log 6500}{\log 0.007} \approx -1.7694. \qquad \text{Rounded to four decimal places}$$

technology connection

To find log 6500/log 0.007 on a graphing calculator, we must use parentheses with care.

1. What keystrokes are needed to create the following?

> log(7)/log(3)
>   1.771243749

The inverse of a logarithmic function is an exponential function. Because of this, on many calculators the **LOG** key doubles as the (10ˣ) key after a **2ND** or SHIFT key is pressed. Calculators lacking a (10ˣ) key may have a key labeled xʸ , aˣ , or . Such a key can raise any positive real number to any real-numbered exponent.

EXAMPLE 2

Use a calculator to approximate $10^{3.417}$ to four decimal places.

Solution   We enter 3.417 and then press (10ˣ). On most graphing calculators, (10ˣ) is pressed first, followed by 3.417 and **ENTER**. Rounding to four decimal places, we have

$$10^{3.417} \approx 2612.1614.$$

The Base e and Natural Logarithms on a Calculator

When interest is compounded n times a year, the compound interest formula is

$$A = P\left(1 + \frac{r}{n}\right)^{nt},$$

where A is the amount that an initial investment P will be worth after t years at interest rate r. Suppose that $1 is invested at 100% interest for 1 year (no bank would pay this). The preceding formula becomes a function A defined in terms of the number of compounding periods n:

$$A(n) = \left(1 + \frac{1}{n}\right)^{n}.$$

Let's find some function values. We round to six decimal places, using a calculator.

technology connection

To visualize the number e, let $y_1 = (1 + 1/x)^x$.

$y_1 = (1 + 1/x)^x$

1. Use (TRACE) or (TABLE) to confirm that as x gets larger, the number e is more closely approximated.
2. Graph $y_2 = e$ and compare y_1 and y_2 for large values of x.
3. Confirm that 0 is not in the domain of this function. Why?

n	$A(n) = \left(1 + \dfrac{1}{n}\right)^n$
1 (compounded annually)	\$2.00
2 (compounded semiannually)	\$2.25
3	\$2.370370
4 (compounded quarterly)	\$2.441406
5	\$2.488320
100	\$2.704814
365 (compounded daily)	\$2.714567
8760 (compounded hourly)	\$2.718127

The numbers in this table approach a very important number in mathematics, called e. Because e is irrational, its decimal representation does not terminate or repeat.

The Number e

$e \approx 2.7182818284\ldots$

Logarithms base e are called **natural logarithms**, or **Napierian logarithms**, in honor of John Napier (1550–1617), who first "discovered" logarithms.

The abbreviation "ln" is generally used with natural logarithms. Thus,

$\ln 53$ means $\log_e 53$.   It is important to remember this abbreviation.

On most scientific calculators, to find the natural logarithm of a number, we enter that number and press (LN). On most graphing calculators, we press (LN), the number, and then (ENTER).

EXAMPLE 3   Use a scientific calculator to approximate $\ln 4568$ to four decimal places.

Solution   We enter 4568 and then press (LN). We find that

$\ln 4568 \approx 8.4268.$ Rounded to four decimal places

On many calculators, the (LN) key doubles as the (e^x) key after a (2ND) or ⎡SHIFT⎤ key has been pressed.

EXAMPLE 4   Use a calculator to approximate $e^{-1.524}$ to four decimal places.

Solution   We enter -1.524 and then press (e^x). On most graphing calculators, (e^x) is pressed first, followed by -1.524 and (ENTER). Since $e^{-1.524}$ is irrational, our answer is approximate:

$e^{-1.524} \approx 0.2178.$ Rounded to four decimal places

Changing Logarithmic Bases

Most calculators can find both common logarithms and natural logarithms. To find a logarithm with some other base, a conversion formula is usually needed.

The Change-of-Base Formula

For any logarithmic bases a and b, and any positive number M,

$$\log_b M = \frac{\log_a M}{\log_a b}.$$

(To find the log, base b, of M, we typically compute $\log M/\log b$ or $\ln M/\ln b$.)

Proof.   Let $x = \log_b M$. Then,

$$b^x = M \qquad \log_b M = x \text{ is equivalent to } b^x = M.$$

$$\log_a b^x = \log_a M \qquad \text{Taking the logarithm, base } a, \text{ on both sides}$$

$$x \log_a b = \log_a M \qquad \text{Using the power rule for logarithms}$$

$$x = \frac{\log_a M}{\log_a b}. \qquad \text{Dividing both sides by } \log_a b$$

But at the outset we stated that $x = \log_b M$. Thus, by substitution, we have

$$\log_b M = \frac{\log_a M}{\log_a b}. \qquad \text{This is the change-of-base formula.}$$

EXAMPLE 5   Find $\log_5 8$ using the change-of-base formula.

Solution   We use the change-of-base formula with $a = 10$, $b = 5$, and $M = 8$:

$$\log_5 8 = \frac{\log_{10} 8}{\log_{10} 5} \qquad \text{Substituting into } \log_b M = \frac{\log_a M}{\log_a b}$$

$$\approx \frac{0.903089987}{0.6989700043} \qquad \text{Using } \boxed{\text{LOG}} \text{ twice}$$

$$\approx 1.2920. \qquad \text{When using a calculator, it is best not to round before dividing.}$$

To check, note that $\ln 8/\ln 5 \approx 1.2920$. We can also use a calculator to verify that $5^{1.2920} \approx 8$.

EXAMPLE 6   Find $\log_4 31$.

Solution   As shown in the check of Example 5, base e can also be used.

$$\log_4 31 = \frac{\log_e 31}{\log_e 4} \qquad \text{Substituting into } \log_b M = \frac{\log_a M}{\log_a b}$$

$$= \frac{\ln 31}{\ln 4} \approx \frac{3.433987204}{1.386294361} \qquad \text{Using } \boxed{LN} \text{ twice}$$

$$\approx 2.4771. \qquad \textit{Check: } 4^{2.4771} \approx 31$$

Graphs of Exponential and Logarithmic Functions, Base e

EXAMPLE 7   Graph $f(x) = e^x$ and $g(x) = e^{-x}$ and state the domain and the range of f and g.

Solution   We use a calculator with an $\boxed{e^x}$ key to find approximate values of e^x and e^{-x}. Using these values, we can graph the functions.

x	e^x	e^{-x}
0	1	1
1	2.7	0.4
2	7.4	0.1
−1	0.4	2.7
−2	0.1	7.4

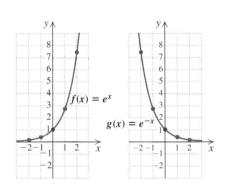

The domain of each function is $\mathbb{R}$ and the range of each function is $(0, \infty)$.

EXAMPLE 8   Graph $f(x) = e^{-x} + 2$ and state the domain and the range of f.

Solution   We find some solutions with a calculator, plot them, and then draw the graph. For example, $f(2) = e^{-2} + 2 \approx 0.1 + 2 \approx 2.1$. The graph is exactly like the graph of $g(x) = e^{-x}$, but is translated up 2 units.

x	$e^{-x} + 2$
0	3
1	2.4
2	2.1
−1	4.7
−2	9.4

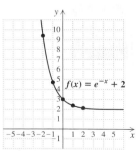

The domain of f is $\mathbb{R}$ and the range is $(2, \infty)$.

For each function given below, (a) determine the domain and the range, (b) set an appropriate window, and (c) draw the graph. Graphs may vary, depending on the scale used.

98. $f(x) = 7.4e^x \ln x$

99. $f(x) = 3.4 \ln x - 0.25e^x$

100. $f(x) = x \ln (x - 2.1)$

101. $f(x) = 2x^3 \ln x$

102. Use a graphing calculator to check your answers to Exercises 53, 61, and 75.

103. Use a graphing calculator to check your answers to Exercises 52, 58, and 68.

104. In an attempt to solve $\ln x = 1.5$, Emma gets the following graph. How can Emma tell at a glance that she has made a mistake?

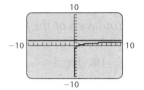

12.6 Solving Exponential and Logarithmic Equations

Solving Exponential Equations •
Solving Logarithmic Equations

Solving Exponential Equations

Equations with variables in exponents, such as $5^x = 12$ and $2^{7x} = 64$, are called **exponential equations**. In Section 12.3, we solved certain exponential equations by using the principle of exponential equality. We restate that principle below.

The Principle of Exponential Equality

For any real number b, where $b \neq -1, 0,$ or $1,$

$$b^x = b^y \quad \text{is equivalent to} \quad x = y.$$

(Powers of the same base are equal if and only if the exponents are equal.)

EXAMPLE 1   Solve: $4^x = 16$.

Solution   Note that $16 = 4^2$. Thus we can write each side as a power of the same base:

$$4^x = 4^2.$$

Since the base is the same, 4, the exponents must be equal. Thus, x must be 2. The solution is 2.

Example 1 is not difficult to solve, but what if the right side of the equation were not a power of 4?

When it seems impossible to write both sides of an equation as powers of the same base, we use the following principle and write an equivalent logarithmic equation.

The Principle of Logarithmic Equality

For any logarithmic base a, and for $x, y > 0$,

$$x = y \quad \text{is equivalent to} \quad \log_a x = \log_a y.$$

(Two expressions are equal if and only if the logarithms of those expressions are equal.)

The principle of logarithmic equality, used together with the power rule for logarithms, allows us to solve equations in which the variable is an exponent.

EXAMPLE 2   Solve: $7^{x-2} = 60$.

Solution   We have

$$7^{x-2} = 60$$

$$\log 7^{x-2} = \log 60 \qquad \text{Using the principle of logarithmic equality to take the common logarithm on both sides. Natural logarithms also would work.}$$

$$(x - 2) \log 7 = \log 60 \qquad \text{Using the power rule for logarithms}$$

$$x - 2 = \frac{\log 60}{\log 7} \quad \longleftarrow \boxed{\textit{Caution!} \quad \text{This is } not \log 60 - \log 7.}$$

$$x = \frac{\log 60}{\log 7} + 2 \qquad \text{Adding 2 to both sides}$$

$$x \approx 4.1041. \qquad \text{Using a calculator and rounding to four decimal places}$$

Since $7^{4.1041-2} \approx 60.0027$, we have a check. We can also note that since $7^{4-2} = 49$, we expect a solution near 4. The solution is $\dfrac{\log 60}{\log 7} + 2$, or approximately 4.1041.

ALGEBRAIC–GRAPHICAL CONNECTION

We can obtain a visual check of the solution of an exponential equation by graphing. For example, the solution of Example 1 can be visualized by graphing $y = 4^x$ and $y = 16$ on the same set of axes. The y-values for both equations are the same where the graphs intersect. The x-value at that point is the solution of the equation. That x-value appears to be 2. Since $4^2 = 16$, we see that this is indeed the case.

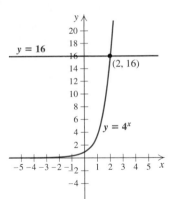

Similarly, the solution of Example 2 can be visualized by graphing $y = 7^{x-2}$ and $y = 60$ and identifying the x-value at the point of intersection. As expected, this value appears to be approximately 4.1.

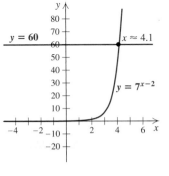

EXAMPLE 3   Solve: $e^{0.06t} = 1500$.

Solution   Since one side is a power of e, it is easiest to take the *natural logarithm* on both sides:

$$\ln e^{0.06t} = \ln 1500 \qquad \text{Taking the natural logarithm on both sides}$$

$$0.06t = \ln 1500 \qquad \text{Finding the logarithm of the base to a power:}$$
$$\log_a a^k = k. \text{ Logarithmic and exponential functions are inverses of each other.}$$

$$t = \frac{\ln 1500}{0.06} \qquad \text{Dividing both sides by 0.06}$$

$$\approx 121.887. \qquad \text{Using a calculator and rounding to three decimal places}$$

To Solve an Equation of the Form $a^t = b$ for t

1. Take the logarithm (either natural or common) of both sides.
2. Use the power rule for exponents so that the variable is no longer written as an exponent.
3. Divide both sides by the coefficient of the variable to isolate the variable.
4. If appropriate, use a calculator to find an approximate solution in decimal form.

Solving Logarithmic Equations

Equations containing logarithmic expressions are called **logarithmic equations**. We saw in Section 12.3 that certain logarithmic equations can be solved by writing an equivalent exponential equation.

EXAMPLE 4   Solve: **(a)** $\log_4 (8x - 6) = 3$; **(b)** $\ln 5x = 27$.

Solution

a) $\log_4 (8x - 6) = 3$

$$4^3 = 8x - 6 \qquad \text{Writing the equivalent exponential equation}$$

$$64 = 8x - 6$$

$$70 = 8x \qquad \text{Adding 6 to both sides}$$

$$x = \tfrac{70}{8}, \text{ or } \tfrac{35}{4}.$$

Check:

$$
\begin{array}{c|c}
\log_4 (8x - 6) = 3 & \\
\hline
\log_4 \left(8 \cdot \tfrac{35}{4} - 6\right) & 3 \\
\log_4 (2 \cdot 35 - 6) & \\
\log_4 64 & \\
3 \overset{?}{=} 3 & \text{TRUE}
\end{array}
$$

The solution is $\tfrac{35}{4}$.

b) $\ln 5x = 27$ Remember: $\ln 5x$ means $\log_e 5x$.

$\quad e^{27} = 5x$ Writing the equivalent exponential equation

$\quad \dfrac{e^{27}}{5} = x$ This is a very large number.

The solution is $\dfrac{e^{27}}{5}$. The check is left to the student.

Often the properties for logarithms are needed. The goal is to first write an equivalent equation in which the variable appears in just one logarithmic expression. We then isolate that expression and solve as in Example 4.

EXAMPLE 5   Solve.

a) $\log x + \log (x - 3) = 1$

b) $\log_2 (x + 7) - \log_2 (x - 7) = 3$

c) $\log_7 (x + 1) + \log_7 (x - 1) = \log_7 8$

Solution

a) To increase understanding, we write in the base, 10.

$$\log_{10} x + \log_{10} (x - 3) = 1$$

$$\log_{10} [x(x - 3)] = 1 \qquad \text{Using the product rule for logarithms to obtain a single logarithm}$$

$$x(x - 3) = 10^1 \qquad \text{Writing an equivalent exponential equation}$$

$$x^2 - 3x = 10$$

$$x^2 - 3x - 10 = 0$$

$$(x + 2)(x - 5) = 0 \qquad \text{Factoring}$$

$$x + 2 = 0 \quad \text{or} \quad x - 5 = 0 \qquad \text{Using the principle of zero products}$$

$$x = -2 \quad \text{or} \qquad x = 5$$

Student Notes _____

It is essential that you remember the properties of logarithms from Section 12.4. Consider reviewing the properties before attempting to solve equations similar to those in Example 5.

Check:

For -2:

$$\underline{\log x + \log (x - 3) = 1}$$

$$\log (-2) + \log (-2 - 3) \overset{?}{=} 1 \quad \text{FALSE}$$

For 5:

$$\underline{\log x + \log (x - 3) = 1}$$

$$\begin{array}{c|c} \log 5 + \log (5 - 3) & 1 \\ \log 5 + \log 2 & \\ \log 10 & \\ 1 \overset{?}{=} 1 & \text{TRUE} \end{array}$$

The number -2 *does not check* because the logarithm of a negative number is undefined. The solution is 5.

b) We have

$$\log_2 (x + 7) - \log_2 (x - 7) = 3$$

$$\log_2 \frac{x + 7}{x - 7} = 3 \qquad \text{Using the quotient rule for logarithms to obtain a single logarithm}$$

$$\frac{x + 7}{x - 7} = 2^3 \qquad \text{Writing an equivalent exponential equation}$$

$$\frac{x + 7}{x - 7} = 8$$

$$x + 7 = 8(x - 7) \qquad \text{Multiplying by the LCD, } x - 7$$

$$x + 7 = 8x - 56 \qquad \text{Using the distributive law}$$

$$63 = 7x$$

$$9 = x. \qquad \text{Dividing by 7}$$

Check:

$$\frac{\log_2 (x + 7) - \log_2 (x - 7) = 3}{\log_2 (9 + 7) - \log_2 (9 - 7) \;\bigm|\; 3}$$

$$\log_2 16 - \log_2 2$$

$$4 - 1$$

$$3 \overset{?}{=} 3 \quad \text{TRUE}$$

The solution is 9.

c) We have

$$\log_7 (x + 1) + \log_7 (x - 1) = \log_7 8$$

$$\log_7 [(x + 1)(x - 1)] = \log_7 8 \qquad \text{Using the product rule for logarithms}$$

$$\log_7 (x^2 - 1) = \log_7 8 \qquad \text{Multiplying. Note that both sides are base-7 logarithms.}$$

$$x^2 - 1 = 8 \qquad \text{Using the principle of logarithmic equality. Study this step carefully.}$$

$$x^2 - 9 = 0$$

$$(x - 3)(x + 3) = 0 \qquad \text{Solving the quadratic equation}$$

$$x = 3 \quad or \quad x = -3.$$

We leave it to the student to show that 3 checks but -3 does not. The solution is 3.

![technology connection logo]

technology connection

To solve exponential and logarithmic equations, we can use INTERSECT to determine the x-coordinate at each intersection.

   For example, to solve $e^{0.5x} - 7 = 2x + 6$, we graph $y_1 = e^{0.5x} - 7$ and $y_2 = 2x + 6$ as shown. We then use the INTERSECT option of the ⟨ CALC ⟩ menu. The x-coordinates at the intersections are approximately -6.48 and 6.52.

   Use a graphing calculator to solve each equation to the nearest hundredth.

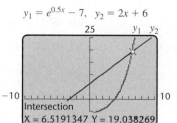

$y_1 = e^{0.5x} - 7, \quad y_2 = 2x + 6$

Intersection
X = 6.5191347   Y = 19.038269
Yscl = 5

1. $e^{7x} = 14$ **2.** $8e^{0.5x} = 3$

3. $xe^{3x-1} = 5$ **4.** $4 \ln (x + 3.4) = 2.5$

5. $\ln 3x = 0.5x - 1$ **6.** $\ln x^2 = -x^2$

Exercise Set

12.6

FOR EXTRA HELP

Student's
Solutions
Manual

Digital Video Tutor
CD 6
Videotape 12

AW Math
Tutor Center

MathXL Tutorials
on CD

Math**XL**
MathXL

MyMathLab
MyMathLab

☙ *Concept Reinforcement   In each of Exercises 1–8, match the equation with an equivalent equation from the column on the right that could be the next step in the solution process.*

1. ____ $5^x = 3$

2. ____ $e^{5x} = 3$

3. ____ $\ln x = 3$

4. ____ $\log_x 5 = 3$

5. ____ $\log_5 x + \log_5(x - 2) = 3$

6. ____ $\log_5 x - \log_5(x - 2) = 3$

7. ____ $\ln x - \ln(x - 2) = 3$

8. ____ $\log x + \log(x - 2) = 3$

a) $\ln e^{5x} = \ln 3$

b) $\log_5 (x^2 - 2x) = 3$

c) $\log (x^2 - 2x) = 3$

d) $\log_5 \dfrac{x}{x - 2} = 3$

e) $\log 5^x = \log 3$

f) $e^3 = x$

g) $\ln \dfrac{x}{x - 2} = 3$

h) $x^3 = 5$

Solve. Where appropriate, include approximations to the nearest thousandth.

9. $2^x = 19$

10. $2^x = 15$

11. $8^{x-1} = 17$

12. $4^{x+1} = 13$

13. $e^t = 1000$

14. $e^t = 100$

15. $e^{0.03t} + 2 = 7$

16. $e^{-0.07t} + 3 = 3.08$

17. $5 = 3^{x+1}$

18. $7 = 3^{x-1}$

Aha! **19.** $2^{x+3} = 16$

20. $4^{x+1} = 64$

21. $4.9^x - 87 = 0$

22. $7.2^x - 65 = 0$

23. $19 = 2e^{4x}$

24. $29 = 3e^{2x}$

25. $7 + 3e^{5x} = 13$

26. $4 + 5e^{4x} = 9$

27. $\log_3 x = 4$

Aha! **28.** $\log_2 x = 6$

29. $\log_2 x = -3$

30. $\log_5 x = 3$

31. $\ln x = 5$

32. $\ln x = 4$

33. $\log_8 x = \frac{1}{3}$

34. $\log_4 x = \frac{1}{2}$

35. $\ln 4x = 3$

36. $\ln 3x = 2$

37. $\log x = 2.5$

38. $\log x = 0.5$

39. $\ln (2x + 1) = 4$

40. $\ln (4x - 2) = 3$

Aha! **41.** $\ln x = 1$

42. $\log x = 1$

43. $5 \ln x = -15$

44. $3 \ln x = -3$

45. $\log_2 (8 - 6x) = 5$

46. $\log_5 (2x - 7) = 3$

47. $\log (x - 9) + \log x = 1$

48. $\log (x + 9) + \log x = 1$

49. $\log x - \log (x + 3) = 1$

50. $\log x - \log (x + 7) = -1$

51. $\log_4 (x + 3) = 2 + \log_4 (x - 5)$

52. $\log_2 (x + 3) = 4 + \log_2 (x - 3)$

53. $\log_7 (x + 1) + \log_7 (x + 2) = \log_7 6$

54. $\log_6 (x + 3) + \log_6 (x + 2) = \log_6 20$

55. $\log_5 (x + 4) + \log_5 (x - 4) = \log_5 20$

56. $\log_4 (x + 2) + \log_4 (x - 7) = \log_4 10$

57. $\ln (x + 5) + \ln (x + 1) = \ln 12$

58. $\ln (x - 6) + \ln (x + 3) = \ln 22$

59. $\log_2 (x - 3) + \log_2 (x + 3) = 4$

60. $\log_3 (x - 4) + \log_3 (x + 4) = 2$

61. $\log_{12} (x + 5) - \log_{12} (x - 4) = \log_{12} 3$

62. $\log_6 (x + 7) - \log_6 (x - 2) = \log_6 5$

63. $\log_2 (x - 2) + \log_2 x = 3$

64. $\log_4 (x + 6) - \log_4 x = 2$

65. Could Example 2 have been solved by taking the natural logarithm on both sides? Why or why not?

66. Christina finds that the solution of $\log_3 (x + 4) = 1$ is -1, but rejects -1 as an answer. What mistake is she making?

SKILL MAINTENANCE

67. Find an equation of variation if y varies directly as x, and $y = 7.2$ when $x = 0.8$. [7.5]

68. Find an equation of variation if y varies inversely as x, and $y = 3.5$ when $x = 6.1$. [7.5]

Solve. [11.3]

69. $T = 2\pi\sqrt{L/32}$, for L

70. $E = mc^2$, for c
(Assume $E, m, c > 0$.)

71. Joni can key in a musical score in 2 hr. Miles takes 3 hr to key in the same score. How long would it take them, working together, to key in the score? [6.7]

72. The side exit at the Flynn Theater can empty a capacity crowd in 25 min. The main exit can empty a capacity crowd in 15 min. How long will it take to empty a capacity crowd when both exits are in use? [6.7]

SYNTHESIS

73. Can the principle of logarithmic equality be expanded to include all functions? That is, is the statement "$m = n$ is equivalent to $f(m) = f(n)$" true for any function f? Why or why not?

74. Explain how Exercises 37 and 38 could be solved using the graph of $f(x) = \log x$.

Solve. If no solution exists, state this.

75. $27^x = 81^{2x-3}$

76. $8^x = 16^{3x+9}$

77. $\log_x (\log_3 27) = 3$

78. $\log_6 (\log_2 x) = 0$

79. $x \log \frac{1}{8} = \log 8$

80. $\log_5 \sqrt{x^2 - 9} = 1$

81. $2^{x^2+4x} = \frac{1}{8}$

82. $\log (\log x) = 5$

83. $\log_5 |x| = 4$

84. $\log x^2 = (\log x)^2$

85. $\log \sqrt{2x} = \sqrt{\log 2x}$

86. $1000^{2x+1} = 100^{3x}$

87. $3^{x^2} \cdot 3^{4x} = \frac{1}{27}$

88. $3^{3x} \cdot 3^{x^2} = 81$

89. $\log x^{\log x} = 25$

90. $3^{2x} - 8 \cdot 3^x + 15 = 0$

91. $(81^{x-2})(27^{x+1}) = 9^{2x-3}$

92. $3^{2x} - 3^{2x-1} = 18$

93. Given that $2^y = 16^{x-3}$ and $3^{y+2} = 27^x$, find the value of $x + y$.

94. If $x = (\log_{125} 5)^{\log_5 125}$, what is the value of $\log_3 x$?

95. Find the value of x for which the natural logarithm is the same as the common logarithm.

96. Use a graphing calculator to check your answers to Exercises 3, 29, 41, and 57.

12.7 Applications of Exponential and Logarithmic Functions

> Applications of Logarithmic Functions •
> Applications of Exponential Functions

We now consider applications of exponential and logarithmic functions.

Applications of Logarithmic Functions

EXAMPLE 1

Sarah Fisher puts in her earplugs in the pits at the Indianapolis Motor Speedway on May 19, 2002. She is the youngest woman to qualify for the Indy 500.

Sound levels.   To measure the volume, or "loudness," of a sound, the *decibel* scale is used. The loudness L, in decibels (dB), of a sound is given by

$$L = 10 \cdot \log \frac{I}{I_0},$$

where I is the intensity of the sound, in watts per square meter (W/m^2), and $I_0 = 10^{-12} \, W/m^2$. (I_0 is approximately the intensity of the softest sound that can be heard by the human ear.)

a) It is common for the intensity of sound at live performances of rock music to reach $10^{-1} \, W/m^2$ (even higher close to the stage). How loud, in decibels, is the sound level?

b) The Occupational Safety and Health Administration (OSHA) considers sound levels of 85 dB and above unsafe. What is the intensity of such sounds?

Solution

a) To find the loudness, in decibels, we use the above formula:

$$L = 10 \cdot \log \frac{I}{I_0}$$

$$= 10 \cdot \log \frac{10^{-1}}{10^{-12}} \qquad \text{Substituting}$$

$$= 10 \cdot \log 10^{11} \qquad \text{Subtracting exponents}$$

$$= 10 \cdot 11 \qquad\qquad \log 10^a = a$$

$$= 110.$$

The volume of the music is 110 decibels.

Study Skills _____

Sorting by Type

When a section contains a variety of problems, try to sort them out by type. For instance, interest compounded continuously, population growth, and the spread of a virus can all be regarded as one type of problem: exponential growth. Once you know how to solve this type of problem, you can focus on determining which problems fall into this category. The solution should then follow in a rather straightforward manner.

b) We substitute and solve for I:

$$L = 10 \cdot \log \frac{I}{I_0}$$

$$85 = 10 \cdot \log \frac{I}{10^{-12}} \qquad \text{Substituting}$$

$$8.5 = \log \frac{I}{10^{-12}} \qquad \text{Dividing both sides by 10}$$

$$8.5 = \log I - \log 10^{-12} \qquad \text{Using the quotient rule for logarithms}$$

$$8.5 = \log I - (-12) \qquad \log 10^a = a$$

$$-3.5 = \log I \qquad \text{Adding} -12 \text{ to both sides}$$

$$10^{-3.5} = I. \qquad \text{Converting to an exponential equation}$$

Earplugs would be recommended for sounds with intensities exceeding $10^{-3.5} \, \text{W/m}^2$.

EXAMPLE 2

Chemistry: pH of liquids.   In chemistry, the pH of a liquid is a measure of its acidity. We calculate pH as follows:

$$\text{pH} = -\log[H^+],$$

where $[H^+]$ is the hydrogen ion concentration in moles per liter.

a) The hydrogen ion concentration of human blood is normally about 3.98×10^{-8} moles per liter. Find the pH.

b) The pH of seawater is about 8.3. Find the hydrogen ion concentration.

Solution

a) To find the pH of blood, we use the above formula:

$$\begin{aligned}
\text{pH} &= -\log[H^+] \\
&= -\log[3.98 \times 10^{-8}] \\
&\approx -(-7.400117) \qquad \text{Using a calculator} \\
&\approx 7.4.
\end{aligned}$$

The pH of human blood is normally about 7.4.

b) We substitute and solve for $[H^+]$:

$$8.3 = -\log[H^+] \qquad \text{Using pH} = -\log[H^+]$$

$$-8.3 = \log[H^+] \qquad \text{Dividing both sides by} -1$$

$$10^{-8.3} = [H^+] \qquad \text{Converting to an exponential equation}$$

$$5.01 \times 10^{-9} \approx [H^+]. \qquad \text{Using a calculator; writing scientific notation}$$

The hydrogen ion concentration of seawater is about 5.01×10^{-9} moles per liter.

Applications of Exponential Functions

EXAMPLE 3   Interest compounded annually.   Suppose that $25,000 is invested at 4% interest, compounded annually. In t years, it will grow to the amount A given by the function

$$A(t) = 25,000(1.04)^t.$$

(See Example 5 in Section 12.2.)

a) How long will it take to accumulate $80,000 in the account?

b) Find the amount of time it takes for the $25,000 to double itself.

Solution

a) We set $A(t) = 80,000$ and solve for t:

$$80,000 = 25,000(1.04)^t$$

$$\frac{80,000}{25,000} = 1.04^t \qquad \text{Dividing both sides by 25,000}$$

$$3.2 = 1.04^t$$

$$\log 3.2 = \log 1.04^t \qquad \text{Taking the common} \\ \text{logarithm on both sides}$$

$$\log 3.2 = t \log 1.04 \qquad \text{Using the power rule for logarithms}$$

$$\frac{\log 3.2}{\log 1.04} = t \qquad \text{Dividing both sides by log 1.04}$$

$$29.7 \approx t. \qquad \text{Using a calculator}$$

Remember that when doing a calculation like this on a calculator, it is best to wait until the end to round off. At an interest rate of 4% per year, it will take about 29.7 yr for $25,000 to grow to $80,000.

Study the different steps in the solution of Example 3(b). Note that if 50,000 and 25,000 are replaced with 8000 and 4000, the doubling time is unchanged.

b) To find the *doubling time*, we replace $A(t)$ with 50,000 and solve for t:

$$50,000 = 25,000(1.04)^t$$

$$2 = (1.04)^t \qquad \text{Dividing both sides by 25,000}$$

$$\log 2 = \log (1.04)^t \qquad \text{Taking the common logarithm} \\ \text{on both sides}$$

$$\log 2 = t \log 1.04 \qquad \text{Using the power rule for} \\ \text{logarithms}$$

$$t = \frac{\log 2}{\log 1.04} \approx 17.7. \qquad \text{Dividing both sides by log 1.04 and} \\ \text{using a calculator}$$

At an interest rate of 4% per year, the doubling time is about 17.7 yr.

Like investments, populations often grow exponentially.

Exponential Growth

An **exponential growth model** is a function of the form

$$P(t) = P_0e^{kt}, \quad k > 0,$$

where P_0 is the population at time 0, $P(t)$ is the population at time t, and k is the **exponential growth rate** for the situation. The **doubling time** is the amount of time necessary for the population to double in size.

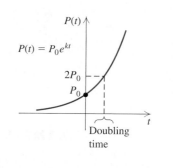

The exponential growth rate is the rate of growth of a population at any *instant* in time. Since the population is continually growing, the percent of total growth after one year will exceed the exponential growth rate.

EXAMPLE 4   Growth of zebra mussel populations.   Zebra mussels, inadvertently imported from Europe, began fouling North American waters in 1988. These mussels are so prolific that lake and river bottoms, as well as water intake pipes, can become blanketed with them, altering an entire ecosystem. In 2000, a portion of the Hudson River contained an average of 10 zebra mussels per square mile. The exponential growth rate was 340% per year.

a) Find the exponential growth function that models the data.

b) Predict the number of mussels per square mile in 2007.

Solution

a) In 2000, at $t = 0$, the population was $10/\text{mi}^2$. We substitute 10 for P_0 and 340%, or 3.4, for k. This gives the exponential growth function

$$P(t) = 10e^{3.4t}.$$

b) In 2007, we have $t = 7$ (since 7 yr have passed since 2000). To find the population in 2007, we compute $P(7)$:

$$P(7) = 10e^{3.4(7)}$$ Using $P(t) = 10e^{3.4t}$ from part (a)

$$= 10e^{23.8}$$

$$\approx 217{,}000{,}000{,}000.$$ Using a calculator

The population of zebra mussels in the specified portion of the Hudson River will reach approximately 217,000,000,000 per square mile in 2007.

EXAMPLE 5   **Spread of a computer virus.** The number of computers infected by a virus t hours after it first appears usually increases exponentially. In 2004, the "MyDoom" worm spread from 100 computers to about 100,000 computers in 24 hr. (*Source*: Based on data from IDG News Service)

a) Find the exponential growth rate and the exponential growth function.

b) Assuming exponential growth, estimate how long it took the MyDoom worm to infect 9000 computers.

Solution

a) We use $N(t) = N_0 e^{kt}$, where t is the number of hours since the first 100 computers were infected. Substituting 100 for N_0 gives

$$N(t) = 100e^{kt}.$$

To find the exponential growth rate, k, note that after 24 hr, 100,000 computers had been infected:

$$\left.\begin{array}{l} N(24) = 100e^{k \cdot 24} \\ 100{,}000 = 100e^{24k} \end{array}\right\}$$ Substituting

$$1000 = e^{24k}$$ Dividing both sides by 100

$$\ln 1000 = \ln e^{24k}$$ Taking the natural logarithm on both sides

$$\ln 1000 = 24k$$ $\ln e^a = a$

$$\frac{\ln 1000}{24} = k$$ Dividing both sides by 24

$$0.288 \approx k.$$ Using a calculator and rounding

The exponential growth rate is 28.8% and the exponential growth function is given by $N(t) = 100e^{0.288t}$.

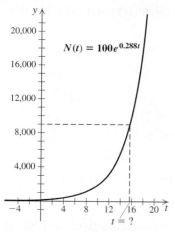

$N(t) = 100e^{0.288t}$

$t = ?$

A visualization of Example 5

b) To estimate how long it took for 9000 computers to be infected, we replace $N(t)$ with 9000 and solve for t:

$$9000 = 100e^{0.288t}$$

$$90 = e^{0.288t} \qquad \text{Dividing both sides by 100}$$

$$\ln 90 = \ln e^{0.288t} \qquad \text{Taking the natural logarithm on both sides}$$

$$\ln 90 = 0.288t \qquad \ln e^a = a$$

$$\frac{\ln 90}{0.288} = t \qquad \text{Dividing both sides by 0.288}$$

$$15.6 \approx t. \qquad \text{Using a calculator}$$

Rounding up to 16, we see that, according to this model, it took about 16 hr for 9000 computers to be infected.

EXAMPLE 6   Interest compounded continuously.   When an amount of money P_0 is invested at interest rate k, compounded *continuously*, interest is computed every "instant" and added to the original amount. The balance $P(t)$, after t years, is given by the exponential growth model

$$P(t) = P_0 e^{kt}.$$

a) Suppose that $30,000 is invested and grows to $44,754.75 in 5 yr. Find the exponential growth function.

b) What is the doubling time?

Solution

a) We have $P(0) = 30,000$. Thus the exponential growth function is

$$P(t) = 30,000e^{kt}, \quad \text{where } k \text{ must still be determined.}$$

Knowing that for $t = 5$ we have $P(5) = 44,754.75$, it is possible to solve for k:

$$44,754.75 = 30,000e^{k(5)} = 30,000e^{5k}$$

$$\frac{44,754.75}{30,000} = e^{5k} \qquad \text{Dividing both sides by 30,000}$$

$$1.491825 = e^{5k}$$

$$\ln 1.491825 = \ln e^{5k} \qquad \text{Taking the natural logarithm on both sides}$$

$$\ln 1.491825 = 5k \qquad \ln e^a = a$$

$$\frac{\ln 1.491825}{5} = k \qquad \text{Dividing both sides by 5}$$

$$0.08 \approx k. \qquad \text{Using a calculator and rounding}$$

The interest rate is about 0.08, or 8%, compounded continuously. Because interest is being compounded continuously, the yearly interest rate is a bit more than 8%. The exponential growth function is

$$P(t) = 30,000e^{0.08t}.$$

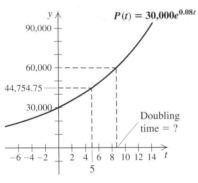

A visualization of Example 6

b) To find the doubling time T, we replace $P(T)$ with 60,000 and solve for T:

$$60{,}000 = 30{,}000e^{0.08T}$$

$$2 = e^{0.08T} \qquad \text{Dividing both sides by 30,000}$$

$$\ln 2 = \ln e^{0.08T} \qquad \text{Taking the natural logarithm on both sides}$$

$$\ln 2 = 0.08T \qquad \ln e^{a} = a$$

$$\frac{\ln 2}{0.08} = T \qquad \text{Dividing both sides by 0.08}$$

$$8.7 \approx T. \qquad \text{Using a calculator and rounding}$$

Thus the original investment of $30,000 will double in about 8.7 yr.

For any specified interest rate, continuous compounding gives the highest yield and the shortest doubling time.

In some real-life situations, a quantity or population is *decreasing* or *decaying* exponentially.

Exponential Decay

An **exponential decay model** is a function of the form

$$P(t) = P_0 e^{-kt}, \quad k > 0,$$

where P_0 is the quantity present at time 0, $P(t)$ is the amount present at time t, and k is the **decay rate**. The **half-life** is the amount of time necessary for half of the quantity to decay.

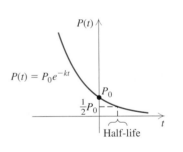

EXAMPLE 7

Chaco Canyon, New Mexico

Carbon dating.   The radioactive element carbon-14 has a half-life of 5750 yr. The percentage of carbon-14 present in the remains of organic matter can be used to determine the age of that organic matter. Recently, while digging in Chaco Canyon, New Mexico, archaeologists found corn pollen that had lost 38.1% of its carbon-14. The age of this corn pollen was evidence that Indians had been cultivating crops in the Southwest centuries earlier than scientists had thought. What was the age of the pollen? (*Source: American Anthropologist*)

Solution   We first find k. To do so, we use the concept of half-life. When $t = 5750$ (the half-life), $P(t)$ will be half of P_0. Then

$$0.5P_0 = P_0 e^{-k(5750)} \qquad \text{Substituting in } P(t) = P_0 e^{-kt}$$

$$0.5 = e^{-5750k} \qquad \text{Dividing both sides by } P_0$$

$$\ln 0.5 = \ln e^{-5750k} \qquad \text{Taking the natural logarithm on both sides}$$

$$\ln 0.5 = -5750k \qquad \ln e^{a} = a$$

$$\frac{\ln 0.5}{-5750} = k \qquad \text{Dividing}$$

$$0.00012 \approx k. \qquad \text{Using a calculator and rounding}$$

Now we have a function for the decay of carbon-14:

$$P(t) = P_0 e^{-0.00012t}.$$ ←—This completes the first part of our solution.

(*Note*: This equation can be used for any subsequent carbon-dating problem.) If the corn pollen has lost 38.1% of its carbon-14 from an initial amount P_0, then $100\% - 38.1\%$, or 61.9%, of P_0 is still present. To find the age t of the pollen, we solve this equation for t:

$$0.619 P_0 = P_0 e^{-0.00012t}$$ We want to find t for which $P(t) = 0.619 P_0$.

$$0.619 = e^{-0.00012t}$$ Dividing both sides by P_0

$$\ln 0.619 = \ln e^{-0.00012t}$$ Taking the natural logarithm on both sides

$$\ln 0.619 = -0.00012t$$ $\ln e^a = a$

$$\frac{\ln 0.619}{-0.00012} = t$$ Dividing

$$4000 \approx t.$$ Using a calculator

The pollen is about 4000 yr old.

Exercise Set

12.7

FOR EXTRA HELP

 Student's Solutions Manual

 Digital Video Tutor CD 6 Videotape 12

 AW Math Tutor Center

 MathXL Tutorials on CD

 MathXL

 MyMathLab

■ *Solve.*

1. *DVD players.*   Yearly sales of DVD players $S(t)$, in millions of dollars, t years after 1997 can be estimated by

$$S(t) = 200 \cdot 2^t.$$

Source: *Statistical Abstract of the United States*, 2003

a) Determine the year in which sales of DVD players first reached $2800 million.

b) What is the doubling time for the yearly sales of DVD players?

2. *Cell phones.*   The number of cell phones in use in the United States, in millions, t years after 1990 can be estimated by

$$N(t) = 7.12(1.3)^t.$$

Source: Cellular Telecommunications and Internet Association

a) In what year did the number of cell phones in use first reach 200 million?

b) What is the doubling time for the number of cell phones in use?

3. *Skateboarding.*   The number of skateboarders of age x, in thousands, can be approximated by

$$N(x) = 1337(0.9)^x, \quad 7 \le x \le 60.$$

Sources: Based on figures from the National Sporting Goods Association and *Statistical Abstract of the United States*, 2003

a) Estimate the number of 21-year-old skateboarders.

b) At what age are there only 6300 skateboarders?

4. *Recycling aluminum cans.*   Approximately one-half of all aluminum cans distributed will be recycled each year. A beverage company distributes 250,000 cans. The number still in use after t years is given by the function

$$N(t) = 250{,}000\left(\tfrac{1}{2}\right)^t.$$

Source: The Aluminum Association, Inc., May 2004

a) After how many years will 60,000 cans still be in use?

b) After what amount of time will only 1000 cans still be in use?

5. *Student loan repayment.*   A college loan of $29,000 is made at 3% interest, compounded annually. After t years, the amount due, A, is given by the function

$$A(t) = 29{,}000(1.03)^t.$$

a) After what amount of time will the amount due reach $35,000?

b) Find the doubling time.

6. *Spread of a rumor.*   The number of people who have heard a rumor increases exponentially. If all who hear a rumor repeat it to two people a day, and if 20 people start the rumor, the number of people N who have heard the rumor after t days is given by

$$N(t) = 20(3)^t.$$

a) After what amount of time will 1000 people have heard the rumor?

b) What is the doubling time for the number of people who have heard the rumor?

7. *Telephone lines.*   As more Americans make cell phones their *only* phones, the percentage of phone lines that are land lines has been shrinking.

The percentage of U.S. phone lines that are land lines $P(t)$, in use t years after 2000, can be estimated by

$$P(t) = 63.03(0.95)^t.$$

Sources: Based on data from Federal Communications Commission; Cellular Telecommunications and Internet Association

a) In what year did/will the percentage of phones that are land lines drop below 50%?

b) In what year will the percentage of phones that are land lines drop below 25%?

8. *Smoking.*   The percentage of smokers who received telephone counseling and had successfully quit smoking for t months is given by

$$P(t) = 21.4(0.914)^t.$$

Sources: *New England Journal of Medicine*; data from California's Smoker's Hotline

a) In what month will 15% of those who quit and used telephone counseling still be smoke-free?

b) In what month will 5% of those who quit and used phone counseling still be smoke-free?

9. *Marine biology.*   As a result of preservation efforts in countries in which whaling was once common, the humpback whale population has grown since the 1970s. The worldwide population $P(t)$, in thousands, t years after 1982 can be estimated by

$$P(t) = 5.5(1.047)^t.$$

a) In what year will the humpback whale population reach 30,000?

b) Find the doubling time.

10. *World population.*   The world population $P(t)$, in billions, t years after 1980 can be approximated by

$$P(t) = 4.495(1.015)^t.$$

Sources: Based on data from U.S. Bureau of the Census; International Data Base

a) In what year will the world population reach 7 billion?

b) Find the doubling time.

Use the pH formula given in Example 2 for Exercises 11–14.

11. *Chemistry.*   The hydrogen ion concentration of fresh-brewed coffee is about 1.3×10^{-5} moles per liter. Find the pH.

12. *Chemistry.*   The hydrogen ion concentration of milk is about 1.6×10^{-7} moles per liter. Find the pH.

13. *Medicine.*   When the pH of a patient's blood drops below 7.4, a condition called *acidosis* sets in. Acidosis can be deadly when the patient's pH reaches 7.0. What would the hydrogen ion concentration of the patient's blood be at that point?

14. *Medicine.*   When the pH of a patient's blood rises above 7.4, a condition called *alkalosis* sets in. Alkalosis can be deadly when the patient's pH reaches 7.8. What would the hydrogen ion concentration of the patient's blood be at that point?

Use the decibel formula given in Example 1 for Exercises 15–18.

15. *Audiology.*   The intensity of sound in normal conversation is about 3.2×10^{-6} W/m^2. How loud in decibels is this sound level?

16. *Audiology.*   The intensity of a riveter at work is about 3.2×10^{-3} W/m^2. How loud in decibels is this sound level?

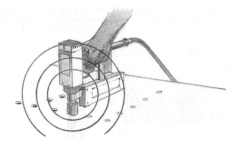

17. *Music.*   The band U2 recently performed and sound measurements of 105 dB were recorded. What is the intensity of such sounds?

18. *Music.*   The band Strange Folk performed in Burlington, VT, and reached sound levels of 111 dB. What is the intensity of such sounds?
    Source: Melissa Garrido, *Burlington Free Press*

Use the compound-interest formula in Example 6 for Exercises 19 and 20.

19. *Interest compounded continuously.*   Suppose that P_0 is invested in a savings account where interest is compounded continuously at 2.5% per year.
    a) Express $P(t)$ in terms of P_0 and 0.025.
    b) Suppose that $5000 is invested. What is the balance after 1 yr? after 2 yr?
    c) When will an investment of $5000 double itself?

20. *Interest compounded continuously.*   Suppose that P_0 is invested in a savings account where interest is compounded continuously at 3.1% per year.
    a) Express $P(t)$ in terms of P_0 and 0.031.
    b) Suppose that $1000 is invested. What is the balance after 1 yr? after 2 yr?
    c) When will an investment of $1000 double itself?

21. *Population growth.*   In 2004, the population of the United States was 292.80 million and the exponential growth rate was 0.9% per year.
    Source: U.S. Bureau of the Census
    a) Find the exponential growth function.
    b) Predict the U.S. population in 2005.
    c) When will the U.S. population reach 325 million?

22. *World population growth.*   In 2004, the world population was 6.3 billion and the exponential growth rate was 1.1% per year.
    Source: U.S. Bureau of the Census
    a) Find the exponential growth function.
    b) Predict the world population in 2009.
    c) When will the world population be 8.0 billion?

23. *iPod sales.*   The number of iPods sold since January 1, 2003, has grown at an exponential growth rate of 10.3% per month. What is the doubling time for iPod sales?
    Source: Based on data from iPodlounge.com

24. *Population growth.*   The exponential growth rate of the population of Saudi Arabia is 3.3% per year (one of the highest in the world). What is the doubling time?
    Sources: Based on data from U.S. Bureau of the Census; International Data Base 2002

25. *World population.*   The function
    $$Y(x) = 67.17 \ln \frac{x}{4.5}$$
    can be used to estimate the number of years $Y(x)$ after 1980 required for the world population to reach x billion people.
    Sources: Based on data from U.S. Bureau of the Census; International Data Base
    a) In what year will the world population reach 7 billion?
    b) In what year will the world population reach 8 billion?
    c) Graph the function.

26. *Marine biology.* The function

$$Y(x) = 21.77 \ln \frac{x}{5.5}$$

can be used to estimate the number of years $Y(x)$ after 1982 required for the world's humpback whale population to reach x thousand whales.

a) In what year will the whale population reach 15,000?

b) In what year will the whale population reach 25,000?

c) Graph the function.

27. *Forgetting.* Students in an English class took a final exam. They took equivalent forms of the exam at monthly intervals thereafter. The average score $S(t)$, in percent, after t months was found to be given by

$$S(t) = 68 - 20 \log (t + 1), \quad t \geq 0.$$

a) What was the average score when they initially took the test, $t = 0$?

b) What was the average score after 4 months? after 24 months?

c) Graph the function.

d) After what time t was the average score 50%?

28. *Advertising.* A model for advertising response is given by

$$N(a) = 2000 + 500 \log a, \quad a \geq 1,$$

where $N(a)$ is the number of units sold and a is the amount spent on advertising, in thousands of dollars.

a) How many units were sold after spending $1000 ($a = 1$) on advertising?

b) How many units were sold after spending $8000?

c) Graph the function.

d) How much would have to be spent in order to sell 5000 units?

29. *Sexually transmitted disease.* Suppose that in 2000 an outbreak of Herpes infected 17 people at a large university, and that by 2001 the number of those infected had grown to 29.

a) Find an exponential growth function that fits the data.

b) Predict the number of people who will be infected in 2006.

30. *iPod sales.* Sales of iPods have grown exponentially since January 1, 2003, at which time 656,000 units had been sold. Approximately 16 months later, in May 2004, the 3-millionth unit was sold.

Source: Based on data from iPodlounge.com

a) Find an exponential growth function that fits the data.

b) Predict the number of units sold as of April 2005.

31. *Decline in farmland.* The number of acres of farmland in the United States has decreased from 987 million acres in 1990 to 941 million acres in 2002. Assume the number of acres of farmland is decreasing exponentially.

Source: *Statistical Abstract of the United States*, 2003

a) Find the value k, and write an equation for an exponential function that can predict the number of acres of U.S. farmland t years after 1990.

b) Predict the number of acres of farmland in 2008.

c) In what year (theoretically) will there be only 800 million acres of U.S. farmland remaining?

32. *Decline in cases of mumps.* The number of cases of mumps has dropped exponentially from 900 in 1995 to 300 in 2001.

Source: U.S. Centers for Disease Control and Prevention

a) Find the value k, and write an exponential function that can be used to estimate the number of cases t years after 1995.

b) Estimate the number of cases of mumps in 2008.

c) In what year (theoretically) will there be only 1 case of mumps?

33. *Archaeology.* When archaeologists found the Dead Sea Scrolls, they determined that the linen wrapping had lost 22.3% of its carbon-14. How old is the linen wrapping? (See Example 7.)

34. *Archaeology.* In 1996, researchers found an ivory tusk that had lost 18% of its carbon-14. How old was the tusk? (See Example 7.)

35. *Chemistry.* The exponential decay rate of iodine-131 is 9.6% per day. What is its half-life?

36. *Chemistry.* The decay rate of krypton-85 is 6.3% per year. What is its half-life?

37. *Home construction.*   The chemical urea formaldehyde was found in some insulation used in houses built during the mid to late 1960s. Unknown at the time was the fact that urea formaldehyde emitted toxic fumes as it decayed. The half-life of urea formaldehyde is 1 yr. What is its decay rate?

38. *Plumbing.*   Lead pipes and solder are often found in older buildings. Unfortunately, as lead decays, toxic chemicals can get in the water resting in the pipes. The half-life of lead is 22 yr. What is its decay rate?

39. *Value of a sports card.*   Legend has it that because he objected to smoking, and because his first baseball card was issued in cigarette packs, the great shortstop Honus Wagner halted production of his card before many were produced. One of these cards was purchased in 1991 by hockey great Wayne Gretzky (and a partner) for $451,000. The same card was sold in 2000 for $1.1 million. For the following questions, assume that the card's value increases exponentially, as it has for many years.

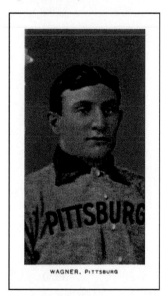

WAGNER, PITTSBURG

a) Find the exponential growth rate k, and determine an exponential function V that can be used to estimate the dollar value, $V(t)$, of the card t years after 1991.
b) Predict the value of the card in 2006.
c) What is the doubling time for the value of the card?
d) In what year will the value of the card first exceed $3,000,000?

40. *Art masterpieces.*   As of August 2004, the most ever paid for a painting is $104,168,000, paid in 2004 for Pablo Picasso's "Garçon à la Pipe." The same painting sold for $30,000 in 1950.
Source: BBC News, 5/6/04

a) Find the exponential growth rate k, and determine the exponential growth function V, for which $V(t)$ is the painting's value, in millions of dollars, t years after 1950.
b) Estimate the value of the painting in 2009.
c) What is the doubling time for the value of the painting?
d) How long after 1950 will the value of the painting be $1 billion?

41. Write a problem for a classmate to solve in which information is provided and the classmate is asked to find an exponential growth function. Make the problem as realistic as possible.

42. Examine the restriction on t in Exercise 27.
   a) What upper limit might be placed on t?
   b) In practice, would this upper limit ever be enforced? Why or why not?

SKILL MAINTENANCE

Graph. [11.7]

43. $y = x^2 - 8x$ **44.** $y = x^2 - 5x - 6$

45. $f(x) = 3x^2 - 5x - 1$ **46.** $g(x) = 2x^2 - 6x + 3$

Solve by completing the square. [11.1]

47. $x^2 - 8x = 7$ **48.** $x^2 + 10x = 6$

SYNTHESIS

49. Will the model used to predict the number of DVD players in Exercise 1 still be realistic in 2020? Why or why not?

50. *Atmospheric pressure.*   Atmospheric pressure P at altitude a is given by

$$P = P_0 e^{-0.00005a},$$

where P_0 is the pressure at sea level $\approx 14.7 \text{ lb/in}^2$ (pounds per square inch). Explain how a barometer, or some other device for measuring atmospheric pressure, can be used to find the height of a skyscraper.

51. *Sports salaries.*   As of November 2004, Alex Rodriguez of the New York Yankees has the largest contract in sports history. As part of the 10-year $252-million deal, he will receive $24 million in 2010 (part from the Yankees and part from his former team, the Texas Rangers). How much money would need to be invested in 2004, at 4% interest compounded continuously, in order to have $24 million for Rodriguez in 2010? (This is much like finding what $24 million in 2010 is worth in 2004 dollars.)
Source: *The San Francisco Chronicle*

52. *Supply and demand.*   The supply and demand for the sale of stereos by Sound Ideas are given by

$$S(x) = e^x \quad \text{and} \quad D(x) = 162{,}755e^{-x},$$

where $S(x)$ is the price at which the company is willing to supply x stereos and $D(x)$ is the demand price for a quantity of x stereos. Find the equilibrium point. (For reference, see Section 3.8.)

53. Use Exercise 7 to form a model for the percentage of U.S. phone lines that are cellular t years after 2000.

54. Use the model developed in Exercise 53 to predict the percentage of U.S. phone lines that will be cellular in 2020. Does your prediction seem plausible? Why or why not?

55. *Nuclear energy.*   Plutonium-239 (Pu-239) is used in nuclear energy plants. The half-life of Pu-239 is 24,360 yr. How long will it take for a fuel rod of Pu-239 to lose 90% of its radioactivity?
Source: *Microsoft Encarta 97 Encyclopedia*

56. *Growth of bacteria.*   The bacteria *Escherichia coli* (*E. coli*) are commonly found in the human bladder. Suppose that 3000 of the bacteria are present at time $t = 0$. Then t minutes later, the number of bacteria present is

$$N(t) = 3000(2)^{t/20}.$$

If 100,000,000 bacteria accumulate, a bladder infection can occur. If, at 11:00 A.M., a patient's bladder contains 25,000 *E. coli* bacteria, at what time can infection occur?

57. Show that for exponential growth at rate k, the doubling time T is given by $T = \dfrac{\ln 2}{k}$.

58. Show that for exponential decay at rate k, the half-life T is given by $T = \dfrac{\ln 2}{k}$.

59. *Heart transplants.*   In 1967, Dr. Christiaan Barnard of South Africa stunned the world by performing the first heart transplant. Since that time, the operation's popularity has both grown and declined, as shown in the table below.

Year	Number of Heart Transplants Worldwide*
1982	189
1983	318
1984	669
1985	1189
1986	2167
1987	2720
1988	3157
1989	3378
1990	4016
1991	4186
1992	4199
1993	4346
1994	4402
1995	4314
1996	4128
1997	4039
1998	3744
1999	3419
2000	3246
2001	3122
2002	3265
2003	3020

Source: International Society for Heart & Lung Transplantation

a) Using 1982 as $t = 0$, graph the data.

b) Does it appear that an exponential function might have ever served as an appropriate model for these data? If so, for what years would this have been the case?

c) Considering *all* of the data points on your graph, which would be the most appropriate model: a linear, a quadratic, or an exponential function? Why?

COLLABORATIVE

CORNER

Investments in Collectibles

Focus: Exponential-growth models

Time: 30 minutes

Group size: 7

Collecting comic books has long been a popular hobby. It can also be quite profitable since many comic books that originally sold for less than $1 are now worth hundreds or, in some cases, thousands of dollars.

Collectors often estimate the future value of their collections by examining the value's growth in the past. As with many collectibles, the value of comic books often grows exponentially.

ACTIVITY

1. Suppose that in 2005, each group member invests in the comic books listed in the following table. Looking only at the approximate value in 2005, each student

should select $1200 worth of comic books. More than one comic of each type can be selected. The comics chosen will become that student's portfolio.

2. Each group member should select a different one of the comic books. That person should then form an exponential growth model for the value of that comic book using the year of issue and the original cost of the comic book.

3. Using the models developed above, each group member should predict the value of his or her portfolio in 2009. Compare the values. Why, when buying a collector's item, is it important to consider its previous worth?

4. Look at the predicted value of each comic book in 2009. Does an exponential growth model seem appropriate? If possible, find the current value of some of the comic books and compare those values with the predicted values.

Comic Book	Approximate Value in 2005	Year of Issue	Original Cost
Bugs Bunny #28	$ 70	1952	15¢
Josie and the Pussycats #45	140	1969	15¢
Amazing Spider-Man #121	250	1973	25¢
Men In Black #1	45	1990	$2.25
Sonic the Hedgehog #1	35	1993	1.25
G. I. Joe #155	35	1994	1.75
Ultimate Spider-Man #1	90	2000	2.99

Source: Prices based on data kindly provided by Tim Reynolds at Comic Carnival, Indianapolis, IN.

Study Summary

Chapter 12 focuses on two special types of functions: **exponential** and **logarithmic** (pp. 794, 803). To understand how these functions relate to each other, it is important to first understand what **composite functions** are and how function **composition** is performed (pp. 782, 783).

The composition of f and g, or $f \circ g$: $(f \circ g)(x) = f(g(x))$

Thus

      if $f(x) = 2x + 1$ and $g(x) = x^2$,

      then $(f \circ g)(3) = f(g(3)) = f(9) = 2 \cdot 9 + 1 = 19.$

Composition of functions is developed so we can discuss **inverse functions** (p. 785). To find a function f^{-1}, which is the inverse of f, f must be **one-to-one**, meaning that no two members of f's domain are paired with the same member of the range (p. 786). One quick test for a one-to-one function is the **horizontal-line test**:

A function f is one-to-one if it is not possible to draw a horizontal line that crosses the graph of f at more than one point (p. 786):

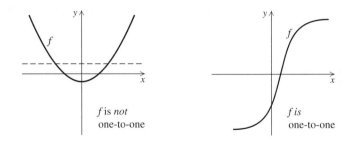

If f is one-to-one, it is then possible to find its inverse:

1. Replace $f(x)$ with y.
2. Interchange x and y.
3. Solve for y.
4. Replace y with $f^{-1}(x)$.

For any two inverse functions f and f^{-1},

$$(f^{-1} \circ f)(x) = (f \circ f^{-1})(x) = x,$$

or, equivalently,

$$f^{-1}(f(x)) = x \text{ and } f(f^{-1}(x)) = x.$$

Probably the most important pair of inverse functions in mathematics are the exponential and logarithmic functions:

f is an exponential function if $f(x) = a^x$ for $a > 0, a \neq 1$.

g is a logarithmic function if $g(x) = \log_a x$ for $a > 0, a \neq 1$.

Note that $y = \log_a x$ means $a^y = x$.

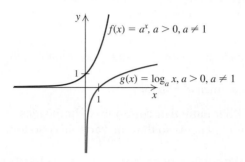

Common (base-10) and **natural** (base-e) logarithms are the most frequently used types of logarithms (pp. 817, 818). Note that $e \approx 2.7$.

Exponential and logarithmic expressions frequently appear in equations. To solve such **exponential** or **logarithmic equations**, we must use certain principles and properties:

Properties of Logarithms

$\log_a (MN) = \log_a M + \log_a N$: $\log_7 10 = \log_7 5 + \log_7 2$;

$\log_a \dfrac{M}{N} = \log_a M - \log_a N$: $\log_5 \dfrac{14}{3} = \log_5 14 - \log_5 3$;

$\log_a M^p = p \cdot \log_a M$: $\log_8 5^{12} = 12 \log_8 5$;

$\log_a 1 = 0$: $\log_9 1 = 0$;

$\log_a a = 1$: $\log_4 4 = 1$;

$\log_a a^k = k$: $\log_3 3^8 = 8$;

$\log M = \log_{10} M$: $\log 43 = \log_{10} 43$;

$\ln M = \log_e M$: $\ln 37 = \log_e 37$;

$\log_b M = \dfrac{\log_a M}{\log_a b}$: $\log_6 31 = \dfrac{\log 31}{\log 6}$

The Principle of Exponential Equality

For any real number b, $b \neq -1$, 0, or 1: $b^x = b^y$ is equivalent to $x = y$.

The Principle of Logarithmic Equality

For any logarithmic base a, and for $x, y > 0$: $x = y$ is equivalent to $\log_a x = \log_a y$.

Thus,

$$25 = 5^x \quad \text{is equivalent to} \quad 5^2 = 5^x, \text{ or } 2 = x,$$

and

$$7^x = 83 \quad \text{is equivalent to} \quad \log 7^x = \log 83, \text{ or } x \log 7 = \log 83, \text{ or } x = \frac{\log 83}{\log 7}.$$

To solve an equation of the form $a^t = b$ for t:

1. Take the logarithm (either natural or common) of both sides.
2. Use the power rule for exponents so that the variable is no longer written as an exponent.
3. Divide both sides by the coefficient of the variable to isolate the variable.
4. If appropriate, use a calculator to find an approximate solution in decimal form.

Exponential and logarithmic equations arise in a wide variety of applications.

Exponential Growth

An **exponential growth model** is a function of the form

$$P(t) = P_0 e^{kt}, \quad k > 0,$$

where P_0 is the population at time 0, $P(t)$ is the population at time t, and k is the **exponential growth rate** for the situation. The **doubling time** is the amount of time necessary for the population to double in size.

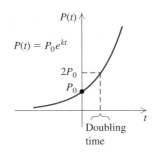

Exponential Decay

An **exponential decay model** is a function of the form

$$P(t) = P_0 e^{-kt}, \quad k > 0,$$

where P_0 is the quantity present at time 0, $P(t)$ is the amount present at time t, and k is the **decay rate**. The **half-life** is the amount of time necessary for half of the quantity to decay.

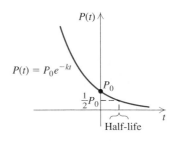

12 Review Exercises

↩ *Concept Reinforcement*   *In each of Exercises 1–10, classify the statement as either true or false.*

1. The functions given by $f(x) = e^x$ and $g(x) = \ln x$ are inverses of each other. [12.3]

2. A function's doubling time is the amount of time t for which $f(t) = 2f(0)$. [12.7]

3. A radioactive isotope's half-life is the amount of time t for which $f(t) = \frac{1}{2} f(0)$. [12.7]

4. $\ln (ab) = \ln a - \ln b$ [12.4]

5. $\log x^a = x \ln a$ [12.4]

6. $\log_a \dfrac{m}{n} = \log_a m - \log_a n$ [12.4]

7. For $f(x) = 3^x$, the domain of f is $[0, \infty)$. [12.2]

8. For $g(x) = \log_2 x$, the domain of g is $[0, \infty)$. [12.3]

9. The function F is not one-to-one if $F(-2) = F(5)$. [12.1]

10. The function g is one-to-one if it passes the vertical-line test. [12.1]

11. Find $(f \circ g)(x)$ and $(g \circ f)(x)$ if $f(x) = x^2 + 1$ and $g(x) = 2x - 3$. [12.1]

12. If $h(x) = \sqrt{3 - x}$, find $f(x)$ and $g(x)$ such that $h(x) = (f \circ g)(x)$. Answers may vary. [12.1]

13. Determine whether $f(x) = 4 - x^2$ is one-to-one. [12.1]

Find a formula for the inverse of each function. [12.1]

14. $f(x) = x - 8$

15. $g(x) = \dfrac{3x + 1}{2}$

16. $f(x) = 27x^3$

Graph.

17. $f(x) = 3^x + 1$ [12.2]   **18.** $x = \left(\frac{1}{4}\right)^y$ [12.2]

19. $y = \log_5 x$ [12.3]

Simplify. [12.3]

20. $\log_3 9$ **21.** $\log_{10} \frac{1}{100}$

22. $\log_5 5^7$ **23.** $\log_9 3$

Rewrite as an equivalent logarithmic equation. [12.3]

24. $10^{-2} = \frac{1}{100}$ **25.** $25^{1/2} = 5$

Rewrite as an equivalent exponential equation. [12.3]

26. $\log_4 16 = x$ **27.** $\log_8 1 = 0$

Express as an equivalent expression using the individual logarithms of x, y, and z. [12.4]

28. $\log_a x^4 y^2 z^3$

29. $\log_a \dfrac{x^5}{yz^2}$

30. $\log \sqrt[4]{\dfrac{z^2}{x^3 y}}$

Express as an equivalent expression that is a single logarithm and, if possible, simplify. [12.4]

31. $\log_a 7 + \log_a 8$

32. $\log_a 72 - \log_a 12$

33. $\frac{1}{2} \log a - \log b - 2 \log c$

34. $\frac{1}{3}[\log_a x - 2 \log_a y]$

Simplify. [12.4]

35. $\log_m m$ **36.** $\log_m 1$

37. $\log_m m^{17}$

Given $\log_a 2 = 1.8301$ and $\log_a 7 = 5.0999$, find each of the following. [12.4]

38. $\log_a 14$ **39.** $\log_a \frac{2}{7}$

40. $\log_a 28$ **41.** $\log_a 3.5$

42. $\log_a \sqrt{7}$ **43.** $\log_a \frac{1}{4}$

▤ *Use a calculator to find each of the following to the nearest ten-thousandth.* [12.5]

44. $\log 75$ **45.** $10^{1.789}$

46. $\ln 0.05$ **47.** $e^{-0.98}$

Find each of the following logarithms using the change-of-base formula. Round answers to the nearest ten-thousandth. [12.5]

48. $\log_5 2$

49. $\log_{12} 70$

Graph and state the domain and the range of each function. [12.5]

50. $f(x) = e^x - 1$

51. $g(x) = 0.6 \ln x$

Solve. Where appropriate, include approximations to the nearest ten-thousandth. [12.6]

52. $2^x = 32$

53. $3^x = \frac{1}{9}$

54. $\log_3 x = -4$

55. $\log_x 16 = 4$

56. $\log x = -3$

57. $3 \ln x = -6$

58. $4^{2x-5} = 19$

59. $2^{x^2} \cdot 2^{4x} = 32$

60. $4^x = 8.3$

61. $e^{-0.1t} = 0.03$

62. $2 \ln x = -6$

63. $\log_3 (2x - 5) = 1$

64. $\log_4 x + \log_4 (x - 6) = 2$

65. $\log x + \log (x - 15) = 2$

66. $\log_3 (x - 4) = 3 - \log_3 (x + 4)$

67. In a business class, students were tested at the end of the course with a final exam. They were then tested again 6 months later. The forgetting formula was determined to be

$$S(t) = 82 - 18 \log (t + 1),$$

where t is the time, in months, after taking the final exam. [12.7]

a) Determine the average score when they first took the exam (when $t = 0$).

b) What was the average score after 6 months?

c) After what time was the average score 54?

68. A color photocopier is purchased for $5200. Its value each year is about 80% of its value in the preceding year. Its value in dollars after t years is given by the exponential function

$$V(t) = 5200(0.8)^t. \quad [12.7]$$

a) After what amount of time will the copier's value be $1200?

b) After what amount of time will the copier's value be half the original value?

69. In 1999, Lucille invested in a building lot that cost $10,000. By 2004, fair-market value for the lot was $19,000. Assume that the value of the lot is increasing exponentially. [12.7]

a) Find the value k, and write an exponential function that describes the value of Lucille's lot t years after 1999.

b) Predict the value of the lot in 2009.

c) In what year will the value of the lot first reach $35,000?

70. The value of Jose's stock market portfolio doubled in 3 yr. What was the exponential growth rate? [12.7]

71. How long will it take $7600 to double itself if it is invested at 4.2%, compounded continuously? [12.7]

72. How old is a skull that has lost 34% of its carbon-14? (Use $P(t) = P_0 e^{-0.00012t}$.) [12.7]

73. What is the pH of a substance if its hydrogen ion concentration is 2.3×10^{-7} moles per liter? (Use $\text{pH} = -\log [\text{H}^+]$.) [12.7]

74. The intensity of the sound of water at the foot of the Niagara Falls is about 10^{-3} W/m². * How loud in decibels is this sound level? [12.7]

$$\left(\text{Use } L = 10 \cdot \log \frac{I}{10^{-12}}. \right)$$

SYNTHESIS

75. Explain why negative numbers do not have logarithms. [12.3]

76. Explain why taking the natural or common logarithm on each side of an equation produces an equivalent equation. [12.6]

Solve. [12.6]

77. $\ln (\ln x) = 3$

78. $2^{x^2+4x} = \frac{1}{8}$

79. Solve the system:

$$5^{x+y} = 25,$$
$$2^{2x-y} = 64. \quad [12.6]$$

Sound and Hearing, Life Science Library. (New York: Time Incorporated, 1965), p. 173.

12 Chapter Test

1. Find $(f \circ g)(x)$ and $(g \circ f)(x)$ if $f(x) = x + x^2$ and $g(x) = 2x + 1$.

2. If
$$h(x) = \frac{1}{2x^2 + 1},$$
find $f(x)$ and $g(x)$ such that $h(x) = (f \circ g)(x)$. Answers may vary.

3. Determine whether $f(x) = |x - 3|$ is one-to-one.

Find a formula for the inverse of each function.

4. $f(x) = 3x + 4$

5. $g(x) = (x + 1)^3$

Graph.

6. $f(x) = 2^x - 3$

7. $g(x) = \log_7 x$

Simplify.

8. $\log_5 125$

9. $\log_{100} 10$

10. $3^{\log_3 18}$

Rewrite as an equivalent logarithmic equation.

11. $4^{-3} = \frac{1}{64}$

12. $256^{1/2} = 16$

Rewrite as an equivalent exponential equation.

13. $m = \log_7 49$

14. $\log_3 81 = 4$

15. Express as an equivalent expression using the individual logarithms of a, b, and c:
$$\log \frac{a^3 b^{1/2}}{c^2}.$$

16. Express as an equivalent expression that is a single logarithm:
$$\tfrac{1}{3} \log_a x + 2 \log_a z.$$

Simplify.

17. $\log_p p$

18. $\log_t t^{23}$

19. $\log_c 1$

Given $\log_a 2 = 0.301$, $\log_a 6 = 0.778$, and $\log_a 7 = 0.845$, find each of the following.

20. $\log_a 14$

21. $\log_a 3$

22. $\log_a 16$

Use a calculator to find each of the following to the nearest ten-thousandth.

23. $\log 12.3$

24. $10^{-0.8}$

25. $\ln 0.035$

26. $e^{4.8}$

27. Find $\log_3 14$ using the change-of-base formula. Round to the nearest ten-thousandth.

Graph and state the domain and the range of each function.

28. $f(x) = e^x + 3$

29. $g(x) = \ln (x - 4)$

Solve. Where appropriate, include approximations to the nearest ten-thousandth.

30. $2^x = \frac{1}{32}$

31. $\log_x 25 = 2$

32. $\log_4 x = \frac{1}{2}$

33. $\log x = 4$

34. $5^{4-3x} = 87$

35. $7^x = 1.2$

36. $\ln x = \frac{1}{4}$

37. $\log (x - 3) + \log (x + 1) = \log 5$

38. The average walking speed R of people living in a city of population P, in thousands, is given by $R = 0.37 \ln P + 0.05$, where R is in feet per second.

   a) The population of Tulsa, Oklahoma, is 878,000. Find the average walking speed.
   b) Baton Rouge, Louisiana, has an average walking speed of about 2.48 ft/sec. Find the population.

39. The population of Nigeria was about 130.5 million in 2002, and the exponential growth rate was 2.4% per year.

   a) Write an exponential function describing the population of Nigeria.
   b) What will the population be in 2007? in 2012?
   c) When will the population be 175 million?
   d) What is the doubling time?

40. The average cost of a year at a private four-year college grew exponentially from \$19,070 in 1997 to \$22,968 in 2003.
Source: National Center for Education Statistics, Digest of Education Statistics, 2002

   a) Find the value k, and write an exponential function that approximates the cost of a year of college t years after 1997.

   b) Predict the cost of a year of college in 2010.

   c) In what year will the average cost of college be \$50,000?

41. An investment with interest compounded continuously doubled itself in 15 yr. What is the interest rate?

42. How old is an animal bone that has lost 43% of its carbon-14? (Use $P(t) = P_0 e^{-0.00012t}$.)

43. The sound of traffic at a busy intersection averages 75 dB. What is the intensity of such a sound?
$$\left(\text{Use } L = 10 \cdot \log \frac{I}{I_0}. \right)$$

44. The hydrogen ion concentration of water is 1.0×10^{-7} moles per liter. What is the pH? (Use $\text{pH} = -\log [\text{H}^+]$.)

SYNTHESIS

45. Solve: $\log_5 |2x - 7| = 4$.

46. If $\log_a x = 2$, $\log_a y = 3$, and $\log_a z = 4$, find
$$\log_a \frac{\sqrt[3]{x^2 z}}{\sqrt[3]{y^2 z^{-1}}}.$$

1–12 Cumulative Review

1. Evaluate $\dfrac{x^0 + y}{-z}$ for $x = 6$, $y = 9$, and $z = -5$. [1.8]

Simplify.

2. $\left| -\frac{5}{2} + \left(-\frac{7}{2} \right) \right|$ [1.8]

3. $(-2x^2 y^{-3})^{-4}$ [4.8]

4. $(-5x^4 y^{-3} z^2)(-4x^2 y^2)$ [4.8]

5. $\dfrac{3x^4 y^6 z^{-2}}{-9x^4 y^2 z^3}$ [4.8]

6. $4x - 3 - 2[5 - 3(2 - x)]$ [1.8]

7. $3^3 + 2^2 - (32 \div 4 - 16 \div 8)$ [1.8]

Solve.

8. $5(2x - 3) = 9 - 5(2 - x)$ [2.2]

9. $4x - 3y = 15,$
$3x + 5y = 4$ [8.2]

10. $x + y - 3z = -1,$
$2x - y + z = 4,$
$-x - y + z = 1$ [8.4]

11. $x(x - 3) = 10$ [5.7]

12. $\dfrac{7}{x^2 - 5x} - \dfrac{2}{x - 5} = \dfrac{4}{x}$ [6.6]

13. $\dfrac{8}{x + 1} + \dfrac{11}{x^2 - x + 1} = \dfrac{24}{x^3 + 1}$ [6.6], [11.2]

14. $\sqrt{4 - 5x} = 2x - 1$ [10.6]

15. $\sqrt[3]{2x} = 1$ [10.6]

16. $3x^2 + 75 = 0$ [11.1]

17. $x - 8\sqrt{x} + 15 = 0$ [11.5]

18. $x^4 - 13x^2 + 36 = 0$ [11.5]

19. $\log_7 x = 1$ [12.3]

20. $\log_x 36 = 2$ [12.3]

21. $9^x = 27$ [12.6]

22. $3^{5x} = 7$ [12.6]

23. $\ln x - \ln (x - 8) = 1$ [12.6]

24. $x^2 + 4x > 5$ [11.9]

25. If $f(x) = x^2 + 6x$, find a such that $f(a) = 11$. [11.2]

26. If $f(x) = |2x - 3|$, find all x for which $f(x) \geq 7$. [9.3]

Solve.

27. $D = \dfrac{ab}{b + a}$, for a [7.5]

28. $\dfrac{1}{p} + \dfrac{1}{q} = \dfrac{1}{f}$, for q [7.5]

29. $M = \dfrac{2}{3}(A + B)$, for B [2.3]

Evaluate. [8.7]

30. $\begin{vmatrix} 6 & -5 \\ 4 & -3 \end{vmatrix}$

31. $\begin{vmatrix} 7 & -6 & 0 \\ -2 & 1 & 2 \\ -1 & 1 & -1 \end{vmatrix}$

32. Find the domain of the function f given by

$$f(x) = \frac{x + 4}{3x^2 - 5x - 2}. \text{ [7.2]}$$

Solve.

33. *Gasoline consumption.* The number of barrels of gasoline consumed per day in the United States has increased from 7.2 million in 1990 to 8.9 million in 2003.

Source: U.S. Department of Energy, Energy Information Administration

   a) At what rate did gasoline consumption increase from 1990 to 2003? [3.4]
   b) Find a linear function g that fits the data. Let t represent the number of years since 1990. [7.3]
   c) Find an exponential function G that fits the data. [12.7]

34. The perimeter of a rectangular garden is 112 m. The length is 16 m more than the width. Find the length and the width. [2.5]

35. In triangle ABC, the measure of angle B is three times the measure of angle A. The measure of angle C is 105° greater than the measure of angle A. Find the angle measures. [2.5]

36. Good's Candies of Indiana makes all their chocolates by hand. It takes Anne 10 min to coat a tray of candies in chocolate. It takes Clay 12 min to coat a tray of candies. How long would it take Anne and Clay, working together, to coat the candies? [6.7]

37. Joe's Thick and Tasty salad dressing gets 45% of its calories from fat. The Light and Lean dressing gets 20% of its calories from fat. How many ounces of each should be mixed in order to get 15 oz of dressing that gets 30% of its calories from fat? [8.3]

38. A fishing boat with a trolling motor can move at a speed of 5 km/h in still water. The boat travels 42 km downriver in the same time that it takes to travel 12 km upriver. What is the speed of the river? [6.7]

39. What is the minimum product of two numbers whose difference is 14? What are the numbers that yield this product? [11.8]

Students in a biology class just took a final exam. A formula for determining what the average exam grade on a similar test will be t months later is

$$S(t) = 78 - 15 \log (t + 1).$$

40. The average score when the students first took the exam occurs when $t = 0$. Find the students' average score on the final exam. [12.7]

41. What would the average score be on a retest after 4 months? [12.7]

The population of Kenya was 33.7 million in 2002, and the exponential growth rate was 1.0% per year. [12.7]

42. Write an exponential function describing the growth of the population of Kenya.

43. Predict what the population will be in 2008 and in 2014.

44. What is the doubling time of the population?

45. y varies directly as the square of x and inversely as z, and $y = 2$ when $x = 5$ and $z = 100$. What is y when $x = 3$ and $z = 4$? [7.5]

Perform the indicated operations and simplify.

46. $(5p^2q^3 + 6pq - p^2 + p) + (2p^2q^3 + p^2 - 5pq - 9)$ [4.3]

47. $(11x^2 - 6x - 3) - (3x^2 + 5x - 2)$ [4.3]

48. $(3x^2 - 2y)^2$ [4.5]

49. $(5a + 3b)(2a - 3b)$ [4.5]

50. $\dfrac{x^2 + 8x + 16}{2x + 6} \div \dfrac{x^2 + 3x - 4}{x^2 - 9}$ [6.2]

51. $\dfrac{1 + \dfrac{3}{x}}{x - 1 - \dfrac{12}{x}}$ [6.5]

52. $\dfrac{a^2 - a - 6}{a^3 - 27} \cdot \dfrac{a^2 + 3a + 9}{6}$ [6.2]

53. $\dfrac{3}{x + 6} - \dfrac{2}{x^2 - 36} + \dfrac{4}{x - 6}$ [6.4]

Factor.

54. $xy + 2xz - xw$ [5.1]

55. $8 - 125x^3$ [5.5]

56. $6x^2 + 8xy - 8y^2$ [5.3]

57. $x^4 - 4x^3 + 7x - 28$ [5.1]

58. $2m^2 + 12mn + 18n^2$ [5.4]

59. $x^4 - 16y^4$ [5.4]

60. For the function described by
$$h(x) = -3x^2 + 4x + 8,$$
find $h(-2)$. [7.1]

61. Divide: $(x^4 - 5x^3 + 2x^2 - 6) \div (x - 3)$. [4.7]

62. Multiply $(5.2 \times 10^4)(3.5 \times 10^{-6})$. Write scientific notation for the answer. [4.8]

For the radical expressions that follow, assume that all variables represent positive numbers.

63. Divide and simplify:
$$\dfrac{\sqrt[3]{40xy^8}}{\sqrt[3]{5xy}}. \quad [10.4]$$

64. Multiply and simplify: $\sqrt{7xy^3} \cdot \sqrt{28x^2y}$. [10.3]

65. Write as an equivalent expression without rational exponents: $(27a^6b)^{4/3}$. [10.2]

66. Rationalize the denominator:
$$\dfrac{3 - \sqrt{y}}{2 - \sqrt{y}}. \quad [10.5]$$

67. Divide and simplify:
$$\dfrac{\sqrt{x + 5}}{\sqrt[5]{x + 5}}. \quad [10.5]$$

68. Multiply these complex numbers:
$$(2 - i\sqrt{3})(6 + 2i\sqrt{3}). \quad [10.8]$$

69. Add: $(8 + 2i) + (5 - 3i)$. [10.8]

70. Find the inverse of f if $f(x) = 9 - 2x$. [12.1]

71. Find a linear equation with a graph that contains the points $(0, -8)$ and $(-1, 2)$. [3.7]

72. Find an equation of the line whose graph has a y-intercept of $(0, 7)$ and is perpendicular to the line given by $2x + y = 6$. [3.6]

Graph.

73. $5x = 15 + 3y$ [3.2]

74. $y = 2x^2 - 4x - 1$ [11.7]

75. $y = \log_3 x$ [12.3]

76. $y = 3^x$ [12.2]

77. $-2x - 3y \leq 12$ [9.4]

78. Graph: $f(x) = 2(x + 3)^2 + 1$. [11.7]
   a) Label the vertex.
   b) Draw the axis of symmetry.
   c) Find the maximum or minimum value.

79. Graph $f(x) = 2e^x$ and determine the domain and the range. [12.5]

80. Express in terms of logarithms of a, b, and c:
$$\log\left(\dfrac{a^2c^3}{b}\right). \quad [12.4]$$

81. Express as a single logarithm:
$$3 \log x - \tfrac{1}{2} \log y - 2 \log z. \quad [12.4]$$

82. Convert to an exponential equation: $\log_a 5 = x$. [12.3]

83. Convert to a logarithmic equation: $x^3 = t$. [12.3]

Find each of the following using a calculator. Round to the nearest ten-thousandth. [12.5]

84. $\log 0.05566$

85. $10^{2.89}$

86. $\ln 12.78$

87. $e^{-1.4}$

SYNTHESIS

Solve.

88. $\dfrac{5}{3x - 3} + \dfrac{10}{3x + 6} = \dfrac{5x}{x^2 + x - 2}$ [6.6]

89. $\log \sqrt{3x} = \sqrt{\log 3x}$ [12.6]

90. A train travels 280 mi at a certain speed. If the speed had been increased by 5 mph, the trip could have been made in 1 hr less time. Find the actual speed. [11.3]

13

Conic Sections

AN APPLICATION

The spotlight on a violin soloist casts an ellipse of light on the floor below her that is 6 ft wide and 10 ft long. Find an equation of that ellipse if the performer is in its center, *x* is the distance from the performer to the side of the ellipse, and *y* is the distance from the performer to the top of the ellipse.

This problem appears as Exercise 49 in Section 13.2.

Tony Penna
LIGHTING DESIGNER
Clemson, South Carolina

As a lighting designer, I use math in almost every aspect of my work. Before the lighting instruments are loaded into the theatre, I must determine the angle at which each instrument will be focused at the stage, which requires a great deal of geometry in three dimensions. For each light I use, I must also choose which type of lighting instrument will produce the appropriate sized beam of light.

*T*he ellipse described in the chapter opener is one example of a conic section, meaning that it can be regarded as a cross section of a cone. This chapter presents a variety of applications and equations with graphs that are conic sections. We have already worked with two conic sections, lines and parabolas, in Chapters 3 and 11.

13.1 Conic Sections: Parabolas and Circles

Parabolas • The Distance and Midpoint Formulas •
Circles

This section and the next two examine curves formed by cross sections of cones. These curves are all graphs of $Ax^2 + By^2 + Cxy + Dx + Ey + F = 0$. The constants A, B, C, D, E, and F determine which of the following shapes will serve as the graph.

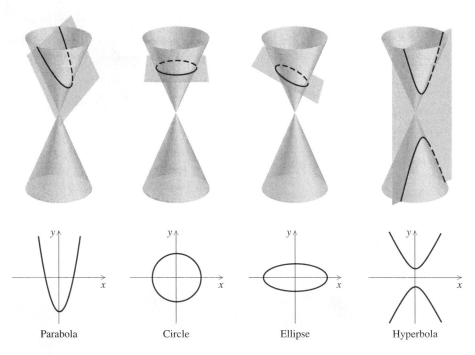

Parabola   Circle   Ellipse   Hyperbola

Parabolas

When a cone is cut as shown in the first figure above, the conic section formed is a **parabola**. Parabolas have many applications in electricity, mechanics, and optics. A cross section of a contact lens or satellite dish is a parabola, and arches that support certain bridges are parabolas.

Equation of a Parabola

A parabola with a vertical axis of symmetry opens upward or downward and has an equation that can be written in the form

$$y = ax^2 + bx + c.$$

A parabola with a horizontal axis of symmetry opens to the right or left and has an equation that can be written in the form

$$x = ay^2 + by + c.$$

Parabolas with equations of the form $f(x) = ax^2 + bx + c$ were graphed in Chapter 11.

EXAMPLE 1 Graph: $y = x^2 - 4x + 9$.

Solution To locate the vertex, we can use either of two approaches. One way is to complete the square:

$y = (x^2 - 4x) + 9$	Note that half of -4 is -2, and $(-2)^2 = 4$.
$\quad = (x^2 - 4x + 4 - 4) + 9$	Adding and subtracting 4
$\quad = (x^2 - 4x + 4) + (-4 + 9)$	Regrouping
$\quad = (x - 2)^2 + 5.$	Factoring and simplifying

The vertex is $(2, 5)$.

A second way to find the vertex is to recall that the x-coordinate of the vertex of the parabola given by $y = ax^2 + bx + c$ is $-b/(2a)$:

$$x = -\frac{b}{2a} = -\frac{-4}{2(1)} = 2.$$

To find the y-coordinate of the vertex, we substitute 2 for x:

$$y = x^2 - 4x + 9 = 2^2 - 4(2) + 9 = 5.$$

Either way, the vertex is $(2, 5)$. Next, we calculate and plot some points on each side of the vertex. As expected for a positive coefficient of x^2, the graph opens upward.

x	y	
2	5	← Vertex
0	9	← y-intercept
1	6	
3	6	
4	9	

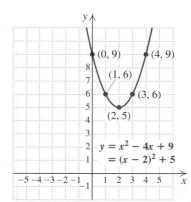

> *To Graph an Equation of the Form* $y = ax^2 + bx + c$
>
> **1.** Find the vertex (h, k) either by completing the square to find an equivalent equation
>
> $$y = a(x - h)^2 + k,$$
>
> or by using $-b/(2a)$ to find the x-coordinate and substituting to find the y-coordinate.
> **2.** Choose other values for x on each side of the vertex, and compute the corresponding y-values.
> **3.** The graph opens upward for $a > 0$ and downward for $a < 0$.

Equations of the form $x = ay^2 + by + c$ represent horizontal parabolas. These parabolas open to the right for $a > 0$, open to the left for $a < 0$, and have axes of symmetry parallel to the x-axis.

EXAMPLE 2   Graph: $x = y^2 - 4y + 9$.

Solution   This equation is like that in Example 1 but with x and y interchanged. The vertex is $(5, 2)$ instead of $(2, 5)$. To find ordered pairs, we choose values for y on each side of the vertex. Then we compute values for x. Note that the x- and y-values of the table in Example 1 are now switched. You should confirm that, by completing the square, we get $x = (y - 2)^2 + 5$.

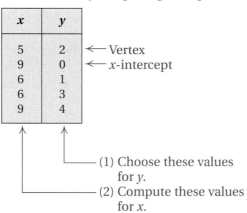

x	y
5	2	← Vertex
9	0	← x-intercept
6	1
6	3
9	4

(1) Choose these values for y.
(2) Compute these values for x.

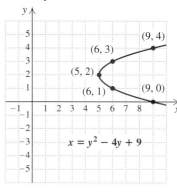

> *To Graph an Equation of the Form* $x = ay^2 + by + c$
>
> **1.** Find the vertex (h, k) either by completing the square to find an equivalent equation
>
> $$x = a(y - k)^2 + h,$$
>
> or by using $-b/(2a)$ to find the y-coordinate and substituting to find the x-coordinate.
> **2.** Choose other values for y that are above and below the vertex, and compute the corresponding x-values.
> **3.** The graph opens to the right if $a > 0$ and to the left if $a < 0$.

EXAMPLE 3   Graph: $x = -2y^2 + 10y - 7$.

Solution   We find the vertex by completing the square:

$$x = -2y^2 + 10y - 7$$
$$= -2(y^2 - 5y \qquad) - 7$$
$$= -2\left(y^2 - 5y + \tfrac{25}{4}\right) - 7 - (-2)\tfrac{25}{4} \qquad \tfrac{1}{2}(-5) = \tfrac{-5}{2}; \left(\tfrac{-5}{2}\right)^2 = \tfrac{25}{4}; \text{ we}$$
add and subtract $(-2)\tfrac{25}{4}$.
$$= -2\left(y - \tfrac{5}{2}\right)^2 + \tfrac{11}{2}. \qquad \text{Factoring and simplifying}$$

The vertex is $\left(\tfrac{11}{2}, \tfrac{5}{2}\right)$.

For practice, we also find the vertex by first computing its y-coordinate, $-b/(2a)$, and then substituting to find the x-coordinate:

$$y = -\frac{b}{2a} = -\frac{10}{2(-2)} = \frac{5}{2}$$
$$x = -2y^2 + 10y - 7 = -2\left(\tfrac{5}{2}\right)^2 + 10\left(\tfrac{5}{2}\right) - 7$$
$$= \tfrac{11}{2}.$$

To find ordered pairs, we choose values for y on each side of the vertex and then compute values for x. A table is shown below, together with the graph. The graph opens to the left because the y^2-coefficient, -2, is negative.

x	y	
$\tfrac{11}{2}$	$\tfrac{5}{2}$	←Vertex
-7	0	←x-intercept
5	2	
5	3	
1	1	
1	4	
-7	5	

(1) Choose these values for y.

(2) Compute these values for x.

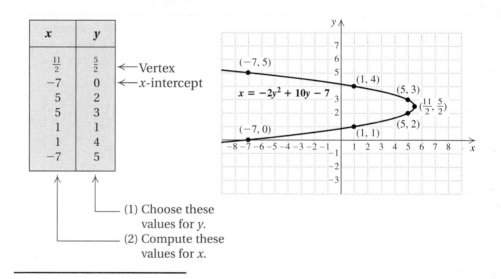

The Distance and Midpoint Formulas

If two points are on a horizontal line, they have the same second coordinate. We can find the distance between them by subtracting their first coordinates. This difference may be negative, depending on the order in which we subtract. So, to make sure we get a positive number, we take the absolute value of this difference. The distance between the points (x_1, y_1) and (x_2, y_1) on a horizontal line is thus $|x_2 - x_1|$. Similarly, the distance between the points (x_2, y_1) and (x_2, y_2) on a vertical line is $|y_2 - y_1|$.

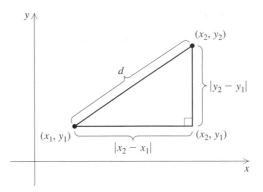

Now consider *any* two points (x_1, y_1) and (x_2, y_2). If $x_1 \neq x_2$ and $y_1 \neq y_2$, these points, along with the point (x_2, y_1), describe a right triangle. The lengths of the legs are $|x_2 - x_1|$ and $|y_2 - y_1|$. We find d, the length of the hypotenuse, by using the Pythagorean theorem:

$$d^2 = |x_2 - x_1|^2 + |y_2 - y_1|^2.$$

Since the square of a number is the same as the square of its opposite, we can replace the absolute-value signs with parentheses:

$$d^2 = (x_2 - x_1)^2 + (y_2 - y_1)^2.$$

Taking the principal square root, we have a formula for distance.

The Distance Formula

The distance d between any two points (x_1, y_1) and (x_2, y_2) is given by

$$d = \sqrt{(x_2 - x_1)^2 + (y_2 - y_1)^2}.$$

EXAMPLE 4   Find the distance between $(5, -1)$ and $(-4, 6)$. Find an exact answer and an approximation to three decimal places.

Solution   We substitute into the distance formula:

$$d = \sqrt{(-4 - 5)^2 + [6 - (-1)]^2}$$ Substituting
$$= \sqrt{(-9)^2 + 7^2}$$
$$= \sqrt{130}$$ This is exact.
$$\approx 11.402.$$ Using a calculator for an approximation

The distance formula is needed to develop the formula for a circle, which follows, and to verify certain properties of conic sections. It is also needed to verify a formula for the coordinates of the *midpoint* of a segment connecting two points. We state the midpoint formula and leave its proof to the exercises.

Student Notes

To help remember the formulas correctly, note that the distance formula (a variation on the Pythagorean theorem) involves both subtraction and addition, whereas the midpoint formula does not include any subtraction.

The Midpoint Formula

If the endpoints of a segment are (x_1, y_1) and (x_2, y_2), then the coordinates of the midpoint are

$$\left(\frac{x_1 + x_2}{2}, \frac{y_1 + y_2}{2} \right).$$

(To locate the midpoint, average the x-coordinates and average the y-coordinates.)

EXAMPLE 5 Find the midpoint of the segment with endpoints $(-2, 3)$ and $(4, -6)$.

Solution Using the midpoint formula, we obtain

$$\left(\frac{-2 + 4}{2}, \frac{3 + (-6)}{2} \right), \quad \text{or} \quad \left(\frac{2}{2}, \frac{-3}{2} \right), \quad \text{or} \quad \left(1, -\frac{3}{2} \right).$$

Circles

One conic section, the **circle**, is a set of points in a plane that are a fixed distance r, called the **radius** (plural, **radii**), from a fixed point (h, k), called the **center**. Note that the word radius can mean either any segment connecting a point on a circle to the center or the length of such a segment. If (x, y) is on the circle, then by the definition of a circle and the distance formula, it follows that

$$r = \sqrt{(x - h)^2 + (y - k)^2}.$$

Squaring both sides gives the equation of a circle in standard form.

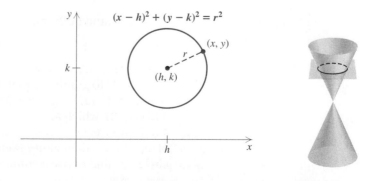

> *Equation of a Circle (Standard Form)*
>
> The equation of a circle, centered at (h, k), with radius r, is given by
>
> $$(x - h)^2 + (y - k)^2 = r^2.$$

Note that for $h = 0$ and $k = 0$, the circle is centered at the origin. Otherwise, the circle is translated $|h|$ units horizontally and $|k|$ units vertically.

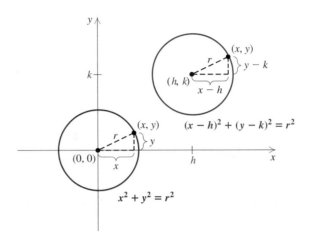

EXAMPLE 6   Find an equation of the circle having center $(4, 5)$ and radius 6.

Solution   Using the standard form, we obtain

$$(x - 4)^2 + (y - 5)^2 = 6^2, \qquad \text{Using } (x - h)^2 + (y - k)^2 = r^2$$

or

$$(x - 4)^2 + (y - 5)^2 = 36.$$

EXAMPLE 7   Find the center and the radius and then graph each circle.

a) $(x - 2)^2 + (y + 3)^2 = 4^2$

b) $x^2 + y^2 + 8x - 2y + 15 = 0$

Solution

a) We write standard form:

$$(x - 2)^2 + [y - (-3)]^2 = 4^2.$$

The center is $(2, -3)$ and the radius is 4. To graph, we plot the points $(2, 1)$, $(2, -7)$, $(-2, -3)$, and $(6, -3)$, which are, respectively, 4 units above, below, left, and right of $(2, -3)$. We then either sketch a circle by hand or use a compass.

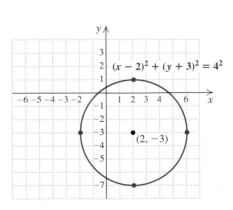

b) To write the equation $x^2 + y^2 + 8x - 2y + 15 = 0$ in standard form, we complete the square twice, once with $x^2 + 8x$ and once with $y^2 - 2y$:

$$x^2 + y^2 + 8x - 2y + 15 = 0$$

$$x^2 + 8x \qquad + y^2 - 2y \qquad = -15 \qquad \text{Grouping the } x\text{-terms and the } y\text{-terms; adding } -15 \text{ to both sides}$$

$$x^2 + 8x + 16 + y^2 - 2y + 1 = -15 + 16 + 1 \qquad \text{Adding } \left(\tfrac{8}{2}\right)^2, \text{ or } 16, \text{ and } \left(-\tfrac{2}{2}\right)^2, \text{ or } 1, \text{ to both sides to get standard form}$$

$$(x + 4)^2 + (y - 1)^2 = 2 \qquad \text{Factoring}$$

$$[x - (-4)]^2 + (y - 1)^2 = \left(\sqrt{2}\right)^2. \qquad \text{Writing standard form}$$

The center is $(-4, 1)$ and the radius is $\sqrt{2}$.

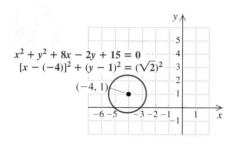

technology connection

Most graphing calculators graph only functions, so graphing the equation of a circle usually requires two steps:

1. Solve the equation for y. The result will include a $\pm$ sign in front of a radical.

2. Graph two functions, one for the $+$ sign and the other for the $-$ sign, on the same set of axes.

For example, to graph $(x - 3)^2 + (y + 1)^2 = 16$, solve for $y + 1$ and then y:

$$(y + 1)^2 = 16 - (x - 3)^2$$

$$y + 1 = \pm\sqrt{16 - (x - 3)^2}$$

$$y = -1 \pm \sqrt{16 - (x - 3)^2},$$

or

$$y_1 = -1 + \sqrt{16 - (x - 3)^2}$$

and

$$y_2 = -1 - \sqrt{16 - (x - 3)^2}.$$

When both functions are graphed (in a "squared" window to eliminate distortion), the result is as follows.

$$y_1 = -1 + \sqrt{16 - (x - 3)^2},$$
$$y_2 = -1 - \sqrt{16 - (x - 3)^2}$$

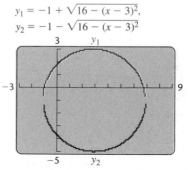

On many calculators, pressing **APPS** and selecting Conics and then Circle accesses a program in which equations in standard form can be graphed directly and then Traced.

Graph each of the following equations.

1. $x^2 + y^2 - 16 = 0$
2. $(x - 1)^2 + (y - 2)^2 = 25$
3. $(x + 3)^2 + (y - 5)^2 = 16$
4. $(x - 5)^2 + (y + 6)^2 = 49$

Exercise Set

 13.1

Concept Reinforcement *In each of Exercises 1–8, match the equation with the graph of that equation from those shown.*

1. ____ $(x - 2)^2 + (y + 5)^2 = 9$

2. ____ $(x + 2)^2 + (y - 5)^2 = 9$

3. ____ $(x - 5)^2 + (y + 2)^2 = 9$

4. ____ $(x + 5)^2 + (y - 2)^2 = 9$

5. ____ $y = (x - 2)^2 - 5$

6. ____ $y = (x - 5)^2 - 2$

7. ____ $x = (y - 2)^2 - 5$

8. ____ $x = (y - 5)^2 - 2$

a)
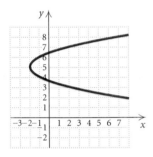

b)
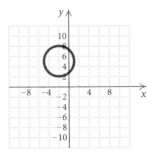

c)
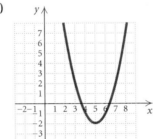

d)
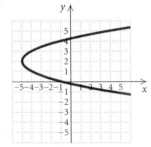

e)
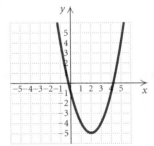

f)
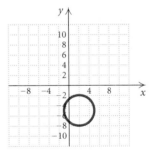

g)
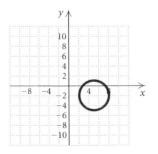

h)
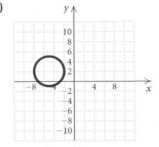

Graph. Be sure to label each vertex.

9. $y = -x^2$

10. $y = 2x^2$

11. $y = -x^2 + 4x - 5$

12. $x = 4 - 3y - y^2$

13. $x = y^2 - 4y + 2$

14. $y = x^2 + 2x + 3$

15. $x = y^2 + 3$

16. $x = 2y^2$

17. $x = -\frac{1}{2}y^2$

18. $x = y^2 - 1$

19. $x = -y^2 - 4y$

20. $x = y^2 + y - 6$

21. $x = 4 - y - y^2$

22. $y = x^2 + 2x + 1$

23. $y = x^2 - 2x + 1$

24. $y = -\frac{1}{2}x^2$

25. $x = -y^2 + 2y - 1$

26. $x = -y^2 - 2y + 3$

27. $x = -2y^2 - 4y + 1$

28. $x = 2y^2 + 4y - 1$

Find the distance between each pair of points. Where appropriate, find an approximation to three decimal places.

29. $(1, 6)$ and $(5, 9)$

30. $(1, 10)$ and $(7, 2)$

31. $(0, -7)$ and $(3, -4)$

32. $(6, 2)$ and $(6, -8)$

33. $(-4, 4)$ and $(6, -6)$

34. $(5, 21)$ and $(-3, 1)$

Aha! **35.** $(8.6, -3.4)$ and $(-9.2, -3.4)$

36. $(5.9, 2)$ and $(3.7, -7.7)$

37. $\left(\frac{5}{7}, \frac{1}{14}\right)$ and $\left(\frac{1}{7}, \frac{11}{14}\right)$

38. $\left(0, \sqrt{7}\right)$ and $\left(\sqrt{6}, 0\right)$

39. $\left(-\sqrt{6}, \sqrt{2}\right)$ and $(0, 0)$

40. $\left(\sqrt{5}, -\sqrt{3}\right)$ and $(0, 0)$

41. $(-4, -2)$ and $(-7, -11)$

42. $(-3, -7)$ and $(-1, -5)$

Find the midpoint of each segment with the given endpoints.

43. $(-7, 6)$ and $(9, 2)$

44. $(6, 7)$ and $(7, -9)$

45. $(2, -1)$ and $(5, 8)$

46. $(-1, 2)$ and $(1, -3)$

47. $(-8, -5)$ and $(6, -1)$

48. $(8, -2)$ and $(-3, 4)$

49. $(-3.4, 8.1)$ and $(2.9, -8.7)$

50. $(4.1, 6.9)$ and $(5.2, -6.9)$

51. $\left(\frac{1}{6}, -\frac{3}{4}\right)$ and $\left(-\frac{1}{3}, \frac{5}{6}\right)$

52. $\left(-\frac{4}{5}, -\frac{2}{3}\right)$ and $\left(\frac{1}{8}, \frac{3}{4}\right)$

53. $\left(\sqrt{2}, -1\right)$ and $\left(\sqrt{3}, 4\right)$

54. $\left(9, 2\sqrt{3}\right)$ and $\left(-4, 5\sqrt{3}\right)$

Find an equation of the circle satisfying the given conditions.

55. Center $(0, 0)$, radius 6

56. Center $(0, 0)$, radius 5

57. Center $(7, 3)$, radius $\sqrt{5}$

58. Center $(5, 6)$, radius $\sqrt{2}$

59. Center $(-4, 3)$, radius $4\sqrt{3}$

60. Center $(-2, 7)$, radius $2\sqrt{5}$

61. Center $(-7, -2)$, radius $5\sqrt{2}$

62. Center $(-5, -8)$, radius $3\sqrt{2}$

63. Center $(0, 0)$, passing through $(-3, 4)$

64. Center $(3, -2)$, passing through $(11, -2)$

65. Center $(-4, 1)$, passing through $(-2, 5)$

66. Center $(-1, -3)$, passing through $(-4, 2)$

Find the center and the radius of each circle. Then graph the circle.

67. $x^2 + y^2 = 64$

68. $x^2 + y^2 = 36$

69. $(x + 1)^2 + (y + 3)^2 = 36$

70. $(x - 2)^2 + (y + 3)^2 = 4$

71. $(x - 4)^2 + (y + 3)^2 = 10$

72. $(x + 5)^2 + (y - 1)^2 = 15$

73. $x^2 + y^2 = 10$

74. $x^2 + y^2 = 7$

75. $(x - 5)^2 + y^2 = \frac{1}{4}$

76. $x^2 + (y - 1)^2 = \frac{1}{25}$

77. $x^2 + y^2 + 8x - 6y - 15 = 0$

78. $x^2 + y^2 + 6x - 4y - 15 = 0$

79. $x^2 + y^2 - 8x + 2y + 13 = 0$

80. $x^2 + y^2 + 6x + 4y + 12 = 0$

81. $x^2 + y^2 + 10y - 75 = 0$

82. $x^2 + y^2 - 8x - 84 = 0$

83. $x^2 + y^2 + 7x - 3y - 10 = 0$

84. $x^2 + y^2 - 21x - 33y + 17 = 0$

85. $36x^2 + 36y^2 = 1$

86. $4x^2 + 4y^2 = 1$

87. Describe a procedure that would use the distance formula to determine whether three points, (x_1, y_1), (x_2, y_2), and (x_3, y_3), are vertices of a right triangle.

88. Does the graph of an equation of a circle include the point that is the center? Why or why not?

SKILL MAINTENANCE

Solve. [6.6]

89. $\dfrac{x}{4} + \dfrac{5}{6} = \dfrac{2}{3}$

90. $\dfrac{t}{6} - \dfrac{1}{9} = \dfrac{7}{12}$

91. A rectangle 10 in. long and 6 in. wide is bordered by a strip of uniform width. If the perimeter of the larger rectangle is twice that of the smaller rectangle, what is the width of the border? [2.5]

92. One airplane flies 60 mph faster than another. To fly a certain distance, the faster plane takes 4 hr and the slower plane takes 4 hr and 24 min. What is the distance? [8.3]

Solve each system. [8.2]

93. $3x - 8y = 5,$
    $2x + 6y = 5$

94. $4x - 5y = 9,$
    $12x - 10y = 18$

SYNTHESIS

95. Outline a procedure that would use the distance formula to determine whether three points,

(x_1, y_1), (x_2, y_2), and (x_3, y_3), are collinear (lie on the same line).

96. Why does the discussion of the distance formula precede the discussion of circles?

Find an equation of a circle satisfying the given conditions.

97. Center $(3, -5)$ and tangent to (touching at one point) the y-axis

98. Center $(-7, -4)$ and tangent to the x-axis

99. The endpoints of a diameter are $(7, 3)$ and $(-1, -3)$.

100. Center $(-3, 5)$ with a circumference of 8π units

101. Find the point on the y-axis that is equidistant from $(2, 10)$ and $(6, 2)$.

102. Find the point on the x-axis that is equidistant from $(-1, 3)$ and $(-8, -4)$.

103. *Wrestling.* The equation $x^2 + y^2 = \frac{81}{4}$, where x and y represent the number of meters from the center, can be used to draw the outer circle on a wrestling mat used in International, Olympic, and World Championship wrestling. The equation $x^2 + y^2 = 16$ can be used to draw the inner edge of the red zone. Find the area of the red zone.
Source: Based on data from the Government of Western Australia

104. *Snowboarding.* Each side edge of the Salomon Freestyle 500 Pro snowboard is an arc of a circle

with a "running length" of 1180 mm and a "side-cut depth" of 21.5 mm (see the figure below).

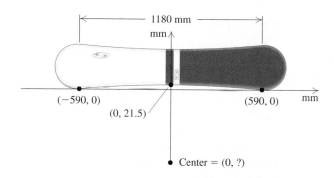

a) Using the coordinates shown, locate the center of the circle. (*Hint*: Equate distances.)
b) What radius is used for the edge of the board?

105. *Snowboarding.* The Elan Jason Evans 155 snowboard has a running length of 1170 mm and a sidecut depth of 23 mm (see Exercise 104). What radius is used for the edge of this snowboard?

106. *Skiing.* The Völkl Supersport 5 Star ski, when lying flat and viewed from above, has edges that are arcs of a circle. (Actually, each edge is made of two arcs of slightly different radii. The arc for the rear half of the ski edge has a slightly larger radius.)

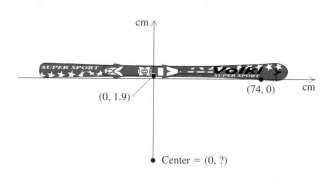

a) Using the coordinates shown, locate the center of the circle. (*Hint*: Equate distances.)

b) What radius is used for the arc passing through (0, 1.9) and (74, 0)?

107. *Doorway construction.* Ace Carpentry needs to cut an arch for the top of an entranceway. The arch needs to be 8 ft wide and 2 ft high. To draw the arch, the carpenters will use a stretched string with chalk attached at an end as a compass.

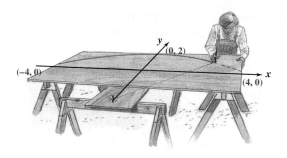

a) Using a coordinate system, locate the center of the circle.
b) What radius should the carpenters use to draw the arch?

108. *Archaeology.* During an archaeological dig, Martina finds the bowl fragment shown below. What was the original diameter of the bowl?

109. *Ferris wheel design.* A ferris wheel has a radius of 24.3 ft. Assuming that the center is 30.6 ft off the ground and that the origin is below the center, as in the following figure, find an equation of the circle.

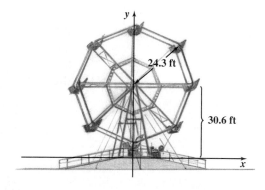

110. Use a graph of the equation $x = y^2 - y - 6$ to approximate to the nearest tenth the solutions of each of the following equations.
a) $y^2 - y - 6 = 2$ (*Hint*: Graph $x = 2$ on the same set of axes as the graph of $x = y^2 - y - 6$.)
b) $y^2 - y - 6 = -3$

111. *Power of a motor.* The horsepower of a certain kind of engine is given by the formula

$$H = \frac{D^2 N}{2.5},$$

where N is the number of cylinders and D is the diameter, in inches, of each piston. Graph this equation, assuming that $N = 6$ (a six-cylinder engine). Let D run from 2.5 to 8.

112. Prove the midpoint formula by showing that

i) the distance from (x_1, y_1) to

$$\left(\frac{x_1 + x_2}{2}, \frac{y_1 + y_2}{2}\right)$$

equals the distance from (x_2, y_2) to

$$\left(\frac{x_1 + x_2}{2}, \frac{y_1 + y_2}{2}\right);$$

and

ii) the points

$$(x_1, y_1), \left(\frac{x_1 + x_2}{2}, \frac{y_1 + y_2}{2}\right),$$

and

$$(x_2, y_2)$$

lie on the same line (see Exercise 95).

113. If the equation $x^2 + y^2 - 6x + 2y - 6 = 0$ is written as $y^2 + 2y + (x^2 - 6x - 6) = 0$, it can be regarded as quadratic in y.

a) Use the quadratic formula to solve for y.

b) Show that the graph of your answer to part (a) coincides with the graph in the Technology Connection on p. 863.

114. How could a graphing calculator best be used to help you sketch the graph of an equation of the form $x = ay^2 + by + c$?

115. Why should a graphing calculator's window be "squared" before graphing a circle?

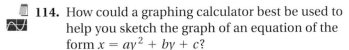

13.2 Conic Sections: Ellipses

Ellipses Centered at (0, 0) • Ellipses Centered at (h, k)

When a cone is cut at an angle, as shown below, the conic section formed is an *ellipse*. To draw an ellipse, stick two tacks in a piece of cardboard. Then tie a loose string to the tacks, place a pencil as shown, and draw an oval by moving the pencil while stretching the string tight.

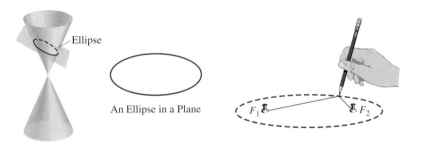

Ellipse

An Ellipse in a Plane

Ellipses Centered at (0, 0)

An **ellipse** is defined as the set of all points in a plane for which the sum of the distances from two fixed points F_1 and F_2 is constant. The points F_1 and F_2 are called **foci** (pronounced fō-sī), the plural of focus. In the figure above, the

Study Skills

Preparing for the Final Exam

It is never too early to begin studying for a final exam. If you have at least three days, consider the following:

- Reviewing the highlighted or boxed information in each chapter;
- Studying the Chapter Tests, Review Exercises, Cumulative Reviews, and Study Summaries;
- Re-taking all quizzes and tests that have been returned to you;
- Attending any review sessions being offered;
- Organizing or joining a study group;
- Using the video or software supplements, or asking a tutor or professor about any trouble spots;
- Asking for previous final exams (and answers) for practice.

tacks are at the foci and the length of the string is the constant sum of the distances. The midpoint of the segment F_1F_2 is the **center**. The equation of an ellipse is as follows. Its derivation is left to the exercises.

Equation of an Ellipse Centered at the Origin

The equation of an ellipse centered at the origin and symmetric with respect to both axes is

$$\frac{x^2}{a^2} + \frac{y^2}{b^2} = 1, \quad a, b > 0. \qquad \text{(Standard form)}$$

To graph an ellipse centered at the origin, it helps to first find the intercepts. If we replace x with 0, we can find the y-intercepts:

$$\frac{0^2}{a^2} + \frac{y^2}{b^2} = 1$$

$$\frac{y^2}{b^2} = 1$$

$$y^2 = b^2 \quad \text{or} \quad y = \pm b.$$

Thus the y-intercepts are $(0, b)$ and $(0, -b)$. Similarly, the x-intercepts are $(a, 0)$ and $(-a, 0)$. If $a > b$, the ellipse is said to be horizontal and $(-a, 0)$ and $(a, 0)$ are referred to as the **vertices** (singular, **vertex**). If $b > a$, the ellipse is said to be vertical and $(0, -b)$ and $(0, b)$ are then the vertices.

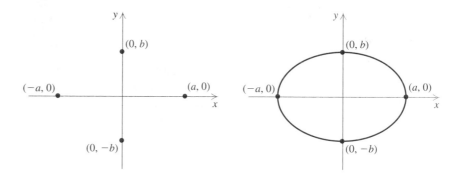

Plotting these four points and drawing an oval-shaped curve, we graph the ellipse. If a more precise graph is desired, we can plot more points.

Using a and b to Graph an Ellipse

For the ellipse

$$\frac{x^2}{a^2} + \frac{y^2}{b^2} = 1,$$

the x-intercepts are $(-a, 0)$ and $(a, 0)$. The y-intercepts are $(0, -b)$ and $(0, b)$. For $a^2 > b^2$, the ellipse is horizontal. For $b^2 > a^2$, the ellipse is vertical.

EXAMPLE 1   Graph the ellipse

$$\frac{x^2}{4} + \frac{y^2}{9} = 1.$$

Solution   Note that

$$\frac{x^2}{4} + \frac{y^2}{9} = \frac{x^2}{2^2} + \frac{y^2}{3^2}.$$ Identifying a and b. Since $b > a$, the ellipse is vertical.

Thus the x-intercepts are $(-2, 0)$ and $(2, 0)$, and the y-intercepts are $(0, -3)$ and $(0, 3)$. We plot these points and connect them with an oval-shaped curve. To plot two other points, we let $x = 1$ and solve for y:

$$\frac{1^2}{4} + \frac{y^2}{9} = 1$$

$$36\left(\frac{1}{4} + \frac{y^2}{9}\right) = 36 \cdot 1$$

$$36 \cdot \frac{1}{4} + 36 \cdot \frac{y^2}{9} = 36$$

$$9 + 4y^2 = 36$$

$$4y^2 = 27$$

$$y^2 = \frac{27}{4}$$

$$y = \pm\sqrt{\frac{27}{4}}$$

$$y \approx \pm 2.6.$$

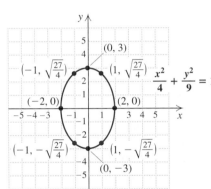

Thus, $(1, 2.6)$ and $(1, -2.6)$ can also be used to draw the graph. Similarly, the points $(-1, 2.6)$ and $(-1, -2.6)$ should appear on the graph.

EXAMPLE 2   Graph: $4x^2 + 25y^2 = 100$.

Solution   To write the equation in standard form, we divide both sides by 100 to get 1 on the right side:

Student Notes _____

Note that any equation of the form $Ax^2 + By^2 = C$ can be rewritten as an equivalent equation in standard form. The graph is an ellipse.

$$\frac{4x^2 + 25y^2}{100} = \frac{100}{100}$$ Dividing by 100 to get 1 on the right side

$$\left.\begin{array}{l} \dfrac{4x^2}{100} + \dfrac{25y^2}{100} = 1 \\[2mm] \dfrac{x^2}{25} + \dfrac{y^2}{4} = 1 \end{array}\right\}$$ Simplifying

$$\frac{x^2}{5^2} + \frac{y^2}{2^2} = 1.$$ $a = 5, b = 2$

The x-intercepts are $(-5, 0)$ and $(5, 0)$, and the y-intercepts are $(0, -2)$ and $(0, 2)$. We plot the intercepts and connect them with an oval-shaped curve. Other points can also be computed and plotted.

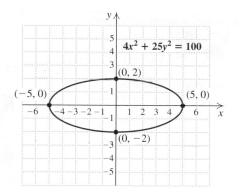

Ellipses Centered at (h, k)

Horizontal and vertical translations, similar to those used in Chapter 8, can be used to graph ellipses that are not centered at the origin.

Equation of an Ellipse Centered at (h, k)

The standard form of a horizontal or vertical ellipse centered at (h, k) is

$$\frac{(x - h)^2}{a^2} + \frac{(y - k)^2}{b^2} = 1.$$

The vertices are $(h + a, k)$ and $(h - a, k)$ if horizontal; $(h, k + b)$ and $(h, k - b)$ if vertical.

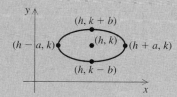

EXAMPLE 3   Graph the ellipse

$$\frac{(x - 1)^2}{4} + \frac{(y + 5)^2}{9} = 1.$$

Solution   Note that

$$\frac{(x - 1)^2}{4} + \frac{(y + 5)^2}{9} = \frac{(x - 1)^2}{2^2} + \frac{(y + 5)^2}{3^2}.$$

Thus, $a = 2$ and $b = 3$. To determine the center of the ellipse, (h, k), note that

$$\frac{(x - 1)^2}{2^2} + \frac{(y + 5)^2}{3^2} = \frac{(x - 1)^2}{2^2} + \frac{(y - (-5))^2}{3^2}.$$

Thus the center is $(1, -5)$. We plot the points 2 units to the left and right of center, as well as the points 3 units above and below center. These are the points $(3, -5)$, $(-1, -5)$, $(1, -2)$, and $(1, -8)$. The graph of the ellipse is shown at left.

Note that this ellipse is the same as the ellipse in Example 1 but translated 1 unit to the right and 5 units down.

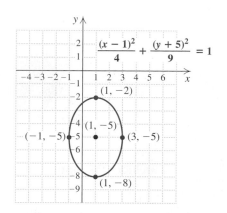

technology connection

Graphing an ellipse on a graphing calculator is much like graphing a circle: We graph it in two pieces after solving for y. To illustrate, let's check Example 2:

$$4x^2 + 25y^2 = 100$$
$$25y^2 = 100 - 4x^2$$
$$y^2 = 4 - \tfrac{4}{25}x^2$$
$$y = \pm\sqrt{4 - \tfrac{4}{25}x^2}.$$

Using a squared window, we have our check:

$$y_1 = -\sqrt{4 - \tfrac{4}{25}x^2}, \quad y_2 = \sqrt{4 - \tfrac{4}{25}x^2}$$

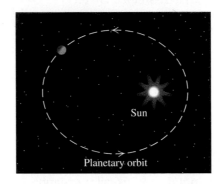

On many calculators, pressing **APPS** and selecting Conics and then Ellipse accesses a program in which equations in Standard Form can be graphed directly.

Ellipses have many applications. Communications satellites move in elliptical orbits with the earth as a focus while the earth itself follows an elliptical path around the sun. A medical instrument, the lithotripter, uses shock waves originating at one focus to crush a kidney stone located at the other focus.

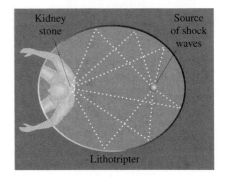

In some buildings, an ellipsoidal ceiling creates a "whispering gallery" in which a person at one focus can whisper and still be heard clearly at the other focus. This happens because sound waves coming from one focus are all reflected to the other focus. Similarly, light waves bouncing off an ellipsoidal mirror are used in a dentist's or surgeon's reflector light. The light source is located at one focus while the patient's mouth or surgical field is at the other.

Exercise Set

13.2

FOR EXTRA HELP

 Student's Solutions Manual

 Digital Video Tutor CD 7 Videotape 13

 AW Math Tutor Center

 MathXL Tutorials on CD

MathXL

MyMathLab

Concept Reinforcement Classify each of the following as either true or false.

1. The graph of $\dfrac{x^2}{9} + \dfrac{y^2}{25} = 1$ includes the points $(-3, 0)$ and $(3, 0)$.

2. The graph of $\dfrac{x^2}{36} + \dfrac{y^2}{25} = 1$ includes the points $(0, -5)$ and $(0, 5)$.

3. The graph of $\dfrac{x^2}{28} + \dfrac{y^2}{48} = 1$ is a vertical ellipse.

4. The graph of $\dfrac{x^2}{30} + \dfrac{y^2}{20} = 1$ is a vertical ellipse.

5. The graph of $\dfrac{x^2}{25} - \dfrac{y^2}{9} = 1$ is a horizontal ellipse.

6. The graph of $\dfrac{-x^2}{20} + \dfrac{y^2}{16} = 1$ is a horizontal ellipse.

7. The graph of $\dfrac{(x+3)^2}{25} + \dfrac{(y-2)^2}{36} = 1$ is an ellipse centered at $(-3, 2)$.

8. The graph of $\dfrac{(x-2)^2}{49} + \dfrac{(y+5)^2}{9} = 1$ is an ellipse centered at $(2, -5)$.

Graph each of the following equations.

9. $\dfrac{x^2}{1} + \dfrac{y^2}{9} = 1$ **10.** $\dfrac{x^2}{9} + \dfrac{y^2}{1} = 1$

11. $\dfrac{x^2}{25} + \dfrac{y^2}{9} = 1$ **12.** $\dfrac{x^2}{16} + \dfrac{y^2}{25} = 1$

13. $4x^2 + 9y^2 = 36$

14. $9x^2 + 4y^2 = 36$

15. $16x^2 + 9y^2 = 144$

16. $9x^2 + 16y^2 = 144$

17. $2x^2 + 3y^2 = 6$

18. $5x^2 + 7y^2 = 35$

Aha! **19.** $5x^2 + 5y^2 = 125$

20. $8x^2 + 5y^2 = 80$

21. $3x^2 + 7y^2 - 63 = 0$

22. $3x^2 + 8y^2 - 72 = 0$

23. $8x^2 = 96 - 3y^2$

24. $6y^2 = 24 - 8x^2$

25. $16x^2 + 25y^2 = 1$

26. $9x^2 + 4y^2 = 1$

27. $\dfrac{(x-3)^2}{9} + \dfrac{(y-2)^2}{25} = 1$

28. $\dfrac{(x-2)^2}{25} + \dfrac{(y-4)^2}{9} = 1$

29. $\dfrac{(x+4)^2}{16} + \dfrac{(y-3)^2}{49} = 1$

30. $\dfrac{(x+5)^2}{4} + \dfrac{(y-2)^2}{36} = 1$

31. $12(x-1)^2 + 3(y+4)^2 = 48$
(*Hint*: Divide both sides by 48.)

32. $4(x-6)^2 + 9(y+2)^2 = 36$

Aha! **33.** $4(x+3)^2 + 4(y+1)^2 - 10 = 90$

34. $9(x+6)^2 + (y+2)^2 - 20 = 61$

35. Is the center of an ellipse part of the ellipse itself? Why or why not?

36. Can an ellipse ever be the graph of a function? Why or why not?

SKILL MAINTENANCE

Solve.

37. $\dfrac{3}{x-2} - \dfrac{5}{x-2} = 9$ [6.6]

38. $\dfrac{7}{x+3} - \dfrac{2}{x+3} = 8$ [6.6]

39. $\dfrac{x}{x-4} - \dfrac{3}{x-5} = \dfrac{2}{x-4}$ [11.2]

40. $\dfrac{7}{x-3} - \dfrac{x}{x-2} = \dfrac{4}{x-2}$ [11.2]

41. $9 - \sqrt{2x+1} = 7$ [10.6]

42. $5 - \sqrt{x+3} = 9$ [10.6]

SYNTHESIS

43. An eccentric person builds a pool table in the shape of an ellipse with a hole at one focus and a tiny dot at the other. Guests are amazed at how many bank shots the owner of the pool table makes. Explain why this occurs.

44. Can a circle be considered a special type of ellipse? Why or why not?

Find an equation of an ellipse that contains the following points.

45. $(-9, 0)$, $(9, 0)$, $(0, -11)$, and $(0, 11)$

46. $(-7, 0)$, $(7, 0)$, $(0, -5)$, and $(0, 5)$

47. $(-2, -1)$, $(6, -1)$, $(2, -4)$, and $(2, 2)$

48. $(4, 3)$, $(-6, 3)$, $(-1, -1)$ and $(-1, 7)$

49. *Theatrical lighting.* The spotlight on a violin soloist casts an ellipse of light on the floor below her that is 6 ft wide and 10 ft long. Find an equation of that ellipse if the performer is in its center, x is the distance from the performer to the side of the ellipse, and y is the distance from the performer to the top of the ellipse.

50. *Astronomy.* The maximum distance of the planet Mars from the sun is 2.48×10^8 mi. The minimum distance is 3.46×10^7 mi. The sun is at one focus of the elliptical orbit. Find the distance from the sun to the other focus.

51. Let $(-c, 0)$ and $(c, 0)$ be the foci of an ellipse. Any point $P(x, y)$ is on the ellipse if the sum of the distances from the foci to P is some constant. Use $2a$ to represent this constant.

    a) Show that an equation for the ellipse is given by

$$\frac{x^2}{a^2} + \frac{y^2}{a^2 - c^2} = 1.$$

    b) Substitute b^2 for $a^2 - c^2$ to get standard form.

52. *President's office.* The Oval Office of the President of the United States is an ellipse 31 ft wide and 38 ft long. Show in a sketch precisely where the President and an adviser could sit to best hear each other using the room's acoustics. (*Hint*: See Exercise 51(b) and the discussion following Example 3.)

53. *Dentistry.* The light source in a dental lamp shines against a reflector that is shaped like a portion of an ellipse in which the light source is one focus of the ellipse. Reflected light enters a patient's mouth at the other focus of the ellipse. If the ellipse from which the reflector was formed is 2 ft wide and 6 ft long, how far should the patient's mouth be from the light source? (*Hint*: See Exercise 51(b).)

F_1 Lamp

54. *Firefighting.* The size and shape of certain forest fires can be approximated as the union of two "half-ellipses." For the blaze modeled below, the equation of the smaller ellipse—the part of the fire moving *into* the wind—is

$$\frac{x^2}{40{,}000} + \frac{y^2}{10{,}000} = 1.$$

The equation of the other ellipse—the part moving *with* the wind—is

$$\frac{x^2}{250{,}000} + \frac{y^2}{10{,}000} = 1.$$

Determine the width and the length of the fire.
Source for figure: "Predicting Wind-Driven Wild Land Fire Size and Shape," Hal E. Anderson, Research Paper INT-305, U.S. Department of Agriculture, Forest Service, February 1983

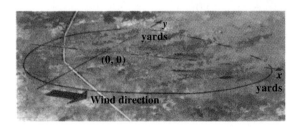

For each of the following equations, complete the square as needed and find an equivalent equation in standard form. Then graph the ellipse.

55. $x^2 - 4x + 4y^2 + 8y - 8 = 0$

56. $4x^2 + 24x + y^2 - 2y - 63 = 0$

57. Use a graphing calculator to check your answers to Exercises 11, 25, 29, and 33.

CORNER

A Cosmic Path

Focus: Ellipses

Time: 20–30 minutes

Group size: 2

Materials: Scientific calculators

In March 1996, the comet Hyakutake came within 21 million mi of the sun, and closer to Earth than any comet in over 500 yr (*Source:* Associated Press newspaper story, 3/20/96). Hyakutake is traveling in an elliptical orbit with the sun at one focus. The comet's average speed is about 100,000 mph (it actually goes much faster near its foci and slower as it gets further from the foci) and one orbit takes about 15,000 yr. (Astronomers estimate the time at 10,000–20,000 yr.)

ACTIVITY

1. The elliptical orbit of Hyakutake is so elongated that the distance traveled in one orbit can be estimated by $4a$ (see the following figure). Use the information above to estimate the distance, in millions of miles, traveled in one orbit. Then determine a.

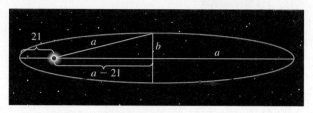

Units are millions of miles.

2. Using the figure above, express b^2 as a function of a. Then solve for b using the value found for a in part (1).

3. Approximately how far will Hyakutake be from the sun at the most distant part of its orbit?

4. Repeat parts (1)–(3), with one group member using the lower estimate of orbit time (10,000 yr) and the other using the upper estimate of orbit time (20,000 yr). By how much do the three answers to part (3) vary?

13.3 Conic Sections: Hyperbolas

Hyperbolas   •   Hyperbolas (Nonstandard Form)   •
Classifying Graphs of Equations

Hyperbolas

A **hyperbola** looks like a pair of parabolas, but the shapes are actually different. A hyperbola has two **vertices** and the line through the vertices is known as the **axis**. The point halfway between the vertices is called the **center**. The two curves that comprise a hyperbola are called **branches**.

  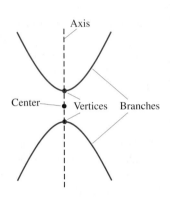

Parabola   Hyperbola in   Hyperbola in a plane
                  three dimensions

Equation of a Hyperbola Centered at the Origin

A hyperbola with its center at the origin* has its equation as follows:

$$\frac{x^2}{a^2} - \frac{y^2}{b^2} = 1 \qquad \text{(Horizontal axis)};$$

$$\frac{y^2}{b^2} - \frac{x^2}{a^2} = 1 \qquad \text{(Vertical axis)}.$$

Note that both equations have a 1 on the right-hand side and a subtraction symbol between the terms. For the discussion that follows, we assume $a, b > 0$.

---

*Hyperbolas with horizontal or vertical axes and centers *not* at the origin are discussed in Exercises 59–64.

To graph a hyperbola, it helps to begin by graphing two lines called **asymptotes**. Although the asymptotes themselves are not part of the graph, they serve as guidelines for an accurate sketch.

As a hyperbola gets farther away from the origin, it gets closer and closer to its asymptotes. The larger $|x|$ gets, the closer the graph gets to an asymptote. The asymptotes act to "constrain" the graph of a hyperbola. Parabolas are *not* constrained by any asymptotes.

Asymptotes of a Hyperbola

For hyperbolas with equations as shown below, the asymptotes are the lines

$$y = \frac{b}{a}x \quad \text{and} \quad y = -\frac{b}{a}x.$$

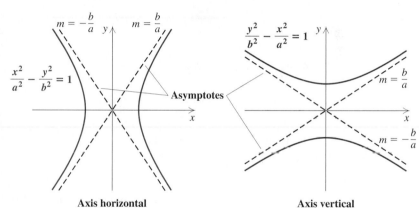

Axis horizontal   Axis vertical

In Section 13.2, we used a and b to determine the width and the length of an ellipse. For hyperbolas, a and b are used to determine the base and the height of a rectangle that can be used as an aid in sketching asymptotes and locating vertices. This is illustrated in the following example.

EXAMPLE 1   Graph: $\dfrac{x^2}{4} - \dfrac{y^2}{9} = 1$.

Solution   Note that

$$\frac{x^2}{4} - \frac{y^2}{9} = \frac{x^2}{2^2} - \frac{y^2}{3^2}, \qquad \text{Identifying } a \text{ and } b$$

so $a = 2$ and $b = 3$. The asymptotes are thus

$$y = \frac{3}{2}x \quad \text{and} \quad y = -\frac{3}{2}x.$$

To help us sketch asymptotes and locate vertices, we use a and b—in this case, 2 and 3—to form the pairs $(-2, 3)$, $(2, 3)$, $(2, -3)$, and $(-2, -3)$. We plot these pairs and lightly sketch a rectangle. The asymptotes pass through the corners and, since this is a horizontal hyperbola, the vertices are where the rectangle intersects the *x*-axis. Finally, we draw the hyperbola, as shown below.

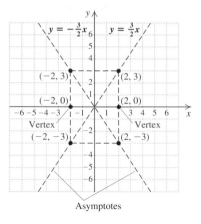 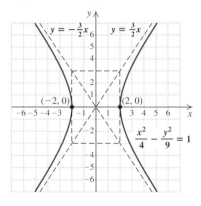

Asymptotes

EXAMPLE 2

Graph: $\dfrac{y^2}{36} - \dfrac{x^2}{4} = 1$.

Solution   Note that

$$\frac{y^2}{36} - \frac{x^2}{4} = \frac{y^2}{6^2} - \frac{x^2}{2^2} = 1.$$

> Whether the hyperbola is horizontal or vertical is determined by the nonnegative term. Here there is a *y* in this term, so the hyperbola is vertical.

Using ± 2 as *x*-coordinates and ± 6 as *y*-coordinates, we plot $(2, 6)$, $(2, -6)$, $(-2, 6)$, and $(-2, -6)$, and lightly sketch a rectangle through them. The asymptotes pass through the corners (see the figure on the left below). Since the hyperbola is vertical, its vertices are $(0, 6)$ and $(0, -6)$. Finally, we draw curves through the vertices toward the asymptotes, as shown below.

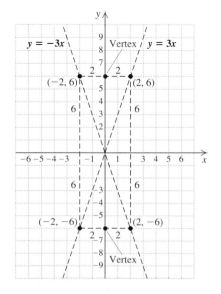 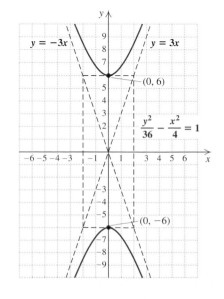

Student Notes —————

Regarding the orientation of a hyperbola, you may find it helpful to think as follows: "The axis is parallel to the *x*-axis if $\dfrac{x^2}{a^2}$ is the positive term. The axis is parallel to the *y*-axis if $\dfrac{y^2}{b^2}$ is the positive term."

Hyperbolas (Nonstandard Form)

The equations for hyperbolas just examined are the standard ones, but there are other hyperbolas. We consider some of them.

> ### Equation of a Hyperbola in Nonstandard Form
>
> Hyperbolas having the x- and y-axes as asymptotes have equations as follows:
>
> $$xy = c, \quad \text{where } c \text{ is a nonzero constant.}$$

EXAMPLE 3   Graph: $xy = -8$.

Solution   We first solve for y:

$$y = -\frac{8}{x}. \qquad \text{Dividing both sides by } x. \text{ Note that } x \neq 0.$$

Next, we find some solutions, keeping the results in a table. Note that x cannot be 0 and that for large values of $|x|$, y will be close to 0. Thus the x- and y-axes serve as asymptotes. We plot the points and draw two curves.

x	y
2	−4
−2	4
4	−2
−4	2
1	−8
−1	8
8	−1
−8	1

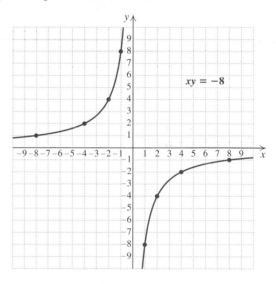

$xy = -8$

Hyperbolas have many applications. A jet breaking the sound barrier creates a sonic boom with a wave front the shape of a cone. The intersection of the cone with the ground is one branch of a hyperbola. Some comets travel in hyperbolic orbits, and a cross section of many lenses is hyperbolic in shape.

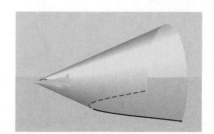

CONNECTING THE CONCEPTS

Recall that the vertical-line test tells us that circles, ellipses, and hyperbolas in standard form do not represent functions. Of the graphs examined in this chapter, only vertical parabolas and hyperbolas similar to the one in Example 3 can represent functions. Because functions are so important, circles and ellipses generally appear in applications of a purely geometric nature, whereas vertical parabolas and nonstandard hyperbolas can be used in applications involving geometry or functions.

In Section 13.4, we return to the challenge of solving real-world problems that translate to a system of equations. There we will find that knowing the general shape of the graph of an equation can help us determine how many solutions, if any, exist.

---

technology connection

The procedure used to graph a hyperbola in standard form is similar to that used to draw a circle or an ellipse. Consider the graph of

$$\frac{x^2}{25} - \frac{y^2}{49} = 1.$$

The student should confirm that solving for y yields

$$y_1 = \frac{\sqrt{49x^2 - 1225}}{5}$$

$$= \frac{7}{5}\sqrt{x^2 - 25}$$

and

$$y_2 = \frac{-\sqrt{49x^2 - 1225}}{5}$$

$$= -\frac{7}{5}\sqrt{x^2 - 25},$$

or $\quad y_2 = -y_1.$

When the two pieces are drawn on the same squared window, the result is as shown. The gaps occur where the graph is nearly vertical.

$$y_1 = \frac{7}{5}\sqrt{x^2 - 25},$$
$$y_2 = -\frac{7}{5}\sqrt{x^2 - 25}$$

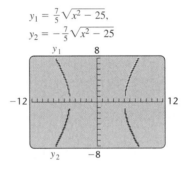

On many calculators, pressing **APPS** and selecting Conics and then Hyperbola accesses a program in which hyperbolas in standard form can be graphed directly.

Graph.

1. $\dfrac{x^2}{16} - \dfrac{y^2}{60} = 1$

2. $16x^2 - 3y^2 = 64$

3. $\dfrac{y^2}{20} - \dfrac{x^2}{64} = 1$

4. $45y^2 - 9x^2 = 441$

Classifying Graphs of Equations

CONNECTING THE CONCEPTS

We summarize the equations and the graphs of the conic sections studied. The examples resume on p. 685.

PARABOLA

$y = ax^2 + bx + c,\ a > 0$
$\quad = a(x - h)^2 + k$

$y = ax^2 + bx + c,\ a < 0$
$\quad = a(x - h)^2 + k$

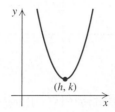

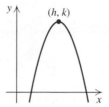

$x = ay^2 + by + c,\ a > 0$
$\quad = a(y - k)^2 + h$

$x = ay^2 + by + c,\ a < 0$
$\quad = a(y - k)^2 + h$

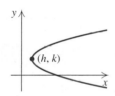

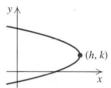

CIRCLE

Center at the origin:
$\quad x^2 + y^2 = r^2$

Center at (h, k):
$\quad (x - h)^2 + (y - k)^2 = r^2$

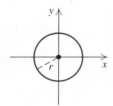

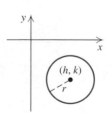

(*continued*)

CONNECTING THE CONCEPTS

HYPERBOLA

Center at the origin:

$$\frac{x^2}{a^2} - \frac{y^2}{b^2} = 1$$

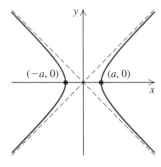

$$\frac{y^2}{b^2} - \frac{x^2}{a^2} = 1$$

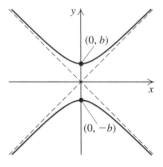

$xy = c, \ c > 0$

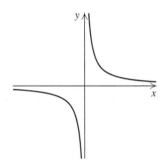

$xy = c, \ c < 0$

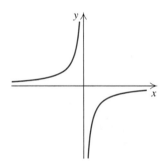

Center at (h, k)*:

$$\frac{(x - h)^2}{a^2} - \frac{(y - k)^2}{b^2} = 1$$

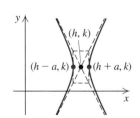

$$\frac{(y - k)^2}{b^2} - \frac{(x - h)^2}{a^2} = 1$$

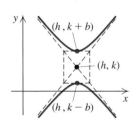

(*continued*)

*See Exercises 59–64.

ELLIPSE

Center at the origin:

$$\frac{x^2}{a^2} + \frac{y^2}{b^2} = 1$$

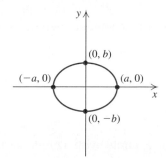

Center at (h, k):

$$\frac{(x - h)^2}{a^2} + \frac{(y - k)^2}{b^2} = 1$$

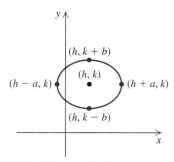

At the beginning of this chapter, we stated that the conic sections represent graphs of $Ax^2 + By^2 + Cxy + Dx + Ey + F = 0$ (we have assumed $C = 0$*):

If A or B (but not both) is 0, the equation can be written in the form $y = ax^2 + bx + c$ or $x = ay^2 + by + c$, and represents a parabola.

If $A = B$, the equation can be written in the form $x^2 + y^2 = c$ or $(x - h)^2 + (y - k)^2 = r^2$, and represents a circle.

If $A \neq B$, but both A and B have the same sign, the equation can be written in the form $b^2x^2 + a^2y^2 = c$ or $b^2(x - h)^2 + a^2(y - k)^2 = c$, and represents an ellipse.

If A and B have opposite signs, the equation can be written in the form $b^2x^2 - a^2y^2 = c$ or $b^2(x - h)^2 - a^2(y - k)^2 = c$, and represents a hyperbola.

Algebraic manipulations may be needed to express an equation in one of the preceding forms.

EXAMPLE 4   Classify the graph of each equation as a circle, an ellipse, a parabola, or a hyperbola.

a) $5x^2 = 20 - 5y^2$

b) $x + 3 + 8y = y^2$

c) $x^2 = y^2 + 4$

d) $x^2 = 16 - 4y^2$

*For $C \neq 0$, the graphs are not symmetric with respect to both axes.

Solution

a) We get the terms with variables on one side by adding $5y^2$:

$$5x^2 + 5y^2 = 20.$$

Since x and y are *both* squared, we do not have a parabola. The fact that the squared terms are *added* tells us that we do not have a hyperbola. Do we have a circle? To find out, we need to get $x^2 + y^2$ by itself. We can do that by factoring the 5 out of both terms on the left and then dividing by 5:

$$5(x^2 + y^2) = 20 \qquad \text{Factoring out 5}$$
$$x^2 + y^2 = 4 \qquad \text{Dividing both sides by 5}$$
$$x^2 + y^2 = 2^2. \qquad \text{This is an equation for a circle.}$$

We can see that the graph is a circle with center at the origin and radius 2.

b) The equation $x + 3 + 8y = y^2$ has only one variable squared, so we solve for the other variable:

$$x = y^2 - 8y - 3. \qquad \text{This is an equation for a parabola.}$$

The graph is a horizontal parabola that opens to the right.

c) In $x^2 = y^2 + 4$, both variables are squared, so the graph is not a parabola. We subtract y^2 on both sides and divide by 4 to obtain

$$\frac{x^2}{2^2} - \frac{y^2}{2^2} = 1. \qquad \text{This is an equation for a hyperbola.}$$

The minus sign here indicates that the graph of this equation is a hyperbola. Because it is the x^2-term that is nonnegative, the hyperbola is horizontal.

d) In $x^2 = 16 - 4y^2$, both variables are squared, so the graph cannot be a parabola. We obtain the following equivalent equation:

$$x^2 + 4y^2 = 16.$$

If the coefficients of the terms were the same, we would have the graph of a circle, as in part (a), but they are not. Dividing both sides by 16 yields

$$\frac{x^2}{16} + \frac{y^2}{4} = 1. \qquad \text{This is an equation for an ellipse.}$$

The graph of this equation is a horizontal ellipse.

Exercise Set

13.3

FOR EXTRA HELP

 Student's Solutions Manual   Digital Video Tutor CD 7 Videotape 13   AW Math Tutor Center   MathXL Tutorials on CD   Math XL MathXL   MyMathLab MyMathLab

✎ *Concept Reinforcement*   *In each of Exercises 1–8, match the conic section with the equation in the column on the right that represents that type of conic section.*

1. ____ A hyperbola with a horizontal axis

2. ____ A hyperbola with a vertical axis

3. ____ An ellipse with its center not at the origin

4. ____ An ellipse with its center at the origin

5. ____ A circle with its center at the origin

6. ____ A circle with its center not at the origin

7. ____ A parabola opening upward or downward

8. ____ A parabola opening to the right or left

a) $\dfrac{x^2}{10} + \dfrac{y^2}{12} = 1$

b) $(x+1)^2 + (y-3)^2 = 30$

c) $y - x^2 = 5$

d) $\dfrac{x^2}{9} - \dfrac{y^2}{10} = 1$

e) $x - 2y^2 = 3$

f) $\dfrac{y^2}{20} - \dfrac{x^2}{35} = 1$

g) $3x^2 + 3y^2 = 75$

h) $\dfrac{(x-1)^2}{10} + \dfrac{(y-4)^2}{8} = 1$

13. $\dfrac{y^2}{36} - \dfrac{x^2}{9} = 1$

14. $\dfrac{x^2}{25} - \dfrac{y^2}{36} = 1$

15. $y^2 - x^2 = 25$

16. $x^2 - y^2 = 4$

17. $25x^2 - 16y^2 = 400$

18. $4y^2 - 9x^2 = 36$

Graph.

19. $xy = -5$

20. $xy = 5$

21. $xy = 4$

22. $xy = -9$

23. $xy = -2$

24. $xy = -1$

25. $xy = 1$

26. $xy = 2$

Classify each of the following as the equation of a circle, an ellipse, a parabola, or a hyperbola.

27. $x^2 + y^2 - 6x + 4y - 30 = 0$

28. $y + 9 = 3x^2$

29. $9x^2 + 4y^2 - 36 = 0$

30. $x + 3y = 2y^2 - 1$

31. $4x^2 - 9y^2 - 72 = 0$

32. $y^2 + x^2 = 8$

33. $x^2 + y^2 = 2x + 4y + 4$

34. $2y + 13 + x^2 = 8x - y^2$

35. $4x^2 = 64 - y^2$

36. $y = \dfrac{7}{x}$

37. $x - \dfrac{8}{y} = 0$

38. $x - 4 = y^2 - 3y$

39. $y + 6x = x^2 + 5$

40. $x^2 = 16 + y^2$

41. $9y^2 = 36 + 4x^2$

42. $3x^2 + 5y^2 + x^2 = y^2 + 49$

Graph each hyperbola. Label all vertices and sketch all asymptotes.

9. $\dfrac{y^2}{16} - \dfrac{x^2}{16} = 1$

10. $\dfrac{x^2}{9} - \dfrac{y^2}{9} = 1$

11. $\dfrac{x^2}{4} - \dfrac{y^2}{25} = 1$

12. $\dfrac{y^2}{16} - \dfrac{x^2}{9} = 1$

43. $3x^2 + y^2 - x = 2x^2 - 9x + 10y + 40$

44. $4y^2 + 20x^2 + 1 = 8y - 5x^2$

45. $16x^2 + 5y^2 - 12x^2 + 8y^2 - 3x + 4y = 568$

46. $56x^2 - 17y^2 = 234 - 13x^2 - 38y^2$

47. What does graphing hyperbolas have in common with graphing ellipses?

48. Is it possible for a hyperbola to represent the graph of a function? Why or why not?

SKILL MAINTENANCE

Solve each system. [8.2]

49. $5x + 6y = -12,$
$3x + 9y = 15$

50. $2x + 6y = -6,$
$3x + 5y = 7$

Solve. [5.7]

51. $y^2 - 3 = 6$

52. $x^2 + 3 = 4$

53. The price of a lawn chair, including 5% sales tax, is $36.75. Find the price of the chair before the tax was added. [2.4]

54. A basketball team increases its score by 7 points in each of the two consecutive games after the home opener. If the team scored a total of 228 points in all three games, what was its score in the home opener? [2.5]

SYNTHESIS

55. What is it in the equation of a hyperbola that controls how wide open the branches are? Explain your reasoning.

56. If, in

$$\frac{x^2}{a^2} - \frac{y^2}{b^2} = 1,$$

$a = b$, what are the asymptotes of the graph? Why?

Find an equation of a hyperbola satisfying the given conditions.

57. Having intercepts $(0, 6)$ and $(0, -6)$ and asymptotes $y = 3x$ and $y = -3x$

58. Having intercepts $(8, 0)$ and $(-8, 0)$ and asymptotes $y = 4x$ and $y = -4x$

The standard equations for horizontal or vertical hyperbolas centered at (h, k) are as follows:

$$\frac{(x - h)^2}{a^2} - \frac{(y - k)^2}{b^2} = 1$$

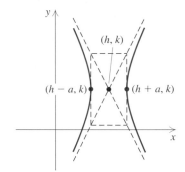

$$\frac{(y - k)^2}{b^2} - \frac{(x - h)^2}{a^2} = 1$$

The vertices are as labeled and the asymptotes are

$$y - k = \frac{b}{a}(x - h) \quad and \quad y - k = -\frac{b}{a}(x - h).$$

For each of the following equations of hyperbolas, complete the square, if necessary, and write in standard form. Find the center, the vertices, and the asymptotes. Then graph the hyperbola.

59. $\dfrac{(x - 5)^2}{36} - \dfrac{(y - 2)^2}{25} = 1$

60. $\dfrac{(x - 2)^2}{9} - \dfrac{(y - 1)^2}{4} = 1$

61. $8(y + 3)^2 - 2(x - 4)^2 = 32$

62. $25(x - 4)^2 - 4(y + 5)^2 = 100$

63. $4x^2 - y^2 + 24x + 4y + 28 = 0$

64. $4y^2 - 25x^2 - 8y - 100x - 196 = 0$

65. Use a graphing calculator to check your answers to Exercises 13, 25, 31, and 59.

13.4 Nonlinear Systems of Equations

Systems Involving One Nonlinear Equation • Systems of Two Nonlinear Equations • Problem Solving

The equations appearing in systems of two equations have thus far in our discussion always been linear. We now consider systems of two equations in which at least one equation is nonlinear.

Systems Involving One Nonlinear Equation

Suppose that a system consists of an equation of a circle and an equation of a line. In what ways can the circle and the line intersect? The figures below represent three ways in which the situation can occur. We see that such a system will have 0, 1, or 2 real solutions.

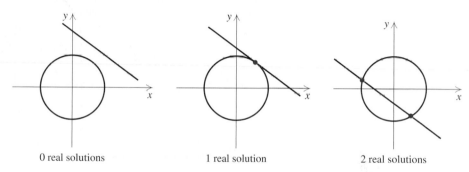

0 real solutions   1 real solution   2 real solutions

Recall that graphing, *elimination*, and *substitution* were all used to solve systems of linear equations. To solve systems in which one equation is of first degree and one is of second degree, it is preferable to use the *substitution* method.

EXAMPLE 1   Solve the system

$$x^2 + y^2 = 25, \quad (1) \quad \text{(The graph is a circle.)}$$
$$3x - 4y = 0. \quad (2) \quad \text{(The graph is a line.)}$$

Solution   First, we solve the linear equation, (2), for x:

$$x = \tfrac{4}{3}y. \quad (3) \quad \text{We could have solved for } y \text{ instead.}$$

Then we substitute $\tfrac{4}{3}y$ for x in equation (1) and solve for y:

$$\left(\tfrac{4}{3}y\right)^2 + y^2 = 25$$
$$\tfrac{16}{9}y^2 + y^2 = 25$$
$$\tfrac{25}{9}y^2 = 25$$
$$y^2 = 9 \qquad \text{Multiplying both sides by } \tfrac{9}{25}$$
$$y = \pm 3. \qquad \text{Using the principle of square roots}$$

Student Notes _____

Be sure to either list each solution of a system as an ordered pair or separately state the value of each variable.

Now we substitute these numbers for y in equation (3) and solve for x:

for $y = 3$, $x = \frac{4}{3}(3) = 4$;

for $y = -3$, $x = \frac{4}{3}(-3) = -4$.

Check: For (4, 3):

$$\begin{array}{c|c} x^2 + y^2 = 25 \\ \hline 4^2 + 3^2 & 25 \\ 16 + 9 & \\ 25 \overset{?}{=} 25 & \text{TRUE} \end{array} \qquad \begin{array}{c|c} 3x - 4y = 0 \\ \hline 3(4) - 4(3) & 0 \\ 12 - 12 & \\ 0 \overset{?}{=} 0 & \text{TRUE} \end{array}$$

It is left to the student to confirm that $(-4, -3)$ also checks in both equations.
The pairs (4, 3) and $(-4, -3)$ check, so they are solutions. We can see the solutions in the graph. Intersections occur at (4, 3) and $(-4, -3)$.

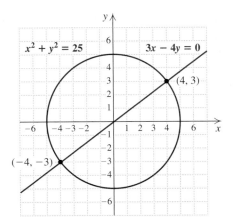

Even if we do not know what the graph of each equation in a system looks like, the algebraic approach of Example 1 can still be used.

EXAMPLE 2   Solve the system

$$y + 3 = 2x, \qquad (1)$$
$$x^2 + 2xy = -1. \qquad (2)$$

Solution   First, we solve the linear equation (1) for y:

$$y = 2x - 3. \qquad (3)$$

Then we substitute $2x - 3$ for y in equation (2) and solve for x:

$$x^2 + 2x(2x - 3) = -1$$
$$x^2 + 4x^2 - 6x = -1$$
$$5x^2 - 6x + 1 = 0$$
$$(5x - 1)(x - 1) = 0 \qquad \text{Factoring}$$
$$5x - 1 = 0 \quad or \quad x - 1 = 0 \qquad \text{Using the principle of zero products}$$
$$x = \tfrac{1}{5} \quad or \qquad x = 1.$$

Now we substitute these numbers for x in equation (3) and solve for y:

$$\text{for } x = \tfrac{1}{5}, \quad y = 2\left(\tfrac{1}{5}\right) - 3 = -\tfrac{13}{5};$$
$$\text{for } x = 1, \quad y = 2(1) - 3 = -1.$$

You can confirm that $\left(\tfrac{1}{5}, -\tfrac{13}{5}\right)$ and $(1, -1)$ check, so they are both solutions.

EXAMPLE 3

technology
connection

Real-number solutions of systems of equations can be found using the INTERSECT option of CALC .

To solve Example 2,

$$y + 3 = 2x,$$
$$x^2 + 2xy = -1,$$

we solve each equation for y and then graph:

$$\left.\begin{array}{l} y_1 = 2x - 3, \\ y_2 = \dfrac{-1 - x^2}{2x}. \end{array}\right\} \quad \begin{array}{l}\text{Note that}\\ x, y \neq 0.\end{array}$$

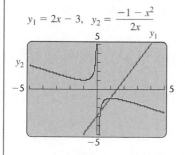

$y_1 = 2x - 3, \quad y_2 = \dfrac{-1 - x^2}{2x}$

Using INTERSECT, we find the solutions to be $(0.2, -2.6)$ and $(1, -1)$.

Solve each system. Round all values to two decimal places.

1. $4xy - 7 = 0,$
    $x - 3y - 2 = 0$
2. $x^2 + y^2 = 14,$
    $16x + 7y^2 = 0$

Solve the system

$$x + y = 5, \quad (1) \quad \text{(The graph is a line.)}$$
$$y = 3 - x^2. \quad (2) \quad \text{(The graph is a parabola.)}$$

Solution   We substitute $3 - x^2$ for y in the first equation:

$$x + 3 - x^2 = 5$$
$$-x^2 + x - 2 = 0 \qquad \text{Adding } -5 \text{ to both sides and rearranging}$$
$$x^2 - x + 2 = 0. \qquad \text{Multiplying both sides by } -1$$

Since $x^2 - x + 2$ does not factor, we need the quadratic formula:

$$x = \frac{-b \pm \sqrt{b^2 - 4ac}}{2a}$$
$$= \frac{-(-1) \pm \sqrt{(-1)^2 - 4 \cdot 1 \cdot 2}}{2(1)} \qquad \text{Substituting}$$
$$= \frac{1 \pm \sqrt{1 - 8}}{2} = \frac{1 \pm \sqrt{-7}}{2} = \frac{1}{2} \pm \frac{\sqrt{7}}{2}i.$$

Solving equation (1) for y gives us $y = 5 - x$. Substituting values for x gives

$$y = 5 - \left(\frac{1}{2} + \frac{\sqrt{7}}{2}i\right) = \frac{9}{2} - \frac{\sqrt{7}}{2}i \quad \text{and}$$
$$y = 5 - \left(\frac{1}{2} - \frac{\sqrt{7}}{2}i\right) = \frac{9}{2} + \frac{\sqrt{7}}{2}i.$$

The solutions are

$$\left(\frac{1}{2} + \frac{\sqrt{7}}{2}i, \frac{9}{2} - \frac{\sqrt{7}}{2}i\right) \quad \text{and} \quad \left(\frac{1}{2} - \frac{\sqrt{7}}{2}i, \frac{9}{2} + \frac{\sqrt{7}}{2}i\right).$$

There are no real-number solutions. Note in the figure at right that the graphs do not intersect. Getting only nonreal solutions tells us that the graphs do not intersect.

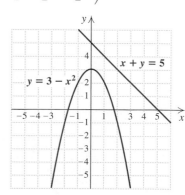

Systems of Two Nonlinear Equations

We now consider systems of two second-degree equations. Graphs of such systems can involve any two conic sections. The following figure shows some ways in which a circle and a hyperbola can intersect.

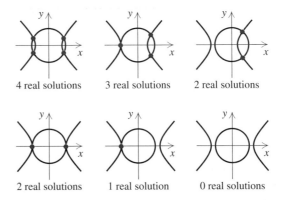

4 real solutions   3 real solutions   2 real solutions

2 real solutions   1 real solution   0 real solutions

To solve systems of two second-degree equations, we either substitute or eliminate. The elimination method is generally better when both equations are of the form $Ax^2 + By^2 = C$. Then we can eliminate an x^2- or y^2-term in a manner similar to the procedure used in Chapter 3.

EXAMPLE 4   Solve the system

$$2x^2 + 5y^2 = 22, \quad (1)$$
$$3x^2 - y^2 = -1. \quad (2)$$

Solution   Here we multiply equation (2) by 5 and then add:

$$\begin{array}{ll} 2x^2 + 5y^2 = 22 & \\ \underline{15x^2 - 5y^2 = -5} & \text{Multiplying both sides of equation (2) by 5} \\ 17x^2 = 17 & \text{Adding} \\ x^2 = 1 & \\ x = \pm 1. & \end{array}$$

There is no x-term, and whether x is -1 or 1, we have $x^2 = 1$. Thus we can simultaneously substitute 1 and -1 for x in equation (2):

$$\left. \begin{array}{l} 3 \cdot (\pm 1)^2 - y^2 = -1 \\ 3 - y^2 = -1 \\ -y^2 = -4 \end{array} \right\} \quad \begin{array}{l} \text{Since } (-1)^2 = 1^2, \text{ we can evaluate for} \\ x = -1 \text{ and } x = 1 \text{ simultaneously.} \end{array}$$
$$y^2 = 4 \quad \text{or} \quad y = \pm 2.$$

Thus, if $x = 1$, then $y = 2$ or $y = -2$; and if $x = -1$, then $y = 2$ or $y = -2$. The four possible solutions are $(1, 2)$, $(1, -2)$, $(-1, 2)$, and $(-1, -2)$.

Check: Since $(2)^2 = (-2)^2$ and $(1)^2 = (-1)^2$, we can check all four pairs at once.

$$\begin{array}{c|c} 2x^2 + 5y^2 = 22 \\ \hline 2(\pm1)^2 + 5(\pm2)^2 & 22 \\ 2 + 20 & \\ 22 \stackrel{?}{=} 22 & \text{TRUE} \end{array} \qquad \begin{array}{c|c} 3x^2 - y^2 = -1 \\ \hline 3(\pm1)^2 - (\pm2)^2 & -1 \\ 3 - 4 & \\ -1 \stackrel{?}{=} -1 & \text{TRUE} \end{array}$$

The solutions are $(1, 2)$, $(1, -2)$, $(-1, 2)$, and $(-1, -2)$.

When a product of variables is in one equation and the other equation is of the form $Ax^2 + By^2 = C$, we often solve for a variable in the equation with the product and then use substitution.

EXAMPLE 5   Solve the system

$$x^2 + 4y^2 = 20, \qquad (1)$$
$$xy = 4. \qquad (2)$$

Solution   First, we solve equation (2) for y:

$$y = \frac{4}{x}. \qquad \text{Dividing both sides by } x. \text{ Note that } x \neq 0.$$

Then we substitute $4/x$ for y in equation (1) and solve for x:

$$x^2 + 4\left(\frac{4}{x}\right)^2 = 20$$

$$x^2 + \frac{64}{x^2} = 20$$

$$x^4 + 64 = 20x^2 \qquad \text{Multiplying by } x^2$$

$$x^4 - 20x^2 + 64 = 0 \qquad \begin{array}{l} \text{Obtaining standard} \\ \text{form. This equation is} \\ \text{reducible to quadratic.} \end{array}$$

$$(x^2 - 4)(x^2 - 16) = 0 \qquad \begin{array}{l} \text{Factoring. If you prefer,} \\ \text{let } u = x^2 \text{ and} \\ \text{substitute.} \end{array}$$

$$(x - 2)(x + 2)(x - 4)(x + 4) = 0 \qquad \text{Factoring again}$$

$$x = 2 \quad or \quad x = -2 \quad or \quad x = 4 \quad or \quad x = -4. \qquad \begin{array}{l} \text{Using the prin-} \\ \text{ciple of zero} \\ \text{products} \end{array}$$

Since $y = 4/x$, for $x = 2$, we have $y = 4/2$, or 2. Thus, $(2, 2)$ is a solution. Similarly, $(-2, -2)$, $(4, 1)$, and $(-4, -1)$ are solutions. You can show that all four pairs check.

technology connection

Before Example 4 can be checked by graphing, each equation must be solved for y. For equation (1), this yields $y_1 = \sqrt{(22 - 2x^2)/5}$ and $y_2 = -\sqrt{(22 - 2x^2)/5}$. For equation (2), this yields $y_3 = \sqrt{3x^2 + 1}$ and $y_4 = -\sqrt{3x^2 + 1}$.

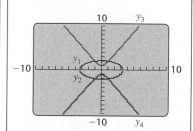

1. Perform a visual check for Example 5.

Problem Solving

We now consider applications that can be modeled by a system of equations in which at least one equation is not linear.

EXAMPLE 6   *Architecture.*   For a college gymnasium, an architect wants to lay out a rectangular piece of land that has a perimeter of 204 m and an area of 2565 m². Find the dimensions of the piece of land.

Solution

1. **Familiarize.**   We draw and label a sketch, letting l = the length and w = the width, both in meters.

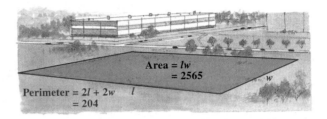

Area = lw
= 2565

Perimeter = $2l + 2w$
= 204

2. **Translate.**   We then have the following translation:

     Perimeter: $2w + 2l = 204;$

        Area: $lw = 2565.$

3. **Carry out.**   We solve the system

$$2w + 2l = 204,$$
$$lw = 2565.$$

Solving the second equation for l gives us $l = 2565/w$. Then we substitute $2565/w$ for l in the first equation and solve for w:

$$2w + 2\left(\frac{2565}{w}\right) = 204$$

$2w^2 + 2(2565) = 204w$ Multiplying both sides by w

$2w^2 - 204w + 2(2565) = 0$ Standard form

$w^2 - 102w + 2565 = 0$ Multiplying by $\frac{1}{2}$

Factoring could be used instead of the quadratic formula, but the numbers are quite large.	$w = \dfrac{-(-102) \pm \sqrt{(-102)^2 - 4 \cdot 1 \cdot 2565}}{2 \cdot 1}$

$$w = \frac{102 \pm \sqrt{144}}{2} = \frac{102 \pm 12}{2}$$

$$w = 57 \quad or \quad w = 45.$$

If $w = 57$, then $l = 2565/w = 2565/57 = 45$. If $w = 45$, then $l = 2565/w = 2565/45 = 57$. Since length is usually considered to be longer than width, we have the solution $l = 57$ and $w = 45$, or $(57, 45)$.

4. **Check.**   If $l = 57$ and $w = 45$, the perimeter is $2 \cdot 57 + 2 \cdot 45$, or 204. The area is $57 \cdot 45$, or 2565. The numbers check.

5. **State.**   The length is 57 m and the width is 45 m.

EXAMPLE 7   HDTV dimensions.   High-definition television (HDTV) offers greater clarity than conventional television. The Kaplans' new HDTV screen has an area of 1296 in^2 and has a $\sqrt{3033}$-in. (about 55-in.) diagonal screen. Find the width and the length of the screen.

Solution

1. **Familiarize.**   We make a drawing and label it. Note the right triangle in the figure. We let $l =$ the length and $w =$ the width, both in inches.

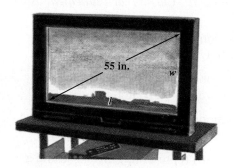

55 in.

w

l

2. **Translate.**   We translate to a system of equations:

$$l^2 + w^2 = \sqrt{3033}^2, \qquad \text{Using the Pythagorean theorem}$$
$$lw = 1296. \qquad\qquad \text{Using the formula for the area of a rectangle}$$

3. **Carry out.**   We solve the system

$$\left.\begin{array}{l} l^2 + w^2 = 3033, \\ lw = 1296 \end{array}\right\} \quad \text{You should complete the solution of this system.}$$

to get $(48, 27)$, $(27, 48)$, $(-48, -27)$, and $(-27, -48)$.

4. **Check.**   Measurements must be positive and length is usually greater than width, so we check only $(48, 27)$. In the right triangle, $48^2 + 27^2 = 2304 + 729 = 3033$ or $\sqrt{3033}^2$. The area is $48 \cdot 27 = 1296$, so our answer checks.

5. **State.**   The length is 48 in. and the width is 27 in.

Exercise Set

13.4

FOR EXTRA HELP

Student's Solutions Manual

Digital Video Tutor CD 7 Videotape 13

 AW Math Tutor Center

 MathXL Tutorials on CD

 Math XL MathXL   MyMathLab MyMathLab

☙ *Concept Reinforcement* *Classify each statement as either true or false.*

1. A system of equations that represent a line and an ellipse can have 0, 1, or 2 solutions.

2. A system of equations that represent a parabola and a circle can have up to 4 solutions.

3. A system of equations representing a hyperbola and a circle can have no fewer than 2 solutions.

4. A system of equations representing an ellipse and a line has either 0 or 2 solutions.

5. Systems containing one first-degree equation and one second-degree equation are most easily solved using the substitution method.

6. Systems containing two second-degree equations of the form $Ax^2 + By^2 = C$ are most easily solved using the elimination method.

Solve. Remember that graphs can be used to confirm all real solutions.

7. $x^2 + y^2 = 25,$
$y - x = 1$

8. $x^2 + y^2 = 100,$
$y - x = 2$

9. $4x^2 + 9y^2 = 36,$
$3y + 2x = 6$

10. $9x^2 + 4y^2 = 36,$
$3x + 2y = 6$

11. $y^2 = x + 3,$
$2y = x + 4$

12. $y = x^2,$
$3x = y + 2$

13. $x^2 - xy + 3y^2 = 27,$
$x - y = 2$

14. $2y^2 + xy + x^2 = 7,$
$x - 2y = 5$

15. $x^2 + 4y^2 = 25,$
$x + 2y = 7$

16. $x^2 - y^2 = 16,$
$x - 2y = 1$

17. $x^2 - xy + 3y^2 = 5,$
$x - y = 2$

18. $m^2 + 3n^2 = 10,$
$m - n = 2$

19. $3x + y = 7,$
$4x^2 + 5y = 24$

20. $2y^2 + xy = 5,$
$4y + x = 7$

21. $a + b = 7,$
$ab = 4$

22. $p + q = -6,$
$pq = -7$

23. $2a + b = 1,$
$b = 4 - a^2$

24. $4x^2 + 9y^2 = 36,$
$x + 3y = 3$

25. $a^2 + b^2 = 89,$
$a - b = 3$

26. $xy = 4,$
$x + y = 5$

Aha! **27.** $y = x^2,$
$x = y^2$

28. $x^2 + y^2 = 25,$
$y^2 = x + 5$

29. $x^2 + y^2 = 9,$
$x^2 - y^2 = 9$

30. $y^2 - 4x^2 = 4,$
$4x^2 + y^2 = 4$

31. $x^2 + y^2 = 25,$
$xy = 12$

32. $x^2 - y^2 = 16,$
$x + y^2 = 4$

33. $x^2 + y^2 = 9,$
$25x^2 + 16y^2 = 400$

34. $x^2 + y^2 = 4,$
$9x^2 + 16y^2 = 144$

35. $x^2 + y^2 = 14,$
$x^2 - y^2 = 4$

36. $x^2 + y^2 = 16,$
$y^2 - 2x^2 = 10$

37. $x^2 + y^2 = 20,$
$xy = 8$

38. $x^2 + y^2 = 5,$
$xy = 2$

39. $x^2 + 4y^2 = 20,$
$xy = 4$

40. $x^2 + y^2 = 13,$
$xy = 6$

41. $2xy + 3y^2 = 7,$
$3xy - 2y^2 = 4$

42. $3xy + x^2 = 34,$
$2xy - 3x^2 = 8$

43. $4a^2 - 25b^2 = 0,$
$2a^2 - 10b^2 = 3b + 4$

44. $xy - y^2 = 2,$
$2xy - 3y^2 = 0$

45. $ab - b^2 = -4,$
$ab - 2b^2 = -6$

46. $x^2 - y = 5,$
$x^2 + y^2 = 25$

Solve.

47. *Computer parts.* Dataport Electronics needs a rectangular memory board that has a perimeter of 28 cm and a diagonal of length 10 cm. What should the dimensions of the board be?

48. *Geometry.* A rectangle has an area of 2 yd^2 and a perimeter of 6 yd. Find its dimensions.

49. *Geometry.* A rectangle has an area of 20 in^2 and a perimeter of 18 in. Find its dimensions.

50. *Tile design.*   The New World tile company wants to make a new rectangular tile that has a perimeter of 6 in. and a diagonal of length $\sqrt{5}$ in. What should the dimensions of the tile be?

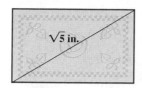

$\sqrt{5}$ in.

51. *Design of a van.*   The cargo area of a delivery van must be 60 ft^2, and the length of a diagonal must accommodate a 13-ft board. Find the dimensions of the cargo area.

13 ft

l

w

52. *Dimensions of a rug.*   The diagonal of a Persian rug is 25 ft. The area of the rug is 300 ft^2. Find the length and the width of the rug.

53. The product of two numbers is 60. The sum of their squares is 136. Find the numbers.

54. *Investments.*   A certain amount of money saved for 1 yr at a certain interest rate yielded $225 in interest. If $750 more had been invested and the rate had been 1% less, the interest would have been the same. Find the principal and the rate.

55. *Garden design.*   A garden contains two square peanut beds. Find the length of each bed if the sum of their areas is 832 ft^2 and the difference of their areas is 320 ft^2.

56. The area of a rectangle is $\sqrt{3}$ m^2, and the length of a diagonal is 2 m. Find the dimensions.

57. The product of the lengths of the legs of a right triangle is 156. The hypotenuse has length $\sqrt{313}$. Find the lengths of the legs.

58. The area of a rectangle is $\sqrt{2}$ m^2, and the length of a diagonal is $\sqrt{3}$ m. Find the dimensions.

59. How can an understanding of conic sections be helpful when a system of nonlinear equations is being solved algebraically?

60. Suppose a system of equations is comprised of one linear equation and one nonlinear equation. Is it possible for such a system to have three solutions? Why or why not?

SKILL MAINTENANCE

Simplify. [1.8]

61. $(-1)^9(-2)^4$

62. $(-1)^{10}(-2)^5$

Evaluate each of the following. [1.8]

63. $\dfrac{(-1)^k}{k-5}$, for $k = 6$

64. $\dfrac{(-1)^k}{k-5}$, for $k = 9$

65. $\dfrac{n}{2}(3+n)$, for $n = 8$

66. $\dfrac{7(1-r^2)}{1-r}$, for $r = 3$

SYNTHESIS

67. Write a problem that translates to a system of two equations. Design the problem so that at least one equation is nonlinear and so that no real solution exists.

68. Write a problem for a classmate to solve. Devise the problem so that a system of two nonlinear equations with exactly one real solution is solved.

69. Find the equation of a circle that passes through $(-2, 3)$ and $(-4, 1)$ and whose center is on the line $5x + 8y = -2$.

70. Find the equation of an ellipse centered at the origin that passes through the points $(2, -3)$ and $\left(1, \sqrt{13}\right)$.

Solve.

71. $p^2 + q^2 = 13,$
$$\frac{1}{pq} = -\frac{1}{6}$$

72. $a + b = \frac{5}{6},$
$$\frac{a}{b} + \frac{b}{a} = \frac{13}{6}$$

73. *Fence design.*   A roll of chain-link fencing contains 100 ft of fence. The fencing is bent at a 90° angle to enclose a rectangular work area of 2475 ft², as shown. Determine the length and the width of the rectangle.

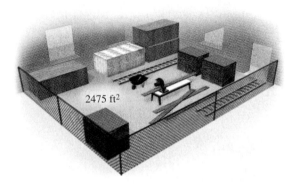

2475 ft²

74. A piece of wire 100 cm long is to be cut into two pieces and those pieces are each to be bent to make a square. The area of one square is to be 144 cm² greater than that of the other. How should the wire be cut?

75. *Box design.*   Four squares with sides 5 in. long are cut from the corners of a rectangular metal sheet that has an area of 340 in². The edges are bent up to form an open box with a volume of 350 in³. Find the dimensions of the box.

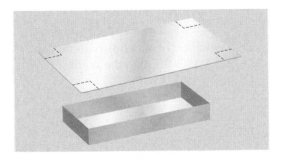

76. *Computer screens.*   The ratio of the length to the height of the screen on a computer monitor is 4 to 3. A Dell Inspiron notebook has a 15-in. diagonal screen. Find the dimensions of the screen.

15 in.

77. *HDTV screens.*   The ratio of the length to the height of an HDTV screen (see Example 7) is 16 to 9. The Remton Lounge has an HDTV screen with a $\sqrt{4901}$-in. (about 70-in.) diagonal screen. Find the dimensions of the screen.

78. *Railing sales.*   Fireside Castings finds that the total revenue R from the sale of x units of railing is given by

$$R = 100x + x^2.$$

Fireside also finds that the total cost C of producing x units of the same product is given by

$$C = 80x + 1500.$$

A break-even point is a value of x for which total revenue is the same as total cost; that is, $R = C$. How many units must be sold to break even?

79. Use a graphing calculator to check your answers to Exercises 13, 25, and 47.

13 Study Summary

The curves formed by cross sections of cones are **conic sections** (p. 856).

Parabola (p. 856):

 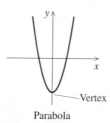

Parabola

$y = ax^2 + bx + c$ (opens upward or downward)
$= a(x - h)^2 + k$ (vertex at (h, k))

$x = ay^2 + by + c$ (opens right or left)
$= a(y - k)^2 + h$ (vertex at (h, k))

Circle (p. 861):

Circle

$x^2 + y^2 = r^2$ (center at $(0, 0)$)

$(x - h)^2 + (y - k)^2 = r^2$ (center at (h, k))

Ellipse (p. 868):

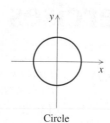

Ellipse

$\dfrac{x^2}{a^2} + \dfrac{y^2}{b^2} = 1$ (center at $(0, 0)$)

$\dfrac{(x - h)^2}{a^2} + \dfrac{(y - k)^2}{b^2} = 1$ (center at (h, k))

Hyperbola (p. 876):

 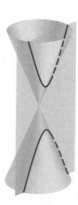 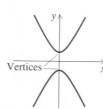

Hyperbola

$\dfrac{x^2}{a^2} - \dfrac{y^2}{b^2} = 1$ (opens right and left)

$\dfrac{y^2}{b^2} - \dfrac{x^2}{a^2} = 1$ (opens upward and downward)

To discuss the conic sections in detail, it is necessary to be able to calculate the **distance** d between any two points (x_1, y_1) and (x_2, y_2):

$$d = \sqrt{(x_2 - x_1)^2 + (y_2 - y_1)^2} \quad \text{(p. 860)}.$$

Using the distance formula, it is possible to develop the formula for the coordinates of the **midpoint** of the segment connecting any two points (x_1, y_1) and (x_2, y_2):

Midpoint: $\left(\dfrac{x_1 + x_2}{2}, \dfrac{y_1 + y_2}{2} \right) \quad$ (p. 861).

13 Review Exercises

↪ *Concept Reinforcement* *Classify each statement as either true or false.*

1. To use the distance formula, one must have an understanding of radical notation. [13.1]

2. The midpoint of the segment connecting (x_1, y_1) and (x_2, y_2) is $(x_1 + x_2, y_1 + y_2)$. [13.1]

3. The center of a circle is part of the circle itself. [13.1]

4. The foci of an ellipse always share the same second coordinate. [13.2]

5. Every parabola that opens upward or downward can represent the graph of a function. [13.1]

6. It is possible for a hyperbola to represent the graph of a function. [13.3]

7. Every system of nonlinear equations has at least one real solution. [13.4]

8. Both substitution and elimination can be used as methods for solving a system of nonlinear equations. [13.4]

Find the distance between each pair of points. Where appropriate, find an approximation to three decimal places. [13.1]

9. $(3, 6)$ and $(7, 6)$

10. $(-1, 1)$ and $(-5, 4)$

11. $(1.4, 3.6)$ and $(4.7, -5.3)$

12. $(2, 3a)$ and $(-1, a)$

Find the midpoint of the segment with the given endpoints. [13.1]

13. $(2, -1)$ and $(7, -1)$

14. $(-1, 10)$ and $(-5, 4)$

15. $\left(1, \sqrt{3}\right)$ and $\left(\frac{1}{2}, -\sqrt{2}\right)$

16. $(2, 3a)$ and $(-1, a)$

Find the center and the radius of each circle. [13.1]

17. $(x + 3)^2 + (y - 2)^2 = 7$

18. $(x - 5)^2 + y^2 = 49$

19. $x^2 + y^2 - 6x - 2y + 1 = 0$

20. $x^2 + y^2 + 8x - 6y = 10$

21. Find an equation of the circle with center $(-4, 3)$ and radius $4\sqrt{3}$. [13.1]

22. Find an equation of the circle with center $(7, -2)$ and radius $2\sqrt{5}$. [13.1]

Classify each equation as a circle, an ellipse, a parabola, or a hyperbola. Then graph.

23. $5x^2 + 5y^2 = 80$ [13.1], [13.3]

24. $9x^2 + 2y^2 = 18$ [13.2], [13.3]

25. $y = -x^2 + 2x - 3$ [13.1], [13.3]

26. $\dfrac{y^2}{9} - \dfrac{x^2}{4} = 1$ [13.3]

27. $xy = 9$ [13.3]

28. $x = y^2 + 2y - 2$ [13.1], [13.3]

29. $\dfrac{(x+1)^2}{3} + (y-3)^2 = 1$ [13.2], [13.3]

30. $x^2 + y^2 + 6x - 8y - 39 = 0$ [13.1], [13.3]

Solve. [13.4]

31. $x^2 - y^2 = 33,$
$\quad x + y = 11$

32. $x^2 - 2x + 2y^2 = 8,$
$\quad 2x + y = 6$

33. $x^2 - y = 3,$
$\quad 2x - y = 3$

34. $x^2 + y^2 = 25,$
$\quad x^2 - y^2 = 7$

35. $x^2 - y^2 = 3,$
$\quad y = x^2 - 3$

36. $x^2 + y^2 = 18,$
$\quad 2x + y = 3$

37. $x^2 + y^2 = 100,$
$\quad 2x^2 - 3y^2 = -120$

38. $x^2 + 2y^2 = 12,$
$\quad xy = 4$

39. A rectangular bandstand has a perimeter of 38 m and an area of 84 m². What are the dimensions of the bandstand? [13.4]

40. One type of carton used by tableproducts.com exactly fits both a rectangular napkin of area 108 in² and a candle of length 15 in., laid diagonally on top of the napkin. Find the length and the width of the carton. [13.4]

15 in.

41. The perimeter of a square mirror is 12 cm more than the perimeter of another square mirror. Its area exceeds the area of the other by 39 cm². Find the perimeter of each mirror. [13.4]

42. The sum of the areas of two circles is 130π ft². The difference of the circumferences is 16π ft. Find the radius of each circle. [13.4]

SYNTHESIS

43. How does the graph of a hyperbola differ from the graph of a parabola? [13.1], [13.3]

44. Explain why function notation rarely appears in this chapter, and list the graphs discussed for which function notation could be used. [13.1], [13.2], [13.3]

45. Solve: [13.4]
$$4x^2 - x - 3y^2 = 9,$$
$$-x^2 + x + y^2 = 2.$$

46. Find the points whose distance from $(8, 0)$ and from $(-8, 0)$ is 10. [13.1]

47. Find an equation of the circle that passes through $(-2, -4)$, $(5, -5)$, and $(6, 2)$. [13.1], [13.4]

48. Find an equation of the ellipse with the following intercepts: $(-9, 0)$, $(9, 0)$, $(0, -5)$, and $(0, 5)$. [13.2]

49. Find the point on the x-axis that is equidistant from $(-3, 4)$ and $(5, 6)$. [13.1]

13 Chapter Test

Find the distance between each pair of points. Where appropriate, find an approximation to three decimal places.

1. $(5, -1)$ and $(-4, 8)$

2. $(3, -a)$ and $(-3, a)$

Find the midpoint of the segment with the given endpoints.

3. $(4, -1)$ and $(-5, 8)$

4. $(3, -a)$ and $(-3, a)$

Find the center and the radius of each circle.

5. $(x + 5)^2 + (y - 1)^2 = 81$

6. $x^2 + y^2 + 4x - 6y + 4 = 0$

Classify the equation as a circle, an ellipse, a parabola, or a hyperbola. Then graph.

7. $y = x^2 - 4x - 1$

8. $x^2 + y^2 + 2x + 6y + 6 = 0$

9. $\dfrac{x^2}{16} - \dfrac{y^2}{9} = 1$

10. $16x^2 + 4y^2 = 64$

11. $xy = -5$

12. $x = -y^2 + 4y$

Solve.

13. $\dfrac{x^2}{4} + \dfrac{y^2}{9} = 1,$
$3x + 4y = 12$

14. $x^2 + y^2 = 16,$
$\dfrac{x^2}{16} - \dfrac{y^2}{9} = 1$

15. $x^2 - 2y^2 = 1,$
$xy = 6$

16. $x^2 + y^2 = 10,$
$x^2 = y^2 + 2$

17. A rectangular bookmark with diagonal of length $5\sqrt{5}$ has an area of 22. Find the dimensions of the bookmark.

18. Two squares are such that the sum of their areas is 8 m^2 and the difference of their areas is 2 m^2. Find the length of a side of each square.

19. A rectangular dance floor has a diagonal of length 40 ft and a perimeter of 112 ft. Find the dimensions of the dance floor.

20. Nikki invested a certain amount of money for 1 yr and earned $72 in interest. Erin invested $240 more than Nikki at an interest rate that was $\frac{5}{6}$ of the rate given to Nikki, but she earned the same amount of interest. Find the principal and the interest rate for Nikki's investment.

SYNTHESIS

21. Find an equation of the ellipse passing through $(6, 0)$ and $(6, 6)$ with vertices at $(1, 3)$ and $(11, 3)$.

22. Find the point on the y-axis that is equidistant from $(-3, -5)$ and $(4, -7)$.

23. The sum of two numbers is 36, and the product is 4. Find the sum of the reciprocals of the numbers.

24. *Theatrical production.* An E.T.C. spotlight for a college's production of *Hamlet* projects an ellipse of light on a stage that is 8 ft wide and 14 ft long. Find an equation of that ellipse if an actor is in its center and x represents the number of feet, horizontally, from the actor to the edge of the ellipse and y represents the number of feet, vertically, from the actor to the edge of the ellipse.

14

Sequences, Series, and the Binomial Theorem

AN APPLICATION

Approximately 534,000 new apartments and houses were built in the United States in 1991. Since then, the number has grown by about 5.35% per year. (*Sources*: Based on data from the U.S. Bureau of the Census and the U.S. Department of Housing and Urban Development) How many new apartments and houses were built in the United States from 1991 through 2004?

This problem appears as Exercise 65 in Section 14.3.

Beverley Dockeray-Ojo
CITY PLANNING DIRECTOR
Atlanta, Georgia

Mathematics is applied in the urban planning field intensively. Specifically used in statistical analysis and demographic projections including population, employment, and income, it is also applied in basic land, floor area, and density calculations. Like many other professions, the numbers tell the story, and provide the basis for problem identification and possible solutions.

*T*he first three sections of this chapter are devoted to sequences *and* series. A sequence is simply an ordered list. For example, when a baseball coach writes a batting order, a sequence is being formed. When the members of a sequence are numbers, they can be added. Such a sum is called a series.

Section 14.4 presents *the* binomial theorem, *which is used to expand expressions of the form* $(a + b)^n$. *Such an expansion is itself a series.*

14.1   Sequences and Series

Sequences   •   Finding the General Term   •
Sums and Series   •   Sigma Notation

Sequences

Suppose that $10,000 is borrowed at 5%, compounded annually. The value of the loan at the start of years 1, 2, 3, 4, and so on, is

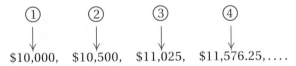

$10,000, $10,500, $11,025, $11,576.25, ...

We can regard this as a function that pairs 1 with $10,000, 2 with $10,500, 3 with $11,025, and so on. A **sequence** (or **progression**) is thus a function, where the domain is a set of consecutive positive integers beginning with 1, and the range varies from sequence to sequence.

If we continue computing the amounts in the account forever, we obtain an **infinite sequence**, with function values

$10,000, $10,500, $11,025, $11,576.25, $12,155.06, ...

The three dots at the end indicate that the sequence goes on without stopping. If we stop after a certain number of years, we obtain a **finite sequence**:

$10,000, $10,500, $11,025, $11,576.25.

Sequences

An *infinite sequence* is a function having for its domain the set of natural numbers: $\{1, 2, 3, 4, 5, \ldots\}$.

A *finite sequence* is a function having for its domain a set of natural numbers: $\{1, 2, 3, 4, 5, \ldots, n\}$, for some natural number n.

As another example, consider the sequence given by

$$a(n) = 2^n, \quad \text{or} \quad a_n = 2^n.$$

The notation a_n means the same as $a(n)$ but is used more commonly with sequences. Some function values (also called *terms* of the sequence) follow:

$$a_1 = 2^1 = 2,$$
$$a_2 = 2^2 = 4,$$
$$a_3 = 2^3 = 8,$$
$$a_6 = 2^6 = 64.$$

The first term of the sequence is a_1, the fifth term is a_5, and the nth term, or **general term**, is a_n. This sequence can also be denoted in the following ways:

$$2, 4, 8, \ldots;$$

or $2, 4, 8, \ldots, 2^n, \ldots$ The 2^n emphasizes that the nth term of this sequence is found by raising 2 to the nth power.

EXAMPLE 1

Find the first four terms and the 57th term of the sequence for which the general term is given by $a_n = (-1)^n/(n + 1)$.

Solution   We have

$$a_1 = \frac{(-1)^1}{1 + 1} = -\frac{1}{2},$$

$$a_2 = \frac{(-1)^2}{2 + 1} = \frac{1}{3},$$

$$a_3 = \frac{(-1)^3}{3 + 1} = -\frac{1}{4},$$

$$a_4 = \frac{(-1)^4}{4 + 1} = \frac{1}{5},$$

$$a_{57} = \frac{(-1)^{57}}{57 + 1} = -\frac{1}{58}.$$

Note that the expression $(-1)^n$ causes the signs of the terms to alternate between positive and negative, depending on whether n is even or odd.

---

technology connection

Sequences are entered and graphed much like functions. The difference is that the SEQUENCE MODE must be selected. You can then enter U_n or V_n using n as the variable. Use this approach to check Example 1 with a table of values for the sequence.

Finding the General Term

When only the first few terms of a sequence are known, it is impossible to be certain what the general term is. Still, a prediction can be made by looking for a pattern.

EXAMPLE 2

For each sequence, predict the general term.

a) $1, 4, 9, 16, 25, \ldots$ **b)** $-1, 2, -4, 8, -16, \ldots$

c) $2, 4, 8, \ldots$

Solution

a) $1, 4, 9, 16, 25, \ldots$

These are squares of consecutive positive integers, so the general term could be n^2.

b) $-1, 2, -4, 8, -16, \ldots$

These are powers of 2 with alternating signs, so the general term may be $(-1)^n[2^{n-1}]$. To check, note that 8 is the fourth term, and

$$(-1)^4[2^{4-1}] = 1 \cdot 2^3$$
$$= 8.$$

c) $2, 4, 8, \ldots$

We regard the pattern as powers of 2, in which case 16 would be the next term and 2^n the general term. The sequence could then be written with more terms as

$$2, 4, 8, 16, 32, 64, 128, \ldots.$$

In part (c) above, suppose that the second term is found by adding 2, the third term by adding 4, the next term by adding 6, and so on. In this case, 14 would be the next term and the sequence would be

$$2, 4, 8, 14, 22, 32, 44, 58, \ldots.$$

This illustrates that the fewer terms we are given, the greater the uncertainty about the nth term.

Sums and Series

> **Series**
>
> Given the infinite sequence
>
> $$a_1, \ a_2, \ a_3, \ a_4, \ \ldots, \ a_n, \ldots,$$
>
> the sum of the terms
>
> $$a_1 + a_2 + a_3 + \cdots + a_n + \cdots$$
>
> is called an *infinite series* and is denoted S_∞. A *partial sum* is the sum of the first n terms:
>
> $$a_1 + a_2 + a_3 + \cdots + a_n.$$
>
> A partial sum is also called a *finite series* and is denoted S_n.

EXAMPLE 3   For the sequence $-2, 4, -6, 8, -10, 12, -14$, find: **(a)** S_2; **(b)** S_3; **(c)** S_7.

Solution

a) $S_2 = -2 + 4 = 2$ This is the sum of the first 2 terms.

b) $S_3 = -2 + 4 + (-6) = -4$ This is the sum of the first 3 terms.

c) $S_7 = -2 + 4 + (-6) + 8 + (-10) + 12 + (-14) = -8$ This is the sum of the first 7 terms.

22.

23.

24.

25.

26.

27.

28.

Loo
nth
29.

30.

31.

32.

33.

34.

35.

36.

37.

38.

39.

40.

41.

42.

43.

44.

Fir

45.

46.

47.

48.

W.

49

Sigma Notation

When the general term of a sequence is known, the Greek letter Σ (capital sigma) can be used to write a series. For example, the sum of the first four terms of the sequence 3, 5, 7, 9, 11, ..., $2k + 1$, ... can be named as follows, using *sigma notation*, or *summation notation*:

$$\sum_{k=1}^{4} (2k + 1).$$

This represents
$(2 \cdot 1 + 1) + (2 \cdot 2 + 1) + (2 \cdot 3 + 1) + (2 \cdot 4 + 1).$

This is read "the sum as k goes from 1 to 4 of $(2k + 1)$." The letter k is called the *index of summation*. The index of summation need not always start at 1.

EXAMPLE 4   Write out and evaluate each sum.

a) $\displaystyle\sum_{k=1}^{5} k^2$ **b)** $\displaystyle\sum_{k=4}^{6} (-1)^k(2k)$ **c)** $\displaystyle\sum_{k=0}^{3} (2^k + 5)$

Solution

a) $\displaystyle\sum_{k=1}^{5} k^2 = 1^2 + 2^2 + 3^2 + 4^2 + 5^2 = 1 + 4 + 9 + 16 + 25 = 55$

Evaluate k^2 for all integers from 1 through 5. Then add.

b) $\displaystyle\sum_{k=4}^{6} (-1)^k(2k) = (-1)^4(2 \cdot 4) + (-1)^5(2 \cdot 5) + (-1)^6(2 \cdot 6)$

$= 8 - 10 + 12 = 10$

c) $\displaystyle\sum_{k=0}^{3} (2^k + 5) = (2^0 + 5) + (2^1 + 5) + (2^2 + 5) + (2^3 + 5)$

$= 6 + 7 + 9 + 13 = 35$

EXAMPLE 5   Write sigma notation for each sum.

a) $1 + 4 + 9 + 16 + 25$

b) $-1 + 3 - 5 + 7$

c) $3 + 9 + 27 + 81 + \cdots$

Solution

a) $1 + 4 + 9 + 16 + 25$

Note that this is a sum of squares, $1^2 + 2^2 + 3^2 + 4^2 + 5^2$, so the general term is k^2. Sigma notation is

$$\sum_{k=1}^{5} k^2.$$ The sum starts with 1^2 and ends with 5^2.

Answers can vary here. For example, another—perhaps less obvious—way of writing $1 + 4 + 9 + 16 + 25$ is

$$\sum_{k=2}^{6} (k - 1)^2.$$

Student Notes _____

A great deal of information is condensed into sigma notation. Be careful to pay attention to what values the index of summation will take on. Evaluate the expression following sigma, the general term, for each value and then add the results.

35. Adam took a job working in a convenience store starting with an hourly wage of $11.50. He was promised a raise of 40¢ per hour every 3 mos for 8 yr. At the end of 8 yr, what will be his hourly wage? [14.2]

36. A stack of poles has 42 poles in the bottom row. There are 41 poles in the second row, 40 poles in the third row, and so on, ending with 1 pole in the top row. How many poles are in the stack? [14.2]

37. Stacey's student loan is in the amount of $12,000. Interest is 4%, compounded annually, and the amount is to be paid off in 7 yr. How much is to be paid back? [14.3]

38. Find the total rebound distance of a ball, given that it is dropped from a height of 12 m and each rebound is one-third of the preceding one. [14.3]

Simplify. [14.4]

39. $7!$

40. $\binom{8}{3}$

41. Find the 3rd term of $(a + b)^{20}$. [14.4]

42. Expand: $(x - 2y)^4$. [14.4]

SYNTHESIS

43. What happens to a_n in a geometric sequence with $|r| < 1$, as n gets larger? Why? [14.3]

44. Compare the two forms of the binomial theorem given in the text. Under what circumstances would one be more useful than the other? [14.4]

45. Find the sum of the first n terms of the geometric series $1 - x + x^2 - x^3 + \cdots$. [14.3]

46. Expand: $(x^{-3} + x^3)^5$. [14.4]

14 Chapter Test

1. Find the first five terms and the 12th term of a sequence with general term $a_n = 6n - 5$.

2. Predict the general term of the sequence
$$\frac{4}{3}, \frac{4}{9}, \frac{4}{27}, \ldots.$$

3. Write out and evaluate:
$$\sum_{k=2}^{6} (3 - 2^k).$$

4. Rewrite using sigma notation:
$$1 + (-8) + 27 + (-64) + 125.$$

5. Find the 13th term, a_{13}, of the arithmetic sequence $9, 4, -1, \ldots.$

Assume arithmetic sequences for Questions 6 and 7.

6. Find the common difference d when $a_1 = 7$ and $a_7 = 9\frac{1}{4}$.

7. Find a_1 and d when $a_5 = 16$ and $a_{10} = -3$.

8. Find the sum of all the multiples of 12 from 24 to 240, inclusive.

9. Find the 6th term of the geometric sequence $72, 18, 4\frac{1}{2}, \ldots.$

10. Find the common ratio of the geometric sequence $22\frac{1}{2}, 15, 10, \ldots.$

11. Find the nth term of the geometric sequence $3, 9, 27, \ldots.$

12. Find the sum of the first nine terms of the geometric series
$$(1 + x) + (2 + 2x) + (4 + 4x) + \cdots.$$

Determine whether each infinite geometric series has a limit. If a limit exists, find it.

13. $0.5 + 0.25 + 0.125 + \cdots$

14. $0.5 + 1 + 2 + 4 + \cdots$

15. $\$1000 + \$80 + \$6.40 + \cdots$

16. Find fraction notation for $0.85858585\ldots$.

17. An auditorium has 31 seats in the first row, 33 seats in the second row, 35 seats in the third row, and so on, for 18 rows. How many seats are in the 17th row?

18. Lindsay's Uncle Ken gave her $100 for her first birthday, $200 for her second birthday, $300 for her third birthday, and so on, until her eighteenth birthday. How much did he give her in all?

19. Each week the price of a $15,000 boat will be reduced 5% of the previous week's price. If we assume that it is not sold, what will be the price after 10 weeks?

20. Find the total rebound distance of a ball that is dropped from a height of 18 m, with each rebound two thirds of the preceding one.

21. Simplify: $\binom{12}{9}$.

22. Expand: $(x^2 - 3y)^5$.

23. Find the 4th term in the expansion of $(a + x)^{12}$.

SYNTHESIS

24. Find a formula for the sum of the first n even natural numbers:
$$2 + 4 + 6 + \cdots + 2n.$$

25. Find the sum of the first n terms of
$$1 + \frac{1}{x} + \frac{1}{x^2} + \frac{1}{x^3} + \cdots.$$

1–14 Cumulative Review

Simplify.

1. $(-7x^2y^3)(5x^4y^{-7})$ [4.8]

2. $|-3.5 + 9.8|$ [1.8]

3. $y - [3 - 4(5 - 2y) - 3y]$ [1.8]

4. $(10 \cdot 8 - 9 \cdot 7)^2 - 54 \div 9 - 3$ [1.8]

5. Evaluate
$$\frac{ab - ac}{bc}$$
for $a = -2$, $b = 3$, and $c = -4$. [1.8]

Perform the indicated operations to create an equivalent expression. Be sure to simplify your result if possible.

6. $(5a^2 - 3ab - 7b^2) - (2a^2 + 5ab + 8b^2)$ [4.3]

7. $(-3x^2 + 4x^3 - 5x - 1) + (9x^3 - 4x^2 + 7 - x)$ [4.3]

8. $(2a - 1)(3a + 5)$ [4.5]

9. $(3a^2 - 5y)^2$ [4.5]

10. $\dfrac{1}{x-2} - \dfrac{4}{x^2-4} + \dfrac{3}{x+2}$ [6.4]

11. $\dfrac{x^2 - 6x + 8}{4x + 12} \cdot \dfrac{x+3}{x^2-4}$ [6.2]

12. $\dfrac{3x + 3y}{5x - 5y} \div \dfrac{3x^2 + 3y^2}{5x^3 - 5y^3}$ [6.2]

13. $\dfrac{x - \dfrac{a^2}{x}}{1 + \dfrac{a}{x}}$ [6.5]

Factor, if possible, to form an equivalent expression.

14. $4x^2 - 12x + 9$ [5.4]

15. $27a^3 - 8$ [5.5]

16. $a^3 + 3a^2 - ab - 3b$ [5.1]

17. $15y^4 + 33y^2 - 36$ [5.3]

18. For the function described by
$$f(x) = 3x^2 - 4x,$$
find $f(-2)$. [7.2]

19. Divide:

$$(7x^4 - 5x^3 + x^2 - 4) \div (x - 2). \ [4.7]$$

Solve.

20. $8(x - 1) - 3(x - 2) = 1$ [2.2]

21. $\dfrac{6}{x} + \dfrac{6}{x + 2} = \dfrac{5}{2}$ [6.6]

22. $2x + 1 > 5 \ or \ x - 7 \le 3$ [9.2]

23. $5x + 3y = -2,$
$3x + 5y = 2$ [8.2]

24. $x + y - z = 0,$
$3x + y + z = 6,$
$x - y + 2z = 5$ [8.4]

25. $3\sqrt{x - 1} = 5 - x$ [10.6]

26. $x^4 - 29x^2 + 100 = 0$ [11.5]

27. $x^2 + y^2 = 8,$
$x^2 - y^2 = 2$ [13.4]

28. $4^x = 7$ [12.6]

29. $\log(x^2 - 25) - \log(x + 5) = 3$ [12.6]

30. $\log_5 x = -2$ [12.6]

31. $7^{2x+3} = 49$ [12.6]

32. $|2x - 1| \le 5$ [9.3]

33. $7x^2 + 14 = 0$ [11.1]

34. $x^2 + 4x = 3$ [11.2]

35. $y^2 + 3y > 10$ [11.9]

36. Let $f(x) = x^2 - 2x$. Find a such that $f(a) \le 48$.
[11.9]

37. If $f(x) = \sqrt{-x + 4} + 3$ and $g(x) = \sqrt{x - 2} + 3$,
find a such that $f(a) = g(a)$. [10.6]

Solve.

38. The perimeter of a rectangular sign is 34 ft. The length of a diagonal is 13 ft. Find the dimensions of the sign. [13.4]

39. A music club offers two types of membership. Limited members pay a fee of $10 a year and can buy CDs for $10 each. Preferred members pay $20 a year and can buy CDs for $7.50 each. For what numbers of annual CD purchases would it be less expensive to be a preferred member? [9.1]

40. Find three consecutive integers whose sum is 198. [2.5]

41. A pentagon with all five sides the same size has a perimeter equal to that of an octagon in which all eight sides are the same size. One side of the pentagon is 2 less than three times one side of the octagon. What is the perimeter of each figure? [8.3]

42. Roger's Organics mixes herbs that cost $2.68 an ounce with herbs that cost $4.60 an ounce to create a seasoning that costs $3.80 an ounce. How many ounces of each herb should be mixed together to make 24 oz of the seasoning? [8.3]

43. An airplane can fly 190 mi with the wind in the same time it takes to fly 160 mi against the wind. The speed of the wind is 30 mph. How fast can the plane fly in still air? [6.7]

44. Bianca can tap the sugar maple trees in Southway Park in 21 hr. Delia can tap the trees in 14 hr. How long would it take them, working together, to tap the trees? [6.7]

45. The centripetal force F of an object moving in a circle varies directly as the square of the velocity v and inversely as the radius r of the circle. If $F = 8$ when $v = 1$ and $r = 10$, what is F when $v = 2$ and $r = 16$? [11.6]

46. The Brighton recreation department plans to fence in a rectangular park next to a river. (Note that no fence will be needed along the river.) What is the area of the largest region that can be fenced in with 200 ft of fencing? [11.8]

Graph.

47. $3x - y = 7$ [3.6]

48. $y - 4 = -\frac{2}{3}(x - 1)$ [3.7]

49. $x^2 + y^2 = 100$ [13.1]

50. $\dfrac{x^2}{36} - \dfrac{y^2}{9} = 1$ [13.3]

51. $y = \log_2 x$ [12.3]

52. $f(x) = 2^x - 3$ [12.2]

53. $2x - 3y < -6$ [9.4]

54. Graph: $f(x) = -2(x - 3)^2 + 1$. [11.7]
  a) Label the vertex.
  b) Draw the axis of symmetry.
  c) Find the maximum or minimum value.

55. Solve $V = P - Prt$ for r. [2.3]

56. Solve $I = \dfrac{R}{R + r}$ for R. [7.5]

57. Find a linear equation whose graph has a y-intercept of $(0, -8)$ and is parallel to the line whose equation is $3x - y = 6$. [3.6]

Find the domain of each function.

58. $f(x) = \sqrt{6 - 8x}$ [9.2]

59. $g(x) = \dfrac{x - 4}{x^2 - 2x + 1}$ [7.2]

60. Multiply $(8.9 \times 10^{-17})(7.6 \times 10^4)$. Write scientific notation for the answer. [4.8]

61. Multiply and simplify: $\sqrt{8x}\,\sqrt{8x^3y}$. [10.3]

62. Simplify: $(25x^{4/3}y^{1/2})^{3/2}$. [10.2]

63. Divide and simplify:
$$\dfrac{\sqrt[3]{25x}}{\sqrt[3]{5y^2}}.\ [10.5]$$

64. Write an equivalent expression by rationalizing the denominator:
$$\dfrac{1 - \sqrt{x}}{1 + \sqrt{x}}.\ [10.5]$$

65. Multiply these complex numbers:
$(3 + 2i)(4 - 7i)$. [10.8]

66. Write a quadratic equation whose solutions are $5\sqrt{2}$ and $-5\sqrt{2}$. [11.4]

67. Find the center and the radius of the circle given by $x^2 + y^2 - 4x + 6y - 23 = 0$. [13.1]

68. Write an equivalent expression that is a single logarithm:
$\frac{2}{3}\log_a x - \frac{1}{2}\log_a y + 5\log_a z$. [12.4]

69. Write an equivalent exponential equation:
$\log_a c = 5$. [12.3]

Use a calculator to find each of the following. [12.5]

70. $\log 5677.2$

71. $10^{-3.587}$

72. $\ln 5677.2$

73. $e^{-3.587}$

74. The number of personal computers in Mexico has grown exponentially from 0.12 million in 1985 to 5.0 million in 2002. [12.7]
Source: Center for International Development
  a) Find the exponential growth rate, k, to three decimal places and write an exponential function describing the number of personal computers in Mexico t years after 1985.
  b) Predict the number of personal computers in Mexico in 2010.

75. Find the distance between the points $(-1, -5)$ and $(2, -1)$. [13.1]

76. Find the 21st term of the arithmetic sequence $19, 12, 5, \ldots$. [14.2]

77. Find the sum of the first 25 terms of the arithmetic series $-1 + 2 + 5 + \cdots$. [14.2]

78. Find the general term of the geometric sequence $16, 4, 1, \ldots$. [14.3]

79. Find the 7th term of $(a - 2b)^{10}$. [14.4]

80. Find the sum of the first nine terms of the geometric series $x + 1.5x + 2.25x + \cdots$. [14.3]

81. On Elyse's 9th birthday, her grandmother opened a savings account for her with $500. The account pays 3% interest, compounded annually. If Elyse neither adds to nor withdraws any money from the bank, how much will be in the account on her 18th birthday? [14.3]

SYNTHESIS

Solve.

82. $\dfrac{9}{x} - \dfrac{9}{x + 12} = \dfrac{108}{x^2 + 12x}$ [6.6]

83. $\log_2(\log_3 x) = 2$ [12.6]

84. y varies directly as the cube of x and x is multiplied by 0.5. What is the effect on y? [11.6]

85. Divide these complex numbers:
$$\dfrac{2\sqrt{6} + 4\sqrt{5}i}{2\sqrt{6} - 4\sqrt{5}i}.\ [10.8]$$

86. Diaphantos, a famous mathematician, spent $\frac{1}{6}$ of his life as a child, $\frac{1}{12}$ as an adolescent, and $\frac{1}{7}$ as a bachelor. Five years after he was married, he had a son who died 4 years before his father at half his father's final age. How long did Diaphantos live? [8.5]

R
Elementary Algebra Review

his chapter is a review of the first six chapters of this text. Each section corresponds to a chapter of the text. For further explanation of the topics in this chapter, refer to the sections or pages referenced in the margin.

R.1   Introduction to Algebraic Expressions

The Real Numbers • Operations on Real Numbers •
Algebraic Expressions

The study of algebra requires a thorough understanding of how numbers are manipulated.

The Real Numbers

Numbers can be represented by points on a number line.

Sets (p. 30)

Some sets of numbers are given specific names.

Sets of Numbers

Natural Numbers: $\{1, 2, 3, \ldots\}$

Whole Numbers: $\{0, 1, 2, 3, \ldots\}$

Integers: $\{\ldots, -3, -2, -1, 0, 1, 2, 3, \ldots\}$

Rational numbers: $\left\{\dfrac{a}{b} \,\middle|\, a \text{ and } b \text{ are integers and } b \neq 0\right\}$

Sets of real numbers
(Section 1.4)

Terminating decimals (p. 33)

Repeating decimals (p. 33)

Irrational numbers (p. 33)

Real numbers (p. 34)

Order (p. 35)

Equation (p. 6)

Inequality (p. 35)

Rational numbers can always be written as **terminating** or **repeating** decimals. **Irrational numbers**, like $\sqrt{2}$ or π, can be thought of as nonterminating and nonrepeating decimals. The set of **real numbers** consists of all rational and irrational numbers, taken together.

We can compare, or **order**, real numbers by their graphs on the number line. For any two numbers, the one to the left is less than the one to the right.

Sentences like $\frac{1}{4} = 0.25$, containing an equals sign, are called **equations**. An **inequality** is a sentence containing $>$ (is greater than), $<$ (is less than), $\geq$ (is greater than or equal to), or $\leq$ (is less than or equal to). Equations and inequalities can be true or false.

EXAMPLE 1   Write true or false for each equation or inequality.

a) $-2\frac{1}{3} = -\frac{7}{3}$ b) $1 = -1$ c) $-5 < -2$

d) $-3 \geq 2$ e) $1.1 \leq 1.1$

Solution

a) $-2\frac{1}{3} = -\frac{7}{3}$ is *true* because $-2\frac{1}{3}$ and $-\frac{7}{3}$ represent the same number.

b) $1 = -1$ is a *false* equation.

c) $-5 < -2$ is *true* because -5 is to the left of -2 on the number line.

d) $-3 \geq 2$ is *false* because neither $-3 > 2$ nor $-3 = 2$ is true.

e) $1.1 \leq 1.1$ is *true* because $1.1 = 1.1$ is true.

Absolute value (p. 36)

The distance of a number from 0 is called the **absolute value** of the number. The notation $|-4|$ represents the absolute value of -4. The absolute value of a number is never negative.

EXAMPLE 2   Find the absolute value: **(a)** $|-4|$; **(b)** $\left|\frac{11}{3}\right|$; **(c)** $|0|$.

Solution

a) $|-4| = 4$ since -4 is 4 units from 0.

b) $\left|\frac{11}{3}\right| = \frac{11}{3}$ since $\frac{11}{3}$ is $\frac{11}{3}$ units from 0.

c) $|0| = 0$ since 0 is 0 units from itself.

Operations on Real Numbers

Addition, subtraction, multiplication, and division of real numbers are defined using absolute values.

Addition (Section 1.5)

> **Rules for Addition of Real Numbers**
>
> 1. *Positive numbers*: Add as usual. The answer is positive.
> 2. *Negative numbers*: Add absolute values and make the answer negative.
> 3. *A positive and a negative number*: Subtract absolute values. Then:
>   a) If the positive number has the greater absolute value, the answer is positive.
>   b) If the negative number has the greater absolute value, the answer is negative.
>   c) If the numbers have the same absolute value, the answer is 0.
> 4. *One number is zero*: The sum is the other number.

Opposite (p. 46)

Every real number has an **opposite**. The opposite of −6 is 6, the opposite of 3.7 is −3.7, and the opposite of 0 is itself. When opposites are added, the result is 0. Finding the opposite of a number is often called "changing its sign."

Subtraction of real numbers is defined in terms of addition and opposites.

Subtraction (Section 1.6)

> ### Subtraction of Real Numbers
>
> To subtract, add the opposite of the number being subtracted.

The rules for multiplication of real numbers are similar to the rules for division.

Multiplication and division
(Section 1.7)

> ### Rules for Multiplication and Division
>
> To multiply or divide two real numbers:
>
> 1. Using the absolute values, multiply or divide, as indicated.
> 2. If the signs are the same, the answer is positive.
> 3. If the signs are different, the answer is negative.

EXAMPLE 3   Perform the indicated operations: **(a)** $-13 + (-9)$; **(b)** $-\frac{4}{5} + \frac{1}{10}$; **(c)** $-6 - (-7.3)$; **(d)** $3(-1.5)$; **(e)** $\left(-\frac{4}{9}\right) \div \left(-\frac{2}{5}\right)$.

Solution

a) $-13 + (-9) = -22$

Two negatives. *Think:* Add the absolute values, 13 and 9, to get 22. Make the answer *negative*, −22.

b) $-\frac{4}{5} + \frac{1}{10} = -\frac{8}{10} + \frac{1}{10} = -\frac{7}{10}$

A negative and a positive. *Think:* The difference of absolute values is $\frac{8}{10} - \frac{1}{10}$, or $\frac{7}{10}$. The negative number has the larger absolute value, so the answer is *negative*, $-\frac{7}{10}$.

c) $-6 - (-7.3) = -6 + 7.3 = 1.3$

Change the subtraction to addition and add the opposite.

d) $3(-1.5) = -4.5$

Think: $3(1.5) = 4.5$. The signs are different, so the answer is negative.

e) $\left(-\frac{4}{9}\right) \div \left(-\frac{2}{5}\right) = \left(-\frac{4}{9}\right) \cdot \left(-\frac{5}{2}\right)$
$= \frac{20}{18} = \frac{10}{9} \cdot \frac{2}{2} = \frac{10}{9}$

Multiplying by the reciprocal. The answer is positive.

Division by 0 (p. 60)

Addition, subtraction, and multiplication are defined for all real numbers, but we cannot **divide by 0**. For example, $\frac{0}{3} = 0 \div 3 = 0$, but $\frac{3}{0} = 3 \div 0$ is **undefined**.

Exponential notation (p. 63)

A product like $2 \cdot 2 \cdot 2 \cdot 2$, in which the factors are the same, is called a **power**. Powers are often written using **exponential notation**:

$$2 \cdot 2 \cdot 2 \cdot 2 = 2^4.$$ There are 4 factors; 4 is the *exponent*.

2 is the *base*.

A number raised to the power of 1 is the number itself; for example, $3^1 = 3$.

An expression containing a series of operations is not necessarily evaluated from left to right. Instead, we perform the operations according to the following rules.

Rules for Order of Operations

1. Calculate within the innermost grouping symbols, ( ), [ ], { }, | |, and above or below fraction bars.
2. Simplify all exponential expressions.
3. Perform all multiplication and division, working from left to right.
4. Perform all addition and subtraction, working from left to right.

EXAMPLE 4

Simplify: $3 - [(4 \times 5) + 12 \div 2^3 \times 6] + 5$.

Solution

$$3 - [(4 \times 5) + 12 \div 2^3 \times 6] + 5$$
$$= 3 - [20 + 12 \div 2^3 \times 6] + 5 \quad \text{Doing the calculations in the innermost parentheses first}$$
$$= 3 - [20 + 12 \div 8 \times 6] + 5 \quad \text{Working inside the brackets; evaluating } 2^3$$
$$= 3 - [20 + 1.5 \times 6] + 5 \quad 12 \div 8 \text{ is the first multiplication or division working from left to right.}$$
$$= 3 - [20 + 9] + 5 \quad \text{Multiplying}$$
$$= 3 - 29 + 5 \quad \text{Completing the calculations within the brackets}$$
$$= -26 + 5$$
$$= -21 \quad \text{Adding and subtracting from left to right}$$

Algebraic expression (p. 3)

Constant (p. 2)

Variable (p. 2)

Substitute (p. 3)

Evaluate (p. 3)

Algebraic Expressions

In an **algebraic expression** like $2xt^3$, the number 2 is a **constant** and x and t are **variables**. When numbers are **substituted** for x and t, we say that we are **evaluating** the expression.

Algebraic expressions containing variables can be evaluated by substituting a number for each variable in the expression and following the rules for order of operations.

EXAMPLE 5   The perimeter P of a rectangle of length l and width w is given by the formula $P = 2l + 2w$. Find the perimeter when l is 16 in. and w is 7.5 in.

Solution   We evaluate, substituting 16 in. for l and 7.5 in. for w and carrying out the operations:

$$P = 2l + 2w$$
$$= 2 \cdot 16 + 2 \cdot 7.5$$
$$= 32 + 15$$
$$= 47 \text{ in.}$$

Expressions that represent the same number are said to be **equivalent**. The laws that follow provide methods for writing equivalent expressions.

Laws and Properties of Real Numbers

Commutative laws:	$a + b = b + a; ab = ba$
Associative laws:	$a + (b + c) = (a + b) + c;$
	$a(bc) = (ab)c$
Distributive law:	$a(b + c) = ab + ac$
Identity property of 1:	$1 \cdot a = a \cdot 1 = a$
Identity property of 0:	$a + 0 = 0 + a = a$
Law of opposites:	$a + (-a) = 0$
Multiplicative property of 0:	$0 \cdot a = a \cdot 0 = 0$
Property of -1:	$-1 \cdot a = -a$
Opposite of a sum:	$-(a + b) = -a + (-b)$

$$\frac{-a}{b} = \frac{a}{-b} = -\frac{a}{b}, \qquad \frac{-a}{-b} = \frac{a}{b}$$

Factor (p. 17)

The distributive law can be used to multiply and to **factor** expressions. We factor an expression when we write an equivalent expression that is a product.

EXAMPLE 6   Write an equivalent expression as indicated.

a) Multiply: $-2(5x - 3)$.   **b)** Factor: $5x + 10y + 5$.

Solution

a) $-2(5x - 3) = -2(5x + (-3))$ Adding the opposite
$$= -2 \cdot 5x + (-2) \cdot (-3)$$ Using the distributive law
$$= (-2 \cdot 5)x + 6$$ Using the associative law for multiplication
$$= -10x + 6$$

b) $5x + 10y + 5 = 5 \cdot x + 5 \cdot 2y + 5 \cdot 1$ The common factor is 5.

$\qquad\qquad\qquad = 5(x + 2y + 1)$ Using the distributive law

Factoring can be checked by multiplying:

$$5(x + 2y + 1) = 5 \cdot x + 5 \cdot 2y + 5 \cdot 1 = 5x + 10y + 5.$$

Terms (p. 16)

Combine like terms (p. 43)

The **terms** of an algebraic expression are separated by plus signs. When two terms have variable factors that are exactly the same, the terms are called **like**, or **similar**, **terms**. The distributive law enables us to **combine**, or **collect**, **like terms**.

EXAMPLE 7

Combine like terms: $-5m + 3n - 4n + 10m$.

Solution

$-5m + 3n - 4n + 10m$

$= -5m + 3n + (-4n) + 10m$ Rewriting as addition

$= -5m + 10m + 3n + (-4n)$ Using the commutative law of addition

$= (-5 + 10)m + (3 + (-4))n$ Using the distributive law

$= 5m + (-n)$

$= 5m - n$ Rewriting as subtraction

We can also use the distributive law to help simplify algebraic expressions containing parentheses.

EXAMPLE 8

Simplify: **(a)** $4x - (y - 2x)$; **(b)** $3(t + 2) - 6(t - 1)$.

Solution

a) $4x - (y - 2x) = 4x - y + 2x$ Removing parentheses and changing the sign of every term

$\qquad\qquad\qquad = 6x - y$ Combining like terms

b) $3(t + 2) - 6(t - 1) = 3t + 6 - 6t + 6$ Multiplying each term of $t + 2$ by 3 and each term of $t - 1$ by -6

$\qquad\qquad\qquad\qquad = -3t + 12$ Combining like terms

Value (p. 3)

Solution (p. 6)

We have seen that algebraic expressions can be evaluated for specified numbers. If the expressions on each side of an equation have the same **value** for a given number, then that number is a **solution** of the equation.

EXAMPLE 9   Determine whether each number is a solution of $x - 2 = -5$.

a) 3   **b)** -3

Solution

a) We have:

$$x - 2 = -5 \qquad \text{Writing the equation}$$
$$\overline{3 - 2 \mid -5} \qquad \text{Substituting 3 for } x$$
$$1 \overset{?}{=} -5 \qquad 1 = -5 \text{ is FALSE}$$

Since $3 - 2 = -5$ is false, 3 is not a solution of $x - 2 = -5$.

b) We have

$$x - 2 = -5$$
$$\overline{-3 - 2 \mid -5}$$
$$-5 \overset{?}{=} -5 \qquad \text{TRUE}$$

Since $-3 - 2 = -5$ is true, -3 is a solution of $x - 2 = -5$.

Translating to algebraic expressions (p. 4)

Translating to equations (p. 6)

Certain word phrases can be translated to algebraic expressions. These in turn can often be used to translate problems to equations.

EXAMPLE 10   Time usage. Translate the following problem to an equation.

The average adult spends 145.6 hr a year shopping for clothes. This is 16 times as many hours as is spent planning for retirement (*Source: Perspective*, September 1996). How many hours a year does the average adult spend planning for retirement?

Solution   We let r represent the number of hours spent planning for retirement. We then reword the problem to make the translation more direct.

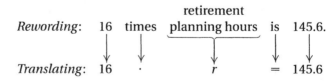

Exercise Set

R.1

FOR EXTRA HELP

 Student's Solutions Manual   Digital Video Tutor CD 8 Videotape 15   Tutor Center AW Math Tutor Center   MathXL Tutorials on CD   Math XL MathXL   MyMathLab MyMathLab

Classify each equation or inequality as true or false.

1. $2.3 = 2.31$

2. $-3 \geq -3$

3. $-10 < -1$

4. $0 \leq -1$

5. $5 > 0$

6. $\frac{1}{10} = 0.1$

Find each absolute value.

7. $|4|$

8. $\left|\frac{11}{4}\right|$

9. $|-1.3|$

10. $|-105|$

Simplify.

11. $(-13) + (-12)$

12. $3 - (-2)$

13. $-\frac{1}{3} - \frac{2}{5}$

14. $\frac{3}{8} \div \frac{3}{5}$

15. $4.2 - 10.7$

16. $(-1.3)(2.8)$

17. $-15 + 0$

18. $\left(-\frac{1}{2}\right) + \frac{1}{8}$

19. $0 \div (-10)$

20. $0 - 32$

21. $\left(-\frac{3}{10}\right) + \left(-\frac{1}{5}\right)$

22. $\left(-\frac{4}{7}\right)\left(\frac{7}{4}\right)$

23. $-3.8 + 9.6$

24. $-0.01 + 1$

25. $(-12) \div 4$

26. $(-3)(30)$

27. $32 - (-7)$

28. $-100 + 35$

29. $(-10)(-17.5)$

30. $-10 - 2.68$

31. $(-68) + 36$

32. $175 \div (-25)$

33. $2 + (-3) + 7 + 10$

34. $-5 + (-15) + 13 + (-1)$

35. $3 \cdot (-2) \cdot (-1) \cdot (-1)$

36. $(-6) \cdot (-5) \cdot (-4) \cdot (-3) \cdot (-2) \cdot (-1)$

37. $(-1)^4 + 2^3$

38. $(-1)^5 + 2^4$

39. $2 \times 6 - 3 \times 5$

40. $12 \div 4 + 15 \div 3$

41. $3 - (2 \cdot 4 + 11)$

42. $3 - 2 \cdot 4 + 11$

43. $4 \cdot 5^2$

44. $7 \cdot 2^3$

45. $25 - 8 \times 3 + 1$

46. $12 - 16 \times 5 + 4$

47. $2 - (3^3 + 16 \div (-2)^3)$

48. $-7 - (8 + 10 \times 2^2)$

49. $|6(-3)| + |(-2)(-9)|$

50. $3 - |2 - 7 + 4|$

51. $\dfrac{7000 + (-10)^3}{10^2 \times (2 + 4)}$

52. $\dfrac{3 - 2 \times 6 - 5}{2(3 + 7)^2}$

53. $2 + 8 \div 2 \times 2$

54. $2 + 8 \div (2 \times 2)$

Evaluate.

55. $x - y$, for $x = 10$ and $y = 3$

56. $2m - n$, for $m = 6$ and $n = 11$

57. $-3 - x^2 + 12x$, for $x = 5$

58. $14 + (y - 5)^2 - 12 \div y$, for $y = -2$

59. The area of a parallelogram with base b and height h is bh. Find the area of the parallelogram when the height is 3.5 cm and the base is 8 cm.

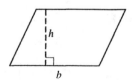

60. The area of a triangle with base b and height h is $\frac{1}{2}bh$. Find the area of the triangle when the height is 2 in. and the base is 6.2 in.

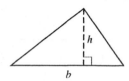

Multiply.

61. $4(2x + 7)$

62. $3(5y + 1)$

63. $5(x - 10)$

64. $4(3x - 2)$

65. $-2(15 - 3x)$

66. $-7(3x - 5)$

67. $2(4a + 6b - 3c)$

68. $5(8p + q - 5r)$

Factor.

69. $8x + 6y$

70. $7p + 14q$

71. $3 + 3w$

72. $4x + 4y$

73. $10x + 50y + 100$

74. $81p + 27q + 36$

Combine like terms.

75. $3p - 2p$

76. $4x + 3x$

77. $4m + 10 - 5m + 12$

78. $3a - 4b - 5b - 6a$

79. $-6x + 7 + 9x$

80. $16r + (-7r) + 3s$

Remove parentheses and simplify.

81. $2p - (7 - 4p)$

82. $4r - (3r + 5)$

83. $2x + 5y - 7(x - y)$

84. $14m - 6(2n - 3m) + n$

85. $6[2a + 4(a - 2b)]$

86. $2[2a + 1 - (3a - 6)]$

87. $3 - 2[5(x - 10y) - (3 + 2y)]$

88. $7 - 4[2(3 - 2x) - 5(4x - 3)]$

Determine whether the given number is a solution of the given equation.

89. $4; 3x - 2 = 10$

90. $12; 100 = 4x + 50$

91. $-3; 4 - x = 1$

92. $-1; 2 = 5 + 3x$

93. $4.6; \dfrac{x}{2} = 2.3$

94. $144; \dfrac{x}{9} = 16$

Translate each problem to an equation. Do not solve.

95. Three times what number is 348?

96. What number added to 256 is 113?

97. *Fast-food calories.* A McDonald's Big Mac® contains 500 calories. This is 69 more calories than a Taco Bell Beef Burrito® provides. How many calories are in a Taco Bell Beef Burrito?

98. *Coca-Cola® consumption.* The average U.S. citizen consumes 296 servings of Coca-Cola each year. This is 7.4 times the international average. What is the international average per capita consumption of Coke?

99. *Vegetable production.* It takes 42 gal of water to produce 1 lb of broccoli. This is twice the amount of water used to produce 1 lb of lettuce. How many gallons of water does it take to produce 1 lb of lettuce?

100. *Sports costs.* The average annual cost for scuba diving is $470. This is $458 more than the average annual cost to play badminton. What is the average annual cost to play badminton?

R.2   Equations, Inequalities, and Problem Solving

Solving Equations and Formulas • Solving Inequalities •
Problem Solving

In this section, we develop a problem-solving approach that can be used to solve many types of problems. Before doing so, we will study some principles used to solve equations and inequalities.

Solving Equations and Formulas

Solution (p. 80)

Any replacement for the variable in an equation that makes the equation true is called a *solution* of the equation. To **solve** an equation means to find all of its solutions.

Equivalent equations (p. 81)

We use the following principles to write **equivalent equations**, or equations with the same solutions.

The addition principle (p. 81)

The Addition and Multiplication Principles for Equations

The Addition Principle

For any real numbers a, b, and c,

$$a = b \text{ is equivalent to } a + c = b + c.$$

The multiplication principle (p. 83)

The Multiplication Principle

For any real numbers a, b, and c, with $c \neq 0$,

$$a = b \text{ is equivalent to } a \cdot c = b \cdot c.$$

To solve $x + a = b$ for x, we add $-a$ to (or subtract a from) both sides.

To solve $ax = b$ for x, we multiply both sides by $\dfrac{1}{a}$ (or divide both sides by a).

To solve an equation like $-3x - 10 = 14$, we first isolate the variable term, $-3x$, using the addition principle. Then we use the multiplication principle to get the variable by itself.

EXAMPLE 1

Solve: $-3x - 10 = 14$.

Solution

$$-3x - 10 = 14$$
$$-3x - 10 + 10 = 14 + 10 \qquad \text{Using the addition principle: Adding 10 to both sides}$$

First isolate the x-term
$$-3x = 24 \qquad \text{Simplifying}$$
$$\frac{-3x}{-3} = \frac{24}{-3} \qquad \text{Dividing both sides by } -3$$

Then isolate x.
$$x = -8 \qquad \text{Simplifying}$$

Check:
$$\begin{array}{c|c} -3x - 10 = 14 \\ \hline -3(-8) - 10 & 14 \\ 24 - 10 & \\ 14 \overset{?}{=} 14 & \text{TRUE} \end{array}$$

The solution is -8.

Clearing fractions (p. 93)

Equations are generally easier to solve when they do not contain fractions. The easiest way to clear an equation of fractions is to multiply *every term on both sides* of the equation by the least common denominator.

EXAMPLE 2   Solve: $\frac{5}{2} - \frac{1}{6}t = \frac{2}{3}$.

Solution   The number 6 is the least common denominator, so we multiply both sides by 6.

$$6\left(\frac{5}{2} - \frac{1}{6}t\right) = 6 \cdot \frac{2}{3}$$ Multiplying both sides by 6

$$6 \cdot \frac{5}{2} - 6 \cdot \frac{1}{6}t = 6 \cdot \frac{2}{3}$$ Using the distributive law. Be sure to multiply every term by 6.

$$15 - t = 4$$ The fractions are cleared.

$$15 - t - 15 = 4 - 15$$ Subtracting 15 from both sides

$$-t = -11$$ $15 - t - 15 = 15 + (-t) + (-15)$
$\qquad\qquad\qquad = -t + 15 + (-15) = -t$

$$(-1)(-t) = (-1)(-11)$$ Multiplying both sides by -1 to change the sign

$$t = 11$$

Check: $\dfrac{5}{2} - \dfrac{1}{6}t = \dfrac{2}{3}$

$$\begin{array}{c|c} \frac{5}{2} - \frac{1}{6}(11) & \frac{2}{3} \\[4pt] \frac{5}{2} - \frac{11}{6} & \\[4pt] \frac{15}{6} - \frac{11}{6} & \\[4pt] & \frac{2}{3} \overset{?}{=} \frac{2}{3} \quad \text{TRUE} \end{array}$$

The solution is 11.

_____

To solve equations that contain parentheses, we can use the distributive law to first remove the parentheses. If like terms appear in an equation, we combine them and then solve.

EXAMPLE 3   Solve: $1 - 3(4 - x) = 2(x + 5) - 3x$.

Solution

$$1 - 3(4 - x) = 2(x + 5) - 3x$$

$$1 - 12 + 3x = 2x + 10 - 3x$$ Using the distributive law

$$-11 + 3x = -x + 10$$ Combining like terms;
$1 - 12 = -11$ and
$2x - 3x = -x$

$$-11 + 3x + x = 10$$ Adding x to both sides to get all x-terms on one side

$$-11 + 4x = 10$$ Combining like terms

$$4x = 10 + 11$$ Adding 11 to both sides to isolate the x-term

$$4x = 21$$ Simplifying

$$x = \frac{21}{4}$$ Dividing both sides by 4

Check:

$$\begin{array}{c|c} \multicolumn{2}{c}{1 - 3(4 - x) = 2(x + 5) - 3x} \\ \hline 1 - 3\left(4 - \frac{21}{4}\right) & 2\left(\frac{21}{4} + 5\right) - 3\left(\frac{21}{4}\right) \\ 1 - 3\left(-\frac{5}{4}\right) & 2\left(\frac{41}{4}\right) - \frac{63}{4} \\ 1 + \frac{15}{4} & \frac{82}{4} - \frac{63}{4} \\ \frac{19}{4} & \stackrel{?}{=} \frac{19}{4} \end{array}$$

TRUE

The solution is $\frac{21}{4}$.

Formulas (Section 2.3)

A **formula** is an equation using two or more letters that represents a relationship between two or more quantities. A formula can be solved for a specified letter using the principles for solving equations.

EXAMPLE 4

The formula

$$A = \frac{a + b + c + d}{4}$$

gives the average A of four test scores a, b, c, and d. Solve for d.

Solution   We have

$$A = \frac{a + b + c + d}{4}$$ We want the letter d alone.

$$4A = a + b + c + d$$ Multiplying by 4 to clear the fraction

$$4A - a - b - c = d.$$ Subtracting $a + b + c$ from (or adding $-a - b - c$ to) both sides. The letter d is now isolated.

We can also write this as $d = 4A - a - b - c$. This formula can be used to determine the test score needed to obtain a specified average if three tests have already been taken.

Solving Inequalities

Solutions of inequalities (p. 127)

A **solution of an inequality** is a replacement of the variable that makes the inequality true.

Graphs of inequalities (p. 128)

The solutions of an inequality in one variable can be **graphed**, or represented by a drawing, on a number line. All points that are solutions are shaded, and dots are used at the endpoints. An open dot indicates an endpoint that is not a solution and a closed dot indicates an endpoint that is a solution.

EXAMPLE 5

Graph each inequality: **(a)** $m \leq 2$; **(b)** $-1 \leq x < 4$.

Solution

a) The solutions of $m \leq 2$ are shown on the number line by shading points to the left of 2 as well as the point at 2. The closed dot at 2 indicates that 2 is a part of the graph (that is, it is a solution of $m \leq 2$).

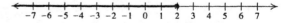

b) In order to be a solution of the inequality $-1 \leq x < 4$, a number must be a solution of both $-1 \leq x$ and $x < 4$. The solutions are shaded on the number line, with an open dot indicating that 4 is not a solution and a closed dot indicating that -1 is a solution.

Equivalent inequalities (p. 129)

As with equations, our goal when solving inequalities is to isolate the variable on one side. We use principles that enable us to write **equivalent inequalities**—inequalities having the same solution set. The addition principle is similar to the addition principle for equations; the multiplication principle contains an important difference.

The Addition and Multiplication Principles for Inequalities

The addition principle for inequalities (p. 129)

The Addition Principle

For any real numbers a, b, and c,

$$a < b \quad \text{is equivalent to} \quad a + c < b + c, \qquad \text{and}$$
$$a > b \quad \text{is equivalent to} \quad a + c > b + c.$$

The multiplication principle for inequalities (p. 131)

The Multiplication Principle

For any real numbers a and b, and for any *positive* number c,

$$a < b \quad \text{is equivalent to} \quad ac < bc, \qquad \text{and}$$
$$a > b \quad \text{is equivalent to} \quad ac > bc.$$

For any real numbers a and b, and for any *negative* number c,

$$a < b \quad \text{is equivalent to} \quad ac > bc, \qquad \text{and}$$
$$a > b \quad \text{is equivalent to} \quad ac < bc.$$

Similar statements hold for $\leq$ and $\geq$.

Note that when we multiply both sides of an inequality by a negative number, we must reverse the direction of the inequality symbol in order to have an equivalent inequality.

EXAMPLE 6   Solve $-2x \geq 5$ and then graph the solution.

Solution   We have

$$-2x \geq 5$$

$$\frac{-2x}{-2} \leq \frac{5}{-2} \qquad \text{Multiplying by } -\frac{1}{2} \text{ or dividing by } -2$$

The symbol must be reversed!

$$x \leq -\frac{5}{2}.$$

Any number less than or equal to $-\frac{5}{2}$ is a solution. The graph is as follows:

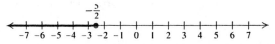

Set-builder notation (p. 130)

In Example 6, note $x \le -\frac{5}{2}$ is an inequality that describes the set of all solutions. Since it is impossible to list all the solutions, we use **set-builder notation**. The solution set of Example 6 is written

$$\left\{x \mid x \le -\tfrac{5}{2}\right\},$$

read "the set of all x such that x is less than or equal to $-\frac{5}{2}$." We can use the addition and multiplication principles together to solve inequalities. We can also combine like terms, remove parentheses, and clear fractions and decimals.

EXAMPLE 7

Solve: $2 - 3(x + 5) > 4 - 6(x - 1)$.

Solution   We have

$$2 - 3(x + 5) > 4 - 6(x - 1)$$

$$2 - 3x - 15 > 4 - 6x + 6 \qquad \text{Using the distributive law to remove parentheses}$$

$$-3x - 13 > -6x + 10 \qquad \text{Simplifying}$$

$$-3x + 6x > 10 + 13 \qquad \text{Adding } 6x \text{ and also } 13, \text{ to get all } x\text{-terms on one side and all other terms on the other side}$$

$$3x > 23 \qquad \text{Combining like terms}$$

$$x > \tfrac{23}{3}. \qquad \text{Multiplying by } \tfrac{1}{3}. \text{ The inequality symbol stays the same because } \tfrac{1}{3} \text{ is positive.}$$

The solution set is $\left\{x \mid x > \tfrac{23}{3}\right\}$.

Problem solving (Section 2.5)

Problem Solving

One of the most important uses of algebra is as a tool for problem solving. The following five steps can be used to help solve problems of many types.

Five Steps for Problem Solving in Algebra

1. *Familiarize* yourself with the problem.
2. *Translate* to mathematical language. (This often means write an equation.)
3. *Carry out* some mathematical manipulation. (This often means *solve* an equation.)
4. *Check* your possible answer in the original problem.
5. *State* the answer clearly.

EXAMPLE 8   Kitchen cabinets.   Cherry kitchen cabinets cost 10% more than oak cabinets. Shelby Custom Cabinets designs a kitchen using $7480 worth of cherry cabinets. How much would the same kitchen cost using oak cabinets?

Solution

Familiarization step (p. 115)

Percent (Section 2.4)

1. **Familiarize.**   The *Familiarize* step is often the most important of the five steps, and may require a significant amount of time. Sometimes it helps to make a drawing or a table, make a guess and check it, or look up further information. For this problem, we could review percent notation. We could also make a guess. Let's suppose that the oak cabinets cost $6500. Then the cherry cabinets would cost 10% more, or an additional $(0.10)(\$6500) = \$650$. Altogether the cherry cabinets would cost $\$6500 + \$650 = \$7150$. Since $\$7150 \neq \$7480$, our guess is incorrect, but we see that 10% of the price of the oak cabinets must be added to the price of the oak cabinets to get the price of the cherry cabinets. We let $c =$ the cost of the oak cabinets.

2. **Translate.**   What we learned in the *Familiarize* step leads to the translation of the problem to an equation.

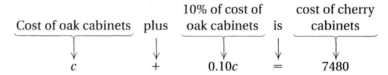

$$
\begin{array}{ccccc}
\text{Cost of oak cabinets} & \text{plus} & \text{10\% of cost of oak cabinets} & \text{is} & \text{cost of cherry cabinets} \\
\downarrow & \downarrow & \downarrow & \downarrow & \downarrow \\
c & + & 0.10c & = & 7480
\end{array}
$$

3. **Carry out.**   We solve the equation:

$$c + 0.10c = 7480$$

$1c + 0.10c = 7480$ Writing c as $1c$ before combining terms

$1.10c = 7480$ Combining like terms

$c = \dfrac{7480}{1.10}$ Dividing by 1.10

$c = 6800.$

4. **Check.**   We check in the wording of the stated problem: Cherry cabinets cost 10% more, so the additional cost is

$$10\% \text{ of } \$6800 = 0.10(\$6800) = \$680.$$

The total cost of the cherry cabinets is then

$$\$6800 + \$680 = \$7480,$$

which is the amount stated in the problem.

5. **State.**   The oak cabinets would cost $6800.

Sometimes the translation of a problem is an inequality.

EXAMPLE 9   Long-distance telephone usage.   Elyse pays a flat rate of 6¢ per minute for long-distance telephone calls. The monthly charge for her local calls is $21.50. How many minutes can she spend calling long distance in a month and not exceed her telephone budget of $50?

Solution

1. **Familiarize.** Suppose that Elyse spends 10 hr, or 600 min, making long-distance calls one month. Then her bill would be the local service charge plus the long-distance charges, or

$$\$21.50 + \$0.06(600) = \$57.50.$$

This exceeds \$50, so we know that the number of long-distance minutes must be less than 600. We let $m =$ the number of minutes of long-distance calls in a month.

2. **Translate.** The *Familiarize* step helps us reword and translate.

Rewording:	The local service charge	plus	the long-distance charges	cannot exceed	\$50.
Translating:	21.50	+	0.06m	≤	50

Solving applications with inequalities (Section 2.7)

3. **Carry out.** We solve the inequality:

$$21.50 + 0.06m \le 50$$
$$0.06m \le 28.50 \qquad \text{Subtracting 21.50 from both sides}$$
$$m \le 475. \qquad \text{Dividing by 0.06. The inequality symbol stays the same.}$$

4. **Check.** As a partial check, note that the telephone bill for 475 min of long-distance charges is

$$\$21.50 + \$0.06(475) = \$50.$$

Since this does not exceed the \$50 budget, and fewer minutes will cost even less, our answer checks. We also note that 475 is less than 600 min, as noted in the *Familiarize* step.

5. **State.** Elyse will not exceed her budget if she talks long distance for no more than 475 min.

Exercise Set

R.2

FOR EXTRA HELP

Student's Solutions Manual

Digital Video Tutor CD 8 Videotape 15

AW Math Tutor Center

MathXL Tutorials on CD

Math XL
MathXL

MyMathLab
MyMathLab

Solve.

1. $y + 5 = 13$

2. $y + 7 = -3$

3. $-3 + m = 9$

4. $-11 = 4 + x$

5. $t + \frac{1}{3} = \frac{1}{4}$

6. $-\frac{2}{3} + p = \frac{1}{6}$

7. $-1.9 = x - 1.1$

8. $x + 4.6 = 1.7$

9. $3y = 13$

10. $2x = 18$

11. $-x = \frac{5}{3}$

12. $-y = -\frac{2}{5}$

13. $-\frac{2}{7}x = -12$

14. $-\frac{1}{4}x = 3$

15. $\dfrac{-t}{5} = 1$

16. $\dfrac{2}{3} = -\dfrac{z}{8}$

17. $3x + 7 = 13$

18. $4x + 3 = -1$

19. $3y - 10 = 15$

20. $12 = 5y - 18$

21. $4x + 7 = 3 - 5x$

22. $2x = 5 + 7x$

23. $2x - 7 = 5x + 1 - x$

24. $a + 7 - 2a = 14 + 7a - 10$

25. $\frac{2}{5} + \frac{1}{3}t = 5$

26. $-\frac{5}{6} + t = \frac{1}{2}$

27. $x + 0.45 = 2.6x$

28. $1.8x + 0.16 = 4.2 - 0.05x$

29. $8(3 - m) + 7 = 47$

30. $2(5 - m) = 5(6 + m)$

31. $4 - (6 + x) = 13$

32. $18 = 9 - (3 - x)$

33. $2 + 3(4 + c) = 1 - 5(6 - c)$

34. $b + (b + 5) - 2(b - 5) = 18 + b$

35. $0.1(a - 0.2) = 1.2 + 2.4a$

36. $\frac{2}{3}\left(\frac{1}{2} - x\right) + \frac{5}{6} = \frac{3}{2}\left(\frac{2}{3}x + 1\right)$

37. $A = lw$, for l

38. $A = lw$, for w

39. $p = 30q$, for q

40. $d = 20t$, for t

41. $I = \dfrac{P}{V}$, for P

42. $b = \dfrac{A}{h}$, for A

43. $q = \dfrac{p + r}{2}$, for p

44. $q = \dfrac{p - r}{2}$, for r

45. $A = \pi r^2 + \pi r^2 h$, for π

46. $ax + by = c$, for a

Determine whether each number is a solution of the given inequality.

47. $x \le -5$

   a) 5

   b) -5

   c) 0

   d) -10

48. $y > 0$

   a) -1

   b) 1

   c) 0

   d) 100

Solve and graph. Write each answer in set-builder notation.

49. $x + 3 \le 15$

50. $y + 7 < -10$

51. $m - 17 > -5$

52. $x + 9 \ge -8$

53. $2x \ge -3$

54. $-\frac{1}{2}n \le 4$

55. $-5t > 15$

56. $3x > 10$

Solve. Write each answer in set-builder notation.

57. $2y - 7 > 13$

58. $2 - 6y \le 18$

59. $6 - 5a \le a$

60. $4b + 7 > 2 - b$

61. $2(3 + 5x) \ge 7(10 - x)$

62. $2(x + 5) < 8 - 3x$

63. $\frac{2}{3}(6 - x) < \frac{1}{4}(x + 3)$

64. $\frac{2}{3}t + \frac{8}{9} \ge \frac{4}{6} - \frac{1}{4}t$

65. $0.7(2 + x) \ge 1.1x + 5.75$

66. $0.4x + 5.7 \le 2.6 - 3(1.2x - 7)$

Solve. Use the five-step problem-solving process.

67. Three less than the sum of 2 and some number is 6. What is the number?

68. Five times some number is 10 less than the number. What is the number?

69. The sum of two consecutive even integers is 34. Find the numbers.

70. The sum of three consecutive integers is 195. Find the numbers.

71. *Reading.* Leisa is reading a 500-page book. She has twice as many pages to read as she has already finished. How many pages has she already read?

72. *Mowing.* It takes Caleb 50 min to mow his lawn. It will take him three times as many minutes to finish as he has already spent mowing. How long has he already spent mowing?

73. *Perimeter of a rectangle.* The perimeter of a rectangle is 28 cm. The width is 5 cm less than the length. Find the width and the length.

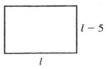

74. *Triangles.* The second angle of a triangle is one third as large as the first. The third angle is 5° more than the first. Find the measure of the second angle.

75. *Water usage.* Rural Water Company charges a monthly service fee of $9.70 plus a volume charge of $2.60 for every hundred cubic feet of water used. How much water was used if the monthly bill is $33.10?

76. *Telephone bills.* Brandon pays $4.95 a month for a long-distance telephone service that offers a flat rate of 7¢ per minute. One month his total long-distance telephone bill was $10.69. How many minutes of long-distance telephone calls were made that month?

77. *Sales prices.* A can of tomatoes is on sale at 20% off for 64¢. What is the normal selling price of the tomatoes?

78. *Plywood.* The price of a piece of plywood rose 5% to $42. What was the original price of the plywood?

R.3 Introduction to Graphing

Points and Ordered Pairs • Graphs and Slope • Linear Equations

The graph of an equation is a drawing representing the solutions of that equation. Every point on the graph is a solution, and every solution is represented by a point.

Points and Ordered Pairs

Graphing ordered pairs (p. 151)

Coordinates (p. 151)

Quadrants (p. 154)

We can represent, or graph, pairs of numbers such as $(2, -5)$ on a plane. To do so, we use two perpendicular number lines called **axes**. The axes cross at a point called the **origin**. Arrows on the axes show the positive directions.

The order of the **coordinates**, or numbers in a pair, is important. The **first coordinate** indicates horizontal position and the **second coordinate** indicates vertical position. Such pairs of numbers are called **ordered pairs**. Thus, the ordered pairs $(1, -2)$ and $(-2, 1)$ correspond to different points, as shown in the accompanying figure.

The axes divide the plane into four regions, or **quadrants**, as indicated by Roman numerals in the figure at right. Points on the axes are not considered to be in any quadrant. The horizontal axis is often labeled the *x*-axis, and the vertical axis the *y*-axis.

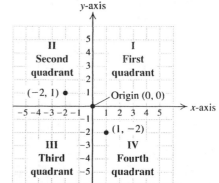

Graphs and Slope

Solutions of equations (p. 159)

When an equation contains two variables, solutions must be ordered pairs. Unless stated otherwise, the first number in each pair replaces the variable that occurs first alphabetically.

EXAMPLE 1   Determine whether $(1, 4)$ is a solution of $y - x = 3$.

Solution   We substitute 1 for x and 4 for y since x occurs first alphabetically:

$$\frac{y - x = 3}{4 - 1 \;\big|\; 3}$$
$$3 \overset{?}{=} 3 \quad \text{TRUE}$$

Since $3 = 3$ is true, the pair $(1, 4)$ *is* a solution.

A curve or line that represents all the solutions of an equation is called its **graph**.

EXAMPLE 2   Graph: $y = -2x + 1$.

Solution   We select a value for x, calculate the corresponding value of y, and form an ordered pair.
   If $x = 0$, then $y = -2 \cdot 0 + 1 = 1$, and $(0, 1)$ is a solution. Repeating this step, we find other ordered pairs and list the results in a table. We then plot the points corresponding to the pairs. They appear to form a straight line, so we draw a line through the points.

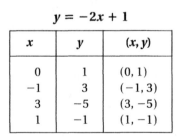

$y = -2x + 1$

x	y	(x, y)
0	1	$(0, 1)$
-1	3	$(-1, 3)$
3	-5	$(3, -5)$
1	-1	$(1, -1)$

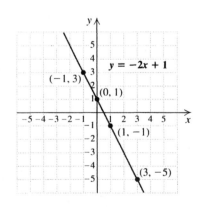

Slope (p. 190)

The graph in Example 2 is a straight line. An equation whose graph is a straight line is a **linear equation**. The *rate of change* of y with respect to x is called the **slope** of a graph. A linear graph has constant slope. It can be found using any two points on a line.

> **Slope**
>
> The *slope* of the line containing points (x_1, y_1) and (x_2, y_2) is given by
>
> $$m = \frac{\text{change in } y}{\text{change in } x} = \frac{\text{rise}}{\text{run}} = \frac{y_2 - y_1}{x_2 - x_1}.$$

EXAMPLE 3   Find the slope of the line containing the points $(-2, 1)$ and $(3, -4)$.

Solution   From $(-2, 1)$ to $(3, -4)$, the change in y, or the rise, is $-4 - 1$, or -5. The change in x, or the run, is $3 - (-2)$, or 5. Thus

$$\text{Slope} = \frac{\text{change in } y}{\text{change in } x} = \frac{\text{rise}}{\text{run}} = \frac{-4 - 1}{3 - (-2)} = \frac{-5}{5} = -1.$$

The slope of a line indicates the direction and steepness of its slant. The larger the absolute value of the slope, the steeper the line. The direction of the slant is indicated by the sign of the slope, as shown in the figures below.

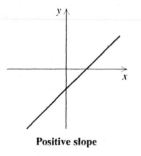

Positive slope   Negative slope   Zero slope   Undefined slope

x-intercept (p. 169)

y-intercept (p. 169)

The **x-intercept** of a line, if it exists, is the point at which the graph crosses the x-axis. To find an x-intercept, we replace y with 0 and calculate x.

The **y-intercept** of a line, if it exists, is the point at which the graph crosses the y-axis. To find a y-intercept, we replace x with 0 and calculate y.

Linear Equations

Any equation that can be written in the **standard form** $Ax + By = C$ is linear. Linear equations can also be written in other forms.

> **Forms of Linear Equations**
>
> | | |
> |---|---|
> | Standard form: | $Ax + By = C$ |
> | Slope-intercept form: | $y = mx + b$ |
> | Point-slope form: | $y - y_1 = m(x - x_1)$ |

The slope and y-intercept of a line can be read from the slope-intercept form of the line's equation.

Slope and y-intercept

For the graph of any equation $y = mx + b$,

- the slope is m, and
- the y-intercept is $(0, b)$.

EXAMPLE 4   Find the slope and the y-intercept of the line given by the equation $4x - 3y = 9$.

Solution   We write the equation in slope-intercept form $y = mx + b$:

$$4x - 3y = 9 \qquad \text{We must solve for } y.$$
$$-3y = -4x + 9 \qquad \text{Adding } -4x \text{ to both sides}$$
$$y = \tfrac{4}{3}x - 3. \qquad \text{Dividing both sides by } -3$$

The slope is $\tfrac{4}{3}$ and the y-intercept is $(0, -3)$.

If we know an equation is a straight line, we can plot two points on the line and draw the line through those points. The intercepts are often convenient points to use.

EXAMPLE 5   Graph $2x - 5y = 10$ using intercepts.

Solution   To find the x-intercept, we let $y = 0$ and solve for x:

$$2x - 5 \cdot 0 = 10 \qquad \text{Replacing } y \text{ with } 0$$
$$2x = 10$$
$$x = 5.$$

To find the y-intercept, we let $x = 0$ and solve for y:

$$2 \cdot 0 - 5y = 10 \qquad \text{Replacing } x \text{ with } 0$$
$$-5y = 10$$
$$y = -2.$$

Thus the x-intercept is $(5, 0)$ and the y-intercept is $(0, -2)$. The graph is a line, since $2x - 5y = 10$ is in the form $Ax + By = C$. It passes through these two points.

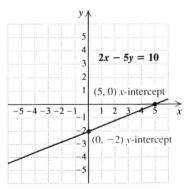

Alternatively, if we know a point on the line and its slope, we can plot the point and "count off" its slope to locate another point on the line.

EXAMPLE 6   Graph: $y = -\dfrac{1}{2}x + 3$.

Solution   The equation is in slope-intercept form, so we can read the slope and y-intercept directly from the equation.

Slope: $-\dfrac{1}{2}$

y-intercept: $(0, 3)$

We plot the y-intercept and use the slope to find another point.

Another way to write the slope is $\dfrac{-1}{2}$.

This means for a run of 2 units, there is a negative rise, or a fall, of 1 unit. Starting at $(0, 3)$, we move 2 units in the positive horizontal direction and then 1 unit down, to locate the point $(2, 2)$. Then we draw the graph. A third point can be calculated and plotted as a check.

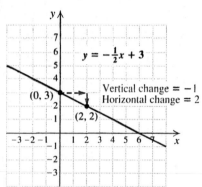

Horizontal and vertical lines intersect only one axis.

Horizontal and Vertical Lines

Horizontal line (p. 174)

Vertical line (p. 174)

Horizontal Line	*Vertical Line*
$y = b$	$x = a$
y-intercept $(0, b)$	x-intercept $(a, 0)$
Slope is 0	Undefined slope
Example: $y = -3$	Example: $x = 2$

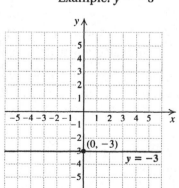

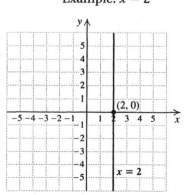

If we know the slope of a line and the coordinates of a point on the line, we can find an equation of the line, using either the slope-intercept equation $y = mx + b$, or the point-slope equation $y - y_1 = m(x - x_1)$.

EXAMPLE 7   Find the slope-intercept equation of a line given the following:

a) The slope is 2, and the y-intercept is $(0, -5)$.

b) The graph contains the points $(-2, 1)$ and $(3, -4)$.

Solution

a) Since the slope and the y-intercept are given, we use the slope-intercept equation:

$$y = mx + b$$
$$y = 2x - 5 \qquad \text{Substituting 2 for } m \text{ and } -5 \text{ for } b$$

b) To use the point-slope equation, we need a point on the line and its slope. The slope can be found from the points given:

$$m = \frac{1 - (-4)}{-2 - 3} = \frac{5}{-5} = -1.$$

Either point can be used for (x_1, y_1). Using $(-2, 1)$, we have

$$y - y_1 = m(x - x_1)$$
$$y - 1 = -1(x - (-2)) \qquad \text{Substituting } -2 \text{ for } x_1, 1$$
$$\qquad\qquad\qquad\qquad\qquad \text{for } y_1, \text{ and } -1 \text{ for } m$$
$$y - 1 = -(x + 2)$$
$$y - 1 = -x - 2$$
$$y = -x - 1. \qquad \text{This is in slope-intercept form.}$$

We can tell from the slopes of two lines whether they are parallel or perpendicular.

Parallel lines (p. 206)

Perpendicular lines (p. 207)

> **Parallel and Perpendicular Lines**
>
> Two lines are parallel if they have the same slope.
>
> Two lines are perpendicular if the product of the slopes is -1.

EXAMPLE 8   Tell whether the graphs of each pair of lines are parallel, perpendicular, or neither.

a) $2x - y = 7,$
  $y = 2x + 3$

b) $4x - y = 8,$
  $x + 4y = 8$

Solution

a) The slope of $y = 2x + 3$ is 2.
To find the slope of $2x - y = 7$, we solve for y:

$$2x - y = 7$$
$$-y = -2x + 7$$
$$y = 2x - 7.$$

The slope of $2x - y = 7$ is also 2. Since the slopes are equal, the lines are parallel.

b) We solve both equations for y in order to determine the slopes of the lines:

$$4x - y = 8$$
$$-y = -4x + 8$$
$$y = 4x - 8.$$

The slope of $4x - y = 8$ is 4.
For the second line, we have

$$x + 4y = 8$$
$$4y = -x + 8$$
$$y = -\tfrac{1}{4}x + 2.$$

The slope of $x + 4y = 8$ is $-\tfrac{1}{4}$. Since $4 \cdot \left(-\tfrac{1}{4}\right) = -1$, the lines are perpendicular.

Exercise Set

R.3

FOR EXTRA HELP

 Student's Solutions Manual   Digital Video Tutor CD 8 Videotape 15   Tutor Center   AW Math Tutor Center   MathXL Tutorials on CD   *Math* XP MathXL   *MyMathLab* MyMathLab

1. Plot these points.
$(2, -3), (5, 1), (0, 2), (-1, 0),$
$(0, 0), (-2, -5), (-1, 1), (1, -1)$

2. Plot these points.
$(0, -4), (-4, 0), (5, -2), (2, 5),$
$(3, 3), (-3, -1), (-1, 4), (0, 1)$

In which quadrant is each point located?

3. $(2, 1)$

4. $(-2, 5)$

5. $(3, -2.6)$

6. $(-1.7, -5.9)$

7. First coordinates are positive in quadrants _____ and _____ .

8. Second coordinates are negative in quadrants _____ and _____ .

Determine whether each equation has the given ordered pair as a solution.

9. $y = 2x - 5;$ $(1, 3)$

10. $4x + 3y = 8;$ $(-1, 4)$

11. $a - 5b = -3;$ $(2, 1)$

12. $c = d + 1;$ $(1, 2)$

Graph.

13. $y = \tfrac{1}{3}x + 3$

14. $y = -x - 2$

15. $y = -4x$

16. $y = \tfrac{3}{4}x + 1$

Find the slope of the line containing each given pair of points.

17. $(3, 6)$ and $(2, 5)$ **18.** $(-1, 7)$ and $(-3, 4)$

19. $\left(-2, -\frac{1}{2}\right)$ and $\left(5, -\frac{1}{2}\right)$

20. $(6.8, 7.5)$ and $(6.8, -3.2)$

Find the slope and the y-intercept of each equation.

21. $y = 2x - 5$ **22.** $y = 4x - 8$

23. $2x + y = 1$ **24.** $x - 2y = 3$

Find the intercepts. Then graph.

25. $3 - y = 2x$ **26.** $2x + 5y = 10$

27. $y = 3x + 5$ **28.** $y = -x + 7$

29. $3x - 2y = 6$ **30.** $2y + 1 = x$

Determine the coordinates of the y-intercept of each equation. Then graph the equation.

31. $y = 2x - 5$ **32.** $y = -\frac{5}{4}x - 3$

33. $2y + 4x = 6$ **34.** $3y + x = 4$

Find the slope of each line, and graph.

35. $y = 4$ **36.** $x = -5$

37. $x = 3$ **38.** $y = -1$

Find the slope–intercept equation of a line given the conditions.

39. The slope is $\frac{1}{3}$ and the *y*-intercept is $(0, 1)$.

40. The slope is -1 and the *y*-intercept is $(0, -5)$.

41. The graph contains the points $(0, 3)$ and $(-1, 4)$.

42. The graph contains the points $(5, 1)$ and $(8, 0)$.

Determine whether each pair of lines is parallel, perpendicular, or neither.

43. $x + y = 5$,   **44.** $2x + y = 3$,
     $x - y = 1$ $y = 4 - 2x$

45. $2x + 3y = 1$,   **46.** $y = \frac{1}{3}x - 7$,
     $2x - 3y = 5$ $y + 3x = 1$

R.4   Polynomials

Exponents • Polynomials • Addition and Subtraction of Polynomials • Multiplication of Polynomials • Division of Polynomials

In this section, we define polynomials and learn to manipulate them. Before doing so, however, we must extend our knowledge of exponents.

Exponents

We know that x^4 means $x \cdot x \cdot x \cdot x$ and that x^1 means x. Exponential notation is also defined for zero and negative exponents.

Zero and Negative Exponents

For any real number a, $a \neq 0$,

$$a^0 = 1 \quad \text{and} \quad a^{-n} = \frac{1}{a^n}.$$

EXAMPLE 1   Simplify: **(a)** $(-36)^0$; **(b)** $(-2x)^0$.

Solution

The exponent zero (p. 233)

a) $(-36)^0 = 1$ since any number (other than 0 itself) raised to the 0 power is 1.

b) $(-2x)^0 = 1$ for any $x \neq 0$.

EXAMPLE 2   Write an equivalent expression using positive exponents:

a) x^{-2} **b)** $\dfrac{1}{x^{-2}}$ **c)** xy^{-1}

Solution

Negative exponents (p. 289)

a) $x^{-2} = \dfrac{1}{x^2}$ x^{-2} is the reciprocal of x^2.

b) $\dfrac{1}{x^{-2}} = x^{-(-2)} = x^2$ The reciprocal of x^{-2} is $x^{-(-2)}$, or x^2.

c) $xy^{-1} = x\left(\dfrac{1}{y^1}\right) = \dfrac{x}{y}$ y^{-1} is the reciprocal of y^1.

The following properties hold for any integers m and n and any real numbers a and b, provided no denominators are 0 and 0^0 is not considered.

Properties of Exponents

The Product Rule: $a^m \cdot a^n = a^{m+n}$

The Quotient Rule: $\dfrac{a^m}{a^n} = a^{m-n}$

The Power Rule: $(a^m)^n = a^{mn}$

Raising a product to a power: $(ab)^n = a^n b^n$

Raising a quotient to a power: $\left(\dfrac{a}{b}\right)^n = \dfrac{a^n}{b^n}$

These properties are often used to simplify exponential expressions.

EXAMPLE 3   Simplify.

a) $(x^2 y^{-1})(xy^{-3})$ **b)** $\dfrac{(3p)^3}{(3p)^{-2}}$

c) $\left(\dfrac{ab^2}{3c^3}\right)^{-4}$

Solution

a) $(x^2y^{-1})(xy^{-3}) = x^2y^{-1}xy^{-3}$ Using an associative law

$= x^2x^1y^{-1}y^{-3}$ Using a commutative law; $x = x^1$

$= x^{2+1}y^{-1+(-3)}$ Using the product rule: Adding exponents

$= x^3y^{-4}$, or $\dfrac{x^3}{y^4}$

b) $\dfrac{(3p)^3}{(3p)^{-2}} = (3p)^{3-(-2)}$ Using the quotient rule: Subtracting exponents

$= (3p)^5$

$= 3^5p^5$ Raising each factor to the fifth power

$= 243p^5$

c) $\left(\dfrac{ab^2}{3c^3}\right)^{-4} = \dfrac{(ab^2)^{-4}}{(3c^3)^{-4}}$ Raising the numerator and the denominator to the -4 power

$= \dfrac{a^{-4}(b^2)^{-4}}{3^{-4}(c^3)^{-4}}$ Raising each factor to the -4 power

$= \dfrac{a^{-4}b^{-8}}{3^{-4}c^{-12}}$ Multiplying exponents

$= \dfrac{3^4c^{12}}{a^4b^8}$, or $\dfrac{81c^{12}}{a^4b^8}$ Rewriting without negative exponents

---

Polynomials

Algebraic expressions like

$$2x^3 + 3x - 5, \qquad 4x, \qquad -7, \quad \text{and} \quad 2a^3b^2 + ab^3$$

are all examples of **polynomials**. All variables in a polynomial are raised to whole-number powers, and there are no variables in a denominator. The **terms** of a polynomial are separated by addition signs.

A polynomial with one term is called a **monomial**. A polynomial with two terms is called a **binomial**, and one with three terms is called a **trinomial**. The **degree of a term** is the number of variable factors in that term. The **leading term** of a polynomial is the term of highest degree. The **degree of a polynomial** is the degree of the leading term. A polynomial is written in *descending order* when the leading term appears first, followed by the term of next highest degree, and so on.

The number -2 in the term $-2y^3$ is called the **coefficient** of that term. The coefficient of the leading term is the **leading coefficient** of the polynomial. To illustrate this terminology, consider the polynomial

$$4y^2 - 8y^5 + y^3 - 6y + 7.$$

The *terms* are $4y^2$, $-8y^5$, y^3, $-6y$,   and   7.

The *coefficients* are   4, -8,   1, -6,   and   7.

The *degree of each term* is   2,   5,   3,   1,   and   0.

The *leading term* is $-8y^5$ and the *leading coefficient* is -8.

The *degree of the polynomial* is 5.

Like, or *similar*, *terms* are either constant terms or terms containing the same variable(s) raised to the same power(s). Polynomials containing like terms can be simplified by *combining* those terms.

EXAMPLE 4   Combine like terms: $4x^2y + 2xy - x^2y + xy^2$.

Solution   The like terms are $4x^2y$ and $-x^2y$. Thus we have

$$4x^2y + 2xy - x^2y + xy^2 = 4x^2y - x^2y + 2xy + xy^2$$
$$= 3x^2y + 2xy + xy^2.$$

A polynomial can be evaluated by replacing the variable or variables with a number or numbers.

EXAMPLE 5   Evaluate $-a^2 + 2ab + 5b^2$ for $a = -1$ and $b = 3$.

Solution   We replace a with -1 and b with 3 and calculate the value using the rules for the order of operations:

Evaluating a polynomial (p. 242)

$$-a^2 + 2ab + 5b^2 = -(-1)^2 + 2 \cdot (-1) \cdot 3 + 5 \cdot 3^2$$
$$= -1 - 6 + 45 = 38.$$

Polynomials can be added, subtracted, multiplied, and divided.

Addition and Subtraction of Polynomials

Addition of polynomials
(Section 4.3)

To add two polynomials, we write a plus sign between them and combine like terms.

EXAMPLE 6   Add: $(4x^3 + 3x^2 + 2x - 7) + (-5x^2 + x - 10)$.

Solution

$$(4x^3 + 3x^2 + 2x - 7) + (-5x^2 + x - 10)$$
$$= 4x^3 + (3 - 5)x^2 + (2 + 1)x + (-7 - 10)$$
$$= 4x^3 - 2x^2 + 3x - 17$$

Opposite of a polynomial (p. 250)

In order to subtract polynomials, we must be able to find the *opposite* of a polynomial. To find the opposite of a polynomial, we replace each term with its opposite. This process is also called *changing the sign* of each term. For example, the opposite of

$$3y^4 - 7y^2 - \tfrac{1}{3}y + 17$$

is

$$-\left(3y^4 - 7y^2 - \tfrac{1}{3}y + 17\right) = -3y^4 + 7y^2 + \tfrac{1}{3}y - 17.$$

Subtraction of polynomials
(Section 4.3)

To subtract polynomials, we add the opposite of the polynomial being subtracted.

EXAMPLE 7   Subtract: $(3a^4 - 2a + 7) - (-a^3 + 5a - 1)$.

Solution

$$(3a^4 - 2a + 7) - (-a^3 + 5a - 1)$$
$$= 3a^4 - 2a + 7 + a^3 - 5a + 1 \qquad \text{Adding the opposite}$$
$$= 3a^4 + a^3 - 7a + 8 \qquad \text{Combining like terms}$$

Multiplication of polynomials
(Section 4.4)

Multiplication of Polynomials

To multiply two monomials, we multiply coefficients and then multiply variables using the product rule for exponents. To multiply a monomial and a polynomial, we multiply each term of the polynomial by the monomial, using the distributive property.

EXAMPLE 8   Multiply: $4x^3(3x^4 - 2x^3 + 7x - 5)$.

Solution

$$\textit{Think:} \quad \overbrace{4x^3 \cdot 3x^4} - \overbrace{4x^3 \cdot 2x^3} + \overbrace{4x^3 \cdot 7x} - \overbrace{4x^3 \cdot 5}$$
$$4x^3(3x^4 - 2x^3 + 7x - 5) = 12x^7 \quad - \quad 8x^6 \quad + \quad 28x^4 \quad - \quad 20x^3$$

To multiply any two polynomials P and Q, we select one of the polynomials—say, P. We then multiply each term of P by every term of Q and combine like terms.

EXAMPLE 9   Multiply: $(2a^3 + 3a - 1)(a^2 - 4a)$.

Solution   It is often helpful to use columns for a long multiplication. We multiply each term at the top by every term at the bottom, write like terms in columns, and add the results.

$$
\begin{array}{r}
2a^3 \quad + 3a \quad - 1 \\
a^2 - 4a \\
\hline
-8a^4 \qquad - 12a^2 + 4a \\
2a^5 \qquad + 3a^3 \quad - a^2 \\
\hline
2a^5 - 8a^4 + 3a^3 - 13a^2 + 4a
\end{array}
$$

Multiplying the top row by $-4a$
Multiplying the top row by a^2
Combining like terms. Be sure that like terms are lined up in columns.

We could multiply two binomials in the same manner in which we multiplied the polynomials in Example 9. However, by observing the pattern of the products formed, we can develop a method of multiplying two binomials more efficiently.

The FOIL Method

To multiply two binomials, $A + B$ and $C + D$, multiply the First terms AC, the Outer terms AD, the Inner terms BC, and then the Last terms BD. Then combine like terms, if possible.

$$(A + B)(C + D) = AC + AD + BC + BD$$

1. Multiply First terms: AC.
2. Multiply Outer terms: AD.
3. Multiply Inner terms: BC.
4. Multiply Last terms: BD.

$\downarrow$

FOIL

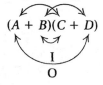

EXAMPLE 10   Multiply: $(3x + 4)(x - 2)$.

Solution

FOIL (p. 266)

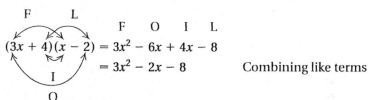

$$= 3x^2 - 2x - 8 \qquad \text{Combining like terms}$$

Two types of products of binomials occur so often that specific formulas or methods for computing them have been developed. Products of this type are called *special products*.

Special Products

The product of a sum and difference of the same two terms:

$$(A + B)(A - B) = \underbrace{A^2 - B^2}$$

This is called a *difference of squares*.

Multiplying sums and differences of two terms (p. 267)

The square of a binomial:

$$(A + B)^2 = A^2 + 2AB + B^2$$
$$(A - B)^2 = A^2 - 2AB + B^2$$

Squaring binomials (p. 269)

EXAMPLE 11   Multiply: **(a)** $(x + 3y)(x - 3y)$; **(b)** $(x^3 + 2)^2$.

Solution

$$(A + B)(A - B) = A^2 - B^2$$

a) $(x + 3y)(x - 3y) = x^2 - (3y)^2$ $A = x$ and $B = 3y$
$$= x^2 - 9y^2$$

$$(A + B)^2 = A^2 + 2 \cdot A \cdot B + B^2$$

b) $(x^3 + 2)^2 = (x^3)^2 + 2 \cdot x^3 \cdot 2 + 2^2$ $A = x^3$ and $B = 2$
$$= x^6 + 4x^3 + 4$$

Division of polynomials
(Section 4.7)

Division of Polynomials

Polynomial division is similar to division in arithmetic. First, let's consider division by a monomial. To divide a polynomial by a monomial, we divide each term by the monomial.

EXAMPLE 12   Divide: $(3x^5 + 8x^3 - 12x) \div 4x$.

Solution   This division can be written

$$\frac{3x^5 + 8x^3 - 12x}{4x} = \frac{3x^5}{4x} + \frac{8x^3}{4x} - \frac{12x}{4x}$$ Dividing each term by $4x$

$$= \frac{3}{4}x^{5-1} + \frac{8}{4}x^{3-1} - \frac{12}{4}x^{1-1}$$ Dividing coefficients and subtracting exponents

$$= \frac{3}{4}x^4 + 2x^2 - 3.$$

To check, we multiply the quotient by $4x$:

$$\left(\tfrac{3}{4}x^4 + 2x^2 - 3\right)4x = 3x^5 + 8x^3 - 12x.$$ The answer checks.

To use long division, we write polynomials in descending order, including terms with 0 coefficients for missing terms. As shown below in Example 13, the procedure ends when the degree of the remainder is less than the degree of the divisor.

EXAMPLE 13   Divide: $(4x^3 - 7x + 1) \div (2x + 1)$.

Solution   The polynomials are already written in descending order, but there is no x^2-term in the dividend. We fill in $0x^2$ for that term.

$$
\begin{array}{r}
2x^2 \\
2x + 1 \overline{\smash{)}4x^3 + 0x^2 - 7x + 1} \\
\underline{4x^3 + 2x^2} \\
-2x^2
\end{array}
$$

Divide the first term of the dividend, $4x^3$, by the first term in the divisor, $2x$: $4x^3/(2x) = 2x^2$.

Multiply $2x^2$ by the divisor, $2x + 1$.

Subtract: $(4x^3 + 0x^2) - (4x^3 + 2x^2) = -2x^2$.

Then we bring down the next term of the dividend, $-7x$.

$$
\begin{array}{r}
2x^2 - x \\
2x + 1 \overline{\smash{)}4x^3 + 0x^2 - 7x + 1} \\
\underline{4x^3 + 2x^2} \\
-2x^2 - 7x \\
\underline{-2x^2 - x} \\
-6x
\end{array}
$$

Divide the first term of $-2x^2 - 7x$ by the first term in the divisor: $-2x^2/(2x) = -x$.

The $-7x$ has been "brought down."

Multiply $-x$ by the divisor, $2x + 1$.

Subtract: $(-2x^2 - 7x) - (-2x^2 - x) = -6x$.

Since the degree of the remainder, $-6x$, is *not* less than the degree of the divisor, we must continue dividing.

$$
\begin{array}{r}
2x^2 - x - 3 \\
2x + 1 \overline{\smash{)}4x^3 + 0x^2 - 7x + 1} \\
\underline{4x^3 + 2x^2} \\
-2x^2 - 7x \\
\underline{-2x^2 - x} \\
-6x + 1 \\
\underline{-6x - 3} \\
4
\end{array}
$$

Divide the first term of $-6x + 1$ by the first term in the divisor: $-6x/(2x) = -3$.

The 1 has been "brought down."

Multiply -3 by $2x + 1$.

Subtract.

The answer is $2x^2 - x - 3$ with R4, or

$$
\text{Quotient} \longrightarrow 2x^2 - x - 3 + \frac{4 \longleftarrow \text{Remainder}}{2x + 1 \longleftarrow \text{Divisor}}.
$$

Check: To check, we can multiply by the divisor and add the remainder:

$$
\begin{aligned}
(2x + 1)(2x^2 - x - 3) + 4 &= 4x^3 - 7x - 3 + 4 \\
&= 4x^3 - 7x + 1.
\end{aligned}
$$

Exercise Set

Solve.

1. a^0, for $a = -25$

2. y^0, for $y = 6.97$

3. $4^0 - 4^1$

4. $8^1 - 8^0$

Write an equivalent expression using positive exponents. Then, if possible, simplify.

5. 8^{-2}

6. 2^{-5}

7. $(-2)^{-3}$

8. $(-3)^{-2}$

9. $(ab)^{-2}$

10. ab^{-2}

11. $\dfrac{1}{y^{-10}}$

12. $\dfrac{1}{x^{-t}}$

Write an equivalent expression using negative exponents.

13. $\dfrac{1}{y^4}$

14. $\dfrac{1}{a^2 b^3}$

15. $\dfrac{1}{x^t}$

16. $\dfrac{1}{n}$

Simplify.

17. $x^5 \cdot x^8$

18. $a^4 \cdot a^{-2}$

19. $\dfrac{a}{a^{-5}}$

20. $\dfrac{p^{-3}}{p^{-8}}$

21. $\dfrac{(4x)^{10}}{(4x)^2}$

22. $\dfrac{a^2 b^9}{a^9 b^2}$

23. $(7^8)^5$

24. $(x^3)^{-7}$

25. $(x^{-2} y^{-3})^{-4}$

26. $(-2a^2)^3$

27. $\left(\dfrac{y^2}{4}\right)^3$

28. $\left(\dfrac{ab^2}{c^3}\right)^4$

29. $\left(\dfrac{2p^3}{3q^4}\right)^{-2}$

30. $\left(\dfrac{2}{x}\right)^{-5}$

Identify the terms of each polynomial.

31. $8x^3 - 6x^2 + x - 7$

32. $-a^2 b + 4a^2 - 8b + 17$

Determine the coefficient and the degree of each term in each polynomial. Then find the degree of each polynomial.

33. $18x^3 + 36x^9 - 7x + 3$

34. $-8y^7 + y + 19$

35. $-x^2 y + 4y^3 - 2xy$

36. $8 - x^2 y^4 + y^7$

Determine the leading term and the leading coefficient of each polynomial.

37. $-p^2 + 4 + 8p^4 - 7p$

38. $13 + 20t - 30t^2 - t^3$

Combine like terms. Write each answer in descending order.

39. $3x^3 - x^2 + x^4 + x^2$

40. $5t - 8t^2 + 4t^2$

41. $3 - 2t^2 + 8t - 3t - 5t^2 + 7$

42. $8x^5 - \frac{1}{3} + \frac{4}{5}x + 1 - \frac{1}{2}x$

Evaluate each polynomial for the given replacements of the variables.

43. $3x^2 - 7x + 10$, for $x = -2$

44. $-y + 3y^2 + 2y^3$, for $y = 3$

45. $a^2 b^3 + 2b^2 - 6a$, for $a = 2$ and $b = -1$

46. $2pq^3 - 5q^2 + 8p$, for $p = -4$ and $q = -2$

The distance s, in feet, traveled by a body falling freely from rest in t seconds is approximated by

$$s = 16t^2.$$

47. A pebble is dropped into a well and takes 3 sec to hit the water. How far down is the surface of the water?

48. An acorn falls from the top of an oak tree and takes 2 sec to hit the ground. How high is the tree?

Add or subtract, as indicated.

49. $(3x^3 + 2x^2 + 8x) + (x^3 - 5x^2 + 7)$

50. $(-6x^4 + 3x^2 - 16) + (4x^2 + 4x - 7)$

51. $(8y^2 - 2y - 3) - (9y^2 - 7y - 1)$

52. $(4t^2 + 6t - 7) - (t + 5)$

53. $(-x^2y + 2y^2 + y) - (3y^2 + 2x^2y - 7y)$

54. $(ab + x^2y^2) + (2ab - x^2y^2)$

Multiply.

55. $4x^2(3x^3 - 7x + 7)$

56. $a^2b(a^3 + b^2 - ab - 2b)$

57. $(2a + y)(4a + b)$

58. $(x + 7y)(y - 3x)$

59. $(x + 7)(x^2 - 3x + 1)$

60. $(2x - 3)(x^2 - x - 1)$

61. $(x + 7)(x - 7)$

62. $(2x + 1)^2$

63. $(x + y)^2$

64. $(xy + 1)(xy - 1)$

65. $(2x^2 + 7)(3x^2 - 2)$

66. $(x^2 + 2)^2$

67. $(a - 3b)^2$

68. $(1.1x^2 + 5)(0.1x^2 - 2)$

69. $(6a - 5y)(7a + 3y)$

70. $(3p^2 - q^3)^2$

Divide and check.

71. $(3t^5 + 9t^3 - 6t^2 + 15t) \div (-3t)$

72. $(4x^5 + 10x^4 - 16x^2) \div (4x^2)$

73. $(15x^2 - 16x - 15) \div (3x - 5)$

74. $(x^3 - 2x^2 - 14x + 1) \div (x - 5)$

75. $(2x^3 - x^2 + 1) \div (x + 1)$

76. $(2x^3 + 3x^2 - 50) \div (2x - 5)$

77. $(5x^3 + 3x^2 - 5x) \div (x^2 - 1)$

78. $(2x^3 + 3x^2 + 6x + 10) \div (x^2 + 3)$

R.5   Polynomials and Factoring

Common Factors and Factoring by Grouping   •   Factoring Trinomials   •
Factoring Special Forms   •   Solving Polynomial Equations by Factoring

Factor (p. 304)

The reverse of multiplication is factoring. To **factor** a polynomial is to find an equivalent expression that is a product. To factor a monomial, we find two monomials whose product is equivalent to the original monomial. Many monomials have multiple factorizations. For example, three factorizations of $50x^6$ are $5 \cdot 10x^6$, $5x^3 \cdot 10x^3$, and $2x \cdot 25x^5$.

Common factor (p. 305)

Common Factors and Factoring by Grouping

If all the terms in a polynomial share a common factor, that factor can be "factored out" of the polynomial. Whenever you are factoring a polynomial with two or more terms, try to first find the largest common factor of the terms, if one exists.

EXAMPLE 1   Factor: $3x^6 + 15x^4 - 9x^3$.

Solution   The largest factor common to 3, 15, and -9 is 3. The largest power of x common to x^6, x^4, and x^3 is x^3. Thus the largest common factor of the terms of the polynomial is $3x^3$. We factor as follows:

$$3x^6 + 15x^4 - 9x^3 = 3x^3 \cdot x^3 + 3x^3 \cdot 5x - 3x^3 \cdot 3 \qquad \text{Factoring each term}$$

$$= 3x^3(x^3 + 5x - 3). \qquad \text{Factoring out } 3x^3$$

Factorizations can always be checked by multiplying:

$$3x^3(x^3 + 5x - 3) = 3x^6 + 15x^4 - 9x^3.$$

A polynomial with two or more terms can be a common factor.

EXAMPLE 2   Factor: $3x^2(x - 2) + 5(x - 2)$.

Solution   The binomial $x - 2$ is a factor of both $3x^2(x - 2)$ and $5(x - 2)$. Thus we have

$$3x^2(x - 2) + 5(x - 2) = (x - 2)(3x^2 + 5). \qquad \text{Factoring out the common factor, } x - 2$$

Factoring by grouping (p. 308)

If a polynomial with four terms can be split into two groups of terms, and both groups share a common binomial factor, the polynomial can be factored. This method is known as **factoring by grouping**.

EXAMPLE 3   Factor by grouping: $2x^3 + 6x^2 - x - 3$.

Solution   First, we consider the polynomial as two groups of terms, $2x^3 + 6x^2$ and $-x - 3$. Then we factor each group separately:

$$2x^3 + 6x^2 - x - 3 = 2x^2(x + 3) - 1(x + 3) \qquad \begin{array}{l}\text{Factoring out } 2x^2 \\ \text{and } -1 \text{ to give the} \\ \text{common binomial} \\ \text{factor, } x + 3\end{array}$$

$$= (x + 3)(2x^2 - 1).$$

The check is left to the student.

Prime polynomial (p. 317)

Not every polynomial with four terms is factorable by grouping. A polynomial that is not factorable is said to be **prime**.

Factoring trinomials of the type $x^2 + bx + c$ (Section 5.2)

Factoring Trinomials

Many trinomials that have no common factor can be written as the product of two binomials. We look first at trinomials of the form

$$x^2 + bx + c,$$

for which the leading coefficient is 1.

Factoring trinomials involves a trial-and-error process. In order for the product of two binomials to be $x^2 + bx + c$, the binomials must look like

$$(x + p)(x + q),$$

where p and q are constants that must be determined. For example, to factor $x^2 + 10x + 16$, we must have

$$x^2 + 10x + 16 = (x + p)(x + q)$$
$$= x^2 + (p + q)x + pq. \quad \text{Using FOIL}$$

Therefore,

$$p + q = 10,$$
$$pq = 16.$$

Thus we look for two numbers whose product is 16 and whose sum is 10.

EXAMPLE 4   Factor.

a) $x^2 + 10x + 16$ **b)** $x^2 - 8x + 15$

c) $x^2 - 2x - 24$ **d)** $3t^2 - 33st + 84s^2$

Solution

a) The factorization is of the form

$$(x + \quad)(x + \quad).$$

Constant term positive (p. 313)

To find the constant terms, we need a pair of factors whose product is 16 and whose sum is 10. Since 16 is positive, its factors will have the same sign as 10—that is, we need consider only positive factors of 16.

We list the possible factorizations in a table and calculate the sum of each pair of factors.

Pairs of Factors of 16	Sums of Factors
1, 16	17
2, 8	10 ←—
4, 4	8

The numbers we seek are 2 and 8.

The factorization of $x^2 + 10x + 16$ is $(x + 2)(x + 8)$. To check, we multiply.

Check: $(x + 2)(x + 8) = x^2 + 8x + 2x + 16 = x^2 + 10x + 16.$

b) For $x^2 - 8x + 15$, c is positive and b is negative. Therefore, the factors of 15 will be negative. Again, we list the possible factorizations in a table.

Pairs of Factors of 15	Sums of Factors
$-1, -15$	-16
$-3, \; -5$	-8 ←

The numbers we need are -3 and -5.

The factorization is $(x - 3)(x - 5)$.

Check: $(x - 3)(x - 5) = x^2 - 5x - 3x + 15 = x^2 - 8x + 15.$

Constant term negative (p. 314)

c) For $x^2 - 2x - 24$, c is negative, so one factor of -24 will be negative and one will be positive. Since b is also negative, the negative factor must have the larger absolute value.

Pairs of Factors of -24	Sums of Factors
$1, -24$	-23
$2, -12$	-10
$3, \; -8$	-5
$4, \; -6$	-2 ←

The numbers we need are 4 and -6.

The factorization is $(x + 4)(x - 6)$.

Check: $(x + 4)(x - 6) = x^2 - 6x + 4x - 24 = x^2 - 2x - 24.$

d) Always look first for a common factor. There is a common factor, 3, which we factor out first:

$$3t^2 - 33st + 84s^2 = 3(t^2 - 11st + 28s^2).$$

Now we consider $t^2 - 11st + 28s^2$. Think of $28s^2$ as the "constant" term c and $-11s$ as the "coefficient" b of the middle term. We try to express $28s^2$ as the product of two factors whose sum is $-11s$. These factors are $-4s$ and $-7s$. Thus the factorization of $t^2 - 11st + 28s^2$ is

$(t - 4s)(t - 7s)$.   This is not the entire factorization of $3t^2 - 33st + 84s^2$.

We now include the common factor, 3, and write

$$3t^2 - 33st + 84s^2 = 3(t - 4s)(t - 7s).$$ This is the factorization.

Check: $3(t - 4s)(t - 7s) = 3(t^2 - 11st + 28s^2) = 3t^2 - 33st + 84s^2.$

Factoring trinomials of the type $ax^2 + bx + c$ (Section 5.3)

When the leading coefficient of a trinomial is not 1, the number of trials needed to find a factorization can increase dramatically. We will consider two methods for factoring trinomials of the type $ax^2 + bx + c$: factoring with FOIL and the grouping method.

Factoring with FOIL (p. 321)

To Factor $ax^2 + bx + c$ Using FOIL

1. Factor out the largest common factor, if one exists.
2. Find two First terms whose product is ax^2:

$$(\quad x + \quad)(\quad + \quad) = ax^2 + bx + c.$$
$$\underset{\text{FOIL}}{\underline{\qquad\qquad\qquad}}$$

3. Find two Last terms whose product is c:

$$(\quad x + \quad)(\quad x + \quad) = ax^2 + bx + c.$$
$$\underset{\text{FOIL}}{\underline{\qquad\qquad\qquad}}$$

4. Repeat steps (2) and (3) until a combination is found for which the sum of the Outer and Inner products is bx:

$$(\quad x + \quad)(\quad x + \quad) = ax^2 + bx + c.$$
$$\text{O} \qquad\qquad \text{FOIL}$$

Always check by multiplying. If no correct combination exists, state that the polynomial is prime.

EXAMPLE 5   Factor: $20x^3 - 22x^2 - 12x$.

Solution

1. First, we factor out the largest common factor, $2x$:

$$20x^3 - 22x^2 - 12x = 2x(10x^2 - 11x - 6).$$

2. Next, in order to factor the trinomial $10x^2 - 11x - 6$, we search for two terms whose product is $10x^2$. The possibilities are

$$(x + \quad)(10x + \quad) \quad \text{or} \quad (2x + \quad)(5x + \quad).$$

3. There are four pairs of factors of -6. Since the first terms of the binomials are different, the order of the factors is important. So there are eight possibilities for the last terms:

$$1, -6 \qquad -1, 6 \qquad 2, -3 \qquad -2, 3$$

and

$$-6, 1 \qquad 6, -1 \qquad -3, 2 \qquad 3, -2.$$

4. Since each of the eight possibilities from step (3) could be used in either of the two possibilities from step (2), there are $2 \cdot 8$, or 16, possible factorizations. We check the possibilities systematically until we find one that gives the correct factorization. Let's first try factors with $(2x + \quad)(5x + \quad)$.

Trial	*Product*	
$(2x + 1)(5x - 6)$	$10x^2 - 7x - 6$	$\longleftarrow$ Wrong middle term
$(2x - 1)(5x + 6)$	$10x^2 + 7x - 6$	$\longleftarrow$ Wrong middle term. Note that changing the signs in the binomials changed the sign of middle term in the product.
$(2x + 2)(5x - 3)$	$10x^2 + 4x - 6$	$\longleftarrow$ Wrong middle term. We need not consider $(2x - 2)(5x + 3)$.
$(2x - 6)(5x + 1)$	$10x^2 - 28x - 6$	$\longleftarrow$ Wrong middle term. We need not consider $(2x + 6)(5x - 1)$.
$(2x - 3)(5x + 2)$	$10x^2 - 11x - 6$	$\longleftarrow$ Correct middle term

We can stop when we find a correct factorization. Including the common factor $2x$, we now have

$$20x^3 - 22x^2 - 12x = 2x(2x - 3)(5x + 2).$$

This can be checked by multiplying.

The grouping method (p. 326)

With practice, some of the trials can be skipped or performed mentally.

The second method of factoring trinomials of the type $ax^2 + bx + c$ involves factoring by grouping.

To Factor $ax^2 + bx + c$, Using the Grouping Method

1. Factor out the largest common factor, if one exists.
2. Multiply the leading coefficient a and the constant c.
3. Find a pair of factors of ac whose sum is b.
4. Rewrite the middle term, bx, as a sum or difference using the factors found in step (3).
5. Factor by grouping.
6. Always check by multiplying.

EXAMPLE 6   Factor: $7x^2 + 31x + 12$.

Solution

1. There is no common factor (other than 1 or -1).
2. We multiply the leading coefficient, 7, and the constant, 12:

$$7 \cdot 12 = 84.$$

3. We look for a pair of factors of 84 whose sum is 31. Since both 84 and 31 are positive, we need consider only positive factors.

Pairs of Factors of 84	Sums of Factors
1, 84	85
2, 42	44
3, 28	31 ←

$3 + 28 = 31$

4. Next, we rewrite $31x$ using the factors 3 and 28:

$$31x = 3x + 28x.$$

5. We now factor by grouping:

$$7x^2 + 31x + 12 = 7x^2 + 3x + 28x + 12$$

Substituting $3x + 28x$ for $31x$

$$= x(7x + 3) + 4(7x + 3)$$

$$= (7x + 3)(x + 4).$$

Factoring out the common factor, $7x + 3$

6. *Check:* $(7x + 3)(x + 4) = 7x^2 + 31x + 12.$

Factoring Special Forms

We can factor certain types of polynomials directly, without using trial and error.

Factoring Formulas

Perfect-square trinomial: $A^2 + 2AB + B^2 = (A + B)^2,$
$A^2 - 2AB + B^2 = (A - B)^2$

Difference of squares: $A^2 - B^2 = (A + B)(A - B)$

Sum of cubes: $A^3 + B^3 = (A + B)(A^2 - AB + B^2)$

Difference of cubes: $A^3 - B^3 = (A - B)(A^2 + AB + B^2)$

Before using the factoring formulas, it is important to check carefully that the expression being factored is indeed in one of the forms listed. Note that there is no factoring formula for the sum of two squares.

EXAMPLE 7   Factor: **(a)** $2x^2 - 2$; **(b)** $x^2y^2 + 20xy + 100$; **(c)** $p^3 - 64$; **(d)** $3y^2 + 27$.

Solution

a) We first factor out a common factor, 2:

$$2x^2 - 2 = 2(x^2 - 1).$$

Recognizing and factoring differences of squares (p. 333)

Looking at $x^2 - 1$, we see that it is a difference of squares, with $A = x$ and $B = 1$. The factorization is thus

$$2x^2 - 2 = 2(x^2 - 1) = 2(x + 1)(x - 1).$$

$$A^2 - B^2 \qquad (A + B)(A - B)$$

Recognizing and factoring perfect-square trinomials (pp. 330–331)

b) First, we check for a common factor; there is none. The polynomial is a perfect-square trinomial, since x^2y^2 and 100 are squares; there is no minus sign before either square; and $20xy$ is $2 \cdot xy \cdot 10$, where xy and 10 are square roots of x^2y^2 and 100, respectively. The factorization is thus

$$x^2y^2 + 20xy + 100 = (xy)^2 + 2 \cdot xy \cdot 10 + 10^2 = (xy + 10)^2.$$

$$A^2 \quad + 2 \cdot A \cdot B + B^2 = (A + B)^2$$

Factoring sums or differences of cubes (Section 5.5)

c) This is a difference of cubes, with $A = p$ and $B = 4$:

$$p^3 - 64 = (p)^3 - (4)^3$$
$$= (p - 4)(p^2 + 4p + 16).$$

d) We factor out the common factor, 3:

$$3y^2 + 27 = 3(y^2 + 9).$$

Since $y^2 + 9$ is a sum of squares, no further factorization is possible.

Factoring completely (p. 334)

A polynomial is said to be *factored completely* when no factor can be factored further.

EXAMPLE 8   Factor completely: $x^4 - 1$.

Solution

$$x^4 - 1 = (x^2 + 1)(x^2 - 1) \qquad \text{Factoring a difference of squares}$$
$$= (x^2 + 1)(x + 1)(x - 1) \qquad \text{The factor } x^2 - 1 \text{ is itself a difference of squares.}$$

Solving Polynomial Equations by Factoring

Polynomial equation (p. 348)

Quadratic equation (p. 348)

A **polynomial equation** is formed by setting two polynomials equal to each other. A **quadratic equation** is a polynomial equation equivalent to one of the form $ax^2 + bx + c = 0$, where $a \neq 0$. Polynomial equations that can be factored can be solved using the principle of zero products.

The principle of zero products (p. 348)

> **The Principle of Zero Products**
>
> An equation $ab = 0$ is true if and only if $a = 0$ or $b = 0$, or both. (A product is 0 if and only if at least one factor is 0.)

If we can write an equation as a product that equals 0, we can try to use the principle of zero products to solve the equation.

EXAMPLE 9   Solve:

a) $x^2 - 11x = 12$

b) $5x^2 + 10x + 5 = 0$

c) $9x^2 = 1$

Solution

a) We must have 0 on one side of the equation before using the principle of zero products:

$$x^2 - 11x = 12$$
$$x^2 - 11x - 12 = 0 \qquad \text{Subtracting 12 from both sides}$$
$$(x - 12)(x + 1) = 0 \qquad \text{Factoring}$$
$$x - 12 = 0 \quad or \quad x + 1 = 0 \qquad \text{Using the principle of zero products}$$
$$x = 12 \quad or \qquad x = -1.$$

The solutions are 12 and -1. The check is left to the student.

b) We have

$$5x^2 + 10x + 5 = 0$$
$$5(x^2 + 2x + 1) = 0 \qquad \text{Factoring out a common factor}$$
$$5(x + 1)(x + 1) = 0 \qquad \text{Factoring completely}$$
$$x + 1 = 0 \quad or \quad x + 1 = 0 \qquad \text{Using the principle of zero products}$$
$$x = -1 \quad or \qquad x = -1.$$

There is only one solution, -1. The check is left to the student.

c) We have

$$9x^2 = 1$$
$$9x^2 - 1 = 0 \qquad \text{Subtracting 1 from both sides to get 0 on one side}$$
$$(3x + 1)(3x - 1) = 0 \qquad \text{Factoring a difference of squares}$$
$$3x + 1 = 0 \quad or \quad 3x - 1 = 0 \qquad \text{Using the principle of zero products}$$
$$3x = -1 \quad or \qquad 3x = 1$$
$$x = -\tfrac{1}{3} \quad or \qquad x = \tfrac{1}{3}.$$

The solutions are $\frac{1}{3}$ and $-\frac{1}{3}$. The check is left to the student.

Quadratic equations can be used to solve problems. One important result that uses squared quantities is the Pythagorean theorem. It relates the lengths of the sides of a **right triangle,** that is, a triangle with a 90° angle. The side opposite the 90° angle is called the **hypotenuse,** and the other sides are called the **legs.**

> ### The Pythagorean Theorem
> The sum of the squares of the legs of a right triangle is equal to the square of the hypotenuse:
> $$a^2 + b^2 = c^2.$$
>
>
>
> This indicates 90°.

EXAMPLE 10   Swing sets.   The length of a slide on a swing set is 5 ft. The distance from the base of the ladder to the base of the slide is 1 ft more than the height of the ladder. Find the height of the ladder.

Solution

1. **Familiarize.**   We first make a drawing and let x = the height of the ladder, in feet. We know then that the other leg of the triangle is $x + 1$, since it is 1 ft longer than the ladder. The hypotenuse has length 5 ft.

2. **Translate.**   Applying the Pythagorean theorem gives us
$$a^2 + b^2 = c^2$$
$$x^2 + (x + 1)^2 = 5^2. \qquad \text{Substituting}$$

3. **Carry out.**   We solve the equation:

$x^2 + (x + 1)^2 = 5^2$	
$x^2 + x^2 + 2x + 1 = 25$	Squaring $x + 1$; squaring 5
$2x^2 + 2x + 1 = 25$	Combining like terms
$2x^2 + 2x - 24 = 0$	Getting 0 on one side
$2(x^2 + x - 12) = 0$	Factoring out a common factor
$2(x + 4)(x - 3) = 0$	Factoring a trinomial
$x + 4 = 0 \quad or \quad x - 3 = 0$	Using the principle of zero products
$x = -4 \quad or \quad x = 3.$	

4. **Check.**   We know that the integer -4 is not a solution because the height of the ladder cannot be negative. When $x = 3$, the distance from the base of the ladder to the base of the slide is $x + 1 = 4$, and $3^2 + 4^2 = 5^2$. So the solution 3 checks.

5. **State.**   The ladder is 3 ft high.

Exercise Set

Factor completely. If a polynomial is prime, state this.

1. $3x^3 + 6x^2 - 9x$

2. $x^2y^4 - 2xy^5 + 3x^3y^6$

3. $y^2 - 6y + 9$

4. $4z^2 - 25$

5. $2p^3(p + 2) + (p + 2)$

6. $6y^2 + y - 1$

7. $16x^2 + 25$

8. $y^3 - 1$

9. $8t^3 + 27$

10. $a^2b^2 + 24ab + 144$

11. $m^2 + 13m + 42$

12. $2x^3 - 6x^2 + x - 3$

13. $x^4 - 81$

14. $x^2 + x + 1$

15. $8x^2 + 22x + 15$

16. $4x^2 - 40x + 100$

17. $x^3 + 2x^2 - x - 2$

18. $(x + 2y)(x - 1) + (x + 2y)(x - 2)$

19. $0.001t^6 - 0.008$

20. $x^2 - 20 - x$

21. $-\frac{1}{16} + x^4$

22. $5x^8 - 5z^{16}$

23. $a^2 + 6a + 9 - y^2$

24. $t^6 - p^6$

25. $5mn + m^2 - 150n^2$

26. $\frac{1}{27} + x^3$

27. $24x^2y - 6y - 10xy$

28. $-3y^2 - 12y - 12$

29. $y^2 + 121 - 22y$

30. $p^2 - m^2 - 2mn - n^2$

Solve.

31. $(x - 2)(x + 7) = 0$

32. $(3x - 5)(7 - 4x) = 0$

33. $8x(4.7 - x) = 0$

34. $(x - 3)(x + 1)(2x - 9) = 0$

35. $x^2 = 100$

36. $8x^2 = 5x$

37. $4x^2 - 18x = 70$

38. $x^2 + 2x + 1 = 0$

39. $2x^2 - 10x = 0$

40. $100x^2 = 81$

41. $(a + 1)(a - 5) = 7$

42. $d(d - 3) = 40$

43. $x^2 + 6x - 55 = 0$

44. $x^2 + 7x - 60 = 0$

45. $\frac{1}{2}x^2 + 5x + \frac{25}{2} = 0$

46. $3 + 10x^2 = 11x$

47. *Landscaping.* A triangular flower garden is 3 ft longer than it is wide. The area of the garden is 20 ft². What are the dimensions of the garden?

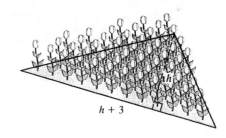

$h + 3$

48. *Page numbers.* The product of the page numbers on two facing pages of a book is 156. Find the page numbers.

49. *Right triangles.* The hypotenuse of a right triangle is 17 ft. One leg is 1 ft shorter than twice the length of the other leg. Find the length of the legs.

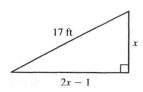

17 ft

x

$2x - 1$

50. *Hiking.* Jenna hiked 500 ft up a steep incline. Her global positioning unit indicated that her horizontal position had changed by 100 ft more than her vertical position had changed. What was the change in altitude?

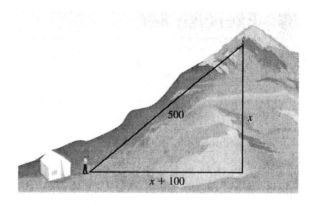

 R.6   # Rational Expressions and Equations

> Multiplication and Division of Rational Expressions   •
> Addition and Subtraction of Rational Expressions   •
> Complex Rational Expressions   •   Solving Rational Equations

Rational expressions (p. 374)

A **rational expression** is a quotient of two polynomials. Because division by 0 is undefined, a rational expression is undefined for any number that will make the denominator 0.

EXAMPLE 1   Find all numbers for which the rational expression

$$\frac{2x + 5}{x^2 - 9x - 10}$$

is undefined.

Solution   We set the denominator equal to 0 and solve:

$$x^2 - 9x - 10 = 0$$
$$(x - 10)(x + 1) = 0 \qquad \text{Factoring}$$
$$x - 10 = 0 \quad or \quad x + 1 = 0 \qquad \text{Using the principle of zero products}$$
$$x = 10 \quad or \qquad x = -1.$$

If x is replaced with 10 or with -1, the denominator is 0. Thus,

$$\frac{2x + 5}{x^2 - 9x - 10} \quad \text{is undefined for } x = 10 \text{ and } x = -1.$$

Multiplication and Division of Rational Expressions

Multiplication and division of rational expressions is similar to multiplication and division with fractions.

> **The Product and the Quotient of Two Rational Expressions**
>
> To multiply two rational expressions, multiply numerators and multiply denominators:
>
> $$\frac{A}{B} \cdot \frac{C}{D} = \frac{AC}{BD}.$$
>
> To divide by a rational expression, multiply by its reciprocal:
>
> $$\frac{A}{B} \div \frac{C}{D} = \frac{A}{B} \cdot \frac{D}{C} = \frac{AD}{BC}.$$

EXAMPLE 2   Simplify: $\dfrac{9x^2 + 12x}{6x^2 - 3x}$.

Solution   We first factor the numerator and the denominator:

$$\frac{9x^2 + 12x}{6x^2 - 3x} = \frac{3x(3x + 4)}{3x(2x - 1)}.$$

We can now write this as a product of two rational expressions using the rule for multiplying rational expressions in reverse. Then we can simplify.

$$\frac{3x(3x + 4)}{3x(2x - 1)} = \frac{3x}{3x} \cdot \frac{3x + 4}{2x - 1} \qquad \text{Rewriting as a product of two rational expressions}$$

$$= 1 \cdot \frac{3x + 4}{2x - 1} \qquad \frac{3x}{3x} = 1$$

$$= \frac{3x + 4}{2x - 1} \qquad \text{Removing the factor 1}$$

Only factors can be removed. Be sure that the numerator and the denominator are factored before you attempt to remove factors equal to 1.

After multiplying or dividing rational expressions, we simplify, if possible.

EXAMPLE 3   Perform each indicated operation and simplify.

a) $\dfrac{x^2 - x - 6}{3x} \cdot \dfrac{12x^3}{x + 2}$

b) $\dfrac{x^2 - 1}{x + 5} \div \dfrac{x^2 + 2x + 1}{2x + 10}$

Solution

Multiplication of rational expressions (p. 381)

a) $\dfrac{x^2 - x - 6}{3x} \cdot \dfrac{12x^3}{x + 2} = \dfrac{(x^2 - x - 6)(12x^3)}{3x(x + 2)}$ Multiplying the numerators and the denominators

$= \dfrac{(x - 3)(x + 2)(3x)(4x^2)}{3x(x + 2)}$ Factoring the numerator. Try to go directly to this step.

$= \dfrac{(x - 3)\cancel{(x + 2)}\cancel{(3x)}(4x^2)}{\cancel{(3x)}\cancel{(x + 2)}}$ Removing a factor equal to 1: $\dfrac{(x + 2)(3x)}{(x + 2)(3x)} = 1$

$= 4x^2(x - 3)$

Division of rational expressions (p. 382)

b) $\dfrac{x^2 - 1}{x + 5} \div \dfrac{x^2 + 2x + 1}{2x + 10} = \dfrac{x^2 - 1}{x + 5} \cdot \dfrac{2x + 10}{x^2 + 2x + 1}$ Multiplying by the reciprocal of the divisor

$= \dfrac{(x + 1)(x - 1)(2)(x + 5)}{(x + 5)(x + 1)(x + 1)}$ Multiplying rational expressions and factoring numerators and denominators

$= \dfrac{\cancel{(x + 1)}(x - 1)(2)\cancel{(x + 5)}}{\cancel{(x + 5)}\cancel{(x + 1)}(x + 1)}$ Removing a factor equal to 1: $\dfrac{(x + 1)(x + 5)}{(x + 1)(x + 5)} = 1$

$= \dfrac{2(x - 1)}{x + 1}$ We leave the numerator in factored form.

Addition and Subtraction of Rational Expressions

Like multiplication and division, addition and subtraction of rational expressions is similar to addition and subtraction of fractions.

The Sum and the Difference of Two Rational Expressions

To add when the denominators are the same, add the numerators and keep the same denominator:

$$\frac{A}{B} + \frac{C}{B} = \frac{A + C}{B}.$$

To subtract when the denominators are the same, subtract the second numerator from the first and keep the same denominator:

$$\frac{A}{B} - \frac{C}{B} = \frac{A - C}{B}.$$

EXAMPLE 4   Add and simplify, if possible:

$$\frac{x - 6}{x^2 - 6x + 5} + \frac{5}{x^2 - 6x + 5}.$$

Solution

Addition of rational expressions
(p. 388)

$$\frac{x-6}{x^2-6x+5}+\frac{5}{x^2-6x+5}=\frac{x-6+5}{x^2-6x+5}$$ Adding numerators

$$=\frac{x-1}{(x-5)(x-1)}$$ Factoring the denominator

$$=\frac{1(x-1)}{(x-5)(x-1)}$$ Removing a factor equal to 1: $\frac{x-1}{x-1}=1$

$$=\frac{1}{x-5}$$

Least common denominator
(p. 390)

Least common multiple (p. 390)

   When two rational expressions do not have a common denominator, we must rewrite them with a common denominator before we can add or subtract them. We generally rewrite them using their **least common denominator** (**LCD**), which is the **least common multiple** (**LCM**) of their denominators.

> *To Find the Least Common Denominator (LCD)*
> 1. Write the prime factorization of each denominator.
> 2. Select one of the factorizations and inspect it to see if it contains the other.
>
>   a) If it does, it represents the LCM of the denominators.
>   b) If it does not, multiply that factorization by any factors of the other denominator that it lacks. The final product is the LCM of the denominators.
>
> The LCD is the LCM of the denominators. It should contain each factor the greatest number of times that it occurs in any of the individual factorizations.

EXAMPLE 5   Add: $\frac{x-3}{x^2-1}+\frac{4x^2}{x^2+4x+3}$.

Solution   We first find the LCD. We write the prime factorization of each denominator and construct the LCM:

$$x^2-1=(x+1)(x-1);$$
$$x^2+4x+3=(x+1)(x+3).$$

The LCM must contain both factorizations. We select the factorization of x^2-1. It does not contain the factor $(x+3)$ from the factorization of x^2+4x+3. We multiply $(x+1)(x-1)$ by $(x+3)$:

$$LCM=(x+1)(x-1)(x+3).$$

The denominator $x^2 - 1 = (x + 1)(x - 1)$ must be multiplied by $x + 3$ in order to obtain the LCD. The denominator $x^2 + 4x + 3 = (x + 1)(x + 3)$ must be multiplied by $x - 1$ in order to obtain the LCD. We multiply each expression by a form of 1 that is made up of these "missing" factors:

$$\frac{x - 3}{x^2 - 1} + \frac{4x^2}{x^2 + 4x + 3} = \frac{x - 3}{(x + 1)(x - 1)} \cdot \frac{x + 3}{x + 3} + \frac{4x^2}{(x + 1)(x + 3)} \cdot \frac{x - 1}{x - 1}$$

$$= \frac{x^2 - 9}{(x + 1)(x - 1)(x + 3)} + \frac{4x^3 - 4x^2}{(x + 1)(x - 1)(x + 3)}$$

$$= \frac{4x^3 - 3x^2 - 9}{(x + 1)(x - 1)(x + 3)}.$$

EXAMPLE 6 Subtract: $\dfrac{x}{x + 2} - \dfrac{2x - 3}{3x - 4}$.

Solution We have

Subtraction of rational expressions (p. 389)

$$\frac{x}{x + 2} - \frac{2x - 3}{3x - 4}$$

$$= \frac{x}{x + 2} \cdot \frac{3x - 4}{3x - 4} - \frac{2x - 3}{3x - 4} \cdot \frac{x + 2}{x + 2} \qquad \text{The LCD is } (x + 2)(3x - 4)$$

$$= \frac{3x^2 - 4x}{(x + 2)(3x - 4)} - \frac{2x^2 + x - 6}{(x + 2)(3x - 4)} \qquad \begin{array}{l}\text{Multiplying out} \\ \text{the numerators} \\ \text{(but not the} \\ \text{denominators)}\end{array}$$

$$= \frac{3x^2 - 4x - (2x^2 + x - 6)}{(x + 2)(3x - 4)} \qquad \begin{array}{l}\text{Parentheses are} \\ \text{important.}\end{array}$$

$$= \frac{3x^2 - 4x - 2x^2 - x + 6}{(x + 2)(3x - 4)} \qquad \begin{array}{l}\text{Removing parentheses} \\ \text{in the numerator;} \\ \text{subtracting every} \\ \text{term}\end{array}$$

$$= \frac{x^2 - 5x + 6}{(x + 2)(3x - 4)}$$

$$= \frac{(x - 2)(x - 3)}{(x + 2)(3x - 4)}. \qquad \begin{array}{l}\text{Factoring the numerator in hopes} \\ \text{of simplifying. There are no common} \\ \text{factors.}\end{array}$$

The result could be written as either of the last two expressions.

Factors that are opposites (p. 401)

When denominators are opposites, we can find a common denominator by multiplying either rational expression by $-1/-1$.

EXAMPLE 7

Add: $\dfrac{a}{a-b}+\dfrac{5}{b-a}$.

Solution

$$\frac{a}{a-b}+\frac{5}{b-a}=\frac{a}{a-b}+\frac{5}{b-a}\cdot\frac{-1}{-1}$$

Writing 1 as $-1/-1$ and multiplying to obtain a common denominator

$$=\frac{a}{a-b}+\frac{-5}{a-b}$$

$(b-a)(-1)=-b+a=a-b$

$$=\frac{a-5}{a-b}$$

Complex Rational Expressions

Complex rational expressions
(Section 6.5)

A **complex rational expression** is a rational expression that has one or more rational expressions within its numerator or denominator. We will consider two methods for simplifying complex rational expressions. The first involves writing the expression as a quotient of two rational expressions.

> *To Simplify a Complex Rational Expression by Dividing*
> 1. Add or subtract, as needed, to get a single rational expression in the numerator.
> 2. Add or subtract, as needed, to get a single rational expression in the denominator.
> 3. Divide the numerator by the denominator (invert and multiply).
> 4. If possible, simplify by removing a factor equal to 1.

EXAMPLE 8

Simplify by dividing: $\dfrac{\dfrac{2}{x+1}}{\dfrac{1}{x+2}+\dfrac{1}{x}}$.

Solution

1. There is already a single rational expression in the numerator.
2. We add to get a single rational expression in the denominator:

$$\frac{\dfrac{2}{x+1}}{\dfrac{1}{x+2}+\dfrac{1}{x}}=\frac{\dfrac{2}{x+1}}{\dfrac{1}{x+2}\cdot\dfrac{x}{x}+\dfrac{1}{x}\cdot\dfrac{x+2}{x+2}}$$

Multiplying by 1 to get the LCD, $x(x+2)$, for the denominator

$$=\frac{\dfrac{2}{x+1}}{\dfrac{x}{x(x+2)}+\dfrac{x+2}{x(x+2)}}=\frac{\dfrac{2}{x+1}}{\dfrac{2x+2}{x(x+2)}}.$$

Adding in the denominator

3. Next, we invert and multiply:

$$\frac{\dfrac{2}{x+1}}{\dfrac{2x+2}{x(x+2)}} = \frac{2}{x+1} \div \frac{2x+2}{x(x+2)} = \frac{2}{x+1} \cdot \frac{x(x+2)}{2x+2}.$$

4. Simplifying, we have:

$$\frac{2}{(x+1)} \cdot \frac{x(x+2)}{2x+2} = \frac{2 \cdot x(x+2)}{2(x+1)(x+1)} \qquad \text{Removing a factor equal to 1: } \tfrac{2}{2} = 1$$

$$= \frac{x(x+2)}{(x+1)^2}.$$

A second method for simplifying complex rational expressions involves multiplying by the LCD.

> **To Simplify a Complex Rational Expression by Multiplying by the LCD**
>
> **1.** Find the LCD of *all* rational expressions within the complex rational expression.
> **2.** Multiply the complex rational expression by a factor equal to 1. Write 1 as the LCD over itself (LCD/LCD).
> **3.** Simplify. No fractional expressions should remain within the complex rational expression.
> **4.** Factor and, if possible, simplify.

EXAMPLE 9   Simplify by multiplying by the LCD: $\dfrac{1 + \dfrac{2}{t}}{\dfrac{4}{t^2} - 1}$.

Solution

1. The denominators *within* the complex rational expression are t and t^2, so the LCD is t^2.

2. We multiply by a form of 1 using t^2/t^2:

$$\frac{1 + \dfrac{2}{t}}{\dfrac{4}{t^2} - 1} = \frac{1 + \dfrac{2}{t}}{\dfrac{4}{t^2} - 1} \cdot \frac{t^2}{t^2}.$$

3. We distribute and simplify:

$$\frac{1 + \dfrac{2}{t}}{\dfrac{4}{t^2} - 1} \cdot \frac{t^2}{t^2} = \frac{1 \cdot t^2 + \dfrac{2}{t} \cdot t^2}{\dfrac{4}{t^2} \cdot t^2 - 1 \cdot t^2}$$

$$= \frac{t^2 + 2t}{4 - t^2}. \qquad \text{No rational expression remains within the numerator or denominator.}$$

4. Finally, we simplify:

$$\frac{t^2 + 2t}{4 - t^2} = \frac{t(t + 2)}{(2 + t)(2 - t)}$$ Factoring and simplifying;
$$\frac{t + 2}{t + 2} = 1$$

$$= \frac{t}{2 - t}.$$

Solving Rational Equations

Solving rational equations
(Section 6.6)

A **rational equation** is an equation containing one or more rational expressions, often with the variable in a denominator.

> **To Solve a Rational Equation**
> 1. List any restrictions that exist. No possible solution can make a denominator equal 0.
> 2. Clear the equation of fractions by multiplying both sides by the LCD of all rational expressions in the equation.
> 3. Solve the resulting equation using the addition principle, the multiplication principle, and the principle of zero products, as needed.
> 4. Check the possible solution(s) in the original equation.

Because a possible solution in step 3 may make a denominator 0, checking is essential when solving rational equations.

EXAMPLE 10   Solve: $x + \dfrac{10}{x} = 7$.

Solution   First we note that x cannot be 0. The LCD is x, so we multiply both sides by x:

$$x + \frac{10}{x} = 7$$

$$x\left(x + \frac{10}{x}\right) = 7x$$ Don't forget the parentheses!

$$x \cdot x + x \cdot \frac{10}{x} = 7x$$ Using the distributive law

$$x^2 + 10 = 7x$$ We have a quadratic equation.

$$x^2 - 7x + 10 = 0$$ Getting 0 on one side

$$(x - 2)(x - 5) = 0$$ Factoring

$$x - 2 = 0 \quad or \quad x - 5 = 0$$ Using the principle of zero products

$$x = 2 \quad or \qquad x = 5.$$

Check: For 2:   For 5:

$$x + \frac{10}{x} = 7 \qquad\qquad x + \frac{10}{x} = 7$$

$$\begin{array}{c|c} 2 + \dfrac{10}{2} & 7 \\ \hline 2 + 5 & \end{array} \qquad\qquad \begin{array}{c|c} 5 + \dfrac{10}{5} & 7 \\ \hline 5 + 2 & \end{array}$$

$$7 \overset{?}{=} 7 \ \text{TRUE} \qquad\qquad 7 \overset{?}{=} 7 \ \text{TRUE}$$

Both numbers check, so there are two solutions, 2 and 5.

Work problems (p. 420)

Many problems translate to rational equations. **Work problems**, which involve the time that it takes to complete a task, can often be solved using the work principle.

> **The Work Principle**
>
> Suppose that A requires a units of time to complete a task and B requires b units of time to complete the same task. Then
>
> A works at a rate of $\dfrac{1}{a}$ tasks per unit of time,
>
> B works at a rate of $\dfrac{1}{b}$ tasks per unit of time, and
>
> A and B together work at a rate of $\dfrac{1}{a} + \dfrac{1}{b}$ tasks per unit of time.
>
> If A and B, working together, require t units of time to complete the task, then all four of the following equations hold:
>
> $$\frac{1}{a}\cdot t + \frac{1}{b}\cdot t = 1; \quad \left(\frac{1}{a} + \frac{1}{b}\right)t = 1; \quad \frac{t}{a} + \frac{t}{b} = 1; \quad \frac{1}{a} + \frac{1}{b} = \frac{1}{t}.$$

EXAMPLE 11   *Drafting.* It takes Kerry 30 hr to draw a set of plans for a house. It takes Jesse 45 hr to draw the same set of plans. How long would it take Kerry and Jesse, working together, to draw the set of plans?

Solution

1. **Familiarize.** We could make some guesses to help us understand the problem and then list our results in a table. We could also reason that if Kerry and Jesse each drew half the plans, it would take Kerry 15 hr and Jesse $22\frac{1}{2}$ hr. So the time it takes them working together should be between 15 and $22\frac{1}{2}$ hr. We let $t =$ the time that it takes them to draw the plans, working together.

2. **Translate.** We will use the work principle to translate the problem:

$$\frac{1}{a}\cdot t + \frac{1}{b}\cdot t = 1 \qquad \begin{array}{l}a \text{ is the time that it takes Kerry to draw the plans;}\\ b \text{ is the time that it takes Jesse to draw the plans.}\end{array}$$

$$\frac{t}{30} + \frac{t}{45} = 1.$$

3. **Carry out.**   We solve the equation:

$$\frac{t}{30} + \frac{t}{45} = 1$$

$$90\left(\frac{t}{30} + \frac{t}{45}\right) = 90 \cdot 1 \qquad \text{The LCD is } 2 \cdot 3 \cdot 3 \cdot 5, \text{ or } 90.$$

$$90 \cdot \frac{t}{30} + 90 \cdot \frac{t}{45} = 90$$

$$3t + 2t = 90$$

$$5t = 90$$

$$t = 18.$$

4. **Check.**   We note that, as predicted in the *Familiarize* step, the answer is between 15 and $22\frac{1}{2}$ hr. Also, if each works 18 hr, Kerry will do $\frac{18}{30}$ of the job and Jesse will do $\frac{18}{45}$ of the job, and

$$\frac{18}{30} + \frac{18}{45} = \frac{3}{5} + \frac{2}{5} = 1. \qquad \text{The entire job will be completed.}$$

5. **State.**   Together it will take them 18 hr to draw the plans.

Motion problems (p. 423)

Problems that deal with distance, speed (or rate), and time, or **motion problems**, can often be translated using the distance formula $d = rt$.

EXAMPLE 12

Driving time.   Karen and Eva are each driving to a sales meeting. Because of road conditions, Karen is able to drive 15 mph faster than Eva. In the same time that it takes Karen to travel 120 mi, Eva travels only 90 mi. Find their speeds.

Solution

1. **Familiarize.**   We let $t =$ the time, in hours, that is spent traveling and $r =$ Karen's speed, in mph. Then Eva's speed $= r - 15$. We set up a table.

$$d \quad = \quad r \quad \cdot \quad t$$

	Distance	Speed	Time
Karen	120	r	t
Eva	90	$r - 15$	t

2. **Translate.**   From the distance formula, we have $t = d/r$, so we can replace the times in the table with expressions involving r.

	Distance	Speed	Time
Karen	120	r	$120/r$
Eva	90	$r - 15$	$90/(r - 15)$

Since the times are the same, we have the equation

$$\frac{120}{r} = \frac{90}{r - 15}.$$

3. Carry out. We solve the equation:

$$\frac{120}{r} = \frac{90}{r-15}$$

$$r(r-15)\frac{120}{r} = r(r-15)\frac{90}{r-15} \qquad \text{The LCD is } r(r-15).$$

$$120(r-15) = 90r \qquad \text{Simplifying}$$

$$120r - 1800 = 90r \qquad \text{Removing parentheses}$$

$$-1800 = -30r \qquad \text{Subtracting } 120r$$

$$60 = r. \qquad \text{Dividing both sides by } -30$$

4. Check.   If $r = 60$, then $r - 15 = 45$. If Karen travels 120 mi at 60 mph, she will have traveled 2 hr. If Eva travels 90 mi at 45 mph, she will also have traveled 2 hr. Since the times are the same, the speeds check.

5. State.   Karen is traveling at 60 mph, while Eva is traveling at 45 mph.

Ratio (p. 426)

Proportion (p. 426)

Another type of problem that translates to a rational equation involves proportions. A **ratio** of two quantities is their quotient. A **proportion** is an equation stating that two ratios are equal.

E X A M P L E 13

Baking.   Rob discovers there is $2\frac{1}{2}$ cups of pancake mix left in the box. The directions on the mix indicate that $1\frac{1}{3}$ cups of milk should be added to 2 cups of mix. How much milk should Rob add to the $2\frac{1}{2}$ cups of mix?

Solution   Since the problem translates directly to a proportion, we will not follow all five steps of the problem-solving process. We write the ratio of mix to milk in two ways:

$$\text{Mix} \longrightarrow \frac{2}{1\frac{1}{3}} = \frac{2\frac{1}{2}}{x} \longleftarrow \text{Mix}$$
$$\text{Milk} \longrightarrow \qquad\quad \longleftarrow \text{Milk}$$

The LCD is $x\left(1\frac{1}{3}\right)$. We solve for x:

$$x\left(1\tfrac{1}{3}\right)\frac{2}{1\frac{1}{3}} = x\left(1\tfrac{1}{3}\right)\frac{2\frac{1}{2}}{x} \qquad \text{Multiplying by the LCD}$$

$$2x = \left(1\tfrac{1}{3}\right)\left(2\tfrac{1}{2}\right) \qquad \text{Simplifying}$$

$$2x = \tfrac{10}{3} \qquad \text{Converting to fraction notation and multiplying}$$

$$x = \tfrac{5}{3}. \qquad \text{Multiplying both sides by } \tfrac{1}{2} \text{ and simplifying}$$

Rob needs to add $\frac{5}{3}$ or $1\frac{2}{3}$ cups of milk.

Exercise Set

R.6

FOR EXTRA HELP

Student's Solutions Manual | Digital Video Tutor CD 8 Videotape 15 | Tutor Center AW Math Tutor Center | MathXL Tutorials on CD | Math XL MathXL | MyMathLab MyMathLab

List all numbers for which each rational expression is undefined.

1. $\dfrac{x-7}{3x+2}$

2. $\dfrac{10-y}{-6y}$

3. $\dfrac{p^2-1}{p^2-100}$

4. $\dfrac{10x}{x^2+9x+8}$

Simplify by removing a factor equal to 1.

5. $\dfrac{16x^2y}{18xy^2}$

6. $\dfrac{2x+10}{6x+30}$

7. $\dfrac{t^2-2t-8}{t^2-16}$

8. $\dfrac{a^3+2a^2+a}{a^2+4a+3}$

9. $\dfrac{2-x}{x^2-4}$

10. $\dfrac{y-8}{8-y}$

Perform each indicated operation. Then, if possible, simplify.

11. $\dfrac{3x}{x+y} \cdot \dfrac{2x+2y}{x^2}$

12. $\dfrac{5}{x+7} \cdot \dfrac{x+7}{10}$

13. $\dfrac{a^2+2a+1}{a} \div \dfrac{a^2}{a^2-1}$

14. $\dfrac{x}{x+3} + \dfrac{3-x}{x+3}$

15. $\dfrac{2x}{x-7} - \dfrac{x+7}{x-7}$

16. $\dfrac{x}{x+y} \div \dfrac{y}{x+y}$

17. $\dfrac{5}{x} + \dfrac{6}{x^2}$

18. $\dfrac{x^2+4x+3}{x^2+x-2} \cdot \dfrac{x^2+3x+2}{x^2+2x-3}$

19. $\dfrac{2a+b}{a-b} - \dfrac{4}{3a-3b}$

20. $(x^2-16) \div \dfrac{4x+16}{3x^2}$

21. $\dfrac{2-x}{5x^2} \div \dfrac{x^2-4}{3x}$

22. $\dfrac{2x}{x-5} + \dfrac{3}{x+4}$

23. $\dfrac{x^3+2x^2+x}{x^2-4} \cdot \dfrac{x^2-x-2}{x^4+x^3}$

24. $\dfrac{-1}{x^2+7x+10} - \dfrac{3}{x^2+8x+15}$

25. $\dfrac{2}{(x+1)^2} + \dfrac{1}{x+1}$

26. $\dfrac{2x}{x^2-3x} \div (x-3)$

27. $\dfrac{x-y}{2x} \cdot \dfrac{3x^2}{y-x}$

28. $\dfrac{1}{x+y} + \dfrac{2}{x^2+y^2}$

29. $\dfrac{x-2}{x+5} - \dfrac{x+3}{x-4}$

30. $\dfrac{z^2+2z+1}{8z} \div \dfrac{z^2-z-2}{4z^2-4}$

Simplify.

31. $\dfrac{\dfrac{2}{x}-\dfrac{1}{x^2}}{\dfrac{x}{4}}$

32. $\dfrac{\dfrac{x}{3}-\dfrac{3}{x}}{\dfrac{1}{x}+\dfrac{1}{3}}$

33. $\dfrac{\dfrac{3}{x-7}}{\dfrac{4x+3}{x+1}}$

34. $\dfrac{\dfrac{a}{a-b}}{\dfrac{a^2}{a^2-b^2}}$

35. $\dfrac{x-\dfrac{3}{x-2}}{x-\dfrac{12}{x+1}}$

36. $\dfrac{t+\dfrac{1}{t}}{t-\dfrac{2}{t}}$

37. $\dfrac{\dfrac{1}{2}-\dfrac{1}{x}}{\dfrac{2-x}{2}}$

38. $\dfrac{\dfrac{x}{2y^2}+\dfrac{y}{3x^2}}{\dfrac{1}{6xy}+\dfrac{2}{x^2y}}$

Solve.

39. $\dfrac{1}{2} + \dfrac{1}{3} = \dfrac{1}{t}$

40. $\dfrac{1}{4} + \dfrac{1}{t} = \dfrac{1}{3}$

41. $x + \dfrac{1}{x} = 2$

42. $\dfrac{x-7}{x+1} = \dfrac{2}{3}$

43. $\dfrac{3}{y+7} = \dfrac{1}{y-8}$

44. $\dfrac{x+1}{x-2} = \dfrac{3}{x-2}$

45. $\dfrac{1}{x-3} - \dfrac{x-4}{x^2-9} = 1$

46. $\dfrac{3}{a+4} = \dfrac{a-1}{4-a}$

47. *Painting.*   Quentin can paint the turret on a Queen Anne house in 40 hr. It takes Austin 50 hr to paint the same turret. How long would it take them, working together, to paint the turret?

48. *Building fences.*   Lindsay can build a fence in 6 hr. Laura can do the same job in 5 hr. How long will it take them, working together, to build the fence?

49. *Snowmobiling.*   Jessica can ride her snowmobile through the fields 20 km/h faster than Josh can ride his through the woods. In the time it takes Jessica to ride 18 km, Josh travels 10 km. Find the speed of each snowmobile.

50. *Bicycling.*   Ani bicycles 8 mi and Lia bicycles 12 mi to meet at a park for lunch. Because Ani's trip is mostly uphill, she rides 5 mph slower than Lia. Ani and Lia leave their homes at the same time and arrive at the park at the same time. Find the speed of each bicyclist.

51. *Elk population.*   To determine the size of a park's elk population, rangers tag 15 elk and set them free. Months later, 40 elk are caught, of which 12 have tags. Estimate the size of the elk population.

52. *Manufacturing pegs.*   A sample of 136 wooden pegs contained 17 defective pegs. How many defective pegs would you expect in a sample of 840 pegs?

Appendixes

A   Mean, Median, and Mode

Mean • Median • Mode

One way to analyze data is to look for a single representative number, called a **center point** or **measure of central tendency**. Those most often used are the **mean** (or **average**), the **median**, and the **mode**.

Mean

Let's first consider the *mean*, or *average*.

> **Mean, or Average**
>
> The *mean*, or *average*, of a set of numbers is the sum of the numbers divided by the number of addends.

EXAMPLE 1   Consider the following data on revenue, in billions of dollars, at McDonald's restaurants in five recent years:

$12.5, $13.2, $14.2, $14.9, $15.9.

What is the mean of the numbers? (*Source*: McDonald's Corporation)

Solution First, we add the numbers:

$$12.5 + 13.2 + 14.2 + 14.9 + 15.9 = 70.7.$$

Then we divide by the number of addends, 5:

$$\frac{(12.5 + 13.2 + 14.2 + 14.9 + 15.9)}{5} = \frac{70.7}{5} = 14.14.$$

The mean, or average, revenue of McDonald's for those five years is $14.14 billion.

Note that $14.14 + 14.14 + 14.14 + 14.14 + 14.14 = 70.7$. If we use this center point, 14.14, repeatedly as the addend, we get the same sum that we do when adding individual data numbers.

Median

The *median* is useful when we wish to de-emphasize extreme scores. For example, suppose five workers in a technology company manufactured the following number of computers during one day's work:

Sarah: 88

Matt: 92

Pat: 66

Jen: 94

Mark: 91

Let's first list the scores in order from smallest to largest:

66   88   91   92   94.

↑

Middle number

The middle number—in this case, 91—is the **median**.

> **Median**
>
> Once a set of data has been arranged from smallest to largest, the *median* of the set of data is the middle number if there is an odd number of data numbers. If there is an even number of data numbers, then there are two middle numbers and the median is the *average* of the two middle numbers.

EXAMPLE 2 Find the median of the following set of household incomes:

$76,000, $58,000, $87,000, $32,500, $64,800, $62,500.

Solution We first rearrange the numbers in order from smallest to largest.

$32,500, $58,000, $62,500, $64,800, $76,000, $87,000

Median

There is an even number of numbers. We look for the middle two, which are $62,500 and $64,800. In this case, the median is the average of $62,500 and $64,800:

$$\frac{\$62,500 + \$64,800}{2} = \$63,650.$$

Mode

The last center point we consider is called the *mode*. A number that occurs most often in a set of data is sometimes considered a representative number or center point.

> **Mode**
>
> The *mode* of a set of data is the number or numbers that occur most often. If each number occurs the same number of times, there is *no* mode.

EXAMPLE 3 Find the mode of the following data:

23, 24, 27, 18, 19, 27.

Solution The number that occurs most often is 27. Thus the mode is 27.

EXAMPLE 4 Find the mode of the following data:

83, 84, 84 84, 85, 86, 87, 87, 87, 88, 89, 90.

Solution There are two numbers that occur most often, 84 and 87. Thus the modes are 84 and 87.

EXAMPLE 5 Find the mode of the following data:

115, 117, 211, 213, 219.

Solution Each number occurs the same number of times. The set of data has *no* mode.

Exercise Set

A

For each set of numbers, find the mean (average), the median, and any modes that exist.

1. 17, 19, 29, 18, 14, 29
2. 72, 83, 85, 88, 92
3. 5, 37, 20, 20, 35, 5, 25
4. 13, 32, 25, 27, 13
5. 4.3, 7.4, 1.2, 5.7, 7.4
6. 13.4, 13.4, 12.6, 42.9
7. 234, 228, 234, 229, 234, 278
8. $29.95, $28.79, $30.95, $29.95
9. *Atlantic storms and hurricanes.* The following bar graph shows the number of Atlantic storms or hurricanes that formed in various months from 1980 to 2000. What is the average number for the 9 months given? the median? the mode?

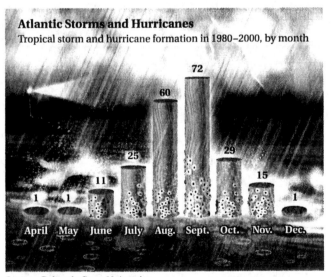

Atlantic Storms and Hurricanes
Tropical storm and hurricane formation in 1980–2000, by month

Source: Colorado State University

10. *Cheddar cheese prices.* The following prices per pound of sharp cheddar cheese were found at five supermarkets:

$5.99, $6.79, $5.99, $6.99, $6.79.

What was the average price per pound? the median price? the mode?

11. *Coffee consumption.* The following lists the annual coffee consumption, in number of cups per person, for various countries. Find the mean, the median, and the mode.

Germany	1113
United States	610
Switzerland	1215
France	798
Italy	750

Source: Beverage Marketing Corporation

12. *NBA tall men.* The following is a list of the heights, in inches, of the tallest men in the NBA in a recent year. Find the mean, the median, and the mode.

Shaquille O'Neal	85
Gheorghe Muresan	91
Shawn Bradley	90
Tim Duncan	84
Yao Ming	89
Bruno Sundov	86

Source: National Basketball Association

13. *Salmon prices.* The following prices per pound of Atlantic salmon were found at five fish markets:

$6.99, $8.49, $8.99, $6.99, $9.49.

What was the average price per pound? the median price? the mode?

14. *PBA scores.*   Chris Barnes rolled scores of 224, 224, 254, and 187 in a recent tournament of the Professional Bowlers Association. What was his average? his median? his mode?
Source: Professional Bowlers Association

15. *Hank Aaron.*   Hank Aaron averaged $34\frac{7}{22}$ home runs per year over a 22-yr career. After 21 yr, Aaron had averaged $35\frac{10}{21}$ home runs per year. How many home runs did Aaron hit in his final year?

16. *Length of pregnancy.*   Marta was pregnant 270 days, 259 days, and 272 days for her first three pregnancies. In order for Marta's average length of pregnancy to equal the worldwide average of 266 days, how long must her fourth pregnancy last?
Source: David Crystal (ed.), *The Cambridge Factfinder.* Cambridge CB2 1RP: Cambridge University Press, 1993, p. 84.

17. The ordered set of data 18, 21, 24, *a*, 36, 37, *b* has a median of 30 and an average of 32. Find *a* and *b*.

18. *Male height.*   Jason's brothers are 174 cm, 180 cm, 179 cm, and 172 cm tall. The average male is 176.5 cm tall. How tall is Jason if he and his brothers have an average height of 176.5 cm?

B   Sets

Naming Sets • Membership • Subsets • Intersections • Unions

A **set** is a collection of objects. In mathematics the objects, or **elements**, of a set are generally numbers. This section provides a basic introduction to sets.

Naming Sets

To name the set of whole numbers less than 6, we can use *roster notation*, as follows:

$$\{0, 1, 2, 3, 4, 5\}.$$

The set of real numbers x for which x is less than 6 cannot be named by listing all its members because there is an infinite number of them. We name such a set using *set-builder notation*, as follows:

$$\{x \mid x < 6\}.$$

This is read

"The set of all x such that x is less than 6."

See Section 2.6 for more on this notation.

Membership

The symbol $\in$ means *is a member of* or *belongs to*, or *is an element of.* Thus,

$$x \in A$$

means

x is a member of A, or x belongs to A, or x is an element of A.

EXAMPLE 1 Classify each of the following as true or false.

a) $1 \in \{1, 2, 3\}$

b) $1 \in \{2, 3\}$

c) $4 \in \{x \mid x \text{ is an even whole number}\}$

d) $5 \in \{x \mid x \text{ is an even whole number}\}$

Solution

a) Since 1 is listed as a member of the set, $1 \in \{1, 2, 3\}$ is true.

b) Since 1 is *not* a member of $\{2, 3\}$, the statement $1 \in \{2, 3\}$ is false.

c) Since 4 is an even whole number, $4 \in \{x \mid x \text{ is an even whole number}\}$ is true.

d) Since 5 is *not* even, $5 \in \{x \mid x \text{ is an even whole number}\}$ is false.

Set membership can be illustrated with a diagram, as shown below.

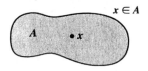

Subsets

If every element of A is also an element of B, then A is a *subset* of B. This is denoted $A \subseteq B$.

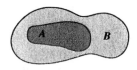

The set of whole numbers is a subset of the set of integers. The set of rational numbers is a subset of the set of real numbers.

EXAMPLE 2 Classify each of the following as true or false.

a) $\{1, 2\} \subseteq \{1, 2, 3, 4\}$

b) $\{p, q, r, w\} \subseteq \{a, p, r, z\}$

c) $\{x \mid x < 6\} \subseteq \{x \mid x \le 11\}$

Solution

a) Since every element of $\{1, 2\}$ is in the set $\{1, 2, 3, 4\}$, it follows that $\{1, 2\} \subseteq \{1, 2, 3, 4\}$ is true.

b) Since $q \in \{p, q, r, w\}$, but $q \notin \{a, p, r, z\}$, it follows that $\{p, q, r, w\} \subseteq \{a, p, r, z\}$ is false.

c) Since every number that is less than 6 is also less than 11, the statement $\{x \mid x < 6\} \subseteq \{x \mid x \leq 11\}$ is true.

Intersections

The *intersection* of sets A and B, denoted $A \cap B$, is the set of members common to both sets.

EXAMPLE 3   Find each intersection.

a) $\{0, 1, 3, 5, 25\} \cap \{2, 3, 4, 5, 6, 7, 9\}$ **b)** $\{a, p, q, w\} \cap \{p, q, t\}$

Solution

a) $\{0, 1, 3, 5, 25\} \cap \{2, 3, 4, 5, 6, 7, 9\} = \{3, 5\}$

b) $\{a, p, q, w\} \cap \{p, q, t\} = \{p, q\}$

Set intersection can be illustrated with a diagram, as shown below.

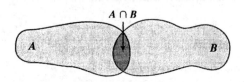

The set without members is known as the *empty set*, and is written $\varnothing$, and sometimes $\{\quad\}$. Each of the following is a description of the empty set:

The set of all 12-ft–tall people;

$\{2, 3\} \cap \{5, 6, 7\}$;

$\{x \mid x$ is an even natural number$\} \cap \{x \mid x$ is an odd natural number$\}$.

Unions

Two sets A and B can be combined to form a set that contains the members of both A and B. The new set is called the *union* of A and B, denoted $A \cup B$.

EXAMPLE 4   Find each union.

a) $\{0, 5, 7, 13, 27\} \cup \{0, 2, 3, 4, 5\}$ **b)** $\{a, c, e, g\} \cup \{b, d, f\}$

Solution

a) $\{0, 5, 7, 13, 27\} \cup \{0, 2, 3, 4, 5\} = \{0, 2, 3, 4, 5, 7, 13, 27\}$

Note that the 0 and the 5 are *not* listed twice in the solution.

b) $\{a, c, e, g\} \cup \{b, d, f\} = \{a, b, c, d, e, f, g\}$

Set union can be illustrated with a diagram, as shown below.

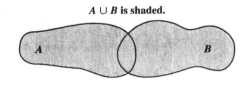

$A \cup B$ **is shaded.**

Exercise Set

B

Name each set using the roster method.

1. The set of whole numbers 3 through 7

2. The set of whole numbers 83 through 89

3. The set of odd numbers between 40 and 50

4. The set of multiples of 5 between 10 and 40

5. $\{x \,|\,$ the square of x is 9$\}$

6. $\{x \,|\, x$ is the cube of 0.2$\}$

Classify each statement as true or false.

7. $2 \in \{x \,|\, x$ is an odd number$\}$

8. $7 \in \{x \,|\, x$ is an odd number$\}$

9. Bruce Springsteen $\in$ The set of all rock stars

10. Apple $\in$ The set of all fruit

11. $-3 \in \{-4, -3, 0, 1\}$

12. $0 \in \{-4, -3, 0, 1\}$

13. $\frac{2}{3} \in \{x \,|\, x$ is a rational number$\}$

14. Heads $\in$ The set of outcomes of flipping a penny

15. $\{4, 5, 8\} \subseteq \{1, 3, 4, 5, 6, 7, 8, 9\}$

16. The set of vowels $\subseteq$ The set of consonants

17. $\{-1, -2, -3, -4, -5\} \subseteq \{-1, 2, 3, 4, 5\}$

18. The set of integers $\subseteq$ The set of rational numbers

Find each intersection.

19. $\{a, b, c, d, e\} \cap \{c, d, e, f, g\}$

20. $\{a, e, i, o, u\} \cap \{q, u, i, c, k\}$

21. $\{1, 2, 5, 10\} \cap \{0, 1, 7, 10\}$

22. $\{0, 1, 7, 10\} \cap \{0, 1, 2, 5\}$

23. $\{1, 2, 5, 10\} \cap \{3, 4, 7, 8\}$

24. $\{a, e, i, o, u\} \cap \{m, n, f, g, h\}$

Find each union.

25. $\{a, e, i, o, u\} \cup \{q, u, i, c, k\}$

26. $\{a, b, c, d, e\} \cup \{c, d, e, f, g\}$

27. $\{0, 1, 7, 10\} \cup \{0, 1, 2, 5\}$

28. $\{1, 2, 5, 10\} \cup \{0, 1, 7, 10\}$

29. $\{a, e, i, o, u\} \cup \{m, n, f, g, h\}$

30. $\{1, 2, 5, 10\} \cup \{a, b\}$

31. What advantage(s) does set-builder notation have over roster notation?

32. What advantage(s) does roster notation have over set-builder notation?

SYNTHESIS

33. Find the union of the set of integers and the set of whole numbers.

34. Find the intersection of the set of odd integers and the set of even integers.

35. Find the union of the set of rational numbers and the set of irrational numbers.

36. Find the intersection of the set of even integers and the set of positive rational numbers.

37. Find the intersection of the set of rational numbers and the set of irrational numbers.

38. Find the union of the set of negative integers, the set of positive integers, and the set containing 0.

39. For a set A, find each of the following.

    a) $A \cup \varnothing$

    b) $A \cup A$

    c) $A \cap A$

    d) $A \cap \varnothing$

40. A set is *closed* under an operation if, when the operation is performed on its members, the result is in the set. For example, the set of real numbers is closed under the operation of addition since the sum of any two real numbers is a real number.

    a) Is the set of even numbers closed under addition?

    b) Is the set of odd numbers closed under addition?

    c) Is the set $\{0, 1\}$ closed under addition?

    d) Is the set $\{0, 1\}$ closed under multiplication?

    e) Is the set of real numbers closed under multiplication?

    f) Is the set of integers closed under division?

41. Experiment with sets of various types and determine whether the following distributive law for sets is true:

$$A \cap (B \cup C) = (A \cap B) \cup (A \cap C).$$

Synthetic Division

Streamlining Long Division • The Remainder Theorem

Streamlining Long Division

To divide a polynomial by a binomial of the type $x - a$, we can streamline the usual procedure to develop a process called *synthetic division*.

    Compare the following. In each stage, we attempt to write a bit less than in the previous stage, while retaining enough essentials to solve the problem. At the end, we will return to the usual polynomial notation.

Stage 1

When a polynomial is written in descending order, the coefficients provide the essential information:

$$
\begin{array}{r}
4x^2 + 5x + 11 \\
x - 2 \overline{)\,4x^3 - 3x^2 + x + 7} \\
\underline{4x^3 - 8x^2} \\
5x^2 + x \\
\underline{5x^2 - 10x} \\
11x + 7 \\
\underline{11x - 22} \\
29
\end{array}
$$

$$
\begin{array}{r}
4 + 5 + 11 \\
1 - 2 \overline{)\,4 - 3 + 1 + 7} \\
\underline{4 - 8} \\
5 + 1 \\
\underline{5 - 10} \\
11 + 7 \\
\underline{11 - 22} \\
29
\end{array}
$$

Because the leading coefficient in the divisor is 1, each time we multiply the divisor by a term in the answer, the leading coefficient of that product duplicates a coefficient in the answer. In the next stage, we don't bother to duplicate these numbers. We also show where -2 is used and drop the 1 from the divisor.

Stage 2

$$
\begin{array}{r}
4x^2 + 5x + 11 \\
x - 2 \overline{)4x^3 - 3x^2 + x + 7} \\
\underline{4x^3 - 8x^2} \\
5x^2 + x \\
\underline{5x^2 - 10x} \\
11x + 7 \\
\underline{11x - 22} \\
29
\end{array}
$$

$$
\begin{array}{r}
4 + 5 + 11 \\
-2 \overline{)4 - 3 + 1 + 7} \\
-8 \\
5 + 1 \\
-10 \\
11 + 7 \\
-22 \\
29
\end{array}
$$

Multiply: $-2 \cdot 4 = -8$.
Subtract: $-3 - (-8) = 5$.
Multiply: $-2 \cdot 5 = -10$.
Subtract: $1 - (-10) = 11$.
Multiply: $-2 \cdot 11 = -22$.
Subtract: $7 - (-22) = 29$.

To simplify further, we now reverse the sign of the -2 in the divisor and, in exchange, *add* at each step in the long division.

Stage 3

$$
\begin{array}{r}
4x^2 + 5x + 11 \\
x - 2 \overline{)4x^3 - 3x^2 + x + 7} \\
\underline{4x^3 - 8x^2} \\
5x^2 + x \\
\underline{5x^2 - 10x} \\
11x + 7 \\
\underline{11x - 22} \\
29
\end{array}
$$

$$
\begin{array}{r}
4 + 5 + 11 \\
2 \overline{)4 - 3 + 1 + 7} \\
8 \\
5 + 1 \\
10 \\
11 + 7 \\
22 \\
29
\end{array}
$$

Replace the -2 with 2.
Multiply: $2 \cdot 4 = 8$.
Add: $-3 + 8 = 5$.
Multiply: $2 \cdot 5 = 10$.
Add: $1 + 10 = 11$.
Multiply: $2 \cdot 11 = 22$.
Add: $7 + 22 = 29$.

The blue numbers can be eliminated if we look at the red numbers instead.

Stage 4

$$
\begin{array}{r}
4x^2 + 5x + 11 \\
x - 2 \overline{)4x^3 - 3x^2 + x + 7} \\
\underline{4x^3 - 8x^2} \\
5x^2 + x \\
\underline{5x^2 - 10x} \\
11x + 7 \\
\underline{11x - 22} \\
29
\end{array}
$$

$$
\begin{array}{r}
4 \quad 5 \quad 11 \\
2 \overline{)4 \quad -3 \quad 1 \quad 7} \\
\underline{8 \quad 10 \quad 22} \\
5 \quad 11 \quad 29
\end{array}
$$

Don't lose sight of how the products 8, 10, and 22 are found. Also, note that the 5 and 11 preceding the remainder 29 coincide with the 5 and 11 following the 4 on the top line. By writing a 4 to the left of 5 on the bottom line, we can eliminate the top line in stage 4 and read our answer from the bottom line. This final stage is commonly called **synthetic division**.

Stage 5

$$
\begin{array}{r}
4 \quad 5 \quad 11 \\
\hline
2)\overline{4 \quad -3 \quad 1 \quad 7} \\
8 \quad 10 \quad 22 \\
\hline
5 \quad 11 \quad 29
\end{array}
$$

$$
\begin{array}{r}
\underline{2\,|}\ 4 \quad -3 \quad 1 \quad 7 \\
8 \quad 10 \quad 22 \\
\hline
4 \quad 5 \quad 11 \,|\, 29
\end{array}
$$

29 ⟵——— This is the remainder.

This is the zero-degree coefficient.

This is the first-degree coefficient.

This is the second-degree coefficient.

The quotient is $4x^2 + 5x + 11$. The remainder is 29.

> Remember that in order for this method to work, the divisor must be of the form $x - a$, that is, a variable minus a constant. The coefficient of the variable must be 1.

EXAMPLE 1   Use synthetic division to divide: $(x^3 + 6x^2 - x - 30) \div (x - 2)$.

Solution

$$
\begin{array}{r}
\underline{2\,|}\ 1 \quad 6 \quad -1 \quad -30 \\
\hline
1
\end{array}
$$

Write the 2 of $x - 2$ and the coefficients of the dividend.

Bring down the first coefficient.

$$
\begin{array}{r}
\underline{2\,|}\ 1 \quad 6 \quad -1 \quad -30 \\
2 \\
\hline
1 \quad 8
\end{array}
$$

Multiply 1 by 2 to get 2.

Add 6 and 2.

$$
\begin{array}{r}
\underline{2\,|}\ 1 \quad 6 \quad -1 \quad -30 \\
2 \quad 16 \\
\hline
1 \quad 8 \quad 15
\end{array}
$$

Multiply 8 by 2.

Add -1 and 16.

$$
\begin{array}{r}
\underline{2\,|}\ 1 \quad 6 \quad -1 \quad -30 \\
2 \quad 16 \quad 30 \\
\hline
1 \quad 8 \quad 15 \quad 0
\end{array}
$$

Multiply 15 by 2 and add.

The answer is $x^2 + 8x + 15$ with R 0, or just $x^2 + 8x + 15$.

EXAMPLE 2   Use synthetic division to divide.

a) $(2x^3 + 7x^2 - 5) \div (x + 3)$

b) $(10x^2 - 13x + 3x^3 - 20) \div (4 + x)$

Solution

a) $(2x^3 + 7x^2 - 5) \div (x + 3)$

The dividend has no x-term, so we need to write 0 for its coefficient of x. Note that $x + 3 = x - (-3)$, so we write -3 inside the ⌋.

$$
\begin{array}{r|rrrr}
-3 & 2 & 7 & 0 & -5 \\
   &   & -6 & -3 & 9 \\
\hline
   & 2 & 1 & -3 & \enspace 4
\end{array}
$$

The answer is $2x^2 + x - 3$, with R 4, or $2x^2 + x - 3 + \dfrac{4}{x + 3}$.

b) We first rewrite $(10x^2 - 13x + 3x^3 - 20) \div (4 + x)$ in descending order:

$$(3x^3 + 10x^2 - 13x - 20) \div (x + 4).$$

Next, we use synthetic division. Note that $x + 4 = x - (-4)$.

$$
\begin{array}{r|rrrr}
-4 & 3 & 10 & -13 & -20 \\
   &   & -12 & 8 & 20 \\
\hline
   & 3 & -2 & -5 & \enspace 0
\end{array}
$$

The answer is $3x^2 - 2x - 5$.

The Remainder Theorem

Because the remainder is 0, Example 1 shows that $x - 2$ is a factor of $x^3 + 6x^2 - x - 30$ and that we can write $x^3 + 6x^2 - x - 30$ as $(x - 2)(x^2 + 8x + 15)$. Using this result and the principle of zero products, we know that if $f(x) = x^3 + 6x^2 - x - 30$, then $f(2) = 0$ (since $x - 2$ is a factor of $f(x)$). Similarly, from Example 2(b), we know that $x + 4$ is a factor of $g(x) = 10x^2 - 13x + 3x^3 - 20$. This tells us that $g(-4) = 0$. In both examples, the remainder from the division, 0, can serve as a function value. Remarkably, this pattern extends to nonzero remainders. To see this, note that the remainder in Example 2(a) is 4, and if $f(x) = 2x^3 + 7x^2 - 5$, then $f(-3)$ is also 4 (you should check this). The fact that the remainder and the function value coincide is predicted by the remainder theorem, which follows.

The Remainder Theorem

The remainder obtained by dividing $P(x)$ by $x - r$ is $P(r)$.

A proof of this result is outlined in Exercise 23.

EXAMPLE 3   Let $f(x) = 8x^5 - 6x^3 + x - 8$. Use synthetic division to find $f(2)$.

Solution   The remainder theorem tells us that $f(2)$ is the remainder when $f(x)$ is divided by $x - 2$. We use synthetic division to find that remainder:

$$
\begin{array}{r|rrrrrr}
2 & 8 & 0 & -6 & 0 & 1 & -8 \\
  &   & 16 & 32 & 52 & 104 & 210 \\
\hline
  & 8 & 16 & 26 & 52 & 105 & 202
\end{array}
$$

Although the bottom line can be used to find the quotient for the division $(8x^5 - 6x^3 + x - 8) \div (x - 2)$, what we are really interested in is the remainder. It tells us that $f(2) = 202$.

Exercise Set

C

Use synthetic division to divide.

1. $(x^3 - 2x^2 + 2x - 7) \div (x + 1)$

2. $(x^3 - 2x^2 + 2x - 7) \div (x - 1)$

3. $(a^2 + 8a + 11) \div (a + 3)$

4. $(a^2 + 8a + 11) \div (a + 5)$

5. $(x^3 - 7x^2 - 13x + 3) \div (x - 2)$

6. $(x^3 - 7x^2 - 13x + 3) \div (x + 2)$

7. $(3x^3 + 7x^2 - 4x + 3) \div (x + 3)$

8. $(3x^3 + 7x^2 - 4x + 3) \div (x - 3)$

9. $(y^3 - 3y + 10) \div (y - 2)$

10. $(x^3 - 2x^2 + 8) \div (x + 2)$

11. $(x^5 - 32) \div (x - 2)$

12. $(y^5 - 1) \div (y - 1)$

13. $(3x^3 + 1 - x + 7x^2) \div \left(x + \frac{1}{3}\right)$

14. $(8x^3 - 1 + 7x - 6x^2) \div \left(x - \frac{1}{2}\right)$

Use synthetic division to find the indicated function value.

15. $f(x) = 5x^4 + 12x^3 + 28x + 9$; $f(-3)$

16. $g(x) = 3x^4 - 25x^2 - 18$; $g(3)$

17. $P(x) = 6x^4 - x^3 - 7x^2 + x + 2$; $P(-1)$

18. $F(x) = 3x^4 + 8x^3 + 2x^2 - 7x - 4$; $F(-2)$

19. $f(x) = x^4 - x^3 - 19x^2 + 49x - 30$; $f(4)$

20. $p(x) = x^4 + 7x^3 + 11x^2 - 7x - 12$; $p(2)$

SYNTHESIS

21. Why is it that we *add* when performing synthetic division, but *subtract* when performing long division?

22. Explain how synthetic division could be useful when factoring a polynomial.

23. To prove the remainder theorem, note that any polynomial $P(x)$ can be rewritten as $(x - r) \cdot Q(x) + R$, where $Q(x)$ is the quotient polynomial that arises when $P(x)$ is divided by $x - r$, and R is some constant (the remainder).

   a) How do we know that R must be a constant?
   b) Show that $P(r) = R$ (this says that $P(r)$ is the remainder when $P(x)$ is divided by $x - r$).

24. Let $f(x) = 4x^3 + 16x^2 - 3x - 45$. Find $f(-3)$ and then solve the equation $f(x) = 0$.

25. Let $f(x) = 6x^3 - 13x^2 - 79x + 140$. Find $f(4)$ and then solve the equation $f(x) = 0$.

Nested evaluation. *One way to evaluate a polynomial function like* $P(x) = 3x^4 - 5x^3 + 4x^2 - 1$ *is to successively factor out x as shown:*

$$P(x) = x(x(x(3x - 5) + 4) + 0) - 1.$$

Computations are then performed using this "nested" form of $P(x)$.

26. Use nested evaluation to find $f(-3)$ in Exercise 24. Note the similarities to the calculations performed with synthetic division.

27. Use nested evaluation to find $f(4)$ in Exercise 25. Note the similarities to the calculations performed with synthetic division.

Tables

TABLE 1 Fraction and Decimal Equivalents

Fraction Notation	$\frac{1}{10}$	$\frac{1}{8}$	$\frac{1}{6}$	$\frac{1}{5}$	$\frac{1}{4}$	$\frac{3}{10}$	$\frac{1}{3}$	$\frac{3}{8}$	$\frac{2}{5}$	$\frac{1}{2}$
Decimal Notation	0.1	0.125	$0.16\overline{6}$	0.2	0.25	0.3	$0.333\overline{3}$	0.375	0.4	0.5
Percent Notation	10%	12.5%, or $12\frac{1}{2}\%$	16.6$\overline{6}$%, or $16\frac{2}{3}\%$	20%	25%	30%	33.3$\overline{3}$%, or $33\frac{1}{3}\%$	37.5%, or $37\frac{1}{2}\%$	40%	50%
Fraction Notation	$\frac{3}{5}$	$\frac{5}{8}$	$\frac{2}{3}$	$\frac{7}{10}$	$\frac{3}{4}$	$\frac{4}{5}$	$\frac{5}{6}$	$\frac{7}{8}$	$\frac{9}{10}$	$\frac{1}{1}$
Decimal Notation	0.6	0.625	$0.666\overline{6}$	0.7	0.75	0.8	$0.83\overline{3}$	0.875	0.9	1
Percent Notation	60%	62.5%, or $62\frac{1}{2}\%$	66.6$\overline{6}$%, or $66\frac{2}{3}\%$	70%	75%	80%	83.3$\overline{3}$%, or $83\frac{1}{3}\%$	87.5%, or $87\frac{1}{2}\%$	90%	100%

TABLE 2   Squares and Square Roots with Approximations to Three Decimal Places

N	$\sqrt{N}$	N^2	N	$\sqrt{N}$	N^2	N	$\sqrt{N}$	N^2	N	$\sqrt{N}$	N^2
1	1	1	26	5.099	676	51	7.141	2601	76	8.718	5776
2	1.414	4	27	5.196	729	52	7.211	2704	77	8.775	5929
3	1.732	9	28	5.292	784	53	7.280	2809	78	8.832	6084
4	2	16	29	5.385	841	54	7.348	2916	79	8.888	6241
5	2.236	25	30	5.477	900	55	7.416	3025	80	8.944	6400
6	2.449	36	31	5.568	961	56	7.483	3136	81	9	6561
7	2.646	49	32	5.657	1024	57	7.550	3249	82	9.055	6724
8	2.828	64	33	5.745	1089	58	7.616	3364	83	9.110	6889
9	3	81	34	5.831	1156	59	7.681	3481	84	9.165	7056
10	3.162	100	35	5.916	1225	60	7.746	3600	85	9.220	7225
11	3.317	121	36	6	1296	61	7.810	3721	86	9.274	7396
12	3.464	144	37	6.083	1369	62	7.874	3844	87	9.327	7569
13	3.606	169	38	6.164	1444	63	7.937	3969	88	9.381	7744
14	3.742	196	39	6.245	1521	64	8	4096	89	9.434	7921
15	3.873	225	40	6.325	1600	65	8.062	4225	90	9.487	8100
16	4	256	41	6.403	1681	66	8.124	4356	91	9.539	8281
17	4.123	289	42	6.481	1764	67	8.185	4489	92	9.592	8464
18	4.243	324	43	6.557	1849	68	8.246	4624	93	9.644	8649
19	4.359	361	44	6.633	1936	69	8.307	4761	94	9.695	8836
20	4.472	400	45	6.708	2025	70	8.367	4900	95	9.747	9025
21	4.583	441	46	6.782	2116	71	8.426	5041	96	9.798	9216
22	4.690	484	47	6.856	2209	72	8.485	5184	97	9.849	9409
23	4.796	529	48	6.928	2304	73	8.544	5329	98	9.899	9604
24	4.899	576	49	7	2401	74	8.602	5476	99	9.950	9801
25	5	625	50	7.071	2500	75	8.660	5625	100	10	10,000

Glossary

A

Absolute value [1.4]   The distance that a number is from 0 on the number line.

Additive inverse [1.6]   A number's opposite. Two numbers are additive inverses of each other if their sum is zero.

Algebraic expression [1.1]   A number or variable or a collection of numbers and variables on which the operations $+$, $-$, $\cdot$, $\div$, $(\quad)^n$, or $\sqrt[n]{(\quad)}$ are performed.

Arithmetic sequence [14.2]   A sequence in which the difference between any two successive terms is constant.

Arithmetic series [14.2]   A series for which the associated sequence is arithmetic.

Ascending order [4.3]   A polynomial in one variable written with the terms arranged according to degree, from least to greatest.

Associative law of addition [1.2]   The statement that when three numbers are added, regrouping the addends gives the same sum.

Associative law of multiplication [1.2]   The statement that when three numbers are multiplied, regrouping the factors gives the same product.

Asymptote [13.3]   A line that a graph approaches more and more closely as x increases or as x decreases.

Average [2.7]   Most commonly, the mean of a set of numbers.

Axes [3.1]   Two perpendicular number lines used to identify points in a plane.

Axis of symmetry [11.6]   A line that can be drawn through a graph such that the part of the graph on one side of the line is an exact reflection of the part on the opposite side.

B

Bar graph [3.1]   A graphic display of data using bars proportional in length to the numbers represented.

Base [1.8]   In exponential notation, the number being raised to a power.

Binomial [4.2]   A polynomial composed of two terms.

Branches [13.3]   The two curves that comprise a hyperbola.

Break-even point [8.8]   In business, the point of intersection of the revenue function and the cost function.

C

Circle [13.1]   A set of points in a plane that are a fixed distance r, called the radius, from a fixed point (h, k), called the center.

Circle graph [3.1]   A graphic display of data using sectors of a circle to represent percents.

Circumference [2.3], [4.2]   The distance around a circle.

Closed interval $[a, b]$ [9.1]   The set of all numbers x for which $a \leq x \leq b$. Thus, $[a, b] = \{x \mid a \leq x \leq b\}$.

Coefficient [2.1]   The numerical multiplier of a variable.

Combined variation [7.5]   A mathematical relationship in which a variable varies directly and/or inversely, at the same time, with more than one other variable.

Common logarithm [12.5]   A logarithm with base 10.

Commutative law of addition [1.2]   The statement that when two numbers are added, changing the order in which the numbers are added does not affect the sum.

Commutative law of multiplication [1.2]   The statement that when two numbers are multiplied, changing the order in which the numbers are multiplied does not affect the product.

Completing the square [11.1]   Adding a particular constant to an expression so that the resulting sum is a perfect square.

Complex number [10.8]   Any number that can be written as $a + bi$, where a and b are real numbers.

Complex rational expression [6.5]   A rational expression that has one or more rational expressions within its numerator and/or denominator.

Complex-number system [10.8]   A number system that contains the real-number system and is designed so that negative numbers have square roots.

Composite function [12.1]   A function in which a quantity depends on a variable that, in turn, depends on another variable.

Composite number [1.3]   A natural number, other than 1, that is not prime.

Compound inequality [9.2]   A statement in which two or more inequalities are combined using the word *and* or the word *or*.

Compound interest [11.1]   Interest computed on the sum of an original principal and the interest previously accrued by that principal.

Conditional equation [2.2]   An equation that is true for some replacements and false for others.

Conic section [13.1]   A curve formed by the intersection of a plane and a cone.

Conjugates [10.5]   Pairs of radical terms, like $\sqrt{a} + \sqrt{b}$ and $\sqrt{a} - \sqrt{b}$, for which the product does not have a radical term.

Conjunction [9.2]   A sentence in which two statements are joined by the word *and*.

Consecutive numbers [2.5]   Integers that are one unit apart.

Consistent system of equations [8.1]   A system of equations that has at least one solution.

Constant [1.1]   A known number.

Constant function [7.3]   A function given by an equation of the form $f(x) = b$, where b is a real number.

Constant of proportionality [7.5]   The constant in an equation of direct or inverse variation.

Constraint [9.5]   A requirement imposed on a problem.

Contradiction [2.2]   An equation that is never true.

Coordinates [3.1]   The numbers in an ordered pair.

Cube root [10.1]   The number c is called the cube root of a if $c^3 = a$.

D

Data point [3.7]   A given ordered pair of a function, usually found experimentally.

Degree of a polynomial [4.2]   The degree of the term of highest degree in a polynomial.

Degree of a term [4.2]   The number of variable factors in a term.

Demand function [8.8]   A function modeling the relationship between the price of a good and the quantity of that good demanded.

Denominator [1.3]   The number below the fraction bar in a fraction.

Dependent equations [8.1]   The equations in a system are dependent if one equation can be removed without changing the solution set.

Descending order [4.2]   A polynomial in one variable written with the terms arranged according to degree, from greatest to least.

Determinant [8.7]   The determinant of a two-by-two matrix $\begin{bmatrix} a & c \\ b & d \end{bmatrix}$ is denoted $\begin{vmatrix} a & c \\ b & d \end{vmatrix}$ and represents $ad - bc$.

Difference of squares [5.4]   An expression that can be written in the form $a^2 - b^2$.

Direct variation [7.5]   A situation that translates to an equation of the form $y = kx$, with k a constant.

Discriminant [11.4]   The expression $b^2 - 4ac$ from the quadratic formula.

Disjunction [9.2]   A sentence in which two statements are joined by the word *or*.

Distributive law [1.2]   The statement that multiplying a factor by the sum of two numbers gives the same result as multiplying the factor by each of the two numbers and then adding.

Domain [7.2]   The set of all first coordinates of the ordered pairs in a function.

Doubling time [12.7]   The time necessary for a population to double in size.

E

Elimination method [8.2]   An algebraic method that uses the addition principle to solve a system of equations.

Ellipse [13.2]   The set of all points in a plane for which the sum of the distances from two fixed points F_1 and F_2 is constant.

Equation [1.1]   A number sentence with the verb =.

Equation of variation [7.5]   An equation used to represent direct, inverse, or combined variation.

Equilibrium point [8.8]   The point of intersection between the demand function and the supply function.

Equivalent equations [2.1]   Equations with the same solutions.

Equivalent expressions [1.2]   Expressions that have the same value for all allowable replacements.

Equivalent inequalities [2.6]   Inequalities that have the same solution set.

Evaluate [1.1]   To substitute a value for each occurrence of a variable in an expression.

Exponent [1.8]   In expressions of the form a^n, the number n is an exponent. For n a natural number, a^n represents n factors of a.

Exponential decay [12.7]   A decrease in quantity over time that can be modeled by an exponential equation of the form $P(t) = P_0 e^{-kt}$, $k > 0$.

Exponential equation [12.6]   An equation in which a variable appears as an exponent.

Exponential function [12.2]   A function that can be described by an exponential equation.

Exponential growth [12.7]   An increase in quantity over time that can be modeled by an exponential function of the form $P(t) = P_0 e^{kt}$, $k > 0$.

Exponential notation [1.8]   A representation of a number using a base raised to a power.

Extrapolation [3.7]   The process of predicting a future value on the basis of given data.

F

Factor [1.2]   *Verb*: to write an equivalent expression that is a product. *Noun*: a multiplier.

Finite sequence [14.1]   A function having for its domain a set of natural numbers: $\{1, 2, 3, 4, 5, \ldots, n\}$, for some natural number n.

Fixed costs [8.8]   In business, costs that are incurred whether or not a product is produced.

Focus [13.2]   One of two fixed points that determine the points of an ellipse.

FOIL [4.5]   To multiply two binomials by multiplying the First terms, the Outside terms, the Inside terms, and then the Last terms.

Formula [2.3]   An equation that uses numbers or letters to represent a relationship between two or more quantities.

Fraction notation [1.3]   A number written using a numerator and a denominator.

Function [7.5]   A correspondence that assigns to each member of a set called the domain exactly one member of a set called the range.

G

General term of a sequence [14.1]   The nth term, denoted a_n.

Geometric sequence [14.3]   A sequence in which the ratio of every pair of successive terms is constant.

Geometric series [14.3]   A series for which the associated sequence is geometric.

Grade [3.5]   The ratio of the vertical distance a road rises over the horizontal distance it runs, expressed as a percent.

Graph [3.1]   A picture or diagram of the data in a table. A line, curve, or collection of points that represents all the solutions of an equation.

Greatest common factor [5.1]   The common factor of a polynomial with the largest possible coefficient and the largest possible exponent(s).

H

Half-life [12.7]   The amount of time necessary for half of a quantity to decay.

Half-open interval [9.1]   An interval that includes exactly one of two endpoints.

Horizontal-line test [12.1]   If it is impossible to draw a horizontal line that intersects the graph of a function more than once, then that function is one-to-one.

Hyperbola [13.3]   The set of all points P in the plane such that the difference of the distance from P to two fixed points is constant.

Hypotenuse [5.8]   In a right triangle, the side opposite the right angle.

I

Identity [2.2]   An equation that is always true.

Identity property of 0 [1.5]   The statement that the sum of a number and 0 is always the original number.

Identity property of 1 [1.3]   The statement that the product of a number and 1 is always the original number.

Imaginary number [10.8]   A number that can be written in the form $a + bi$, where a and b are real numbers and $b \neq 0$.

Imaginary number i [10.8]   The square root of -1. That is, $i = \sqrt{-1}$ and $i^2 = -1$.

Inconsistent system of equations [8.1]   A system of equations for which there is no solution.

Independent equations [8.1]   Equations that are not dependent.

Index [10.1]   In the radical $\sqrt[n]{a}$, the number n is called the index.

Inequality [1.4]   A mathematical sentence using $<, >, \leq, \geq,$ or $\neq$.

Infinite geometric series [14.3]   The sum of the terms of an infinite geometric sequence.

Infinite sequence [14.1]   A function having for its domain the set of natural numbers: $\{1, 2, 3, 4, 5, \ldots\}$.

Input [7.1]   A member of the domain of a function.

Integers [1.4]   The whole numbers and their opposites.

Interpolation [3.7]   The process of estimating a value between given values.

Intersection of two sets [9.2]   The set of all elements that are common to both sets.

Interval notation [9.1]   The use of a pair of numbers inside parentheses and brackets to represent the set of all numbers between those two numbers. *See also* Closed and Open intervals.

Inverse relation [12.1]   The relation formed by interchanging the members of the domain and the range of a relation.

Inverse variation [7.5]   A situation that translates to an equation of the form $y = k/x$, with k a constant.

Irrational number [1.4]   A real number that cannot be named as a ratio of two integers.

Isosceles right triangle [10.7]   A right triangle in which both legs have the same length.

J

Joint variation [7.5]   A situation that translates to an equation of the form $y = kxz$, with k a constant.

L

Leading coefficient [4.2]   The coefficient of the term of highest degree in a polynomial.

Leading term [4.2]   The term of highest degree in a polynomial.

Least common denominator [6.3]   The least common multiple of the denominators.

Legs [5.8]   In a right triangle, the two sides that form the right angle.

Like radicals [10.5]   Radical expressions that have a common radical factor.

Like terms [1.5]   Terms that have exactly the same variable factors.

Line graph [3.1]   A graph in which quantities are represented as points connected by straight-line segments.

Linear equation [3.2]   Any equation that can be written in the form $y = mx + b$, or $Ax + By = C$, where x and y are variables.

Linear function [7.3]   A function that can be described by an equation of the form $y = mx + b$, where x and y are variables.

Linear inequality [9.4]   An inequality whose related equation is a linear equation.

Linear programming [9.5]   A branch of mathematics involving graphs of inequalities and their constraints.

Logarithmic equation [12.6]   An equation containing a logarithmic expression.

Logarithmic function, base a [12.3]   The inverse of an exponential function with base a.

M

Matrix [8.6]   A rectangular array of numbers.

Maximum value [12.6]   The largest function value (output) achieved by a function.

Mean [2.7]   The sum of a set of numbers divided by the number of addends.

Minimum value [12.6]   The smallest function value (output) achieved by a function.

Monomial [4.2]   A constant, a variable, or a product of a constant and one or more variables.

Motion problem [6.7]   A problem that deals with distance, speed, and time.

Multiplicative inverses [1.3]   Reciprocals; two numbers whose product is 1.

Multiplicative property of zero [1.7]   The statement that the product of 0 and any real number is 0.

N

Natural logarithm [12.5]   A logarithm with base e.

Natural numbers [1.3]   The counting numbers: $1, 2, 3, 4, 5, \ldots$.

Nonlinear function [7.3]   A function whose graph is not a straight line.

Numerator [1.3]   The number above the fraction bar in a fraction.

O

Objective function [9.5]   In linear programming, the function in which the expression being maximized or minimized appears.

One-to-one function [12.1]   A function for which different inputs have different outputs.

Open interval (a, b) [9.1]   The set of all numbers x for which $a < x < b$. Thus, $(a, b) = \{x \mid a < x < b\}$.

Opposite [1.6]   The opposite, or additive inverse, of a number a is written $-a$. Opposites are the same distance from 0 on the number line but on different sides of 0.

Ordered pair [3.1]   A pair of numbers of the form (h, k) for which the order in which the numbers are listed is important.

Origin [3.1]   The point on a graph where the two axes intersect.

Output [7.1]   A member of the range of a function.

P

Parabola [11.6]   A graph of a quadratic function.

Parallel lines [3.6]   Lines that extend indefinitely without intersecting.

Pascal's triangle [14.4]   A triangular array of coefficients of the expansion $(a + b)^n$ for $n = 0, 1, 2, \ldots$.

Perfect square [10.1]   A rational number for which there exists a number a for which $a^2 = p$.

Perfect-square trinomial [5.4]   A trinomial that is the square of a binomial.

Perpendicular lines [3.6]   Lines that form a right angle.

Point–slope equation [3.7]   An equation of the type $y - y_1 = m(x - x_1)$, where x and y are variables.

Polynomial [4.2]   A monomial or a sum of monomials.

Polynomial equation [5.7]   An equation in which two polynomials are set equal to each other.

Polynomial inequality [11.9]   An inequality that is equivalent to an inequality with a polynomial as one side and 0 as the other.

Prime factorization [1.3]   The factorization of a whole number into a product of its prime factors.

Prime number [1.3]   A natural number that has exactly two different factors: the number itself and 1.

Principal square root [10.1]   The nonnegative square root of a number.

Proportion [6.7]   An equation stating that two ratios are equal.

Pure imaginary number [10.8]   A complex number of the form $a + bi$, with $a = 0$ and $b \neq 0$.

Pythagorean theorem [5.8]   In any right triangle, if a and b are the lengths of the legs and c is the length of the hypotenuse, then $a^2 + b^2 = c^2$.

Q

Quadrants [3.1]   The four regions into which the axes divide a plane.

Quadratic equation [5.7]   An equation equivalent to one of the form $ax^2 + bx + c = 0$, where $a \neq 0$.

Quadratic formula [11.2]   The solutions of $ax^2 + bx + c, a \neq 0$, are given by the equation
$$x = \frac{-b \pm \sqrt{b^2 - 4ac}}{2a}.$$

Quadratic function [11.1]   A second-degree polynomial function in one variable.

Quadratic inequality [11.9]   A second-degree polynomial inequality in one variable.

R

Radical equation [10.6]   An equation in which a variable appears in a radicand.

Radical expression [10.1]   An algebraic expression in which a radical sign appears.

Radical sign [10.1]   The symbol $\sqrt{}$.

Radical term [10.5]   A term in which a radical sign appears.

Radicand [10.1]   The expression under the radical sign.

Radius [13.1]   The distance from the center of a circle to a point on the circle. Also, a segment connecting the center to a point on the circle.

Range [7.2]   The set of all second coordinates of the ordered pairs in a function.

Rate [3.4]   A ratio that indicates how two quantities change with respect to each other.

Ratio [6.7]   The ratio of a to b is a/b, also written $a:b$.

Rational equation [6.6]   An equation containing one or more rational expressions.

Rational expression [6.1]   A quotient of two polynomials.

Rational inequality [11.9]   An inequality containing a rational expression.

Rational number [1.4]   A number that can be written in the form $\frac{a}{b}$, where a and b are integers and $b \neq 0$.

Rationalizing the denominator [10.4]   A procedure for finding an equivalent expression without a radical in the denominator.

Rationalizing the numerator [10.4]   A procedure for finding an equivalent expression without a radical in the numerator.

Real number [1.4]   Any number that is either rational or irrational.

Reciprocal [1.3]   A multiplicative inverse. Two numbers are reciprocals if their product is 1.

Reflection [11.6]   The mirror image of a graph.

Relation [7.1]   A correspondence between the domain and the range of a function such that each member of the domain corresponds to at least one member of the range.

Repeating decimal [1.4]   A decimal in which a number pattern repeats indefinitely.

Right triangle [5.8]   A triangle that includes a right angle.

Row-equivalent operations [11.6]   Operations used to produce equivalent systems of equations.

S

Scientific notation [4.8]   A number written in the form $N \times 10^{m}$, where m is an integer, $1 \leq N < 10$, and N is expressed in decimal notation.

Sequence [14.1]   A function for which the domain is a set of consecutive positive integers beginning with 1.

Series [14.1]   The sum of specified terms in a sequence.

Set [1.4]   A collection of objects.

Set-builder notation [2.6]   The naming of a set by describing basic characteristics of the elements in the set.

Sigma notation [14.1]   The naming of a sum using the Greek letter Σ (sigma) as part of an abbreviated form.

Similar triangles [10.7]   Triangles in which corresponding sides are proportional.

Simplify   To rewrite an expression in an equivalent, abbreviated, form.

Slope [3.5]   The ratio of the rise to the run for any two points on a line.

Slope–intercept equation [3.6]   An equation of the form $y = mx + b$, where x and y are variables.

Solution [1.1]   A replacement or substitution that makes an equation or inequality true.

Solution set [2.6]   The set of all solutions of an equation, an inequality, or a system of equations or inequalities.

Solve [2.1]   To find all solutions of an equation, an inequality, or a system of equations or inequalities; to find the solution(s) of a problem.

Speed [6.7]   The ratio of distance traveled to the time required to travel that distance.

Square matrix [8.7]   A matrix with the same number of rows and columns.

Square root [10.1]   The number c is a square root of a if $c^2 = a$.

Substitute [1.1]   To replace a variable with a number.

Substitution method [8.2]   An algebraic method for solving systems of equations.

Supply function [11.8]   A function modeling the relationship between the price of a good and the quantity of that good supplied.

System of equations [11.1]   A set of two or more equations that are to be solved simultaneously.

T

Term [1.2]   A number, a variable, or a product or a quotient of numbers and/or variables.

Terminating decimal [1.4]   A decimal that can be written using a finite number of decimal places.

Total cost [8.8]   The amount spent to produce a product.

Total profit [8.8]   The amount taken in less the amount spent, or total revenue minus total cost.

Total revenue [8.8]   The amount taken in from the sale of a product.

Trinomial [4.2]   A polynomial that is composed of three terms.

U

Union of A and B [9.2]   The set of all elements belonging to either A or B.

Undefined [1.7]   An expression that has no meaning attached to it.

V

Value [1.1]   The numerical result after a number has been substituted into an expression.

Variable [1.1]   A letter that represents an unknown number.

Variable costs [8.8]   In business, costs that vary according to the amount of products produced.

Variable expression [1.1]   An expression containing a variable.

Vertex [11.6]   The point at which the graph of a quadratic equation crosses its axis of symmetry.

Vertical-line test [7.3]   The statement that a graph represents a function if it is impossible to draw a vertical line that intersects the graph more than once.

W

Whole numbers [1.3]   The natural numbers and 0: 0, 1, 2, 3, . . .

X

***x*-intercept** [3.3]   The point at which a graph crosses the *x*-axis.

Y

***y*-intercept** [3.3]   The point at which a graph crosses the *y*-axis.

Z

Zeros [11.9]   The *x*-values for which $f(x)$ is 0, for any function f.

Photo Credits

Answers

CHAPTER 1

Technology Connection, p. 7

1. 3438 **2.** 47,531

Exercise Set 1.1, pp. 9–12

1. Expression **3.** Equation **5.** Equation **7.** Expression
9. Equation **11.** Expression **13.** 36 **15.** 56 **17.** 5
19. 4 **21.** 5 **23.** 6 **25.** 24 ft^2 **27.** 15 cm^2 **29.** 0.368
31. Let r represent Ron's age; $r + 5$, or $5 + r$ **33.** $b + 6$,
or $6 + b$ **35.** $c - 9$ **37.** $6 + q$, or $q + 6$ **39.** Let p
represent Phil's speed; $9p$, or $p \cdot 9$ **41.** $y - x$

43. $x \div w$, or $\dfrac{x}{w}$ **45.** $n - m$

47. Let l represent the length of the box and h represent
the height; $l + h$, or $h + l$ **49.** $9 \cdot 2m$, or $2m \cdot 9$ **51.** Let y
represent "some number"; $\frac{1}{4}y$, or $\frac{y}{4}$ **53.** Let w represent
the number of women attending; 64% of w, or $0.64w$
55. Yes **57.** No **59.** Yes **61.** Yes **63.** Let x represent
the unknown number; $73 + x = 201$ **65.** Let x represent
the unknown number; $42x = 2352$ **67.** Let s represent the
number of unoccupied squares; $s + 19 = 64$ **69.** Let w
represent the amount of solid waste generated, in millions
of tons; 27% of $w = 56$, or $0.27w = 56$ **71.** (f) **73.** (d)
75. (g) **77.** (e) **79.** ▨ **81.** ▨ **83.** $337.50 **85.** 2
87. 6 **89.** $w + 4$ **91.** $l + w + l + w$, or $2l + 2w$
93. $t + 8$ **95.** ▨

Exercise Set 1.2, pp. 18–19

1. Commutative **3.** Associative **5.** Distributive
7. Associative **9.** Commutative **11.** $x + 7$ **13.** $c + ab$
15. $3y + 9x$ **17.** $5(1 + a)$ **19.** $a \cdot 2$ **21.** ts **23.** $5 + ba$
25. $(a + 1)5$ **27.** $a + (5 + b)$ **29.** $(r + t) + 7$

31. $ab + (c + d)$ **33.** $8(xy)$ **35.** $(2a)b$ **37.** $(3 \cdot 2)(a + b)$
39. $(r + t) + 6$; $(t + 6) + r$ **41.** $17(ab)$; $b(17a)$
43. $(5 + x) + 2 = (x + 5) + 2$ Commutative law
            $= x + (5 + 2)$ Associative law
            $= x + 7$ Simplifying
45. $(m \cdot 3)7 = m(3 \cdot 7)$ Associative law
          $= m \cdot 21$ Simplifying
          $= 21m$ Commutative law
47. $4a + 12$ **49.** $6 + 6x$ **51.** $3x + 3$ **53.** $24 + 8y$
55. $18x + 54$ **57.** $5r + 10 + 15t$ **59.** $2a + 2b$

61. $5x + 5y + 10$ **63.** $x, xyz, 19$ **65.** $2a, \dfrac{a}{b}, 5b$

67. $2(a + b)$ **69.** $7(1 + y)$ **71.** $3(6x + 1)$
73. $5(x + 2 + 3y)$ **75.** $3(4x + 3)$ **77.** $3(a + 3b)$
79. $11(4x + y + 2z)$ **81.** s, t **83.** $3, (x + y)$ **85.** $7, a$
87. $(a - b), (x - y)$ **89.** ▨ **91.** Let k represent Kara's

salary; $2k$ **92.** $\dfrac{1}{2} \cdot m$, or $\dfrac{m}{2}$ **93.** ▨

95. Yes; distributive law **97.** Yes; distributive law and
commutative law of multiplication **99.** No; for example,
let $x = 1$ and $y = 2$. Then $30 \cdot 2 + 1 \cdot 15 = 60 + 15 = 75$
and $5[2(1 + 3 \cdot 2)] = 5[2(7)] = 5 \cdot 14 = 70$. **101.** ▨

Exercise Set 1.3, pp. 28–30

1. Composite **3.** Prime **5.** Composite **7.** Prime
9. Neither **11.** (b) **13.** (d) **15.** $2 \cdot 25$; $5 \cdot 10$; 1, 2, 5, 10,
25, 50 **17.** $3 \cdot 14$; $6 \cdot 7$; 1, 2, 3, 6, 7, 14, 21, 42 **19.** $2 \cdot 13$
21. $2 \cdot 3 \cdot 5$ **23.** $3 \cdot 3 \cdot 3$ **25.** $2 \cdot 3 \cdot 3$ **27.** $2 \cdot 2 \cdot 2 \cdot 5$
29. Prime **31.** $2 \cdot 3 \cdot 5 \cdot 7$ **33.** $5 \cdot 23$ **35.** $\frac{2}{3}$ **37.** $\frac{2}{7}$
39. $\frac{1}{8}$ **41.** 7 **43.** $\frac{1}{4}$ **45.** 6 **47.** $\frac{21}{25}$ **49.** $\frac{60}{41}$ **51.** $\frac{15}{7}$

53. $\frac{3}{14}$ **55.** $\frac{27}{8}$ **57.** $\frac{1}{2}$ **59.** $\frac{7}{6}$ **61.** $\dfrac{3b}{7a}$ **63.** $\dfrac{7}{a}$ **65.** $\frac{5}{6}$

67. 1 **69.** $\frac{5}{18}$ **71.** 0 **73.** $\frac{35}{18}$ **75.** $\frac{10}{3}$ **77.** 28 **79.** 1
81. $\frac{6}{35}$ **83.** 18 **85.** ▨ **87.** $5(3 + x)$; answers may vary

88. $7 + (b + a)$, or $(a + b) + 7$ **89.** 🖳
91. Row 1: 7, 2, 36, 14, 8, 8; row 2: 9, 18, 2, 10, 12, 21
93. $\frac{2}{5}$ **95.** $\frac{3q}{t}$ **97.** $\frac{6}{25}$ **99.** $\frac{5ap}{2cm}$ **101.** $\frac{23r}{18t}$ **103.** $\frac{28}{45}\,\text{m}^2$
105. $14\frac{2}{9}\,\text{m}$ **107.** $27\frac{3}{5}\,\text{cm}$

Technology Connection, p. 34

1. 2.236067977   **2.** 2.645751311   **3.** 3.605551275
4. 5.196152423   **5.** 6.164414003   **6.** 7.071067812

Exercise Set 1.4, pp. 37–39

1. Repeating   **3.** Integer   **5.** Rational number
7. Natural number   **9.** $-1349, 29{,}035$ **11.** $950{,}000{,}000$,
-460 **13.** $2, -6$ **15.** $750, -125$ **17.** Jets: -34; Strikers: 34
19.
21.
23.
25. 0.875   **27.** -0.75
29. $1.1\overline{6}$ **31.** $0.\overline{6}$ **33.** -0.5 **35.** 0.13   **37.** $<$ **39.** $>$
41. $<$ **43.** $<$ **45.** $>$ **47.** $<$ **49.** $<$ **51.** $x < -7$
53. $y \geq -10$ **55.** True   **57.** False   **59.** True   **61.** 58
63. 17   **65.** 5.6   **67.** 329   **69.** $\frac{9}{7}$ **71.** 0   **73.** 8
75. $-83, -4.7, 0, \frac{5}{9}, 8.31, 62$ **77.** $-83, 0, 62$
79. $-83, -4.7, 0, \frac{5}{9}, \pi, \sqrt{17}, 8.31, 62$ **81.** 🖳   **83.** 42
84. $ba + 5$, or $5 + ab$ **85.** 🖳   **87.** 🖳   **89.** $-23, -17, 0, 4$
91. $-\frac{4}{3}, \frac{4}{9}, \frac{4}{8}, \frac{4}{6}, \frac{4}{5}, \frac{4}{3}, \frac{4}{2}$ **93.** $<$ **95.** $=$ **97.** $-7, 7$
99. $-4, -3, 3, 4$ **101.** $\frac{3}{3}$ **103.** $\frac{70}{9}$ **105.** 🖳

Exercise Set 1.5, pp. 44–46

1. (f)   **3.** (e)   **5.** (b)   **7.** -3 **9.** 4   **11.** 0   **13.** -8
15. -27 **17.** -8 **19.** 0   **21.** -41 **23.** 0   **25.** 7
27. -2 **29.** 11   **31.** -33 **33.** 0   **35.** 18   **37.** -45
39. 0   **41.** 20   **43.** -1.7 **45.** -9.1 **47.** $\frac{1}{5}$ **49.** $\frac{-6}{7}$
51. $-\frac{1}{15}$ **53.** $\frac{2}{9}$ **55.** -3 **57.** 0   **59.** The price rose 9¢.
61. Her new balance was $95.   **63.** The total gain was
22 yd.   **65.** Lyle owes $85.   **67.** The elevation of the peak
is 13,796 ft.   **69.** $14a$ **71.** $9x$ **73.** $13t$ **75.** $-2m$
77. $-7a$ **79.** $1 - 2x$ **81.** $12x + 17$ **83.** $7r + 8t + 16$
85. $18n + 16$ **87.** 🖳   **89.** $21z + 7y + 14$ **90.** $\frac{28}{3}$ **91.** 🖳
93. $65.25   **95.** $-5y$ **97.** $-7m$ **99.** $-7t, -23$
101. 1 under par

Exercise Set 1.6, pp. 51–54

1. (d)   **3.** (f)   **5.** (a)   **7.** (b)   **9.** Four minus ten
11. Two minus negative nine   **13.** Nine minus the

opposite of t **15.** The opposite of x minus y
17. Negative three minus the opposite of n **19.** -39
21. 9   **23.** 3.14   **25.** -23 **27.** $\frac{14}{3}$ **29.** -0.101 **31.** 72
33. $-\frac{2}{5}$ **35.** 1   **37.** -7 **39.** -2 **41.** -5 **43.** -6
45. -10 **47.** -6 **49.** 0   **51.** -5 **53.** -10 **55.** 2
57. 0   **59.** 0   **61.** 8   **63.** -11 **65.** 16   **67.** -19
69. -1 **71.** 17   **73.** -5 **75.** -3 **77.** -21 **79.** 5
81. -8 **83.** 10   **85.** -23 **87.** -68 **89.** -58
91. -5.5 **93.** -0.928 **95.** $-\frac{7}{11}$ **97.** $-\frac{4}{5}$ **99.** $\frac{5}{17}$
101. $3.8 - (-5.2)$; 9   **103.** $114 - (-79)$; 193   **105.** -58
107. 34   **109.** 41   **111.** -62 **113.** -139 **115.** 0
117. $-7x, -4y$ **119.** $9, -5t, -3st$ **121.** $-3x$
123. $-5a + 4$ **125.** $-7n - 9$ **127.** $-6x + 5$
129. $-8t - 7$ **131.** $-12x + 3y + 9$ **133.** $8x + 66$
135. 150°C   **137.** 30,384 ft   **139.** 116 m   **141.** 🖳
143. $432\,\text{ft}^2$ **144.** $2 \cdot 2 \cdot 2 \cdot 2 \cdot 2 \cdot 3 \cdot 3 \cdot 3$ **145.** 🖳
147. 11:00 P.M., August 14   **149.** False. For example,
let $m = -3$ and $n = -5$. Then $-3 > -5$, but
$-3 + (-5) = -8 \not> 0$.   **151.** True. For example, for $m = 4$
and $n = -4$, $4 = -(-4)$ and $4 + (-4) = 0$; for $m = -3$ and
$n = 3$, $-3 = -3$ and $-3 + 3 = 0$.
153. (-) 9 − (-) 7 ENTER

Exercise Set 1.7, pp. 60–62

1. 1   **3.** 0   **5.** 0   **7.** 1   **9.** 1   **11.** -24 **13.** -56
15. -24 **17.** -72 **19.** 42   **21.** 45   **23.** 190   **25.** -144
27. 1200   **29.** 98   **31.** -78 **33.** 21.7   **35.** $-\frac{2}{5}$ **37.** $\frac{1}{12}$
39. -11.13 **41.** $-\frac{5}{12}$ **43.** 252   **45.** 0   **47.** $\frac{1}{28}$ **49.** 150
51. 0   **53.** -720 **55.** $-30{,}240$ **57.** -7 **59.** -4 **61.** -7
63. 4   **65.** -8 **67.** 2   **69.** -12 **71.** -8 **73.** Undefined
75. -4 **77.** 0   **79.** 0   **81.** $-\frac{8}{3}; \frac{8}{-3}$ **83.** $-\frac{29}{35}, \frac{-29}{35}$
85. $\frac{-7}{3}; \frac{7}{-3}$ **87.** $-\frac{x}{2}; \frac{x}{-2}$ **89.** $-\frac{5}{4}$ **91.** $-\frac{13}{47}$ **93.** $-\frac{1}{10}$
95. $\frac{1}{4.3}$, or $\frac{10}{43}$ **97.** $-\frac{4}{9}$ **99.** Does not exist   **101.** $\frac{21}{20}$
103. $\frac{12}{55}$ **105.** -1 **107.** 1   **109.** $-\frac{9}{11}$ **111.** $-\frac{7}{4}$
113. -12 **115.** -3 **117.** 1   **119.** 7   **121.** $-\frac{2}{9}$ **123.** $\frac{1}{10}$
125. $-\frac{7}{6}$ **127.** $\frac{6}{7}$ **129.** $-\frac{14}{15}$ **131.** 🖳   **133.** $\frac{22}{39}$
134. $12x - 2y - 9$ **135.** 🖳   **137.** For 2 and 3, the
reciprocal of the sum is $1/(2 + 3)$ or $1/5$. But
$1/5 \neq 1/2 + 1/3$.   **139.** Negative   **141.** Negative
143. Negative   **145.** (a) m and n have different signs;
(b) either m or n is zero; (c) m and n have the same sign.
147. 🖳

Exercise Set 1.8, pp. 70–72

1. (a) Division; (b) subtraction; (c) addition;
(d) multiplication; (e) subtraction; (f) multiplication
3. 2^3 **5.** x^7 **7.** $(3t)^5$ **9.** 9   **11.** 16   **13.** -16 **15.** 64
17. 625   **19.** 7   **21.** $81t^4$ **23.** $-343x^3$ **25.** 26   **27.** 86
29. 7   **31.** 5   **33.** 1   **35.** 298   **37.** 11   **39.** -36
41. 1291   **43.** 14   **45.** 152   **47.** 36   **49.** 1   **51.** -26

53. −2 **55.** −$\frac{9}{2}$ **57.** −11 **59.** −3 **61.** −15 **63.** 9
65. 30 **67.** 6 **69.** −17 **71.** −9x − 1 **73.** −5 + 6x
75. −4a + 3b − 7c **77.** −3x² − 5x + 1 **79.** 2x − 7
81. −3a + 9 **83.** 5x − 6 **85.** −3t − 11r **87.** 9y − 25z
89. x² + 2 **91.** −t³ − 2t **93.** 37a² − 23ab + 35b²
95. −22t³ − t² + 9t **97.** 2x − 25 **99.** 🖉 **101.** Let n
represent the number; 2n + 9, or 9 + 2n **102.** Let m and
n represent the two numbers; $\frac{1}{2}(m + n)$ **103.** 🖉
105. −6r − 5t + 21 **107.** −2x − f **109.** 🖉 **111.** True
113. False **115.** 0 **117.** 39,000 **119.** 44x³

Review Exercises: Chapter 1, pp. 75–77

1. True **2.** True **3.** False **4.** True **5.** False **6.** False
7. True **8.** False **9.** False **10.** True **11.** 15 **12.** 4
13. −7 **14.** −5 **15.** z − 7 **16.** xz **17.** Let m and n
represent the numbers; mn + 1, or 1 + mn **18.** No
19. Let d represent the number of digital photos taken in
2003, in billions; 29.8 = d + 18.49 **20.** t · 3 + 5
21. 2x + (y + z) **22.** (4x)y, 4(yx), (4y)x; answers may vary
23. 18x + 30y **24.** 40x + 24y + 16 **25.** 3(7x + 5y)
26. 7(5x + 2 + y) **27.** 2 · 2 · 13 **28.** $\frac{5}{12}$ **29.** $\frac{9}{4}$ **30.** $\frac{31}{36}$
31. $\frac{3}{16}$ **32.** $\frac{3}{5}$ **33.** $\frac{72}{25}$ **34.** −45, 72
35.
$$\xleftarrow{\qquad} \overset{-\frac{1}{3}}{\underset{-5\ -4\ -3\ -2\ -1\ 0\ 1\ 2\ 3\ 4\ 5}{\bullet}} \xrightarrow{\qquad}$$
36. x > −3
37. True **38.** False **39.** −0.875 **40.** 1 **41.** −9
42. −3 **43.** −$\frac{7}{12}$ **44.** 0 **45.** −5 **46.** 5 **47.** −$\frac{7}{5}$
48. −7.9 **49.** 54 **50.** −9.18 **51.** −$\frac{2}{7}$ **52.** −140
53. −7 **54.** −3 **55.** $\frac{3}{4}$ **56.** 92 **57.** 62 **58.** 48
59. 168 **60.** $\frac{21}{8}$ **61.** $\frac{103}{17}$ **62.** 7a − 3b **63.** −2x + 5y
64. 7 **65.** −$\frac{1}{7}$ **66.** (2x)⁴ **67.** −125x³ **68.** −3a + 9
69. −2b + 21 **70.** −3x + 9 **71.** 12y − 34 **72.** 5x + 24
73. 🖉 The value of a constant never varies. A variable can
represent a variety of numbers. **74.** 🖉 A term is one of
the parts of an expression that is separated from the other
parts by plus signs. A factor is part of a product.
75. 🖉 The distributive law is used in factoring algebraic
expressions, multiplying algebraic expressions, combining
like terms, finding the opposite of a sum, and subtracting
algebraic expressions. **76.** 🖉 A negative number raised
to an even power is positive; a negative number raised to
an odd power is negative. **77.** 25,281
78. (a) $\frac{3}{11}$; (b) $\frac{10}{11}$ **79.** −$\frac{5}{8}$ **80.** −2.1 **81.** (i) **82.** (j)
83. (a) **84.** (h) **85.** (k) **86.** (b) **87.** (c) **88.** (e)
89. (d) **90.** (f) **91.** (g)

Test: Chapter 1, p. 78

1. [1.1] 4 **2.** [1.1] Let x represent the number; x − 9
3. [1.1] 240 ft² **4.** [1.2] q + 3p **5.** [1.2] (x · 4) · y
6. [1.1] No **7.** [1.1] Let p represent the maximum
production capability; p − 282 = 2518 **8.** [1.2] 35 − 7x
9. [1.7] −5y + 10 **10.** [1.2] 11(1 − 4x)

11. [1.2] 7(x + 3 + 2y) **12.** [1.3] 2 · 2 · 3 · 5 · 5
13. [1.3] $\frac{2}{7}$ **14.** [1.4] < **15.** [1.4] > **16.** [1.4] $\frac{9}{4}$
17. [1.4] 2.7 **18.** [1.6] −$\frac{2}{3}$ **19.** [1.7] −$\frac{7}{4}$ **20.** [1.6] 8
21. [1.4] −2 ≥ x **22.** [1.6] 7.8 **23.** [1.5] −8
24. [1.6] −2.5 **25.** [1.6] $\frac{7}{8}$ **26.** [1.7] −48 **27.** [1.7] $\frac{3}{16}$
28. [1.7] −6 **29.** [1.7] $\frac{3}{4}$ **30.** [1.7] −9.728 **31.** [1.8] −173
32. [1.6] 15 **33.** [1.8] −4 **34.** [1.8] 448
35. [1.6] 21a + 22y **36.** [1.8] 16x⁴ **37.** [1.8] x + 7
38. [1.8] 9a − 12b − 7 **39.** [1.8] 68y − 8 **40.** [1.1] 5
41. [1.8] 9 − (3 − 4) + 5 = 15 **42.** [1.8] 15 **43.** [1.8] 4a
44. [1.8] False

CHAPTER 2

Exercise Set 2.1, pp. 87–88

1. (f) **3.** (a) **5.** (d) **7.** 17 **9.** −11 **11.** −21
13. −31 **15.** 13 **17.** 19 **19.** −4 **21.** $\frac{7}{3}$ **23.** −$\frac{13}{10}$
25. $\frac{41}{24}$ **27.** −$\frac{1}{20}$ **29.** 1.5 **31.** −5 **33.** 14 **35.** 4
37. 12 **39.** −23 **41.** 8 **43.** −7 **45.** 8 **47.** −88
49. 20 **51.** −54 **53.** $\frac{5}{9}$ **55.** 1 **57.** $\frac{9}{2}$ **59.** −7.6
61. −2.5 **63.** −15 **65.** 18 **67.** −6 **69.** −128
71. −$\frac{1}{2}$ **73.** −15 **75.** 12 **77.** 310.756 **79.** 🖉
81. −34 **82.** 41 **83.** 1 **84.** −16 **85.** 🖉 **87.** 9.4
89. 2 **91.** −13, 13 **93.** 9000 **95.** 250

Technology Connection, p. 92

1.

X	Y1
0	5
1	4
2	3
3	2
4	1
5	0
6	−1

X = 0

2.

X	Y1	Y2
0	5	17
1	4	13
2	3	9
3	2	5
4	1	1
5	0	−3
6	−1	−7

X = 0

3. 4; not reliable because, depending on the choice of
ΔTbl, it is easy to scroll past a solution without realizing it.

Exercise Set 2.2, pp. 95–97

1. (c) **3.** (a) **5.** (b) **7.** 8 **9.** 7 **11.** 5 **13.** 14
15. −7 **17.** −11 **19.** −24 **21.** 19 **23.** $\frac{10}{9}$ **25.** 3
27. 15 **29.** −4 **31.** −$\frac{28}{3}$ **33.** All real numbers; identity
35. −3 **37.** 5 **39.** 2 **41.** 0 **43.** 8 **45.** 0 **47.** 10
49. 4 **51.** 0 **53.** 2 **55.** −8 **57.** 2 **59.** No solution;
contradiction **61.** −$\frac{2}{5}$ **63.** $\frac{64}{3}$ **65.** $\frac{2}{5}$ **67.** 3 **69.** −4
71. 1.$\overline{6}$ **73.** −$\frac{40}{37}$ **75.** 11 **77.** 6 **79.** $\frac{16}{15}$ **81.** −$\frac{51}{31}$ **83.** 2
85. 🖉 **87.** −7 **88.** 15 **89.** −15 **90.** −28 **91.** 🖉
93. $\frac{1136}{909}$, or 1.$\overline{2497}$ **95.** No solution; contradiction
97. No solution; contradiction **99.** $\frac{2}{3}$ **101.** 0 **103.** 0
105. −2

Technology Connection, p. 98

1. 72,930

Exercise Set 2.3, pp. 101–104

1. 2 mi   3. 1423 students   5. 54,000 Btu's   7. 255 mg

9. $b = \dfrac{A}{h}$ 11. $r = \dfrac{d}{t}$ 13. $P = \dfrac{I}{rt}$ 15. $m = 65 - H$

17. $l = \dfrac{P - 2w}{2}$, or $l = \dfrac{P}{2} - w$ 19. $\pi = \dfrac{A}{r^2}$ 21. $h = \dfrac{2A}{b}$

23. $m = \dfrac{E}{c^2}$ 25. $d = 2Q - c$ 27. $b = 3A - a - c$

29. $A = Ms$ 31. $C = \frac{5}{9}(F - 32)$ 33. $t = \dfrac{A}{a + b}$

35. $h = \dfrac{2A}{a + b}$ 37. $L = W - \dfrac{N(R - r)}{400}$, or

$L = \dfrac{400W - NR + Nr}{400}$ 39. 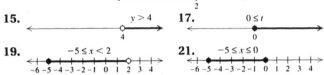   41. 0   42. 9.18

43. -13 44. 65   45.   47. 35 yr   49. 27 in^3

51. $a = \dfrac{w}{c} \cdot d$ 53. $c = \dfrac{d}{a - b}$ 55. $a = \dfrac{c}{3 + b + d}$

57. $K = 917 + 13.2276w + 2.3622h - 6a$

Exercise Set 2.4, pp. 109–113

1. (d)   3. (e)   5. (c)   7. (f)   9. (b)   11. 0.3   13. 0.02
15. 0.77   17. 0.09   19. 0.6258   21. 0.007   23. 1.25
25. 64%   27. 10.6%   29. 42%   31. 90%   33. 0.49%
35. 108%   37. 230%   39. 80%   41. 32%   43. 25%
45. 24%   47. $46\frac{2}{3}$, or $\frac{140}{3}$ 49. 2.5   51. 84   53. 125%
55. 0.8   57. 50%   59. $198   61. $1584   63. $528
65. 75 credits   67. About 626 at-bats   69. (a) 16%;
(b) $29   71. About 72%; about 28%   73. $280
75. 285 women   77. $18/hr   79. 150%   81. $36
83. $148.50   85. About 31.5 lb   87. 7410 brochures
89. About 165 calories   91.   93. Let n represent the
number; $n + 5$ 94. Let t represent Tino's weight; $t - 4$
95. $8 \cdot 2a$ 96. Let x and y represent the two numbers;
$xy + 1$ 97.   99. 18,500 people   101. About 5 ft 6 in.
103. About 27%   105.

Exercise Set 2.5, pp. 122–127

1. 8   3. 11   5. $85   7. $85   9. Approximately $62\frac{2}{3}$ mi
11. 190 mi   13. 1204 and 1205   15. 396 and 398
17. 19, 20, 21   19. Bride: 102 yr; groom: 83 yr
21. Bathrooms: $$11\frac{2}{3}$ billion; kitchens: $$23\frac{1}{3}$ billion
23. 140 and 141   25. Width: 100 ft; length: 160 ft; area:
16,000 ft^2 27. Width: 50 ft; length: 84 ft   29. $1\frac{3}{4}$ in. by
$3\frac{1}{2}$ in.   31. 30°, 90°, 60°   33. 95°   35. Bottom: 144 ft;
middle: 72 ft; top: 24 ft   37. $10\frac{1}{16}$ mi   39. $128\frac{1}{3}$ mi

41. 65°, 25°   43. Length: 27.9 cm; width: 21.6 cm
45. $6600   47. 1049 points   49. 160 chirps per minute
51.   53. <   54. <   55. <   56. >   57.
59. $37   61. 20   63. Half-dollars: 5; quarters: 10; dimes:
20; nickels: 60   65. 120 apples   67. 30 games   69. 76
71.   73. Width: 23.31 cm; length: 27.56 cm

Exercise Set 2.6, pp. 133–135

1. ≥   3. <   5. Equivalent   7. Equivalent   9. (a) Yes;
(b) yes; (c) yes; (d) no; (e) yes   11. (a) No; (b) no; (c) yes;
(d) yes; (e) no   13. $y < 2$

15. $y > 4$ 17. $0 \le t$

19. $-5 \le x < 2$ 21. $-5 \le x \le 0$

23. $\{x \mid x > -4\}$ 25. $\{x \mid x \le 2\}$ 27. $\{x \mid x < -1\}$
29. $\{x \mid x \ge 0\}$ 31. $\{y \mid y > 3\}$,
33. $\{x \mid x \le -21\}$,
35. $\{x \mid x < 17\}$,
37. $\{y \mid y > -6\}$,
39. $\{x \mid x \le 9\}$,
41. $\{y \mid y \le \frac{1}{2}\}$,
43. $\{t \mid t > \frac{5}{8}\}$,
45. $\{x \mid x < 0\}$,
47. $\{t \mid t < 23\}$,
49. $\{x \mid x < 7\}$,
51. $\{x \mid x > -\frac{13}{7}\}$,
53. $\{t \mid t < -3\}$,
55. $\{y \mid y \ge -\frac{2}{7}\}$,
57. $\{y \mid y \ge -\frac{1}{10}\}$,
59. $\{x \mid x > \frac{4}{5}\}$,

61. $\{x \mid x < 9\}$ 63. $\{y \mid y \ge 4\}$ 65. $\{t \mid t \le 7\}$
67. $\{y \mid y < -4\}$ 69. $\{x \mid x > -4\}$ 71. $\{y \mid y < -\frac{10}{3}\}$
73. $\{x \mid x > -10\}$ 75. $\{y \mid y < 2\}$ 77. $\{y \mid y \ge 3\}$
79. $\{x \mid x > -4\}$ 81. $\{x \mid x > -4\}$ 83. $\{n \mid n \ge 70\}$
85. $\{x \mid x \le 15\}$ 87. $\{t \mid t < 14\}$ 89. $\{y \mid y < 6\}$
91. $\{t \mid t \le -4\}$ 93. $\{r \mid r > -3\}$ 95. $\{x \mid x \ge 8\}$
97. $\{x \mid x < \frac{11}{18}\}$ 99.   101. Let n represent "some
number"; $3 + n$ 102. Let x and y represent the two

numbers; $2(x + y)$ **103.** Let x represent the number; $2x - 3$ **104.** Let y represent the number; $2y + 5$
105. 🗔   **107.** $\{x \mid x \text{ is a real number}\}$ **109.** $\left\{x \mid x \le \frac{5}{6}\right\}$
111. $\{x \mid x > 7\}$ **113.** $\left\{x \mid x < \dfrac{y - b}{a}\right\}$
115. $\{x \mid x \text{ is a real number}\}$

Exercise Set 2.7, pp. 138–142

1. $b \le a$ **3.** $a \le b$ **5.** $b \le a$ **7.** $b < a$ **9.** Let n represent the number; $n \ge 8$ **11.** Let t represent the temperature; $t \le -3$ **13.** Let p represent the price of Pat's PT Cruiser; $p > 21,900$ **15.** Let d represent the distance to Normandale Community College; $d \le 15$ **17.** Let n represent the number; $n > -2$ **19.** Let p represent the number of people attending the Million Man March; $400,000 < p < 1,200,000$ **21.** More than 2.5 hr
23. More than 18 one-way trips per month   **25.** Scores greater than or equal to 97   **27.** 8 credits or more
29. 21 calls or more   **31.** Lengths greater than 6 cm
33. Depths less than 437.5 ft   **35.** Blue-book value is greater than or equal to $10,625   **37.** Lengths greater than or equal to 5 in.   **39.** Temperatures greater than 37°C
41. Heights at least 4 ft   **43.** A serving contains at least 16 g of fat.   **45.** Dates after September 16   **47.** 14 or fewer copies   **49.** Years after 1995   **51.** Mileages less than or equal to 193   **53.** 🗔   **55.** 2   **56.** $\frac{1}{2}$ **57.** $-\frac{10}{3}$
58. $-\frac{1}{5}$ **59.** 🗔   **61.** Temperatures between $-15°C$ and $-9\frac{4}{9}°C$ **63.** Lengths less than or equal to 8 cm
65. They contain at least 7.5 g of fat per serving.
67. At least $42   **69.** 🗔

Review Exercises: Chapter 2, pp. 144–145

1. True   **2.** False   **3.** True   **4.** True   **5.** True   **6.** False
7. True   **8.** True   **9.** -25 **10.** 7   **11.** -65 **12.** 1
13. -5 **14.** 1.11   **15.** $\frac{1}{2}$ **16.** $-\frac{15}{64}$ **17.** $\frac{38}{5}$ **18.** -8
19. -5 **20.** $-\frac{1}{3}$ **21.** 4   **22.** 3   **23.** 4   **24.** 16   **25.** 7
26. $-\frac{7}{5}$ **27.** 12   **28.** No solution; contradiction
29. $d = \dfrac{C}{\pi}$ **30.** $B = \dfrac{3V}{h}$ **31.** $b = 2A - a$ **32.** 0.009
33. 44%   **34.** 70%   **35.** 140   **36.** Yes   **37.** No   **38.** Yes
39. $5x - 6 < 2x + 3$ [number line: $-5 -4 -3 -2 -1\ 0\ 1\ 2\ 3\ 4\ 5$]   **40.** $-2 < x \le 5$ [number line: $-5 -4 -3 -2 -1\ 0\ 1\ 2\ 3\ 4\ 5$]
41. $t > 0$ [number line: $-5 -4 -3 -2 -1\ 0\ 1\ 2\ 3\ 4\ 5$]   **42.** $\left\{t \mid t \ge -\frac{1}{2}\right\}$
43. $\{x \mid x \ge 7\}$ **44.** $\{y \mid y > 3\}$ **45.** $\{y \mid y \le -4\}$
46. $\{x \mid x < -11\}$ **47.** $\{y \mid y > -7\}$ **48.** $\{x \mid x > -6\}$
49. $\left\{x \mid x > -\frac{9}{11}\right\}$ **50.** $\{t \mid t \le -12\}$ **51.** $\{x \mid x \le -8\}$
52. 20 bottles   **53.** 15 ft, 17 ft   **54.** $126 billion
55. 57, 59   **56.** Width: 11 cm; length: 17 cm   **57.** $160
58. $46,987.95   **59.** 35°, 85°, 60°   **60.** $105 or less
61. Widths greater than 17 cm

62. 🗔 Multiplying both sides of an equation by *any* nonzero number results in an equivalent equation. When multiplying on both sides of an inequality, the sign of the number being multiplied by must be considered. If the number is positive, the direction of the inequality symbol remains unchanged; if the number is negative, the direction of the inequality symbol must be reversed to produce an equivalent inequality.   **63.** 🗔 The solutions of an equation can usually each be checked. The solutions of an inequality are normally too numerous to check. Checking a few numbers from the solution set found cannot guarantee that the answer is correct, although if any number does not check, the answer found is incorrect.
64. 25 hr 39 min   **65.** Nile: 6673 km; Amazon: 6440 km
66. $18,600   **67.** $-23, 23$ **68.** $-20, 20$
69. $a = \dfrac{y - 3}{2 - b}$

Test: Chapter 2, p. 146

1. [2.1] 9   **2.** [2.1] 15   **3.** [2.1] -3 **4.** [2.1] 49
5. [2.1] -12 **6.** [2.2] 2   **7.** [2.1] -8 **8.** [2.1] $-\frac{7}{20}$
9. [2.2] 7   **10.** [2.2] $-\frac{5}{3}$ **11.** [2.2] $\frac{23}{8}$ **12.** [2.2] All real numbers; identity   **13.** [2.6] $\{x \mid x > -5\}$
14. [2.6] $\{x \mid x > -13\}$ **15.** [2.6] $\left\{x \mid x < \frac{21}{8}\right\}$
16. [2.6] $\{y \mid y \le -13\}$ **17.** [2.6] $\{y \mid y \le -8\}$
18. [2.6] $\left\{x \mid x \le -\frac{1}{20}\right\}$ **19.** [2.6] $\{x \mid x < -6\}$
20. [2.6] $\{x \mid x \le -1\}$ **21.** [2.3] $r = \dfrac{A}{2\pi h}$
22. [2.3] $l = 2w - P$ **23.** [2.4] 2.3   **24.** [2.4] 5.4%
25. [2.4] 16   **26.** [2.4] 44%
27. [2.6]   **28.** [2.6]
[number line: $y < 4$; $-10 -8 -6 -4 -2\ 0\ 2\ 4\ 6\ 8\ 10$]   [number line: $-2 \le x \le 2$; $-5 -4 -3 -2 -1\ 0\ 1\ 2\ 3\ 4\ 5$]
29. [2.5] Width: 7 cm; length: 11 cm   **30.** [2.5] 60 mi
31. [2.5] 81 mm, 83 mm, 85 mm   **32.** [2.4] $65
33. [2.7] Mileages less than or equal to 525.8 mi
34. [2.3] $d = \dfrac{a}{3}$ **35.** [1.4], [2.2] $-15, 15$
36. [2.5] 60 tickets

CHAPTER 3

Exercise Set 3.1, pp. 154–158

1. (a)   **3.** (b)   **5.** 2 drinks
7. The person weighs more than 200 lb.
9. About 2,920,000   **11.** About 1,460,000
13. About 24.8 million tons
15. About 2.9 million tons
17. 120,000,000 phones
19. 2004

21.

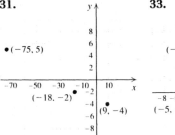

23.

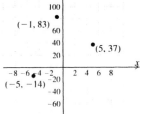

25.

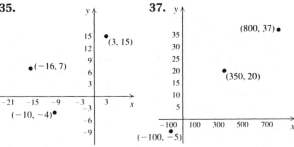

27. $A(-4, 5)$; $B(-3, -3)$; $C(0, 4)$; $D(3, 4)$; $E(3, -4)$
29. $A(4, 1)$; $B(0, -5)$; $C(-4, 0)$; $D(-3, -2)$; $E(3, 0)$

31.

33.

35.

37.

39.

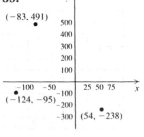

41. IV   **43.** III   **45.** I

47. II   **49.** I and IV   **51.** I and III   **53.** 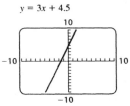   **55.** -18
56. -31 **57.** 6   **58.** 1   **59.** $y = \frac{3}{2}x - 3$
60. $y = \frac{7}{4}x - \frac{7}{2}$ **61.** 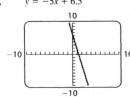   **63.** II or IV   **65.** $(-1, -5)$

67.

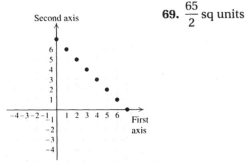

69. $\dfrac{65}{2}$ sq units

71. Latitude 27°North; longitude 81° West   **73.**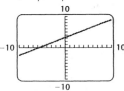

Technology Connection, p. 165

1. $y = -5x + 6.5$

2. $y = 3x + 4.5$

3. $7y - 4x = 22$, or
$y = \frac{4}{7}x + \frac{22}{7}$

4. $5y + 11x = -20$, or
$y = -\frac{11}{5}x - 4$

5. $2y - x^2 = 0$, or
$y = 0.5x^2$

6. $y + x^2 = 8$, or
$y = -x^2 + 8$

Exercise Set 3.2, pp. 166–168

1. No   **3.** No   **5.** Yes   **7.**

$y = x + 3$	
2	$-1 + 3$
$2 \overset{?}{=} 2$	True

$y = x + 3$	
7	$4 + 3$
$7 \overset{?}{=} 7$	True

$(2, 5)$; answers may vary

9.

$y = \frac{1}{2}x + 3$	
5	$\frac{1}{2} \cdot 4 + 3$
	$2 + 3$
$5 \overset{?}{=} 5$	True

$y = \frac{1}{2}x + 3$	
2	$\frac{1}{2}(-2) + 3$
	$-1 + 3$
$2 \overset{?}{=} 2$	True

$(0, 3)$; answers may vary

11.
$$\begin{array}{c|c} y + 3x = 7 \\ \hline 1 + 3 \cdot 2 & 7 \\ 1 + 6 & \end{array}$$
$$7 \overset{?}{=} 7 \text{ True}$$
(1, 4); answers may vary

$$\begin{array}{c|c} y + 3x = 7 \\ \hline -5 + 3 \cdot 4 & 7 \\ -5 + 12 & \end{array}$$
$$7 \overset{?}{=} 7 \text{ True}$$

13.
$$\begin{array}{c|c} 4x - 2y = 10 \\ \hline 4 \cdot 0 - 2(-5) & 10 \\ 0 + 10 & \end{array}$$
$$10 \overset{?}{=} 10 \text{ True}$$
(2, −1); answers may vary

$$\begin{array}{c|c} 4x - 2y = 10 \\ \hline 4 \cdot 4 - 2 \cdot 3 & 10 \\ 16 - 6 & \end{array}$$
$$10 \overset{?}{=} 10 \text{ True}$$

15.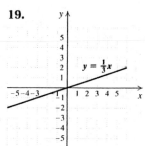

17.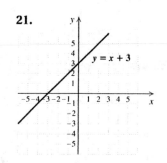

19.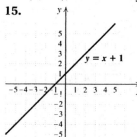

21.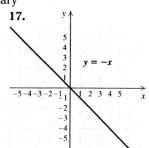

23.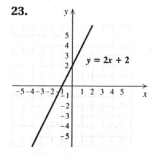

25.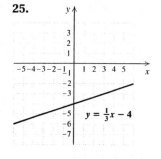

27.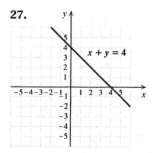

29.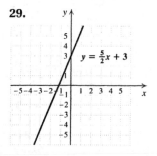

31.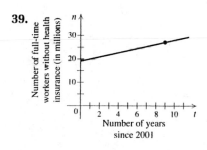

33.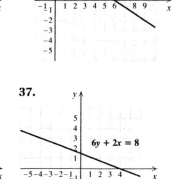

35.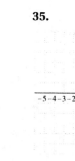

37.

39. 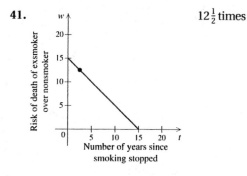   27 million workers

41. $12\frac{1}{2}$ times

43.  $300

45.
$1000

47.
24°F **49.** 🗒 **51.** $\dfrac{12}{5}$

52. $\dfrac{9}{2}$ **53.** $-\dfrac{5}{2}$ **54.** $p = \dfrac{w}{q+1}$ **55.** $y = \dfrac{C - Ax}{B}$

56. $Q = 2A - T$ **57.** 🗒
59. $s + n = 18$

61. $x + y = 2$, or $y = -x + 2$ **63.** $5x - 3y = 15$, or $y = \dfrac{5}{3}x - 5$ **65.** l

Answers may vary. 1 dinner, 40 lunches;
5 dinners, 20 lunches; 8 dinners, 5 lunches

67.
$y = -|x|$

69.
$y = -|x| + 2$

71. $y = -2.8x + 3.5$

73. $y = 2.8x - 3.5$

75. $y = x^2 + 4x + 1$

77. 🗒

Technology Connection, p. 172

1. $y = -0.72x - 15$
Xscl = 5, Yscl = 5

2. $y - 2.13x = 27$, or $y = 2.13x + 27$
Xscl = 5, Yscl = 5

3. $5x + 6y = 84$, or $y = -\dfrac{5}{6}x + 14$
Xscl = 5, Yscl = 5

4. $2x - 7y = 150$, or $y = \dfrac{2}{7}x - \dfrac{150}{7}$
Xscl = 10, Yscl = 5

5. $19x - 17y = 200$, or $y = \dfrac{19}{17}x - \dfrac{200}{17}$

6. $6x + 5y = 159$, or $y = -\dfrac{6}{5}x + \dfrac{159}{5}$
Xscl = 5, Yscl = 5

Exercise Set 3.3, pp. 175–177

1. (f)   **3.** (d)   **5.** (b)   **7.** (a) $(0, 5)$; (b) $(2, 0)$
9. (a) $(0, -4)$; (b) $(3, 0)$ **11.** (a) $(0, -2)$; (b) $(-3, 0)$
13. (a) $(0, 5)$; (b) $(3, 0)$ **15.** (a) $(0, -14)$; (b) $(4, 0)$
17. (a) $(0, 50)$; (b) $\left(-\frac{75}{2}, 0\right)$ **19.** (a) $(0, 9)$; (b) none
21. (a) None; (b) $(-7, 0)$

23.
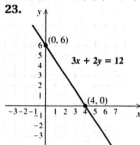

25.
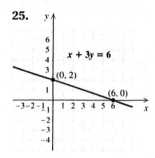

27.
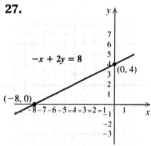

29.
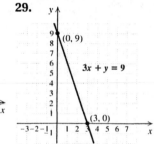

31.
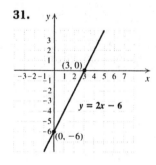

33.
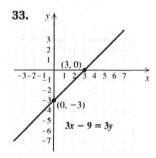

35.
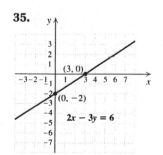

37.
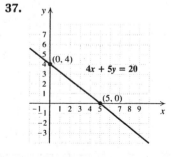

39.
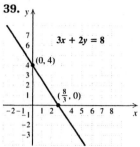

41.
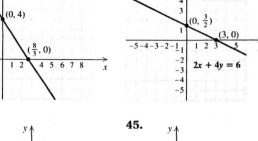

43.
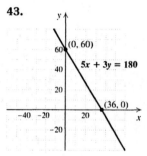

45.
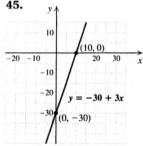

47.
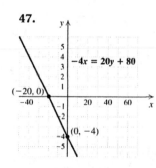

49.
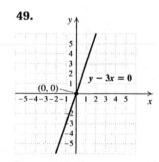

51.
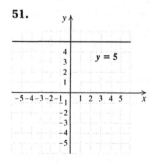

53.
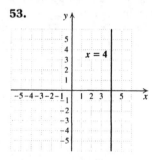

55.
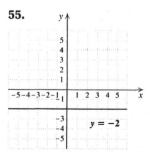

57.
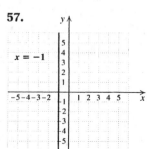

59.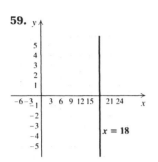

61.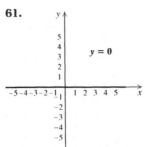

15.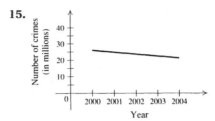

17.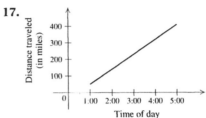

63.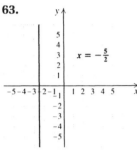

65.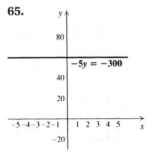

19.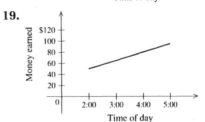

67.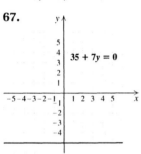

69. $y = -1$ **71.** $x = 4$

21.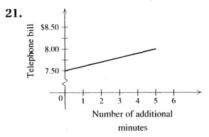

73. $y = 0$ **75.** 🔲   **77.** $d - 7$ **78.** $w + 5$, or $5 + w$
79. Let n represent the number; $2 + n$ **80.** Let n
represent the number; $3n$ **81.** Let x and y represent the
numbers; $2(x + y)$ **82.** Let a and b represent the
numbers; $\frac{1}{2}(a + b)$ **83.** 🔲   **85.** $y = 0$ **87.** $x = -2$
89. $(-3, -3)$ **91.** $-5x + 3y = 15$, or $y = \frac{5}{3}x + 5$
93. -24 **95.** $(0, 25)$; $\left(\frac{50}{3}, 0\right)$, or $(16.\overline{6}, 0)$ **97.** $(0, -9)$;
$(45, 0)$ **99.** $\left(0, -\frac{1}{20}\right)$, or $(0, -0.05)$; $\left(\frac{1}{25}, 0\right)$, or $(0.04, 0)$

23. 2 haircuts/hr   **25.** 75 mi/hr   **27.** 7¢/min
29. $-\$500$/yr   **31.** 0.04 gal/mi   **33.** (e)   **35.** (d)
37. (b)   **39.** 🔲   **41.** 5   **42.** -6 **43.** -1 **44.** $-\frac{4}{3}$
45. $-\frac{4}{3}$ **46.** $-\frac{4}{5}$ **47.** 🔲   **49.**

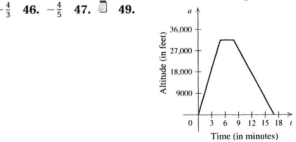

Exercise Set 3.4, pp. 181–186

1. (a) 21 mpg; (b) \$39.33/day; (c) 91 mi/day; (d) 43¢/mile
3. (a) 6 mph; (b) \$4/hr; (c) \$0.67/mi   **5.** (a) \$16/hr;
(b) 4.5 pages/hr; (c) \$3.56/page   **7.** \$16/yr
9. (a) 14.5 floors/min; (b) 4.14 sec/floor
11. (a) 3.71 ft/min; (b) 0.27 min/ft
13.

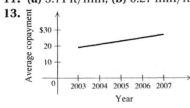

51. 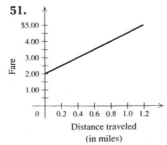   **53.** 13 ft/sec

55. About 41.7 min   **57.** 4:20 P.M.

Exercise Set 3.5, pp. 194–200

1. Positive   **3.** Negative   **5.** Positive   **7.** Zero
9. Negative   **11.** 2.5 million people/yr   **13.** 1.3%/yr
15. 1 point/$1000 income   **17.** $-2.1°$/min   **19.** $\frac{3}{4}$
21. $\frac{3}{2}$ **23.** $\frac{1}{3}$ **25.** -1 **27.** 0   **29.** $-\frac{1}{3}$ **31.** Undefined
33. $-\frac{1}{4}$ **35.** $\frac{3}{2}$ **37.** 0   **39.** -3 **41.** $\frac{3}{2}$ **43.** $-\frac{4}{5}$ **45.** $\frac{7}{9}$
47. $-\frac{2}{3}$ **49.** $-\frac{1}{2}$ **51.** 0   **53.** $-\frac{11}{6}$ **55.** Undefined
57. Undefined   **59.** 0   **61.** Undefined   **63.** 0   **65.** 8%
67. $8.\overline{3}$%   **69.** $\frac{29}{98}$, or about 30%   **71.** About 29%   **73.**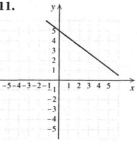
75. $y = \dfrac{c - ax}{b}$ **76.** $r = \dfrac{p + mn}{x}$ **77.** $y = \dfrac{ax - c}{b}$
78. $t = \dfrac{q - rs}{n}$ **79.** 3   **80.** 2   **81.**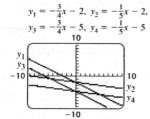
83. 0.364, or 36.4%   **85.** $\left\{m \mid m \geq \frac{5}{2}\right\}$ **87.** $\frac{1}{2}$

Technology Connection, p. 205

1.
$$y_1 = -\tfrac{3}{4}x - 2, \ y_2 = -\tfrac{1}{5}x - 2,$$
$$y_3 = -\tfrac{3}{4}x - 5, \ y_4 = -\tfrac{1}{5}x - 5$$

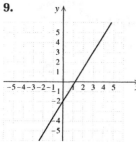

Exercise Set 3.6, pp. 208–210

1. (c)   **3.** (f)   **5.** (d)   **7.**

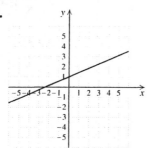

9.

11.

13.

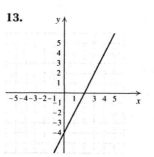

15.

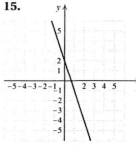

17. $-\frac{2}{7}$; (0, 5)   **19.** $\frac{5}{8}$; (0, 3)   **21.** $\frac{9}{5}$; (0, −4)   **23.** 3; (0, 7)
25. $-\frac{5}{2}$; (0, 4)   **27.** 0; (0, 4)   **29.** $\frac{2}{5}$; $\left(0, \frac{8}{5}\right)$ **31.** $y = 3x + 7$
33. $y = \frac{7}{8}x - 1$ **35.** $y = -\frac{5}{3}x - 8$ **37.** $y = 3$
39. $y = \frac{8}{9}x + 9$, where y is the number of gallons per person and x is the number of years since 1990
41. $y = 15x + 250$, where y is the number of jobs, in thousands, and x is the number of years since 1998

43.

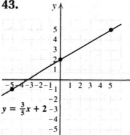

45.

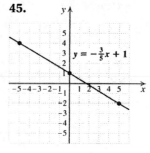

47.

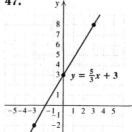

49.

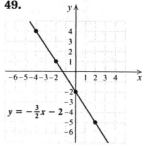

51.

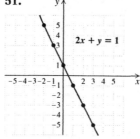

53.

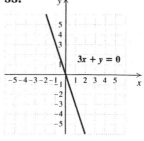

55.

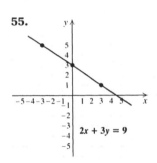

57.

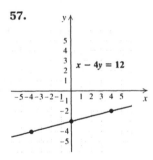

37. $y = 2x - 7$ **39.** $y = \frac{5}{3}x - \frac{28}{3}$ **41.** $y = 2x - 8$
43. $y = -\frac{5}{3}x - \frac{41}{3}$ **45.** $y = -\frac{1}{2}x + 6$

47.

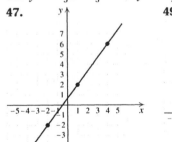

49.

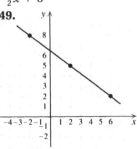

59. Yes **61.** No **63.** Yes **65.** Yes **67.** No **69.** Yes
71. $y = 5x + 11$ **73.** $y = \frac{1}{2}x$ **75.** $y = x + 3$
77. $y = x - 4$ **79.** ▨ **81.** $y = m(x - h) + k$
82. $y = -2(x + 4) + 9$ **83.** 2 **84.** 16 **85.** −9
86. −10 **87.** ▨
89. When $x = 0$, $y = b$, so $(0, b)$ is on the line. When
$x = 1$, $y = m + b$, so $(1, m + b)$ is on the line. Then

$$\text{slope} = \frac{(m + b) - b}{1 - 0} = m.$$

91. $y = \frac{1}{3}x + 3$ **93.** $y = -\frac{5}{3}x + 3$ **95.** $y = -\frac{2}{3}x$ **97.** ▨

51.

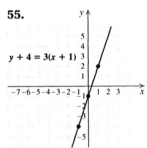

53.

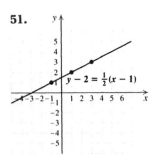

Technology Connection, p. 213

1. $y_1 = \frac{3}{4}x + 2;\ y_2 = -\frac{4}{3}x - 1$ **2.** $y_1 = -\frac{2}{5}x - 4;\ y_2 = \frac{5}{2}x + 3$

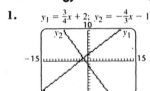 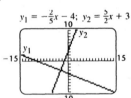

3. $y_1 = \frac{31}{40}x + 2;\ y_2 = -\frac{40}{30}x - 1$ No: $-\frac{40}{30} \neq -\frac{1}{\frac{31}{40}}$

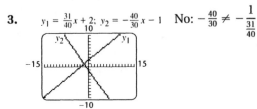

Although the lines appear to be perpendicular, they are
not, because the product of their slopes is not -1:
$$\frac{31}{40}\left(-\frac{40}{30}\right) = -\frac{1240}{1200} \neq -1.$$

Exercise Set 3.7, pp. 218–221

1. (g) **3.** (e) **5.** (b) **7.** (f) **9.** (c) **11.** (d)
13. $y - 2 = 5(x - 6)$ **15.** $y - 1 = -4(x - 3)$
17. $y - (-4) = \frac{3}{2}(x - 5)$ **19.** $y - 6 = \frac{5}{4}(x - (-2))$
21. $y - (-1) = -2(x - (-4))$ **23.** $y - 8 = 1(x - (-2))$
25. $y = 2x - 3$ **27.** $y = \frac{7}{4}x - 9$ **29.** $y = -3x + 3$
31. $y = -4x - 9$ **33.** $y = -\frac{5}{6}x + 4$ **35.** $y = -\frac{1}{2}x + 9$

55.

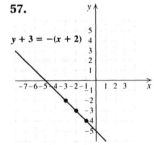

57.

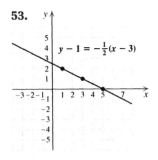

59.

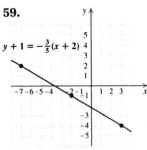

61. (a) 49.14 births per 1000 females; (b) 34.56 births per
1000 females **63.** (a) About 40.6%; (b) about 22.3%
65. (a) 65.1 million students; (b) 72.3 million students
67. (a) 33.3 million residents; (b) 38.7 million residents
69. $y = -x + 6$ **71.** $y = \frac{2}{3}x + 3$ **73.** $y = \frac{2}{5}x - 2$
75. $y = \frac{3}{4}x - \frac{5}{2}$ **77.** ▨ **79.** −125 **80.** 64 **81.** 8
82. 24 **83.** −72 **84.** −4 **85.** ▨

87.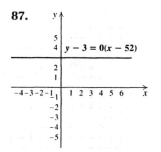

89. $y = 2x - 9$

91. $y = -\frac{4}{3}x + \frac{23}{3}$ **93.** $y - 7 = -\frac{2}{3}(x - (-4))$
95. $y = -4x + 7$ **97.** $y = \frac{10}{3}x + \frac{25}{3}$ **99.** 🗎

Review Exercises: Chapter 3, pp. 223–225

1. True **2.** True **3.** False **4.** False **5.** True **6.** True
7. True **8.** False **9.** True **10.** True **11.** $54,000
12. $269.50 **13.–15.**

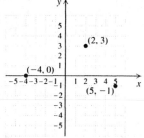

16. IV **17.** III **18.** II **19.** $(-5, -1)$ **20.** $(-2, 5)$
21. $(3, 0)$ **22.**   **23.** (a) Yes; (b) no

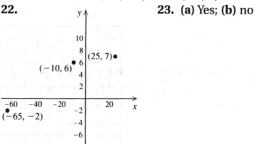

24.

$$\begin{array}{c|c} 2x - y = 3 \\ \hline 2 \cdot 0 - (-3) & 3 \\ 0 + 3 & \\ & 3 \overset{?}{=} 3 \text{ True} \end{array} \qquad \begin{array}{c|c} 2x - y = 3 \\ \hline 2 \cdot 2 - 1 & 3 \\ 4 - 1 & \\ & 3 \overset{?}{=} 3 \text{ True} \end{array}$$

$(-1, -5)$; answers may vary

25. 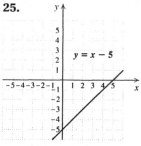   **26.**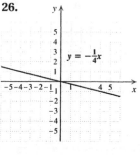

27. 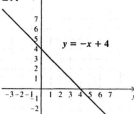   **28.**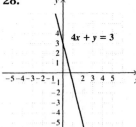

29. 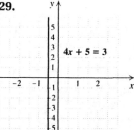   **30.**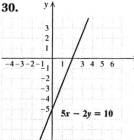

31. (a) $\frac{4}{9}$ meal/min; (b) $2\frac{1}{4}$ min/meal **32.** 12 mpg **33.** 0
34. $\frac{7}{3}$ **35.** $-\frac{3}{7}$ **36.** $\frac{3}{2}$ **37.** 0 **38.** Undefined **39.** 2
40. 28% **41.** x-intercept: $(6, 0)$; y-intercept: $(0, 9)$
42. $-\frac{1}{2}$; $(0, 5)$ **43.** Perpendicular **44.** Parallel
45. $y = -\frac{3}{4}x + 6$ **46.** $y - 6 = -\frac{1}{2}(x - 3)$ **47.** (a) $3100;
(b) $4900 **48.** $y = 4x + 5$ **49.** $y = -\frac{5}{3}x - \frac{5}{3}$

50. 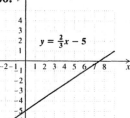   **51.**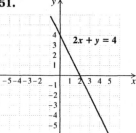

52. 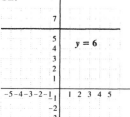   **53.**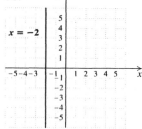

54.

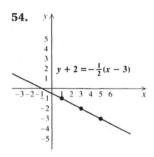

$y + 2 = -\frac{1}{2}(x - 3)$

55. ▢ Two perpendicular lines share the same y-intercept if their point of intersection is on the y-axis.   **56.** ▢ The y-intercept is the point at which the graph crosses the y-axis. Since a point on the y-axis is neither left nor right of the origin, the first coordinate of the point is 0.   **57.** -1
58. 19   **59.** Area: 45 sq units; perimeter: 28 units
60. $(0, 4), (1, 3), (-1, 3)$; answers may vary

Test: Chapter 3, pp. 225–226

1. [3.1] $205.20   **2.** [3.1] $638   **3.** [3.1] II   **4.** [3.1] III
5. [3.1] $(3, 4)$ **6.** [3.1] $(0, -4)$ **7.** [3.1] $(-5, 2)$
8. [3.2]

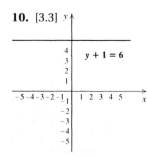

$y = 2x - 1$

9. [3.3]

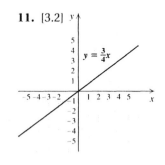

$2x - 4y = -8$

10. [3.3]

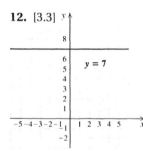

$y + 1 = 6$

11. [3.2]

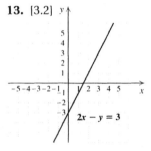

$y = \frac{3}{4}x$

12. [3.3]

13. [3.2]

$y = 7$

$2x - y = 3$

14. [3.3]

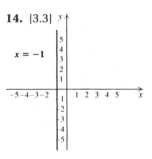

$x = -1$

15. [3.3] x-intercept: $(6, 0)$; y-intercept: $(0, -10)$
16. [3.3] x-intercept: $(10, 0)$; y-intercept: $\left(0, \frac{5}{2}\right)$ **17.** [3.5] $\frac{9}{2}$
18. [3.5] $\frac{7}{12}$ **19.** [3.4] $\frac{1}{3}$ km/min   **20.** [3.5] 31.5%
21. [3.6] 3; $(0, 7)$
22. [3.6]

23. [3.7]

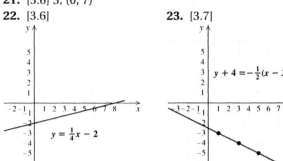

$y = \frac{1}{4}x - 2$

$y + 4 = -\frac{1}{2}(x - 3)$

24. [3.6] Parallel   **25.** [3.6] Perpendicular
26. [3.7] $y - 8 = -3(x - 6)$ **27.** [3.7] $y = -x + 10$
28. [3.7] **(a)** 40 hr; **(b)** 58 hr   **29.** [3.6] $y = \frac{2}{5}x + 9$
30. [3.1] Area: 25 sq units; perimeter: 20 units   **31.** [3.2], [3.7] $(0, 12), (-3, 15), (5, 7)$

Cumulative Review: Chapters 1–3, pp. 226–228

1. 7   **2.** $12x - 15y + 21$ **3.** $3(5x - 3y + 1)$ **4.** $2 \cdot 3 \cdot 7$
5. 0.45   **6.** 4   **7.** $\frac{1}{4}$ **8.** -4 **9.** $-x - y$ **10.** 0.785
11. $\frac{11}{60}$ **12.** 2.6   **13.** 7.28   **14.** $-\frac{5}{12}$ **15.** -3 **16.** 27
17. $-2y - 7$ **18.** $5x + 11$ **19.** -1.2 **20.** -21 **21.** 9
22. $-\frac{20}{3}$ **23.** 2   **24.** $\frac{13}{8}$ **25.** $-\frac{17}{21}$ **26.** -17 **27.** 2
28. $\{x \mid x < 16\}$ **29.** $\{x \mid x \le -\frac{11}{8}\}$ **30.** $h = \dfrac{A - \pi r^2}{2\pi r}$
31. IV   **32.** $-1 < x \le 2$

33.   **34.**

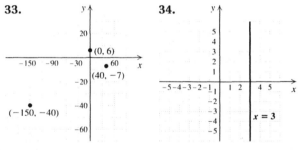

$(0, 6)$
$(40, -7)$
$(-150, -40)$

$x = 3$

35.

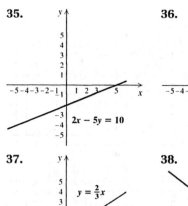

$2x - 5y = 10$

36.

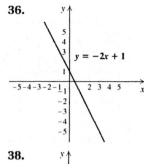

$y = -2x + 1$

37.

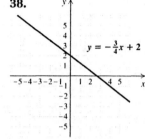

$y = \frac{2}{3}x$

38.

$y = -\frac{3}{4}x + 2$

39. $(10.5, 0)$; $(0, -3)$ **40.** $(-1.25, 0)$; $(0, 5)$
41. 160 million **42.** 15.6 million **43.** \$120
44. 50 m, 53 m, 40 m **45.** No more than 8 hr
46. \$40/person **47.** $-\frac{1}{3}$ **48.** $y = \frac{2}{7}x - 4$
49. $-\frac{1}{3}$; $(0, 3)$ **50.** $y = -\frac{1}{2}x + 5$ **51.** **(a)** 17.8%;
(b) 24.56% **52.** \$25,000 **53.** $-4, 4$ **54.** 2 **55.** -5
56. 3 **57.** No solution; contradiction **58.** $Q = \dfrac{2 - pm}{p}$
59. $y = -\frac{7}{3}x + 7$; $y = -\frac{7}{3}x - 7$; $y = \frac{7}{3}x - 7$; $y = \frac{7}{3}x + 7$

CHAPTER 4

Exercise Set 4.1, pp. 236–238

1. (b) **3.** (e) **5.** (g) **7.** (c) **9.** r^{10} **11.** 9^8 **13.** a^7
15. 8^{11} **17.** $(3y)^{12}$ **19.** $(5t)^7$ **21.** $a^5 b^9$ **23.** $(x + 1)^{12}$
25. r^{10} **27.** $x^4 y^7$ **29.** 7^3 **31.** x^{12} **33.** t^4 **35.** $5a$
37. 1 **39.** $\frac{3}{4}m^3$ **41.** $4a^7 b^6$ **43.** $m^9 n^4$ **45.** 1 **47.** 5
49. 2 **51.** -4 **53.** x^{28} **55.** 5^{16} **57.** m^{35} **59.** t^{80}
61. $49x^2$ **63.** $-8a^3$ **65.** $16m^6$ **67.** $a^{14} b^7$ **69.** $x^8 y^7$
71. $24x^{19}$ **73.** $\dfrac{a^3}{64}$ **75.** $\dfrac{49}{25a^2}$ **77.** $\dfrac{a^{20}}{b^{15}}$ **79.** $\dfrac{y^6}{4}$ **81.** $\dfrac{x^8 y^4}{z^{12}}$
83. $\dfrac{a^{12}}{16b^{20}}$ **85.** $\dfrac{125x^{21} y^3}{8z^{12}}$ **87.** 1 **89.** 🖍 **91.** $3(s - r + t)$
92. $-7(x - y + z)$ **93.** $8x$ **94.** $-3a - 6b$ **95.** $2y + 3x$
96. $5z + 2xy$ **97.** 🖍 **99.** 🖍 **101.** Let $a = 1$; then
$(a + 5)^2 = 36$, but $a^2 + 5^2 = 26$. **103.** Let $a = 0$; then
$\dfrac{a + 7}{7} = 1$, but $a = 0$. **105.** a^{8k} **107.** $\frac{16}{375}$ **109.** 13
111. $<$ **113.** $<$ **115.** $>$ **117.** 4,000,000; 4,194,304;
194,304 **119.** 2,000,000,000; 2,147,483,648; 147,483,648
121. 1,536,000 bytes, or approximately 1,500,000 bytes

Technology Connection, p. 243

1. 79

Exercise Set 4.2, pp. 244–248

1. (b) **3.** (d) **5.** (g) **7.** (c) **9.** $7x^4, x^3, -5x, 8$
11. $-t^4, 7t^3, -3t^2, 6$ **13.** Coefficients: 4, 7; degrees: 5, 1
15. Coefficients: 9, -3, 4; degrees: 2, 1, 0
17. Coefficients: 7, 9, 1; degrees: 4, 1, 3 **19.** Coefficients:
1, -1, 4, -3; degrees: 4, 3, 1, 0 **21.** **(a)** 1, 2, 6; **(b)** $3x^6$, 3;
(c) 6 **23.** **(a)** 2, 0, 4; **(b)** $2a^4$, 2; **(c)** 4 **25.** **(a)** 0, 2, 1, 5;
(b) $-x^5$, -1; **(c)** 5
27.

Term	Coefficient	Degree of the Term	Degree of the Polynomial
$8x^5$	8	5	
$-\frac{1}{2}x^4$	$-\frac{1}{2}$	4	
$-4x^3$	-4	3	5
$7x^2$	7	2	
6	6	0	

29. Trinomial **31.** None of these **33.** Binomial
35. Monomial **37.** $11x^2 + 3x$ **39.** $4a^4$ **41.** $6x^2 - 3x$
43. $5x^3 - x + 5$ **45.** $-x^4 - x^3$ **47.** $\frac{1}{15}x^4 + 10$
49. $3.4x^2 + 1.3x + 5.5$ **51.** -17; 25 **53.** 16; 34
55. -67; 17 **57.** -27; 81 **59.** -117; -63
61. \$2.17 trillion **63.** 1112 ft **65.** 62.8 cm
67. 153.86 m^2 **69.** 5 million gigawatt hours
71. 4.5 million gigawatt hours **73.** About 9 words
75. About 6 **77.** Approximately 1.8 million;
approximately 4.4 million **79.** 🖍 **81.** 5 **82.** -9
83. $5(x + 3)$ **84.** $7(a - 3)$ **85.** 6.25¢/mi **86.** 274 and
275 **87.** 🖍 **89.** $2x^5 + 4x^4 + 6x^3 + 8$; answers may vary
91. \$2510 **93.** $3x^6$ **95.** 5, 13, 80 **97.** 85.0
99.

t	$-t^2 + 10t - 18$
3	3
4	6
5	7
6	6
7	3

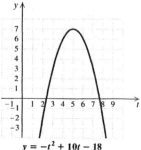

$y = -t^2 + 10t - 18$

Technology Connection, p. 253

1. In each case, let y_1 = the expression before the addition or subtraction has been performed, y_2 = the simplified sum or difference, and $y_3 = y_2 - y_1$; and note that the graph of y_3 coincides with the x-axis. That is, $y_3 = 0$.

Exercise Set 4.3, pp. 254–256

1. $-2x + 6$ **3.** $x^2 - 5x - 1$ **5.** $9t^2 + 5t - 3$
7. $8m^3 + 3m^2 - 3m - 7$ **9.** $7 + 13a + 6a^2 + 14a^3$
11. $9x^8 + 8x^7 - 3x^4 + 2x^2 - 2x + 5$
13. $-\frac{1}{2}x^4 + \frac{2}{3}x^3 + x^2 + 2$
15. $4.2t^3 + 3.5t^2 - 6.4t - 1.8$ **17.** $-3x^4 + 3x^2 + 4x$
19. $1.05x^4 + 0.36x^3 + 14.22x^2 + x + 0.97$
21. $-(-t^3 + 4t^2 - 9);\ t^3 - 4t^2 + 9$
23. $-(12x^4 - 3x^3 + 3);\ -12x^4 + 3x^3 - 3$ **25.** $-8x + 9$
27. $-3a^4 + 5a^2 - 9$ **29.** $4x^4 - 6x^2 - \frac{3}{4}x + 8$
31. $9x + 3$ **33.** $-t^2 - 8t + 7$
35. $6x^4 + 3x^3 - 4x^2 + 3x - 4$
37. $4.6x^3 + 9.2x^2 - 3.8x - 23$ **39.** 0
41. $1 + 2a + 7a^2 - 3a^3$ **43.** $\frac{3}{4}x^3 - \frac{1}{2}x$
45. $0.05t^3 - 0.07t^2 + 0.01t + 1$ **47.** $3x + 5$
49. $11x^4 + 12x^3 - 10x^2$ **51.** (a) $5x^2 + 4x$; (b) 145; 273
53. $\frac{23}{2}a + 12$ **55.** $(r + 11)(r + 9);\ 9r + 99 + 11r + r^2$
57. $(x + 3)^2;\ x^2 + 3x + 9 + 3x$ **59.** $\pi r^2 - 25\pi$
61. $xy - 21$ **63.** $(x^2 - 12)\,\text{ft}^2$ **65.** $(z^2 - 16\pi)\,\text{ft}^2$
67. $\left(144 - \dfrac{d^2}{4}\pi\right)\text{m}^2$ **69.** 🔲   **71.** 0 **72.** 0
73. $13t + 14$ **74.** $14t - 15$ **75.** $\left\{x \mid x < \frac{14}{3}\right\}$
76. $\{x \mid x \le 12\}$ **77.** 🔲   **79.** $9t^2 - 20t + 11$
81. $-10y^2 - 2y - 10$ **83.** $250.591x^3 + 2.812x$
85. $20w + 42$ **87.** $2x^2 + 20x$ **89.** $8x + 24$ **91.** 🔲

Technology Connection, p. 262

1. Let $y_1 = (-2x^2 - 3)(5x^3 - 3x + 4)$ and $y_2 = -10x^5 - 9x^3 - 8x^2 + 9x - 12$. With the table set in AUTO mode, note that the values in the Y1- and Y2-columns match, regardless of how far we scroll up or down.   **2.** Use TRACE, a table, or a boldly drawn graph to confirm that y_3 is always 0.

Exercise Set 4.4, pp. 262–264

1. (b)   **3.** (d)   **5.** $36x^3$ **7.** $-x^7$ **9.** x^8 **11.** $24a^4$
13. $-0.12x^9$ **15.** $-\frac{1}{20}x^{12}$ **17.** $5n^3$ **19.** $72y^{10}$
21. $8x^2 - 12x$ **23.** $3x^2 + 6x$ **25.** $3a^2 + 27a$
27. $x^5 + x^2$ **29.** $6x^3 - 18x^2 + 3x$ **31.** $15t^3 + 30t^2$
33. $-6x^4 - 6x^3$ **35.** $4a^9 - 8a^7 - \frac{5}{12}a^4$
37. $x^2 + 8x + 12$ **39.** $x^2 + 3x - 10$ **41.** $a^2 - 13a + 42$
43. $x^2 - 9$ **45.** $25 - 15x + 2x^2$ **47.** $t^2 + \frac{17}{6}t + 2$

49. $\frac{3}{16}a^2 + \frac{5}{4}a - 2$ **51.**

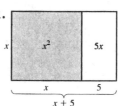

53. 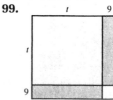   **55.**

57. $x^3 + 4x + 5$ **59.** $2a^3 - a^2 - 11a + 10$
61. $2y^5 - 13y^3 + y^2 - 7y - 7$ **63.** $27x^2 + 39x + 14$
65. $x^4 - 2x^3 - x + 2$ **67.** $6t^4 - 17t^3 - 6t^2 + \frac{3}{2}t - 2$
69. $x^4 + 8x^3 + 12x^2 + 9x + 4$ **71.** 🔲   **73.** 6   **74.** 31
75. 0   **76.** 0   **77.** 🔲   **79.** $75y^2 - 45y$ **81.** 5
83. $V = 4x^3 - 48x^2 + 144x\ \text{in}^3$; $S = -4x^2 + 144\ \text{in}^2$
85. $x^3 + 2x^2 - 210\ \text{m}^3$ **87.** 16 ft by 8 ft   **89.** 0   **91.** 0

Exercise Set 4.5, pp. 271–274

1. True   **3.** False   **5.** $x^3 + 3x^2 + 5x + 15$
7. $x^4 + 2x^3 + 6x + 12$ **9.** $y^2 - y - 6$
11. $9x^2 + 21x + 10$ **13.** $5x^2 + 6x - 8$ **15.** $2 + 3t - 9t^2$
17. $2x^2 - 13x + 20$ **19.** $p^2 - \frac{1}{16}$ **21.** $x^2 - 0.01$
23. $-2x^2 - 11x + 6$ **25.** $a^2 + 18a + 81$
27. $1 - 2t - 15t^2$ **29.** $x^5 + 3x^3 - x^2 - 3$
31. $3x^6 - 2x^4 - 6x^2 + 4$ **33.** $4t^6 + 16t^3 + 15$
35. $8x^5 + 16x^3 + 5x^2 + 10$ **37.** $4x^3 - 12x^2 + 3x - 9$
39. $x^2 - 49$ **41.** $4x^2 - 1$ **43.** $25m^2 - 4$ **45.** $9x^8 - 1$
47. $x^8 - 49$ **49.** $t^2 - \frac{9}{16}$ **51.** $x^2 + 4x + 4$
53. $49x^6 + 14x^3 + 1$ **55.** $a^2 - \frac{4}{5}a + \frac{4}{25}$
57. $t^6 + 10t^3 + 25$ **59.** $4 - 12x^4 + 9x^8$
61. $25 + 60t^2 + 36t^4$ **63.** $49x^2 - 4.2x + 0.09$
65. $10a^5 - 5a^3$ **67.** $a^3 - a^2 - 10a + 12$
69. $9 - 12x^3 + 4x^6$ **71.** $5x^3 + 30x^2 - 10x$
73. $t^6 - 2t^3 + 1$ **75.** $15t^5 - 3t^4 + 3t^3$
77. $36x^8 - 36x^4 + 9$ **79.** $12x^3 + 8x^2 + 15x + 10$
81. $25 - 60x^4 + 36x^8$ **83.** $a^3 + 1$ **85.** $a^2 + 2a + 1$
87. $x^2 + 7x + 10$ **89.** $x^2 + 14x + 49$ **91.** $t^2 + 10t + 24$
93. $t^2 + 13t + 36$ **95.** $9x^2 + 24x + 16$
97.   **99.**

101.

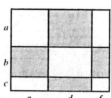

3 | x

103.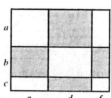

105. Lamps: 500 watts; air conditioner: 2000 watts; television: 50 watts   **106.** II   **107.** $y = \dfrac{8}{5x}$ **108.** $a = \dfrac{c}{3b}$

109. $x = \dfrac{b + c}{a}$ **110.** $t = \dfrac{u - r}{s}$ **111.**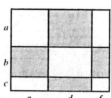

113. $16x^4 - 81$ **115.** $81t^4 - 72t^2 + 16$

117. $t^{24} - 4t^{18} + 6t^{12} - 4t^6 + 1$ **119.** 396   **121.** -7

123. $17F + 7(F - 17)$, $F^2 - (F - 17)(F - 7)$; other equivalent expressions are possible.

125. $x^2 - 9$, $(x - 3)^2 + 3(x - 3) + 3(x - 3)$; other equivalent expressions are possible.

127. $100 - 40x + 4x^2$ **129.**

Technology Connection, p. 278

1. 36.22   **2.** 22,312

Exercise Set 4.6, pp. 278–282

1. (a)   **3.** (b)   **5.** (c)   **7.** (a)   **9.** -7 **11.** -92

13. 2.97 L   **15.** About 2494 calories   **17.** 20.60625 in^2

19. 66.4 m

21. Coefficients: 1, -2, 3, -5; degrees: 4, 2, 2, 0; 4

23. Coefficients: 17, -3, -7; degrees: 5, 5, 0; 5

25. $3a - 2b$ **27.** $3x^2y - 2xy^2 + x^2 + 5x$

29. $8u^2v - 5uv^2 + 7u^2$ **31.** $6a^2c - 7ab^2 + a^2b$

33. $3x^2 - 4xy + 3y^2$ **35.** $-6a^4 - 8ab + 7ab^2$

37. $-6r^2 - 5rt - t^2$ **39.** $3x^3 - x^2y + xy^2 - 3y^3$

41. $10y^4x^2 - 8y^3x$ **43.** $-8x + 8y$ **45.** $6z^2 + 7uz - 3u^2$

47. $x^2y^2 + 3xy - 28$ **49.** $4a^2 - b^2$ **51.** $15r^2t^2 - rt - 2$

53. $m^6n^2 + 2m^3n - 48$ **55.** $30x^2 - 28xy + 6y^2$

57. $0.01 - p^2q^2$ **59.** $x^2 + 2xh + h^2$

61. $16a^2 + 40ab + 25b^2$ **63.** $c^4 - d^2$ **65.** $a^2b^2 - c^2d^4$

67. $a^2 + 2ab + b^2 - c^2$ **69.** $a^2 - b^2 - 2bc - c^2$

71. $a^2 + ab + ac + bc$ **73.** $x^2 - z^2$

75. $x^2 + y^2 + z^2 + 2xy + 2xz + 2yz$

77. $\frac{1}{2}x^2 + \frac{1}{2}xy - y^2$

79. We draw a rectangle with dimensions $r + s$ by $u + v$.

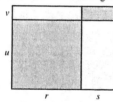

81.

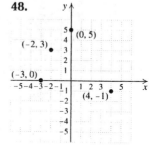

83. 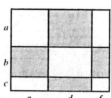   **85.** 12   **86.** 5

87. 27   **88.** 36   **89.** 7   **90.** 5   **91.**   **93.** $4xy - 4y^2$

95. $2xy + \pi x^2$ **97.** $x^3 + 2y^3 + x^2y + xy^2$

99. $2\pi nh + 2\pi mh + 2\pi n^2 - 2\pi m^2$ **101.**

103. $P + 2Pr + Pr^2$ **105.** \$15,638.03

Exercise Set 4.7, pp. 287–288

1. $4x^5 - 3x$ **3.** $1 - 2u + u^6$ **5.** $6t^2 - 8t + 2$

7. $-5x^4 + 4x^2 + 1$ **9.** $6t^2 - 10t + \frac{3}{2}$

11. $4x^2 - 5x + \frac{1}{2}$ **13.** $x^4 + \frac{3}{2}x^2 + \frac{1}{x}$

15. $-3rs - r + 2s$ **17.** $x + 6$ **19.** $t - 5 + \dfrac{-45}{t - 5}$

21. $2x - 1 + \dfrac{1}{x + 6}$ **23.** $a^2 - 2a + 4$ **25.** $t + 4 + \dfrac{3}{t - 4}$

27. $x + 4$ **29.** $3a + 1 + \dfrac{3}{2a + 5}$ **31.** $t^2 - 3t + 1$

33. $t^2 - 2t + 3 + \dfrac{-4}{t + 1}$ **35.** $t^2 + 1 + \dfrac{4t - 2}{t^2 - 3}$

37. $2x^2 + 1 + \dfrac{-x}{2x^2 - 3}$ **39.**   **41.** -17 **42.** -23

43. -2 **44.** 5   **45.** 167.5 ft   **46.** 2

47.

48.

49.   **51.** $5x^{6k} - 16x^{3k} + 14$ **53.** $3t^{2h} + 2t^h - 5$

55. $a + 3 + \dfrac{5}{5a^2 - 7a - 2}$ **57.** $2x^2 + x - 3$ **59.** 3

61. -1

Technology Connection, p. 295

1. 1.71×10^{17} **2.** $5.\overline{370} \times 10^{-15}$ **3.** 3.68×10^{16}

Exercise Set 4.8, pp. 295–297

1. $\dfrac{1}{7^2} = \dfrac{1}{49}$ **3.** $\dfrac{1}{10^4} = \dfrac{1}{10,000}$ **5.** $\dfrac{1}{(-2)^6} = \dfrac{1}{64}$ **7.** $\dfrac{1}{x^8}$

9. $\dfrac{x}{y^2}$ **11.** $\dfrac{t}{r^5}$ **13.** t^8 **15.** h^8 **17.** $\dfrac{1}{7}$ **19.** $\left(\dfrac{5}{3}\right)^2 = \dfrac{25}{9}$

21. $\left(\dfrac{2}{a}\right)^3 = \dfrac{8}{a^3}$ **23.** $\left(\dfrac{t}{s}\right)^7 = \dfrac{t^7}{s^7}$ **25.** 6^{-2} **27.** t^{-6}

29. a^{-4} **31.** p^{-7} **33.** 5^{-1} **35.** t^{-1} **37.** 2^3, or 8

39. $\dfrac{1}{x^9}$ **41.** $\dfrac{1}{t^2}$ **43.** $\dfrac{1}{a^{18}}$ **45.** t^{18} **47.** $\dfrac{1}{t^{12}}$ **49.** $\dfrac{1}{m^7 n^7}$

51. $\dfrac{9}{x^8}$ **53.** $\dfrac{25t^6}{r^8}$ **55.** t^{10} **57.** $\dfrac{1}{y^4}$ **59.** $3y^5$ **61.** $2x^5$

63. $\dfrac{3b^9}{2a^7}$ **65.** 1   **67.** $\dfrac{3y^6 z^2}{x^5}$ **69.** $\dfrac{1}{27x^{12}y^{15}}$ **71.** $x^{24}y^8$

73. $\dfrac{b^5 c^4}{a^8}$ **75.** $\dfrac{9}{a^8}$ **77.** $\dfrac{n^{12}}{m^3}$ **79.** $\dfrac{27b^{12}}{8a^6}$ **81.** 1   **83.** $\dfrac{2b^3}{a^4}$

85. $\dfrac{5y^4 z^{10}}{4x^{11}}$ **87.** 71,200   **89.** 0.00892   **91.** 904,000,000

93. 0.0000000002764   **95.** 42,090,000   **97.** 4.9×10^5

99. 5.83×10^{-3} **101.** 7.8×10^{10} **103.** 5.27×10^{-7}

105. 1.8×10^{-8} **107.** 1.094×10^{15} **109.** 8×10^{12}

111. 2.47×10^8 **113.** 3.915×10^{-16} **115.** 2.5×10^{13}

117. 5×10^{-4} **119.** 3×10^{-21} **121.** 🔳   **123.** 15

124. 49   **125.** 78   **126.** 6   **127.** -15 **128.** -7

129.

130. $t = \dfrac{r - cx}{b}$ **131.** 🔳

133. 8×10^5 **135.** 2^{-12} **137.** 5   **139.** 7×10^{23}
141. $4.894179894 \times 10^{26}$ **143.** 3.12×10^{43}
145. (a) False; (b) false; (c) false
147. About 2.5×10^{12} bytes
149. Approximately 1.15385×10^{12} times

Review Exercises: Chapter 4, pp. 299–301

1. False   **2.** True   **3.** True   **4.** False   **5.** True   **6.** False
7. True   **8.** True   **9.** y^{11} **10.** $(3x)^{14}$ **11.** t^6 **12.** 4^3, or
64   **13.** 1   **14.** $\dfrac{9t^8}{4s^6}$ **15.** $-8x^3 y^6$ **16.** $18x^5$ **17.** $a^7 b^6$

18. $3x^2, 6x, \dfrac{1}{2}$ **19.** $-4y^5, 7y^2, -3y, -2$ **20.** $9, -1, 7$
21. $4, 6, -5, \dfrac{5}{3}$ **22.** (a) 2, 0, 5; (b) $15t^2$, 15; (c) 5
23. (a) 5, 0, 2, 1; (b) $-2x^5$, -2; (c) 5   **24.** Binomial
25. None of these   **26.** Monomial   **27.** $-x^2 + 7x$
28. $-\dfrac{1}{4}x^3 + 4x^2 + 7$ **29.** $-3x^5 + 25$
30. $-2x^2 - 3x + 2$ **31.** $10x^4 - 7x^2 - x - \dfrac{1}{2}$ **32.** -15
33. 10   **34.** $x^5 + 8x^4 + 6x^3 - 2x - 9$
35. $-x^5 + 3x^4 - x^3 - 2x^2$ **36.** $2x^2 - 4x - 6$
37. $x^5 - 3x^3 - 2x^2 + 8$ **38.** $\dfrac{3}{4}x^4 + \dfrac{1}{4}x^3 - \dfrac{1}{3}x^2 - \dfrac{7}{4}x + \dfrac{3}{8}$

39. $-x^5 + x^4 - 5x^3 - 2x^2 + 2x$ **40.** (a) $4w + 6$;
(b) $w^2 + 3w$ **41.** $-12x^3$ **42.** $49x^2 + 14x + 1$
43. $a^2 - 3a - 28$ **44.** $m^2 - 25$
45. $12x^3 - 23x^2 + 13x - 2$ **46.** $x^2 - 16x + 64$
47. $15t^5 - 6t^4 + 12t^3$ **48.** $a^2 - 81$ **49.** $x^2 - 1.3x + 0.4$
50. $x^7 + x^5 - 3x^4 + 3x^3 - 2x^2 + 5x - 3$
51. $9x^2 - 30x + 25$ **52.** $2t^4 - 11t^2 - 21$
53. $a^2 + \dfrac{1}{6}a - \dfrac{1}{3}$ **54.** $9x^2 - 49$ **55.** 49
56. Coefficients: 1, -7, 9, -8; degrees: 6, 2, 2, 0; 6
57. Coefficients: 1, -1, 1; degrees: 16, 40, 23; 40
58. $-y + 9w - 5$ **59.** $6m^3 + 4m^2 n - mn^2$
60. $-x^2 - 10xy$ **61.** $11x^3 y^2 - 8x^2 y - 6x^2 - 6x + 6$
62. $2x^2 - xy - 15y^2$ **63.** $9a^8 - 2a^4 b^3 + \dfrac{1}{9}b^6$
64. $\dfrac{1}{2}x^2 - \dfrac{1}{2}y^2$ **65.** $5x^2 - \dfrac{1}{2}x + 4$

66. $3x^2 - 7x + 4 + \dfrac{1}{2x + 3}$ **67.** $t^3 + 2t - 3$ **68.** $\dfrac{1}{m^4}$

69. a^{-9} **70.** $\dfrac{1}{7^2}$, or $\dfrac{1}{49}$ **71.** $\dfrac{2}{a^{13}b^7}$ **72.** $\dfrac{1}{x^{12}}$ **73.** $\dfrac{x^6}{4y^2}$

74. $\dfrac{y^3}{8x^3}$ **75.** 8,300,000   **76.** 3.28×10^{-5} **77.** 2.09×10^4

78. 5.12×10^{-5} **79.** 2.28×10^{11} platelets   **80.** 🔳 In the
expression $5x^3$, the exponent refers only to the x. In the
expression $(5x)^3$, the entire expression $5x$ is the base.
81. 🔳 It is possible to determine two possibilities for the
binomial that was squared by using the equation
$(A - B)^2 = A^2 - 2AB + B^2$ in reverse. Since, in
$x^2 - 6x + 9$, $A^2 = x^2$ and $B^2 = 9$, or 3^2, the binomial that
was squared was $A - B$, or $x - 3$. If the polynomial is
written $9 - 6x + x^2$, then $A^2 = 9$ and $B^2 = x^2$, so the
binomial that was squared was $3 - x$. We cannot
determine without further information whether the
binomial squared was $x - 3$ or $3 - x$.   **82.** (a) 4; (b) 2
83. $64x^{16}$ **84.** $8x^4 + 4x^3 + 5x - 2$
85. $-16x^6 + x^2 - 10x + 25$ **86.** $\dfrac{94}{13}$

Test: Chapter 4, p. 302

1. [4.1] a^{10} **2.** [4.1] 4^3, or 64   **3.** [4.1] 1   **4.** [4.1] x^6

5. [4.1] $-27y^6$ **6.** [4.1] $\dfrac{25}{16a^6}$ **7.** [4.1] $-24x^{17}$

8. [4.1] $a^6 b^5$ **9.** [4.2] Binomial   **10.** [4.2] $\dfrac{1}{3}, -1, 7$
11. [4.2] Degrees of terms: 3, 1, 5, 0; leading term: $7t^5$;
leading coefficient: 7; degree of polynomial: 5
12. [4.2] -7 **13.** [4.2] $5a^2 - 6$ **14.** [4.2] $\dfrac{7}{4}y^2 - 4y$
15. [4.2] $x^5 + 2x^3 + 4x^2 - 8x + 3$
16. [4.3] $4x^5 + x^4 + 5x^3 - 8x^2 + 2x - 7$
17. [4.3] $5x^4 + 5x^2 + x + 5$
18. [4.3] $-4x^4 + x^3 - 8x - 3$
19. [4.3] $-x^5 + 1.3x^3 - 0.8x^2 - 3$
20. [4.4] $-6x^4 + 6x^3 + 10x^2$ **21.** [4.5] $x^2 - \dfrac{2}{3}x + \dfrac{1}{9}$
22. [4.5] $25t^2 - 49$ **23.** [4.5] $3b^2 - 4b - 15$
24. [4.5] $x^{14} - 4x^8 + 4x^6 - 16$ **25.** [4.5] $48 + 34y - 5y^2$
26. [4.4] $6x^3 - 7x^2 - 11x - 3$ **27.** [4.5] $64a^2 + 48a + 9$

28. [4.6] 24   **29.** [4.6] $-4x^3y - x^2y^2 + xy^3 - y^3 + 19$
30. [4.6] $8a^2b^2 + 6ab + 6ab^2 + ab^3 - 4b^3$
31. [4.6] $9x^{10} - y^2$ **32.** [4.7] $4x^2 + 3x - 5$
33. [4.7] $2x^2 - 4x - 2 + \dfrac{17}{3x+2}$ **34.** [4.8] $\dfrac{1}{5^3}$
35. [4.8] y^{-8} **36.** [4.8] $\dfrac{1}{t^6}$ **37.** [4.8] $\dfrac{y^5}{x^5}$ **38.** [4.8] $\dfrac{b^4}{16a^{12}}$
39. [4.8] $\dfrac{c^3}{a^3b^3}$ **40.** [4.8] 3.9×10^9 **41.** [4.8] 0.00000005
42. [4.8] 1.75×10^{17} **43.** [4.8] 1.296×10^{22}
44. [4.4], [4.5] $V = l(l-2)(l-1) = l^3 - 3l^2 + 2l$
45. [2.2], [4.5] $\frac{100}{21}$ **46.** [4.8] 3.0×10^5 sound files

CHAPTER 5

Technology Connection, p. 310

1. Correct   **2.** Correct   **3.** Not correct   **4.** Not correct
5. Not correct   **6.** Correct   **7.** Not correct   **8.** Correct

Exercise Set 5.1, pp. 311–312

1. (h)   **3.** (b)   **5.** (c)   **7.** (d)   **9.** Answers may vary.
$(10x)(x^2), (5x^2)(2x), (-2)(-5x^3)$ **11.** Answers may vary.
$(-15)(a^4), (-5a)(3a^3), (-3a^2)(5a^2)$ **13.** Answers may vary.
$(2x)(13x^4), (13x^5)(2), (-x^3)(-26x^2)$ **15.** $7(x-2)$
17. $t(3t+1)$ **19.** $-4a(a+2)$, or $4a(-a-2)$
21. $x^2(x+6)$ **23.** $8x^2(x^2-3)$ **25.** $2(x^2+x-4)$
27. $-a^2(7a^4 - 10a^2 + 14)$ **29.** $6x^2(x^6 + 2x^4 - 4x^2 + 5)$
31. $x^2y^2(x^3y^3 + x^2y + xy - 1)$
33. $-5a^2b^2(ab^2 - 2b + 3a)$ **35.** $(y-2)(y+7)$
37. $(x+3)(x^2-7)$ **39.** $(y+8)(y^2+1)$
41. $(x+3)(x^2+4)$ **43.** $(a+3)(5a^2+2)$
45. $(3x-4)(3x^2+1)$ **47.** $(t-5)(4t^2+3)$
49. $(7x+2)(x^2-2)$ **51.** $(6a-7)(a^2+1)$
53. $(x+8)(x^2-3)$ **55.** $(x+6)(2x^2-5)$
57. Not factorable by grouping   **59.** $(y+8)(y^2-2)$
61. $(x-4)(2x^2-9)$ **63.** ▨   **65.** $x^2 + 8x + 15$
66. $x^2 + 9x + 14$ **67.** $a^2 - 4a - 21$ **68.** $a^2 - 3a - 40$
69. $6x^2 + 7x - 20$ **70.** $12t^2 - 13t - 14$
71. $9t^2 - 30t + 25$ **72.** $4t^2 - 36t + 81$ **73.** ▨
75. $(2x^3 + 3)(2x^2 + 3)$ **77.** $(x^5 + 1)(x^7 + 1)$
79. $(x-1)(5x^4 + x^2 + 3)$ **81.** Answers may vary.
$8x^4y^3 - 24x^2y^4 + 16x^3y^4$

Exercise Set 5.2, pp. 318–319

1. Positive; positive   **3.** Negative; positive   **5.** Positive
7. $(x+6)(x+1)$ **9.** $(x+3)(x+4)$ **11.** $(x-3)^2$
13. $(x+2)(x+7)$ **15.** $(b-4)(b-1)$ **17.** $(a+6)(a-2)$
19. $(d-2)(d-5)$ **21.** $(x-5)(x+3)$ **23.** $(x+5)(x-3)$
25. $3(y+4)(y-7)$ **27.** $-x(x+6)(x-7)$
29. $(x-5)(x+12)$ **31.** $(x-6)(x+12)$

33. $-5(b-3)(b+8)$ **35.** $x^3(x-2)(x+1)$ **37.** Prime
39. $(t+5)(t+10)$ **41.** $(x+9)(x+11)$
43. $2x(x-8)(x-12)$ **45.** $-4(x+5)^2$
47. $(y-9)(y-12)$ **49.** $-a^4(a-6)(a+15)$ **51.** $\left(t+\frac{1}{3}\right)^2$
53. Prime   **55.** $(p+5q)(p-2q)$ **57.** Prime
59. $(s-5t)(s+3t)$ **61.** $6a^8(a+2)(a-7)$ **63.** ▨
65. $\frac{8}{3}$ **66.** $-\frac{7}{2}$ **67.** $3x^2 + 22x + 24$
68. $49w^2 + 84w + 36$ **69.** 29,443 people
70. 100°, 25°, 55°   **71.** ▨   **73.** $-5, 5, -23, 23, -49, 49$
75. $(y+0.2)(y-0.4)$ **77.** $-\frac{1}{3}a(a-3)(a+2)$
79. $(x^m+4)(x^m+7)$ **81.** $(a+1)(x+2)(x+1)$
83. $(x+3)^3$, or $x^3 + 9x^2 + 27x + 27$ cubic meters
85. $x^2(\pi-1)$ **87.** $x^2(9 - \frac{1}{2}\pi)$ **89.** $(x+5)(x+7)$

Exercise Set 5.3, pp. 328–330

1. (c)   **3.** (d)   **5.** $(2x-1)(x+4)$ **7.** $(3t-5)(t+3)$
9. $(3x-1)(2x-7)$ **11.** $(7x+1)(x+2)$
13. $(3a+2)(3a-4)$ **15.** $2(3x+1)(x-2)$
17. $6(2t+1)(t-1)$ **19.** $(5x+3)(3x+2)$
21. $-1(7x+4)(5x+2)$, or $-(7x+4)(5x+2)$ **23.** Prime
25. $(5x+4)^2$ **27.** $(8a+3)(2a+9)$ **29.** $2(3t-1)(3t+5)$
31. $-1(x-3)(2x+5)$, or $-(x-3)(2x+5)$
33. $-3(2x+1)(x+5)$ **35.** $5(4x-1)(x-1)$
37. $4(3x-1)(x+6)$ **39.** $(3x+1)(x+1)$
41. $(y+4)(y-2)$ **43.** $(4t-3)(2t-7)$
45. $(3x+2)(2x+3)$ **47.** $(t+3)(2t-1)$
49. $(a-4)(3a-1)$ **51.** $(9t+5)(t+1)$
53. $-1(4x+1)(4x+7)$, or $-(4x+1)(4x+7)$
55. $5(2a-1)(a+3)$ **57.** $3x(3x-1)(2x+3)$
59. $(x+1)(25x+64)$ **61.** $3x(7x+1)(8x+1)$
63. $-t^2(2t-3)(7t+1)$ **65.** $3(5x-3)(3x+2)$
67. $(2a+b)(a+2b)$ **69.** $(2s+3t)(4s+3t)$
71. $6(3x-4y)(x+y)$ **73.** $-2(3a-2b)(4a-3b)$
75. $x^2(4x+7)(2x+5)$ **77.** $a^6(3a+4)(3a+2)$
79. ▨   **81.** 6369 km, 3949 mi   **82.** 40°   **83.** $9x^2 + 6x + 1$
84. $25x^2 - 20x + 4$ **85.** $16t^2 - 40t + 25$
86. $49a^2 + 14a + 1$ **87.** $25x^2 - 4$ **88.** $4x^2 - 9$
89. $4t^2 - 49$ **90.** $16a^2 - 49$ **91.** ▨
93. $(3xy+2)(6xy-5)$ **95.** Prime   **97.** $(4t^5-1)^2$
99. $-1(10x^n+3)(2x^n+1)$, or $-(10x^n+3)(2x^n+1)$
101. $a(a^n-1)^2$ **103.** $-2(a+1)^n(a+3)^2(a+6)$

Exercise Set 5.4, pp. 336–337

1. Difference of squares   **3.** None of these   **5.** Perfect-
square trinomial   **7.** Prime polynomial   **9.** Perfect-
square trinomial   **11.** Yes   **13.** No   **15.** No   **17.** No
19. $(x+8)^2$ **21.** $(x-7)^2$ **23.** $3(x+1)^2$ **25.** $(2-x)^2$, or
$(x-2)^2$ **27.** $2(3x+1)^2$ **29.** $(7-4y)^2$, or $(4y-7)^2$
31. $-x^3(x-9)^2$ **33.** $2x(x-1)^2$ **35.** $5(2x+5)^2$
37. $(7-3x)^2$, or $(3x-7)^2$ **39.** $(4x+3)^2$ **41.** $2(1+5x)^2$,
or $2(5x+1)^2$ **43.** $(2p+3q)^2$ **45.** Prime
47. $-1(8m+n)^2$, or $-(8m+n)^2$ **49.** $-2(4s-5t)^2$
51. No   **53.** Yes   **55.** No   **57.** $(y+2)(y-2)$

59. $(p + 3)(p - 3)$ **61.** $(7 + t)(-7 + t)$, or $(t + 7)(t - 7)$
63. $6(a + 3)(a - 3)$ **65.** $(7x - 1)^2$ **67.** $2(10 - t)(10 + t)$
69. $-5(4a - 3)(4a + 3)$ **71.** $5(t + 4)(t - 4)$
73. $2(2x + 7)(2x - 7)$ **75.** $x(6 + 7x)(6 - 7x)$ **77.** Prime
79. $(t - 1)(t + 1)(t^2 + 1)$ **81.** $-3x(x - 4)^2$
83. $3(4t + 3)(4t - 3)$ **85.** $a^6(a - 1)^2$ **87.** $7(a + b)(a - b)$
89. $(5x + 2y)(5x - 2y)$ **91.** $2(3t + 2s)(3t - 2s)$ **93.** 🖊
95. 3.125 L **96.** Scores ≥ 77 **97.** $x^{12}y^{12}$ **98.** $25a^4b^6$
99.

$y = \frac{3}{2}x - 3$

$3x - 5y = 30$

101. 🖊 **103.** $(x^4 + 2^4)(x^2 + 2^2)(x + 2)(x - 2)$, or
$(x^4 + 16)(x^2 + 4)(x + 2)(x - 2)$ **105.** $2x(3x - \frac{2}{5})(3x + \frac{2}{5})$
107. $(y^2 - 10y + 25 + z^4)(y - 5 + z^2)(y - 5 - z^2)$
109. $-1(x^2 + 1)(x + 3)(x - 3)$, or $-(x^2 + 1)(x + 3)(x - 3)$
111. $(y + 4)^2$ **113.** $(3x - 7)^2(3x + 7)$
115. $(9 + b^{2k})(3 + b^k)(3 - b^k)$ **117.** $2x^3 - x^2 - 1$
119. $(y + x + 7)(y - x - 1)$ **121.** 16
123. $(x + 1)^2 - x^2 = [(x + 1) + x][(x + 1) - x] = 2x + 1 =$
$(x + 1) + x$

Exercise Set 5.5, pp. 340–341

1. $(t + 2)(t^2 - 2t + 4)$ **3.** $(a - 4)(a^2 + 4a + 16)$
5. $(z + 5)(z^2 - 5z + 25)$ **7.** $(2a - 1)(4a^2 + 2a + 1)$
9. $(y - 3)(y^2 + 3y + 9)$ **11.** $(4 + 5x)(16 - 20x + 25x^2)$
13. $(5p - 1)(25p^2 + 5p + 1)$
15. $(3m + 4)(9m^2 - 12m + 16)$
17. $(p - q)(p^2 + pq + q^2)$ **19.** $(x + \frac{1}{2})(x^2 - \frac{1}{2}x + \frac{1}{4})$
21. $2(y - 4)(y^2 + 4y + 16)$ **23.** $3(2a + 1)(4a^2 - 2a + 1)$
25. $r(s - 4)(s^2 + 4s + 16)$
27. $5(x + 2z)(x^2 - 2xz + 4z^2)$
29. $(x + 0.1)(x^2 - 0.1x + 0.01)$
31. $3z^2(z - 1)(z^2 + z + 1)$ **33.** $(t^2 + 1)(t^4 - t^2 + 1)$
35. $(p + q)(p^2 - pq + q^2)(p - q)(p^2 + pq + q^2)$ **37.** 🖊
39. $9x^2 - 25$ **40.** $9x^2 + 30x + 25$ **41.** $x^2 - 3x - 28$
42. $x^3 + 1$ **43.** 24 million **44.** 32.8 million barrels
45. 🖊 **47.** $(5c^2 + 2d^2)(25c^4 - 10c^2d^2 + 4d^4)$
49. $3(x^a - 2y^b)(x^{2a} + 2x^ay^b + 4y^{2b})$
51. $\frac{1}{3}(\frac{1}{2}xy + z)(\frac{1}{4}x^2y^2 - \frac{1}{2}xyz + z^2)$ **53.** $2x(x^2 + 75)$
55. $(t - 8)(t - 1)(t^2 + t + 1)$

Exercise Set 5.6, pp. 346–347

1. Common factor **3.** Grouping **5.** $10(a + 8)(a - 8)$
7. $(y - 7)^2$ **9.** $(2t + 3)(t + 4)$ **11.** $x(x - 9)^2$
13. $(x - 5)^2(x + 5)$ **15.** $3t(3t + 1)(3t - 1)$

17. $3x(3x - 5)(x + 3)$ **19.** Prime **21.** $3(x + 3)(2x - 5)$
23. $-2a^4(a - 2)^2$ **25.** $5x(x^2 + 4)(x + 2)(x - 2)$
27. $(t^2 + 3)(t^2 - 3)$ **29.** $-x^4(x^2 - 2x + 7)$
31. $(x - y)(x^2 + xy + y^2)$ **33.** $a(x^2 + y^2)$
35. $9mn(4 - mn)$ **37.** $2\pi r(h + r)$ **39.** $(a + b)(5a + 3b)$
41. $(x + 1)(x + y)$ **43.** $(a - 3)(a + y)$
45. $(3x - 2y)(x + 5y)$ **47.** $(a - 2b)^2$ **49.** $(4x + 3y)^2$
51. Prime **53.** $(2t + 1)(4t^2 - 2t + 1)(2t - 1)(4t^2 + 2t + 1)$
55. $p(4p^2 + 4pq - q^2)$ **57.** $(3b - a)(b + 6a)$
59. $-1(xy + 2)(xy + 6)$, or $-(xy + 2)(xy + 6)$
61. $(pq + 6)(pq + 1)$ **63.** $2a(3a + 2b)(9a^2 - 6ab + 4b^2)$
65. $x^4(x + 2y)(x - y)$ **67.** $(6a - \frac{5}{4})^2$ **69.** $(\frac{1}{9}x - \frac{4}{3})^2$
71. $(1 + 4x^6y^6)(1 + 2x^3y^3)(1 - 2x^3y^3)$ **73.** $(2ab + 3)^2$
75. $a(a^2 + 8)(a + 8)$ **77.** 🖊
79. For $(-1, 11)$:

$\dfrac{y = -4x + 7}{11 \;\bigg|\; \begin{array}{l} -4(-1) + 7 \\ 4 + 7 \end{array}}$

$11 \overset{?}{=} 11$ True

For $(0, 7)$:

$\dfrac{y = -4x + 7}{7 \;\bigg|\; \begin{array}{l} -4 \cdot 0 + 7 \\ 0 + 7 \end{array}}$

$7 \overset{?}{=} 7$ True

For $(3, -5)$:

$\dfrac{y = -4x + 7}{-5 \;\bigg|\; \begin{array}{l} -4 \cdot 3 + 7 \\ -12 + 7 \end{array}}$

$-5 \overset{?}{=} -5$ True

80. $\frac{4}{5}$ **81.** $-\frac{7}{3}$ **82.** $-\frac{9}{2}$ **83.** $\frac{9}{4}$
84.

$y = -\frac{1}{2}x + 4$

85. 🖊

87. $-x(x^2 + 9)(x^2 - 2)$
89. $-3(a + 1)(a - 1)(a + 2)(a - 2)$
91. $(y + 1)(y - 7)(y + 3)$ **93.** $(2x - 2 + 3y)(3x - 3 - y)$
95. $(a + 3)^2(2a + b + 4)(a - b + 5)$

Technology Connection, p. 354

1. $-4.65, 0.65$ **2.** $-0.37, 5.37$ **3.** $-8.98, -4.56$
4. No solution **5.** $0, 2.76$

Exercise Set 5.7, pp. 354–356

1. (c) **3.** (a) **5.** $-7, -5$ **7.** $-4, \frac{9}{2}$ **9.** $-\frac{7}{4}, \frac{9}{10}$
11. $-2, 0$ **13.** $\frac{1}{21}, \frac{18}{11}$ **15.** $-\frac{9}{2}, 0$ **17.** $50, 70$ **19.** $-5, \frac{2}{3}, 1$
21. $1, 6$ **23.** $-7, 3$ **25.** $0, 1, 2$ **27.** $0, 6$ **29.** $-6, 0$
31. $-\frac{2}{3}, \frac{2}{3}$ **33.** -5 **35.** 1 **37.** $0, 2$ **39.** $-\frac{5}{3}, 4$
41. $-5, -1$ **43.** 3 **45.** $0, \frac{3}{2}$ **47.** $-\frac{5}{9}, \frac{5}{9}$ **49.** $-1, \frac{6}{5}$

51. $-2, 9$ **53.** $-1, 0, \frac{3}{2}$ **55.** $-7, -\frac{8}{3}, \frac{5}{2}$ **57.** $-3, 2$
59. $-1, 3$ **61.** $(-4, 0), (1, 0)$ **63.** $(-3, 0), (5, 0)$
65. $\left(-\frac{5}{2}, 0\right), (2, 0)$ **67.** 🖉   **69.** $(a + b)^2$ **70.** $a^2 + b^2$
71. Let x represent the first integer; $x + (x + 1)$
72. Let x represent the number; $2x + 5 < 19$
73. Let x represent the number; $\frac{1}{2}x - 7 > 24$
74. Let x represent the number; $x - 3 \geq 34$ **75.** 🖉
77. **(a)** $x^2 - x - 20 = 0$; **(b)** $x^2 - 6x - 7 = 0$;
(c) $4x^2 - 13x + 3 = 0$; **(d)** $6x^2 - 5x + 1 = 0$;
(e) $12x^2 - 17x + 6 = 0$; **(f)** $x^3 - 4x^2 + x + 6 = 0$
79. $-5, 4$ **81.** $-\frac{3}{5}, \frac{3}{5}$ **83.** $-4, 2$
85. **(a)** $2x^2 + 20x - 4 = 0$; **(b)** $x^2 - 3x - 18 = 0$;
(c) $(x + 1)(5x - 5) = 0$; **(d)** $(2x + 8)(2x - 5) = 0$;
(e) $4x^2 + 8x + 36 = 0$; **(f)** $9x^2 - 12x + 24 = 0$ **87.** 🖉
89. $-0.25, 0.88$ **91.** $-3.23, 4.55$ **93.** $-3.76, 0$

Exercise Set 5.8, pp. 363–367

1. $-4, 5$ **3.** 9 cm, 12 cm, 15 cm   **5.** 9, 10   **7.** -17 and
-15; 15 and 17   **9.** Length: 12 ft; width: 2 ft
11. Length: 6 cm; width: 4 cm   **13.** Base: 14 cm; height:
4 cm   **15.** Foot: 7 ft; height: 12 ft   **17.** 1 min, 3 min
19. 16 teams   **21.** 105 handshakes   **23.** 12 players
25. 9 ft   **27.** 25 ft   **29.** Dining room: 12 ft by 12 ft;
kitchen: 12 ft by 10 ft   **31.** 20 ft   **33.** 1 sec, 2 sec
35. 🖉   **37.** $-\frac{8}{21}$ **38.** $-\frac{35}{45}$ **39.** $-\frac{35}{54}$ **40.** $-\frac{5}{16}$ **41.** $-\frac{2}{21}$
42. $-\frac{26}{45}$ **43.** $\frac{1}{18}$ **44.** $-\frac{11}{24}$ **45.** 🖉   **47.** \$1200
49. 39 cm   **51.** 15 cm by 30 cm   **53.** 35 ft
55. 2 hr, 4.2 hr   **57.** 3 hr

Review Exercises: Chapter 5, pp. 369–370

1. False   **2.** True   **3.** True   **4.** False   **5.** True   **6.** False
7. True   **8.** False   **9.** Answers may vary.
$(12x)(3x^2), (-9x^2)(-4x), (6x)(6x^2)$ **10.** Answers may vary.
$(-4x^3)(5x^2), (2x^4)(-10x), (-5x)(4x^4)$ **11.** $6x^3(2x - 3)$
12. $4a(2a - 3)$ **13.** $(2t - 3)(2t + 3)$ **14.** $(x - 2)(x + 6)$
15. $(x + 7)^2$ **16.** $3x(2x + 1)^2$ **17.** $(2x + 3)(3x^2 + 1)$
18. $(6t + 1)(t - 1)$ **19.** $(5t - 3)^2$ **20.** $2(24t^2 - 14t + 3)$
21. $(9a^2 + 1)(3a + 1)(3a - 1)$ **22.** $3x(3x - 5)(x + 3)$
23. $2(x - 5)(x^2 + 5x + 25)$ **24.** $(x + 4)(x^3 - 2)$
25. $(ab^2 - 6)(ab^2 + 6)$ **26.** $-4x^4(2x^2 - 8x + 1)$
27. $3(2x - 5)^2$ **28.** Prime   **29.** $-x(x - 6)(x + 5)$
30. $(2x + 5)(2x - 5)$ **31.** $2z(2z - 3)$ **32.** $5z(3 + 2z)$
33. $(4t + 5)(t + 2)$ **34.** $(2t + 1)(t - 4)$
35. $7x(x + 1)(x + 4)$ **36.** $5x(x + 2)(x + 5)$
37. $2(3x - 1)^2$ **38.** $-3(x + 3)(x - 3)$ **39.** $(5 - x)(3 - x)$
40. $(2y + 3x^2)(4y^2 - 6x^2y + 9x^4)$ **41.** $(xy - 3)(xy + 4)$
42. $3(2a + 7b)^2$ **43.** $(m + 5)(m + t)$
44. $32(x^2 + 2y^2z^2)(x^2 - 2y^2z^2)$ **45.** $(2m + n)(3m + n)$
46. Prime   **47.** $-8, 7$ **48.** $-7, 0, 5$ **49.** $-\frac{1}{3}, \frac{1}{3}$ **50.** $\frac{2}{3}, 1$
51. $-\frac{3}{2}, 4$ **52.** $-2, 3$ **53.** $0, \frac{3}{4}$ **54.** $0, \frac{4}{3}$ **55.** $-3, 4$
56. 10 teams   **57.** $(-1, 0), \left(\frac{5}{2}, 0\right)$
58. Height: 40 cm; base: 40 cm   **59.** 24 ft

60. 🖉 Answers may vary. Because Edith did not first factor
out the largest common factor, 4, her factorization will not
be "complete" until she removes a common factor of 2
from each binomial. The answer should be $4(x - 5)(x + 5)$.
Awarding 3 to 7 points would seem reasonable.
61. 🖉 The equations solved in this chapter have an
x^2-term (are quadratic), whereas those solved previously
have no x^2-term (are linear). The principle of zero
products is used to solve quadratic equations and is not
used to solve linear equations.   **62.** 2.5 cm   **63.** 0, 2
64. Length: 12 cm; width: 6 cm   **65.** 100 cm², 225 cm²
66. $-3, 2, \frac{5}{2}$ **67.** No real solution

Test: Chapter 5, pp. 370–371

1. [5.1] $(2x)(4x^3), (-4x^2)(-2x^2), (8x)(x^3)$
2. [5.2] $(x - 2)(x - 5)$ **3.** [5.4] $(x - 5)^2$
4. [5.1] $2y^2(2y^2 - 4y + 3)$ **5.** [5.1] $(x + 1)(x^2 + 2)$
6. [5.1] $t^5(t^2 - 3)$ **7.** [5.2] $x(x + 3)(x - 1)$
8. [5.3] $2(5x - 6)(x + 4)$ **9.** [5.4] $(2t + 5)(2t - 5)$
10. [5.2] $(x - 4)(x + 3)$ **11.** [5.3] $-3m(2m + 1)(m + 1)$
12. [5.4] $3(w + 5)(w - 5)$ **13.** [5.4] $5(3r + 2)^2$
14. [5.4] $3(x^2 + 4)(x + 2)(x - 2)$ **15.** [5.4] $(7t + 6)^2$
16. [5.3] $(5x - 1)(x - 5)$ **17.** [5.1] $(x + 2)(x^3 - 3)$
18. [5.5] $2(m^2 + 2)(m^4 - 2m^2 + 4)$
19. [5.3] $(2x + 3)(2x - 5)$ **20.** [5.3] $3t(2t + 5)(t - 1)$
21. [5.3] $3(m - 5n)(m + 2n)$ **22.** [5.7] $-5, 4$
23. [5.7] $-\frac{3}{2}, 0, 5$ **24.** [5.7] $-4, 7$ **25.** [5.7] $(-1, 0), \left(\frac{8}{3}, 0\right)$
26. [5.8] Length: 8 m; width: 6 m   **27.** [5.8] 5 ft
28. [5.8] 4 in., 6 in.   **29.** [5.8] Width: 3; length: 15
30. [5.2] $(a - 4)(a + 8)$ **31.** [5.7] $-\frac{8}{3}, 0, \frac{2}{5}$

CHAPTER 6

Technology Connection, p. 377

1. Correct   **2.** Correct   **3.** Not correct   **4.** Not correct

Exercise Set 6.1, pp. 379–381

1. (e)   **3.** (d)   **5.** (c)   **7.** 0   **9.** -8 **11.** 4   **13.** $-4, 7$
15. $-6, 0, \frac{1}{2}$ **17.** $\frac{5a}{4b^2}$ **19.** $\frac{4}{3xy^4}$ **21.** $\frac{3}{4}$ **23.** $\frac{a - 3}{a + 1}$
25. $\frac{3}{2x^3}$ **27.** $\frac{y - 3}{4y}$ **29.** $\frac{t + 4}{t + 5}$ **31.** $\frac{a + 4}{2(a - 4)}$ **33.** $\frac{x + 4}{x - 4}$
35. $t - 1$ **37.** $\frac{1}{a^2 + 2a + 4}$ **39.** $\frac{y^2 + 4}{y + 2}$ **41.** $\frac{1}{2}$
43. $\frac{y}{2y + 1}$ **45.** $\frac{2x - 3}{5x + 2}$ **47.** -1 **49.** -7 **51.** $-\frac{1}{3}$
53. $-\frac{3}{2}$ **55.** -1 **57.** 🖉   **59.** $-\frac{4}{7}$ **60.** $-\frac{10}{33}$ **61.** $-\frac{15}{4}$
62. $-\frac{21}{16}$ **63.** $\frac{13}{63}$ **64.** $\frac{5}{48}$ **65.** 🖉   **67.** $-(2y + x)$

69. $\dfrac{x^3 + 4}{(x^3 + 2)(x^2 + 2)}$ **71.** $\dfrac{(t-1)(t-9)^2}{(t+1)(t^2+9)}$

73. $\dfrac{(x-y)^3}{(x+y)^2(x-5y)}$ **75.** ▢

Technology Connection, p. 384

1. Let $y_1 = ((x^2 + 3x + 2)/(x^2 + 4))/(5x^2 + 10x)$ and $y_2 = (x+1)/((x^2+4)(5x))$. With the table set in AUTO mode, note that the values in the Y1- and Y2-columns match except for $x = -2$.
2. ERROR messages occur when division by 0 is attempted. Since the simplified expression has no factor of $x + 5$ or $x + 1$ in a denominator, no ERROR message occurs in Y2 for $x = -5$ or -1.

Exercise Set 6.2, pp. 384–386

1. $\dfrac{7x(x-5)}{5(2x+1)}$ **3.** $\dfrac{(a-4)(a+2)}{(a+6)^2}$ **5.** $\dfrac{(2x+3)(x+1)}{4(x-5)}$

7. $\dfrac{(a-4)(a+4)}{(a^2+4)(a^2-4)}$ **9.** $\dfrac{(x+6)(x-1)}{(3+x)(x+1)}$ **11.** $\dfrac{5a^2}{3}$

13. $\dfrac{4}{c^2d}$ **15.** $\dfrac{x+2}{x-2}$ **17.** $\dfrac{(a^2+25)(a-5)}{(a-3)(a-1)(a+5)}$

19. $\dfrac{7(a+3)}{a(a+4)}$ **21.** $\dfrac{2a}{a-2}$ **23.** $\dfrac{t-5}{t+5}$ **25.** $\dfrac{5(a+6)}{a-1}$

27. 1   **29.** $\dfrac{t+4}{t+2}$ **31.** $\dfrac{x+2}{x+3}$ **33.** $c(c-2)$ **35.** $\dfrac{7}{3x}$

37. $\dfrac{1}{a^3-8a}$ **39.** $\frac{35}{24}$ **41.** $\dfrac{x^2}{20}$ **43.** $\dfrac{a^3}{b^3}$ **45.** $\dfrac{y+5}{2y}$

47. $4(y-2)$ **49.** $-\dfrac{a}{b}$ **51.** $\dfrac{(y+3)(y^2+1)}{y+1}$ **53.** $\frac{15}{16}$

55. $\dfrac{a-5}{3(a-1)}$ **57.** $\dfrac{(2x-1)(2x+1)}{x-5}$ **59.** $\dfrac{(a-5)(3a-4)}{(a+4)(2a-7)}$

61. $\dfrac{1}{(c-5)(5c-3)}$ **63.** $\dfrac{(x-4y)(x-y)}{(x+y)^3}$

65. $\dfrac{x^2+4x+16}{(x+4)^2}$ **67.** $\dfrac{(2a+b)^2}{2(a+b)}$ **69.** ▢   **71.** $\frac{19}{12}$

72. $\frac{41}{24}$ **73.** $\frac{1}{18}$ **74.** $-\frac{1}{6}$ **75.** $-\frac{37}{20}$ **76.** $\frac{49}{45}$ **77.** ▢

79. $\dfrac{a}{(c-3d)(2a+5b)}$ **81.** $\dfrac{a^2-2b}{a^2+3b}$ **83.** $\dfrac{(z+4)^3}{3(z-4)^2}$

85. $\dfrac{x(x^2+1)}{3(x+y-1)}$ **87.** $\dfrac{3(y+2)^3}{y(y-1)}$ **89.** ▨

Exercise Set 6.3, pp. 394–397

1. Numerators; denominator   **3.** Least common denominator; LCD   **5.** $\dfrac{10}{x}$ **7.** $\dfrac{3x+5}{12}$ **9.** $\dfrac{9}{a+3}$

11. $\dfrac{6}{a+2}$ **13.** $\dfrac{2y+7}{2y}$ **15.** 11   **17.** $\dfrac{3x+5}{x+1}$ **19.** $a+5$

21. $x-4$ **23.** 0   **25.** $\dfrac{1}{x+2}$ **27.** $\dfrac{t-4}{t+3}$ **29.** $\dfrac{x+5}{x-6}$

31. $-\dfrac{5}{x-4}$, or $\dfrac{5}{4-x}$ **33.** $-\dfrac{1}{x-1}$, or $\dfrac{1}{1-x}$ **35.** 135

37. 72   **39.** 126   **41.** $12x^3$ **43.** $30a^4b^8$ **45.** $6(y-3)$

47. $(x-2)(x+2)(x+3)$ **49.** $t(t-4)(t+2)^2$

51. $30x^2y^2z^3$ **53.** $(a+1)(a-1)^2$ **55.** $(m-3)(m-2)^2$

57. $12x^3(x-5)(x-3)(x-1)$

59. $2(x+1)(x-1)(x^2+x+1)$

61. $\dfrac{3a^3}{10a^6}, \dfrac{2b}{10a^6}$ **63.** $\dfrac{21y}{9x^4y^3}, \dfrac{4x^3}{9x^4y^3}$

65. $\dfrac{2x(x+3)}{(x-2)(x+2)(x+3)}, \dfrac{4x(x-2)}{(x-2)(x+2)(x+3)}$

67. ▢   **69.** $-\frac{7}{9}, \frac{-7}{9}$ **70.** $\frac{-3}{2}, \frac{3}{-2}$ **71.** $-\frac{11}{36}$ **72.** $-\frac{7}{60}$

73. $x^2-9x+18$ **74.** $s^2-\pi r^2$ **75.** ▢   **77.** $\dfrac{18x+5}{x-1}$

79. $\dfrac{x}{3x+1}$ **81.** 30 strands   **83.** 60 strands

85. $72(t+1)(t-1)^4$ **87.** 70 minutes   **89.** 7:55 A.M.

91. ▢

Exercise Set 6.4, pp. 403–405

1. LCD   **3.** Numerators; LCD   **5.** $\dfrac{4x+9}{x^2}$ **7.** $-\dfrac{5}{24r}$

9. $\dfrac{2d^2+7c}{c^2d^3}$ **11.** $\dfrac{-2xy-18}{3x^2y^3}$ **13.** $\dfrac{5x+7}{18}$ **15.** $\dfrac{-x-4}{6}$

17. $\dfrac{a^2+16a+16}{16a^2}$ **19.** $\dfrac{7z-12}{12z}$ **21.** $\dfrac{x^2+4xy+y^2}{x^2y^2}$

23. $\dfrac{4x^2-13xt+9t^2}{3x^2t^2}$ **25.** $\dfrac{6x}{(x+2)(x-2)}$

27. $\dfrac{2x-40}{(x-5)(x+5)}$ **29.** $\dfrac{11x+2}{3x(x+1)}$ **31.** $\dfrac{3-5t}{2t(t-1)}$

33. $\dfrac{x^2+6x}{(x-4)(x+4)}$ **35.** $\dfrac{16}{3(z+4)}$ **37.** $\dfrac{3x-1}{(x-1)^2}$

39. $\dfrac{1}{m^2+m+1}$ **41.** $\dfrac{9a}{4(a-5)}$ **43.** 0

45. $\dfrac{10}{(a-3)(a+2)}$ **47.** $\dfrac{x-5}{(x+5)(x+3)}$

49. $\dfrac{3z^2+19z-20}{(z-2)^2(z+3)}$ **51.** $\dfrac{-5}{x^2+17x+16}$ **53.** $\dfrac{5x-3}{5}$

55. $y+3$ **57.** $\dfrac{2b-14}{b^2-16}$ **59.** $\dfrac{p^2+7p+1}{(p-5)(p+5)}$

61. $\dfrac{13x+20}{(4+x)(4-x)}$ **63.** $\dfrac{-a-2}{(a+1)(a-1)}$, or $\dfrac{a+2}{(1+a)(1-a)}$

65. $\dfrac{10x+6y}{(x-y)(x+y)}$ **67.** $\dfrac{2x-3}{2-x}$ **69.** 2   **71.** 0   **73.** ▢

75. $-\frac{13}{14}$ **76.** $-\frac{5}{9}$ **77.** $\frac{2}{15}$ **78.** $\frac{7}{6}$

79.

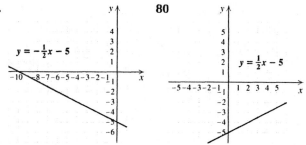

80.

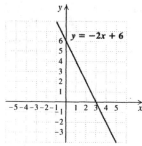

81.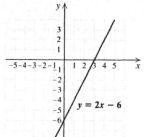

83. Perimeter: $\dfrac{10x - 14}{(x - 5)(x + 4)}$; area: $\dfrac{6}{(x - 5)(x + 4)}$

85. $\dfrac{30}{(x - 3)(x + 4)}$ **87.** $\dfrac{x^4 + 4x^3 - 5x^2 - 126x - 441}{(x + 2)^2(x + 7)^2}$

89. $\dfrac{-x^2 - 3}{(2x - 3)(x - 3)}$ **91.** $\dfrac{a}{a - b} + \dfrac{3b}{b - a}$; answers may vary.

93.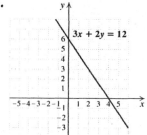

Technology Connection, p. 410

1. $(1 - 1/x)/(1 - 1/x^2)$ **2.** Parentheses are needed to group separate terms into factors. When a fraction bar is replaced with a division sign, we need parentheses to preserve the groupings that had been created by the fraction bar. This holds for denominators and numerators alike.

Exercise Set 6.5, pp. 410–412

1. (d)   **3.** (b)   **5.** $\frac{6}{5}$ **7.** $\frac{117}{22}$ **9.** $\dfrac{4s^2}{9 + 3s^2}$ **11.** $\dfrac{4x}{3x + 2}$

13. $\dfrac{4a - 10}{a - 7}$ **15.** $x - 4$ **17.** $-\dfrac{1}{x}$ **19.** $\dfrac{1 + t^2}{t - t^2}$ **21.** $\dfrac{x}{x - y}$

23. $\dfrac{2a^2 + 7a}{5 - 3a^2}$ **25.** 1 **27.** $\dfrac{3a^2 + 4b^3}{5b^3 - 3a^2b^3}$ **29.** $\dfrac{2x^4 - 3x^2}{2x^4 + 3}$

31. $\dfrac{t^2 - 2}{t^2 + 5}$ **33.** $\dfrac{a^2b^2}{b^2 - ab + a^2}$ **35.** $\dfrac{3a^2b^3 + 4a}{3b^2 + ab^2}$

37. $\dfrac{t^2 + 5t + 3}{(t + 1)^2}$ **39.** $\dfrac{x^2 - 2x - 1}{x^2 - 5x - 4}$ **41.**   **43.** -4

44. -4 **45.** $\frac{19}{3}$ **46.** $-\frac{14}{27}$ **47.** $-3, 10$ **48.** $-10, 2$

49.   **51.** $6, 7, 8$ **53.** $-\frac{4}{5}, \frac{9}{2}$ **55.** $\dfrac{P(i + 12)^2}{12(i + 24)}$

57. $\dfrac{(x - 8)(x - 1)(x + 1)}{x^2(x - 2)(x + 2)}$ **59.** 0 **61.** $\dfrac{2z(5z - 2)}{(z + 2)(13z - 6)}$

63.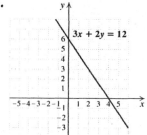

Exercise Set 6.6, pp. 418–419

1. False   **3.** True   **5.** $-\frac{1}{2}$ **7.** $\frac{6}{7}$ **9.** $\frac{24}{7}$ **11.** $-5, -1$

13. $-6, 6$ **15.** 3 **17.** $\frac{14}{3}$ **19.** $\frac{35}{3}$ **21.** $-4, -3$ **23.** 5

25. $\frac{5}{2}$ **27.** -1 **29.** No solution   **31.** -10 **33.** $\frac{10}{7}$

35. $-2, \frac{7}{3}$ **37.** No solution   **39.** 2 **41.** No solution

43. No solution   **45.** 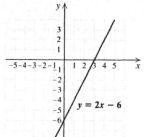   **47.** $137, 139$ **48.** 14 yd

49. Base: 9 cm; height: 12 cm   **50.** $-8, -6$; $6, 8$

51. 0.06 cm per day   **52.** 0.28 in. per day   **53.**

55. -2 **57.** $-\frac{1}{6}$ **59.** $-1, 0$ **61.** 4 **63.**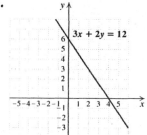

Exercise Set 6.7, pp. 429–433

1. 12 min   **3.** $\frac{48}{7}$ hr, or 6 hr, $51\frac{3}{7}$ min   **5.** $\frac{14}{3}$ min, or $4\frac{2}{3}$ min

7. $8\frac{4}{7}$ hr   **9.** Canon: 36 min; HP: 72 min   **11.** Erickson Air-Crane: 10 hr; S-58T: 40 hr   **13.** Mariah: $\frac{4}{3}$ hr; Stan: 4 hr

15. 8 hr

17.

	Distance (in km)	Speed (in km/h)	Time (in hours)
B & M	330	$r - 14$	$\dfrac{330}{r - 14}$
AMTRAK	400	r	$\dfrac{400}{r}$

AMTRAK: 80 km/h; B & M: 66 km/h

19. Bill: 50 mph; Hillary: 80 mph   **21.** 3 hr   **23.** 7 mph

25. 4.3 ft/sec   **27.** Freight: 66 mph; passenger: 80 mph

29. 9 km/h   **31.** 2 km/h   **33.** 10.5   **35.** $\frac{8}{3}$ **37.** $3\frac{3}{4}$ in.

39. 20 ft   **41.** $2\frac{2}{3}$ ft   **43.** 12.6   **45.** 105 steps per minute

47. 702 photos   **49.** \$32,340   **51.** 20 duds   **53.** 184

55. (a) 1.92 T; (b) 28.8 lb   **57.**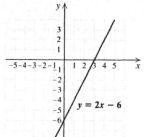

59.

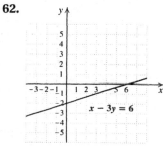

60.

61.

62.

63.

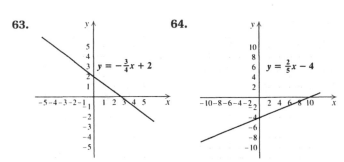

$y = -\frac{3}{4}x + 2$

64.

$y = \frac{2}{5}x - 4$

65. 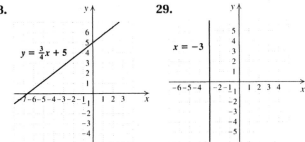   **67.** Michelle: 6 hr; Sal: 3 hr; Kristen: 4 hr
69. $30\frac{22}{31}$ hr   **71.** Add 80 oz of gasoline.   **73.** $\frac{36}{68}$
75. $\frac{B}{A} = \frac{D}{C}; \frac{A}{C} = \frac{B}{D}; \frac{C}{A} = \frac{D}{B}$ **77.**

Review Exercises: Chapter 6, pp. 436–437

1. False   **2.** True   **3.** False   **4.** True   **5.** True   **6.** False
7. False   **8.** False   **9.** 0   **10.** 4   **11.** $-6, 6$ **12.** $-6, 5$
13. -2 **14.** $\frac{x-2}{x+1}$ **15.** $\frac{7x+3}{x-3}$ **16.** $\frac{y-5}{y+5}$
17. $-5(x+2y)$ **18.** $\frac{a-6}{5}$ **19.** $\frac{8(t+1)}{(2t-1)(t-1)}$ **20.** $-32t$
21. $\frac{2x(x-1)}{x+1}$ **22.** $\frac{(x^2+1)(2x+1)}{(x-2)(x+1)}$ **23.** $\frac{(t+4)^2}{t+1}$
24. $24a^5b^9$ **25.** $x^4(x-1)(x+1)$
26. $(y-2)(y+2)(y+1)$ **27.** $\frac{15-3x}{x+3}$ **28.** -1
29. $\frac{4}{x-4}$ **30.** $\frac{x+5}{2x}$ **31.** $\frac{2x+5}{x-2}$ **32.** $\frac{2a}{a-1}$ **33.** $d+c$
34. $\frac{-x^2+x+26}{(x+1)(x-5)(x+5)}$ **35.** $\frac{2(x-2)}{x+2}$ **36.** $\frac{19x+8}{10x(x+2)}$
37. $\frac{z}{1-z}$ **38.** $\frac{x^3(2xy^2+1)}{y(1+x)}$ **39.** $c-d$ **40.** 8   **41.** $-\frac{1}{2}$
42. $-5, 3$ **43.** $5\frac{1}{7}$ hr   **44.** Celeron: 45 sec; Pentium 4:
30 sec   **45.** Car: 105 km/h; train: 90 km/h   **46.** 24 mph
47. 60   **48.** 6   **49.** The LCM of denominators is used
to clear fractions when simplifying a complex rational
expression using the method of multiplying by the LCD,
and when solving rational equations.   **50.** Although
multiplying the denominators of the expressions being
added results in a common denominator, it is often not
the *least* common denominator. Using a common
denominator other than the LCD makes the expressions
more complicated, requires additional simplifying after
the addition has been performed, and leaves more room
for error.
51. $\frac{5(a+3)^2}{a}$ **52.** $\frac{10a}{(a-b)(b-c)}$ **53.** 0   **54.** 44%

Test: Chapter 6, p. 438

1. [6.1] 0   **2.** [6.1] -8 **3.** [6.1] $-7, 7$ **4.** [6.1] 1, 2
5. [6.1] $\frac{3x+7}{x+3}$ **6.** [6.2] $\frac{-2(a+5)}{3}$ **7.** [6.2] $\frac{(5y+1)(y+1)}{3y(y+2)}$
8. [6.2] $\frac{(2x+1)(2x-1)(x^2+1)}{(x-1)^2(x-2)}$ **9.** [6.2] $(x+3)(x-3)$
10. [6.3] $(y-3)(y+3)(y+7)$ **11.** [6.3] $\frac{-3x+9}{x^3}$
12. [6.3] $\frac{-2t+8}{t^2+1}$ **13.** [6.4] $\frac{3}{3-x}$ **14.** [6.4] $\frac{2x-5}{x-3}$
15. [6.4] $\frac{11t-8}{t(t-2)}$ **16.** [6.4] $\frac{-x^2-7x-15}{(x+4)(x-4)(x+1)}$
17. [6.4] $\frac{x^2+2x-7}{(x+1)(x-1)^2}$ **18.** [6.5] $\frac{3y+1}{y}$
19. [6.5] $\frac{a^2(3b^2-2a)}{b^2(a^3+2)}$ **20.** [6.6] 12   **21.** [6.6] $-3, 5$
22. [6.7] 12 min   **23.** [6.7] $2\frac{1}{7}$ cups   **24.** [6.7] Craig:
65 km/h; Marilyn: 45 km/h   **25.** [6.7] Rema: 4 hr;
Reggie: 10 hr   **26.** [6.5] a **27.** [6.7] -1

Cumulative Review: Chapters 1–6, pp. 439–440

1. $2b+a$ **2.** $>$ **3.** 25   **4.** $-8x+28$ **5.** $-\frac{43}{8}$ **6.** 1
7. -6.2 **8.** 8   **9.** 10   **10.** $-7, 7$ **11.** $-\frac{10}{3}$ **12.** -3
13. $\frac{8}{3}$ **14.** $-10, -1$ **15.** -8 **16.** 1, 4   **17.** $\{y \mid y \le -\frac{2}{3}\}$
18. -17 **19.** $-4, \frac{1}{2}$ **20.** $\{x \mid x > 43\}$ **21.** 5   **22.** $-\frac{7}{2}, 5$
23. -13 **24.** $b = 3a - c + 9$ **25.** $y = \frac{4z - 3x}{6}$
26. $\frac{3}{2}x + 2y - 3z$ **27.** $-4x^3 - \frac{1}{7}x^2 - 2$
28.

$y = \frac{3}{4}x + 5$

29.

$x = -3$

30.

$4x + 5y = 20$

31.

$y = 6$

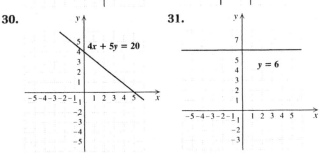

32. -2 **33.** $\frac{1}{2}$; $(0, -2)$ **34.** $y = -3x + 1$

35. (a) $y = -0.1x + 13.1$; (b) 7.1 miles per gallon **36.** $\frac{1}{x^2}$

37. y^{-6}, or $\frac{1}{y^6}$ **38.** $-4a^4b^{14}$ **39.** $-y^3 - 2y^2 - 2y + 7$

40. $15a - 10b + 5c$ **41.** $2x^5 + x^3 - 6x^2 - x + 3$

42. $36x^2 - 60xy + 25y^2$ **43.** $2x^2 + 11x - 40$ **44.** $4x^6 - 1$

45. $2x(3 - x - 12x^3)$ **46.** $(4x + 9)(4x - 9)$

47. $(t - 4)(t - 6)$ **48.** $(4x + 3)(2x + 1)$

49. $2(3x - 2)(x - 4)$ **50.** $4(t + 3)(t - 3)$ **51.** $(5t + 4)^2$

52. $10(t^2 - 2)(t^4 + 2t^2 + 4)$ **53.** $(x + 2)(x^3 - 3)$

54. $\dfrac{y + 6}{2}$ **55.** 1 **56.** $\dfrac{a^2 + 7ab + b^2}{(a + b)(a - b)}$ **57.** $\dfrac{2x + 5}{4 - x}$

58. $\dfrac{x}{x - 2}$ **59.** $\dfrac{t(2t^2 + 1)}{t^3 - 2}$ **60.** $6x^2 - 5x + 2 + \dfrac{4}{x} + \dfrac{1}{x^2}$

61. $15x^3 - 57x^2 + 177x - 529 + \dfrac{1605}{x + 3}$

62. At most 225 sheets **63.** \$3.60 **64.** 14 ft

65. $-278, -276$ **66.** 30 min **67.** 50 **68.** 26 in. **69.** 12

70. $-144, 144$ **71.** $16y^6 - y^4 + 6y^2 - 9$

72. $2(a^{16} + 81b^{20})(a^8 + 9b^{10})(a^4 + 3b^5)(a^4 - 3b^5)$

73. $-7, 4, 12$ **74.** -7 **75.** 18 **76.** $66\frac{2}{3}\%$ **77.** \$8.32

CHAPTER 7

Exercise Set 7.1, pp. 449–454

1. Domain **3.** Exactly **5.** 5 **7.** x **9.** Yes **11.** Yes

13. Yes **15.** No **17.** Function **19.** Function

21. (a) -1; (b) -3 **23.** (a) 3; (b) 3 **25.** (a) 3; (b) 0

27. (a) 3; (b) -3 **29.** (a) 1; (b) 3 **31.** (a) 4; (b) $-1, 3$

33. (a) 2; (b) $\{x \mid 0 < x \le 2\}$

35. (a) 5; (b) 1; (c) -2; (d) 13; (e) $a + 7$; (f) $a + 7$

37. (a) 0; (b) 1; (c) 57; (d) $5t^2 + 4t$; (e) $20a^2 + 8a$; (f) 48

39. (a) $\frac{3}{5}$; (b) $\frac{1}{3}$; (c) $\frac{4}{7}$; (d) 0; (e) $\dfrac{x - 1}{2x - 1}$

41. $4\sqrt{3}$ cm$^2 \approx 6.93$ cm^2 **43.** 36π in$^2 \approx 113.10$ in^2

45. $1\frac{20}{33}$ atm; $1\frac{10}{11}$ atm; $4\frac{1}{33}$ atm **47.** 159.48 cm **49.** 14°F

51. 75 heart attacks per 10,000 men **53.** 56%

55. 60 watts; 140 watts

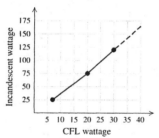

57. 3.5 drinks; 6 drinks

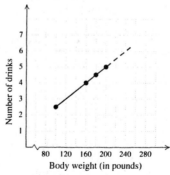

59. 57,000; 50,000

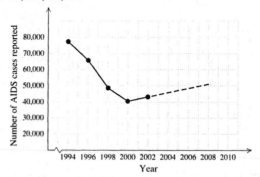

61. \$257,000; \$306,000

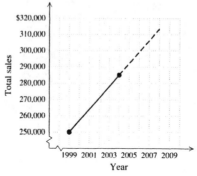

63. 🖻 **65.** $\frac{1}{3}$ **66.** -1 **67.** $l = \dfrac{S - 2wh}{2h + 2w}$

68. $w = \dfrac{S - 2lh}{2l + 2h}$ **69.** $y = -\frac{2}{3}x + 2$ **70.** $y = \frac{5}{4}x - 2$

71. 🖻 **73.** 26; 99 **75.** Worm **77.** About 2 min, 50 sec

79. 1 every 3 min **81.** $g(x) = \frac{15}{4}x - \frac{13}{4}$

Exercise Set 7.2, pp. 461–464

1. (c) **3.** (d) **5.** (c)

7. Domain: $\{2, 9, -2, -4\}$; range: $\{8, 3, 10, 4\}$

9. Domain: $\{0, 4, -5, -1\}$; range: $\{0, -2\}$

11. Domain: $\{-4, -2, 0, 2, 4\}$; range: $\{-2, -1, 0, 1, 2\}$

13. Domain: $\{-5, -3, -1, 0, 2, 4\}$; range: $\{-1, 1\}$

15. Domain: $\{x \mid -4 \le x \le 3\}$; range: $\{y \mid -3 \le y \le 4\}$

17. Domain: $\{x \mid -4 \le x \le 5\}$; range: $\{y \mid -2 \le y \le 4\}$

19. Domain: $\{x \mid -4 \leq x \leq 4\}$; range: $\{-3, -1, 1\}$
21. Domain: $\mathbb{R}$; range: $\mathbb{R}$ **23.** Domain: $\mathbb{R}$; range: $\{4\}$
25. Domain: $\mathbb{R}$; range: $\{y \mid y \geq 1\}$
27. Domain: $\{x \mid x$ is a real number $and\ x \neq -2\}$; range:
$\{y \mid y$ is a real number $and\ y \neq -4\}$
29. Domain: $\{x \mid x \geq 0\}$; range: $\{y \mid y \geq 0\}$
31. $\{x \mid x$ is a real number $and\ x \neq 3\}$
33. $\{x \mid x$ is a real number $and\ x \neq \frac{1}{2}\}$ **35.** $\mathbb{R}$ **37.** $\mathbb{R}$
39. $\{x \mid x$ is a real number $and\ x \neq 3\ and\ x \neq -3\}$ **41.** $\mathbb{R}$
43. $\{x \mid x$ is a real number $and\ x \neq -1\ and\ x \neq -7\}$
45. $\{t \mid 0 \leq t < 624\}$ **47.** $\{p \mid \$0 \leq p \leq \$10.60\}$
49. $\{d \mid d \geq 0\}$ **51.** $\{t \mid 0 \leq t \leq 5\}$ **53.** (a) -5;
(b) 1; (c) 21   **55.** (a) 0; (b) 2; (c) 7   **57.** (a) 100;
(b) 100; (c) 131   **59.**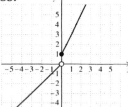

61. 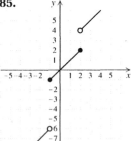   **62.**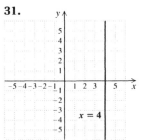

63. Slope: $\frac{2}{3}$; y-intercept: $(0, -4)$
64. Slope: $-\frac{1}{4}$; y-intercept: $(0, 6)$
65. Slope: $\frac{4}{3}$; y-intercept: $(0, 0)$
66. Slope: -5; y-intercept: $(0, 0)$ **67.**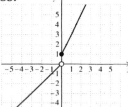

69. 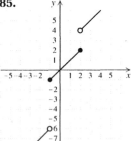   **71.**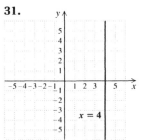

73. Domain: $\{x \mid x$ is a real number $and\ x \neq 0\}$;
range: $\{y \mid y$ is a real number $and\ y \neq 0\}$
75. Domain: $\{x \mid x < -2\ or\ x > 0\}$; range:
$\{y \mid y < -2\ or\ y > 3\}$
77. Domain: $\mathbb{R}$; range: $\{y \mid y \geq 0\}$
79. Domain: $\{x \mid x$ is a real number $and\ x \neq 2\}$; range: $\{y \mid y$
is a real number $and\ y \neq 0\}$ **81.** $\{h \mid 0 \leq h \leq 144\}$
83. 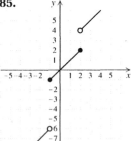   **85.**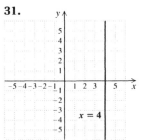

87. 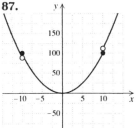   **89.**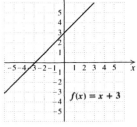

Exercise Set 7.3, pp. 473–477

1. False   **3.** False   **5.** True   **7.** Yes   **9.** Yes   **11.** No
13. No   **15.** Yes   **17.** No
19. 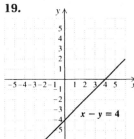   **21.**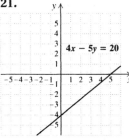

23. 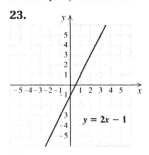   **25.**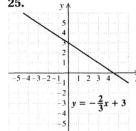

27. 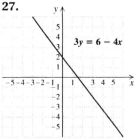   **29.**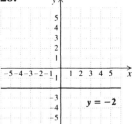

31.   **33.**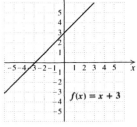

35.

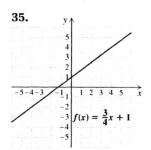

37.

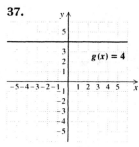

39. $C(t) = 25t + 50$; 4 months   **41.** $L(t) = \frac{1}{2}t + 1$; 4 months after the cut   **43.** $C(d) = \$0.75d + 2$; 3 mi
45. (a) $C(t) = \frac{335}{29}t + 1542$; **(b)** 1981 calories; **(c)** approximately 2011
47. (a) $E(t) = 0.23t + 71.8$; **(b)** 76.2 yr
49. (a) $A(t) = 10.34t + 178.6$; **(b)** \$344 million
51. (a) $N(t) = 4t + 48$; **(b)** 88 million Americans; **(c)** 2013
53. (a) $A(t) = 0.55t + 74.9$; **(b)** 83.15 million acres
55. Linear function; $\mathbb{R}$ **57.** Quadratic function; $\mathbb{R}$
59. Rational function; $\{t \mid t$ is a real number $and\ t \neq -\frac{4}{3}\}$
61. Polynomial function; $\mathbb{R}$ **63.** Rational function; $\{x \mid x$ is a real number $and\ x \neq \frac{5}{2}\}$ **65.** Rational function; $\{n \mid n$ is a real number $and\ n \neq -1\ and\ n \neq -2\}$ **67.** Linear function; $\mathbb{R}$ **69.** $\{y \mid y \geq 0\}$ **71.** $\mathbb{R}$ **73.** $\{y \mid y \leq 0\}$

75.

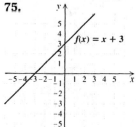

77.

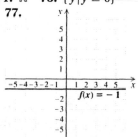

Domain: $\mathbb{R}$; range: $\mathbb{R}$ Domain: $\mathbb{R}$; range: $\{-1\}$
79.   **81.**

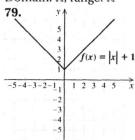

Domain: $\mathbb{R}$;   Domain: $\mathbb{R}$;
range: $\{y \mid y \geq 1\}$ range: $\{y \mid y \geq 0\}$
83. 🔲   **85.** $4x^2 + 2x - 1$
86. $2x^3 - x^2 - x + 7$ **87.** $2x^2 - 13x - 7$
88. $x^2 + x - 12$ **89.** $x^3 - 2x^2 - 3x + 5$
90. $x^3 + 2x^2 + x + 4$ **91.** 🔲   **93.** False
95. False   **97.** 21.1°C   **99.** \$30
101. (a) $g(x) = x - 8$; **(b)** -10; **(c)** 83
103. $f(x) = 0.299x - 515.3622222$

Exercise Set 7.4, pp. 483–486
1. Domain   **3.** Evaluate   **5.** Excluding   **7.** 1   **9.** -41
11. 12   **13.** $\frac{13}{18}$ **15.** 5   **17.** $x^2 - 3x + 3$ **19.** $x^2 - x + 3$
21. 23   **23.** 5   **25.** 56   **27.** $\frac{x^2 - 2}{5 - x}, x \neq 5$ **29.** $\frac{2}{7}$
31. 4%   **33.** $1.3 + 2.2 = 3.5$ million   **35.** About 50 million; the number of passengers using Newark Liberty and LaGuardia in 1998   **37.** About 81 million; the number of passengers using the three airports in 2002
39. About 51 million; the number of passengers using LaGuardia and Newark Liberty in 2002   **41.** $\mathbb{R}$
43. $\{x \mid x$ is a real number $and\ x \neq 3\}$
45. $\{x \mid x$ is a real number $and\ x \neq 0\}$
47. $\{x \mid x$ is a real number $and\ x \neq 1\}$
49. $\{x \mid x$ is a real number $and\ x \neq 2\ and\ x \neq 4\}$
51. $\{x \mid x$ is a real number $and\ x \neq 3\}$
53. $\{x \mid x$ is a real number $and\ x \neq 4\}$
55. $\{x \mid x$ is a real number $and\ x \neq 4\ and\ x \neq 5\}$
57. $\{x \mid x$ is a real number $and\ x \neq -1\ and\ x \neq -\frac{5}{2}\}$
59. 4; 3   **61.** 5; -1 **63.** $\{x \mid 0 \leq x \leq 9\}$; $\{x \mid 3 \leq x \leq 10\}$; $\{x \mid 3 \leq x \leq 9\}$; $\{x \mid 3 \leq x \leq 9\}$
65.

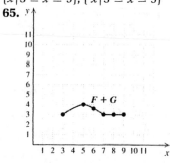

67. 🔲   **69.** $x = \frac{7}{4}y + 2$ **70.** $y = \frac{3}{8}x - \frac{5}{8}$
71. $y = -\frac{5}{2}x - \frac{3}{2}$ **72.** $x = -\frac{5}{6}y - \frac{1}{3}$
73. Let n represent the number; $2n + 5 = 49$
74. Let x represent the number; $\frac{1}{2}x - 3 = 57$
75. Let x represent the first integer; $x + (x + 1) = 145$
76. Let n represent the number; $n - (-n) = 20$
77. 🔲   **79.** $\{x \mid x$ is a real number $and\ x \neq -\frac{5}{2}\ and$ $x \neq -3\ and\ x \neq 1\ and\ x \neq -1\}$
81. Answers may vary.

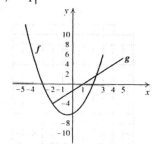

83. $\{x \mid x$ is a real number $and -1 < x < 5 \ and \ x \neq \frac{3}{2}\}$

85. Answers may vary. $f(x) = \dfrac{1}{x+2}, g(x) = \dfrac{1}{x-5}$ **87.**

Exercise Set 7.5, pp. 494–499

1. LCD   **3.** Factor   **5.** Inverse   **7.** Direct   **9.** Inverse

11. $d = \dfrac{L}{f}$ **13.** $v_1 = \dfrac{2s}{t} - v_2$, or $\dfrac{2s - tv_2}{t}$ **15.** $b = \dfrac{at}{a-t}$

17. $R = \dfrac{2V}{I} - 2r$, or $\dfrac{2V - 2Ir}{I}$ **19.** $g = \dfrac{Rs}{s-R}$

21. $n = \dfrac{IR}{E - Ir}$ **23.** $q = \dfrac{pf}{p-f}$ **25.** $t_1 = \dfrac{H}{Sm} + t_2$, or

$\dfrac{H + Smt_2}{Sm}$ **27.** $r = \dfrac{Re}{E-e}$ **29.** $r = 1 - \dfrac{a}{S}$, or $\dfrac{S-a}{S}$

31. $a + b = \dfrac{f}{c^2}$ **33.** $r = \dfrac{A}{P} - 1$, or $\dfrac{A-P}{P}$

35. $t_2 = \dfrac{d_2 - d_1}{v} + t_1$, or $\dfrac{d_2 - d_1 + t_1 v}{v}$ **37.** $b^2 = \dfrac{a^2 y^2}{a^2 - x^2}$

39. $Q = \dfrac{2Tt - 2AT}{A - q}$ **41.** $k = 7; y = 7x$

43. $k = 1.7; y = 1.7x$ **45.** $k = 6; y = 6x$

47. $k = 60; y = \dfrac{60}{x}$ **49.** $k = 112; y = \dfrac{112}{x}$

51. $k = 9; y = \dfrac{9}{x}$ **53.** 241,920,000 cans   **55.** 6 amperes

57. 3.5 hr   **59.** 32 kg   **61.** 50 min   **63.** About 21 min

65. 122,269,230 tons   **67.** $y = \frac{2}{3}x^2$ **69.** $y = \dfrac{54}{x^2}$

71. $y = 0.3xz^2$ **73.** $y = \dfrac{4wx^2}{z}$ **75.** About 2.9 sec

77. 308 cm³   **79.** About 57.42 mph   **81.** ▨   **83.** $\frac{13}{2}$

84. $\frac{5}{3}$ **85.** $-\frac{3}{2}$ **86.** $-\frac{5}{3}, \frac{7}{2}$ **87.** No solution; contradiction

88. All real numbers; identity   **89.** ▨   **91.** 567 mi

93. Ratio is $\dfrac{a + 12}{a + 6}$; percent increase is $\dfrac{6}{a+6} \cdot 100\%$,

or $\dfrac{600}{a+6}\%$ **95.** $t_1 = t_2 + \dfrac{(d_2 - d_1)(t_4 - t_3)}{a(t_4 - t_2)(t_4 - t_3) + d_3 - d_4}$

97. The intensity is halved.   **99.** About 1.697 m

101. $d(s) = \dfrac{28}{s}$; 70 yd

Review Exercises: Chapter 7, pp. 502–505

1. True   **2.** True   **3.** False   **4.** True   **5.** False   **6.** True
7. True   **8.** True   **9.** True   **10.** False   **11. (a)** 3;
(b) $\{x \mid -2 \le x \le 4\}$; **(c)** -1 **(d)** $\{y \mid 1 \le y \le 5\}$ **12.** $\frac{3}{2}$
13. $4a^2 + 4a - 3$ **14.** 10.53 yr

15. About $3.50;

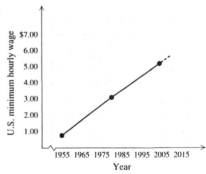

16. About $5.60   **17. (a)** Yes; **(b)** domain: $\mathbb{R}$;
range: $\{y \mid y \ge 0\}$ **18. (a)** No   **19. (a)** No   **20. (a)** Yes;
(b) domain: $\mathbb{R}$; range: $\{-2\}$ **21.** $\mathbb{R}$
22. $\{x \mid x$ is a real number $and \ x \neq 1\}$
23. $\{t \mid t$ is a real number $and \ t \neq -1 \ and \ t \neq -4\}$
24. $\{x \mid x \ge 0\}$ **25.** $\{t \mid 0 \le t \le 34\}$ **26. (a)** 5; **(b)** 4;
(c) 16; **(d)** 35   **27.** $C(t) = 15t + 75$; 7 months
28. (a) $v(t) = -2.2t + 48.5$; **(b)** 44.1 million visitors
29. Absolute-value function   **30.** Polynomial function
31. Quadratic function   **32.** Linear function
33. Rational function

34.

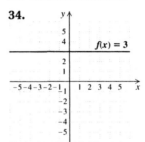

Domain: $\mathbb{R}$; range: $\{3\}$

35.

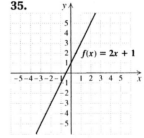

Domain: $\mathbb{R}$; range: $\mathbb{R}$

36.

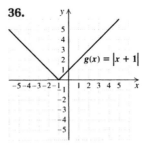

Domain: $\mathbb{R}$; range: $\{y \mid y \ge 0\}$
37. 102   **38.** -17 **39.** $-\frac{9}{2}$ **40.** $\mathbb{R}$
41. $\{x \mid x$ is a real number $and \ x \neq 2\}$ **42.** $y = \frac{15}{2}x$

43. $y = \dfrac{\frac{3}{4}}{x}$ **44.** $y = \dfrac{1}{2} \cdot \dfrac{xw^2}{z}$ **45.** About 22 lb   **46.** 64 L

47. ▨   Two functions that have the same domain and
range are not necessarily identical. For example, the
functions $f: \{(-2, 1), (-3, 2)\}$ and $g: \{(-2, 2), (-3, 1)\}$ have
the same domain and range but are different functions.

48. 📝 Jenna is not correct. Any value of the variable that makes a denominator 0 is not in the domain; 0 itself may or may not make a denominator 0.
49. $f(x) = 3.09x + 3.75$
50. Domain: $\{x \mid x \geq -4 \text{ and } x \neq 2\}$; range: $\{y \mid y \geq 0 \text{ and } y \neq 3\}$
51. No; the rate of change is not constant. Each year the amount of the raise will be higher since the current year's salary is higher than the previous year's salary.

Test: Chapter 7, pp. 505–506

1. [7.1], [7.2] **(a)** 1; **(b)** $\{x \mid -3 \leq x \leq 4\}$; **(c)** 3;
(d) $\{y \mid -1 \leq y \leq 2\}$ **2.** [7.1] 2   **3.** [7.1] 46 million
4. (a) [7.3] Yes; **(b)** [7.2] domain: $\mathbb{R}$; range: $\mathbb{R}$
5. (a) [7.3] Yes; **(b)** [7.2] domain: $\mathbb{R}$; range: $\{y \mid y \geq 1\}$
6. (a) [7.3] No   **7.** [7.2] $\{t \mid 0 \leq t \leq 4\}$
8. [7.2] **(a)** -5; **(b)** 10
9. [7.3] $c(n) = 25n + 75$; 17 people
10. [7.3] **(a)** $C(m) = 0.3m + 25$; **(b)** \$175
11. [7.3] Linear function; $\mathbb{R}$
12. [7.3] Rational function; $\{x \mid x \text{ is a real number and } x \neq 5\}$ **13.** [7.3] Quadratic function; $\mathbb{R}$
14. [7.3]   **15.** [7.3]

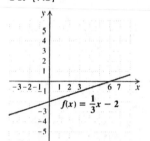

Domain: $\mathbb{R}$; range: $\mathbb{R}$ Domain: $\mathbb{R}$; range: $\{y \mid y \geq -1\}$

16. [7.3]

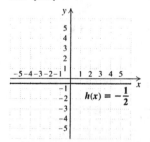

Domain: $\mathbb{R}$; range: $\left\{-\frac{1}{2}\right\}$

17. [7.1] $\frac{1}{4}$ **18.** [7.1] -10 **19.** [7.1] $\dfrac{1}{2a + 4}$
20. [7.4] $-\frac{8}{3}$ **21.** [7.2] $\{x \mid x \text{ is a real number and } x \neq -4\}$
22. [7.2] $\mathbb{R}$ **23.** [7.4] $\{x \mid x \text{ is a real number and } x \neq -4\}$
24. [7.4] $\{x \mid x \text{ is a real number and } x \neq -4 \text{ and } x \neq 7\}$
25. [7.5] $y = \frac{1}{2}x$ **26.** [7.5] 30 workers   **27.** [7.5] $\frac{833}{125}$, or 6.664 in^2 **28.** [7.3] **(a)** 30 mi; **(b)** 15 mph
29. [7.4] $h(x) = 7x - 2$

CHAPTER 8

Technology Connection, p. 513

1. $(1.53, 2.58)$ **2.** $(-0.26, 57.06)$ **3.** $(2.23, 1.14)$
4. $(0.87, -0.32)$

Exercise Set 8.1, pp. 514–516

1. True   **3.** True   **5.** True   **7.** False   **9.** Yes   **11.** No
13. Yes   **15.** Yes   **17.** $(4, 1)$ **19.** $(2, -1)$ **21.** $(4, 3)$
23. $(-3, -2)$ **25.** $(-3, 2)$ **27.** $(3, -7)$ **29.** $(7, 2)$
31. $(4, 0)$ **33.** No solution   **35.** $\{(x, y) \mid y = 3 - x\}$
37. All except 33   **39.** 35   **41.** Let x represent the first number and y the second number; $x + y = 50, x = 0.25y$
43. Let m represent the number of ounces of mineral oil and v the number of ounces of vinegar; $m + v = 16, m = 2v + 4$ **45.** Let x and y represent the angles; $x + y = 180, x = 2y - 3$ **47.** Let x represent the number of two-point shots and y the number of foul shots; $x + y = 64, 2x + y = 100$ **49.** Let x represent the number of \$8.50 brushes sold and y the number of \$9.75 brushes sold; $x + y = 45, 8.50x + 9.75y = 398.75$
51. Let h represent the number of vials of Humulin sold and n the number of vials of Novolin Velosulin; $h + n = 50, 27.06h + 34.39n = 1565.57$ **53.** Let l represent the length, in feet, and w the width, in feet; $2l + 2w = 288, l = w + 44$ **55.** 📝   **57.** 15   **58.** $\frac{19}{12}$
59. $\frac{9}{20}$ **60.** $\frac{13}{3}$ **61.** $y = -\frac{3}{4}x + \frac{7}{4}$ **62.** $y = \frac{2}{5}x - \frac{9}{5}$ **63.** 📝
65. Answers may vary. **(a)** $x + y = 6, x - y = 4$;
(b) $x + y = 1, 2x + 2y = 3$; **(c)** $x + y = 1, 2x + 2y = 2$
67. $A = -\frac{17}{4}, B = -\frac{12}{5}$ **69.** Let x and y represent the number of years that Lou and Juanita have taught at the university, respectively; $x + y = 46, x - 2 = 2.5(y - 2)$
71. Let s and v represent the number of ounces of baking soda and vinegar needed, respectively; $s = 4v, s + v = 16$
73. $(0, 0), (1, 1)$ **75.** $(0.07, -7.95)$ **77.** $(0.00, 1.25)$

Exercise Set 8.2, pp. 523–524

1. (d)   **3.** (a)   **5.** (c)   **7.** $(2, -3)$ **9.** $(-4, 3)$ **11.** $(2, -2)$ **13.** $\{(x, y) \mid 2x - 3 = y\}$ **15.** $(-2, 1)$ **17.** $\left(\frac{1}{2}, \frac{1}{2}\right)$
19. $\left(\frac{25}{23}, -\frac{11}{23}\right)$ **21.** No solution   **23.** $(1, 2)$ **25.** $(2, 7)$
27. $(-1, 2)$ **29.** $\left(\frac{128}{31}, -\frac{17}{31}\right)$ **31.** $(6, 2)$ **33.** No solution
35. $\left(\frac{110}{19}, -\frac{12}{19}\right)$ **37.** $(3, -1)$ **39.** $\{(x, y) \mid -4x + 2y = 5\}$
41. $\left(\frac{140}{13}, -\frac{50}{13}\right)$ **43.** $(-2, -9)$ **45.** $(30, 6)$
47. $\{(x, y) \mid x = 2 + 3y\}$ **49.** No solution   **51.** $(140, 60)$
53. $\left(\frac{1}{3}, -\frac{2}{3}\right)$ **55.** 📝   **57.** 4 mi   **58.** 86
59. \$11$\frac{2}{3}$ billion on bathrooms; \$23$\frac{1}{3}$ billion on kitchens
60. 30 m, 90 m, 360 m   **61.** 450.5 mi   **62.** 460.5 mi
63. 📝   **65.** $m = -\frac{1}{2}, b = \frac{5}{2}$ **67.** $a = 5, b = 2$
69. $\left(-\frac{32}{17}, \frac{38}{17}\right)$ **71.** $\left(-\frac{1}{5}, \frac{1}{10}\right)$ **73.** 📝

Exercise Set 8.3, pp. 535–539

1. 10, 40 **3.** Mineral oil: 12 oz; vinegar: 4 oz **5.** 119°, 61°
7. Two-point shots: 36; foul shots: 28 **9.** $8.50-brushes:
32; $9.75-brushes: 13 **11.** Humulin vials: 21; Novolin
Velosulin vials: 29 **13.** Width: 50 ft; length: 94 ft
15. Nonrecycled sheets: 38; recycled sheets: 112
17. General Electric bulbs: 60; SLi bulbs: 140 **19.** HP
cartridges: 15; Apple cartridges: 35 **21.** Kenyan: 8 lb;
Sumatran: 12 lb **23.** 10 lb of each **25.** Deep Thought:
12 lb; Oat Dream: 8 lb **27.** $7500 at 6%; $4500 at 9%
29. Arctic Antifreeze: 12.5 L; Frost No-More: 7.5 L
31. 87-octane: 4 gal; 93-octane: 8 gal **33.** Whole milk:
$169\frac{3}{13}$ lb; cream: $30\frac{10}{13}$ lb **35.** 375 km **37.** 24 mph
39. About 1489 mi **41.** Length: 265 ft; width: 165 ft
43. Simon: 122 properties; DeBartolo: 61 properties
45. 30-sec commercials: 4; 60-sec commercials: 8
47. Quarters: 17; fifty-cent pieces: 13 **49.** 🖫 **51.** 16
52. 11 **53.** −28 **54.** −10 **55.** $\frac{49}{12}$ **56.** $\frac{13}{10}$ **57.** 🖫
59. 0%: 20 reams; 30%: 40 reams **61.** 1.8 L
63. 180 members **65.** Brown: 0.8 gal; neutral: 0.2 gal
67. City: 261 mi; highway: 204 mi **69.** $P(x) = \dfrac{0.1 + x}{1.5}$

(This expresses the percent as a decimal quantity.)

Exercise Set 8.4, pp. 545–547

1. True **3.** False **5.** True **7.** No **9.** (4, 0, 2)
11. (2, −2, 2) **13.** (3, −2, 1) **15.** No solution
17. (2, 1, 3) **19.** (2, −5, 6) **21.** The equations are
dependent. **23.** $\left(\frac{1}{2}, 4, -6\right)$ **25.** $\left(\frac{1}{2}, \frac{1}{3}, \frac{1}{6}\right)$ **27.** $\left(\frac{1}{2}, \frac{2}{3}, -\frac{5}{6}\right)$
29. (15, 33, 9) **31.** (3, 4, −1) **33.** (10, 23, 50) **35.** No
solution **37.** The equations are dependent. **39.** 🖫
41. Let x and y represent the numbers; $x = 2y$ **42.** Let x
and y represent the numbers; $x + y = 3x$ **43.** Let x
represent the first number; $x + (x + 1) + (x + 2) = 45$
44. Let x and y represent the numbers; $x + 2y = 17$
45. Let x, y, and z represent the numbers; $x + y = 5z$
46. Let x and y represent the numbers; $xy = 2(x + y)$
47. 🖫 **49.** (1, −1, 2) **51.** (−3, −1, 0, 4)
53. $\left(-\frac{1}{2}, -1, -\frac{1}{3}\right)$ **55.** 14 **57.** $z = 8 − 2x − 4y$

Exercise Set 8.5, pp. 551–554

1. 16, 19, 22 **3.** 8, 21, −3 **5.** 32°, 96°, 52° **7.** Individual
adult: $64; spouse: $57; child: $43 **9.** Bran muffin: 1.5 g;
banana: 3 g; 1 cup Wheaties: 3 g **11.** Basic price: $24,695;
4WD: $1970; sunroof: $800 **13.** Elrod: 20 ft/hr; Dot:
24 ft/hr; Wendy: 30 ft/hr **15.** 12-oz cups: 17; 16-oz cups:
25; 20-oz cups: 13 **17.** Small: 10; medium: 25; large: 5
19. Roast beef: 2 servings; baked potato: 1 serving;
broccoli: 2 servings **21.** Asia: 4.8 billion; Africa: 1.8
billion; rest of world: 2.5 billion **23.** Two-point field
goals: 32; three-point field goals: 5; foul shots: 13
25. 🖫 **27.** −8 **28.** 33 **29.** −55 **30.** −71
31. $−14x + 21y − 35z$ **32.** $−24a − 42b + 54c$ **33.** $−5a$

34. $11x$ **35.** 🖫 **37.** Applicant: $102; spouse: $58; first
child: $43; second child: $40 **39.** 20 yr **41.** 35 tickets

Exercise Set 8.6, pp. 558–559

1. Horizontal; columns **3.** Entry **5.** Multiple
7. $\left(-\frac{1}{3}, -4\right)$ **9.** (−4, 3) **11.** $\left(\frac{3}{2}, \frac{5}{2}\right)$ **13.** $\left(2, \frac{1}{2}, -2\right)$
15. (2, −2, 1) **17.** $\left(4, \frac{1}{2}, -\frac{1}{2}\right)$ **19.** (1, −3, −2, −1)
21. Dimes: 18; nickels: 24 **23.** $4.05-granola: 5 lb;
$2.70-granola: 10 lb **25.** $400 at 7%; $500 at 8%;
$1600 at 9% **27.** 🖫 **29.** 13 **30.** −22 **31.** 37 **32.** 422
33. 🖫 **35.** 1324

Exercise Set 8.7, pp. 563–564

1. True **3.** False **5.** False **7.** 18 **9.** 36 **11.** 27
13. −3 **15.** −5 **17.** (−3, 2) **19.** $\left(\frac{9}{19}, \frac{51}{38}\right)$
21. $\left(-1, -\frac{6}{7}, \frac{11}{7}\right)$ **23.** (2, −1, 4) **25.** (1, 2, 3) **27.** 🖫
29. $\frac{333}{245}$ **30.** −12 **31.** One piece: 20.8 ft; other piece: 12 ft
32. Scientific calculators: 18; graphing calculators: 27
33. Mazzas: 28 rolls; Kranepools: 8 rolls **34.** Buckets:
17; dinners: 11 **35.** 🖫 **37.** 12 **39.** 10

Exercise Set 8.8, pp. 569–571

1. (b) **3.** (e) **5.** (h) **7.** (g)
9. (a) $P(x) = 20x − 300,000$; (b) (15,000 units, $975,000)
11. (a) $P(x) = 50x − 120,000$; (b) (2400 units, $144,000)
13. (a) $P(x) = 45x − 22,500$; (b) (500 units, $42,500)
15. (a) $P(x) = 18x − 16,000$; (b) (889 units, $35,560)
17. (a) $P(x) = 50x − 100,000$; (b) (2000 units, $250,000)
19. ($70, 300) **21.** ($22, 474) **23.** ($50, 6250)
25. ($10, 1070) **27.** (a) $C(x) = 125,300 + 450x$;
(b) $R(x) = 800x$; (c) $P(x) = 350x − 125,300$; (d) $90,300
loss, $14,700 profit; (e) (358 computers, $286,400)
29. (a) $C(x) = 16,404 + 6x$; (b) $R(x) = 18x$;
(c) $P(x) = 12x − 16,404$; (d) $19,596 profit, $4404 loss;
(e) (1367 dozen caps, $24,606) **31.** 🖫 **33.** 12 **34.** 15
35. $\frac{8}{3}$ **36.** 4 **37.** $\frac{9}{2}$ **38.** $\frac{1}{3}$ **39.** 🖫 **41.** ($5, 300 yo-yo's)
43. (a) $8.74; (b) 24,509 units

Review Exercises: Chapter 8, pp. 574–575

1. Substitution **2.** Elimination **3.** Approximate
4. Dependent **5.** Inconsistent **6.** Infinite **7.** Parallel
8. Square **9.** Determinant **10.** Zero **11.** (−2, 1)
12. (3, 2) **13.** $\left(-\frac{11}{15}, -\frac{43}{30}\right)$ **14.** No solution **15.** $\left(-\frac{4}{5}, \frac{2}{5}\right)$
16. $\left(\frac{37}{19}, \frac{53}{19}\right)$ **17.** $\left(\frac{76}{17}, -\frac{2}{119}\right)$ **18.** (2, 2)
19. $\{(x, y) | 3x + 4y = 6\}$ **20.** DVD: $17; videocassette: $14
21. 4 hr **22.** 8% juice: 10 L; 15% juice: 4 L
23. (4, −8, 10) **24.** The equations are dependent.
25. (2, 0, 4) **26.** No solution **27.** $\left(\frac{8}{9}, -\frac{2}{3}, \frac{10}{9}\right)$
28. A: 90°; B: 67.5°; C: 22.5°
29. Oil: $21\frac{1}{3}$ oz; lemon juice: $10\frac{2}{3}$ oz

30. Lumber: 29 pallets; plywood: 13 pallets   **31.** $\left(55, -\frac{89}{2}\right)$
32. $(-1, 1, 3)$ **33.** 2   **34.** 9   **35.** $(6, -2)$ **36.** $(-3, 0, 4)$
37. $(\$3, 81)$ **38. (a)** $C(x) = 0.75x + 9000$;
(b) $R(x) = 5.25x$; **(c)** $P(x) = 4.5x - 9000$; **(d)** \$2250 loss;
\$13,500 profit; **(e)** (2000 pints of honey, \$10,500)
39. 🖉 To solve a problem involving four variables, go
through the *Familiarize* and *Translate* steps as usual. The
resulting system of equations can be solved using the
elimination method just as for three variables but likely
with more steps.   **40.** 🖉 A system of equations can be
both dependent and inconsistent if it is equivalent to a
system with fewer equations that has no solution. An
example is a system of three equations in three unknowns
in which two of the equations represent the same plane,
and the third represents a parallel plane.   **41.** 8000 pints
42. $(0, 2), (1, 3)$
43. $a = -\frac{2}{3}, b = -\frac{4}{3}, c = 3; f(x) = -\frac{2}{3}x^2 - \frac{4}{3}x + 3$

Test: Chapter 8, p. 576

1. [8.1] $(2, 4)$ **2.** [8.2] $\left(3, -\frac{11}{3}\right)$ **3.** [8.2] $\left(\frac{15}{7}, -\frac{18}{7}\right)$
4. [8.2] $\left(-\frac{3}{2}, -\frac{3}{2}\right)$ **5.** [8.2] No solution   **6.** [8.3] Length:
30 units; width: 18 units   **7.** [8.3] Pepperidge Farm
Goldfish: 120 g; Rold Gold Pretzels: 500 g   **8.** [8.4] The
equations are dependent.   **9.** [8.4] $\left(2, -\frac{1}{2}, -1\right)$
10. [8.4] No solution   **11.** [8.4] $(0, 1, 0)$
12. [8.6] $\left(\frac{34}{107}, -\frac{104}{107}\right)$ **13.** [8.6] $(3, 1, -2)$ **14.** [8.7] 34
15. [8.7] 133   **16.** [8.7] $\left(\frac{13}{18}, \frac{7}{27}\right)$ **17.** [8.5] Electrician:
3.5 hr; carpenter: 8 hr; plumber: 10 hr   **18.** [8.8] $(\$3, 55)$
19. [8.8] **(a)** $C(x) = 25x + 40{,}000$; **(b)** $R(x) = 70x$;
(c) $P(x) = 45x - 40{,}000$; **(d)** \$26,500 loss, \$500 profit;
(e) (889 hammocks, \$62,230)
20. [3.6], [8.3] $m = 7, b = 10$ **21.** [8.5] Adults' tickets:
1346; senior citizens' tickets: 335; children's tickets: 1651

CHAPTER 9

Exercise Set 9.1, pp. 584–586

1. Equivalent inequalities   **3.** Equivalent equations
5. Not equivalent   **7.** Equivalent expressions   **9.** Not
equivalent
11. $(-\infty, 6), \{y \mid y < 6\}$
13. $[-4, \infty), \{x \mid x \geq -4\}$
15. $(-3, \infty), \{t \mid t > -3\}$
17. $(-\infty, -7], \{x \mid x \leq -7\}$
19. $\{y \mid y > -9\}$, or $(-9, \infty)$
21. $\{y \mid y \leq 14\}$, or $(-\infty, 14]$
23. $\{t \mid t < -9\}$, or $(-\infty, -9)$
25. $\{x \mid x \leq 0.9\}$, or $(-\infty, 0.9]$

27. $\left\{x \mid x \leq \frac{5}{6}\right\}$, or $\left(-\infty, \frac{5}{6}\right]$
29. $\{x \mid x < -26\}$, or $(-\infty, -26)$
31. $\left\{t \mid t \geq -\frac{13}{3}\right\}$, or $\left[-\frac{13}{3}, \infty\right)$
33. $\{x \mid x \geq 6\}$, or $[6, \infty)$
35. $\{x \mid x \geq 2\}$, or $[2, \infty)$
37. $\left\{x \mid x > \frac{2}{3}\right\}$, or $\left(\frac{2}{3}, \infty\right)$
39. $\left\{x \mid x \geq \frac{1}{2}\right\}$, or $\left[\frac{1}{2}, \infty\right)$
41. $\left\{y \mid y \leq -\frac{53}{6}\right\}$, or $\left(-\infty, -\frac{53}{6}\right]$ **43.** $\left\{t \mid t < \frac{29}{5}\right\}$, or $\left(-\infty, \frac{29}{5}\right)$
45. $\left\{m \mid m > \frac{7}{3}\right\}$, or $\left(\frac{7}{3}, \infty\right)$ **47.** $\{x \mid x \geq 2\}$, or $[2, \infty)$
49. $\{y \mid y < 5\}$, or $(-\infty, 5)$ **51.** $\left\{x \mid x \leq \frac{4}{7}\right\}$, or $\left(-\infty, \frac{4}{7}\right]$
53. For 1175 min or more   **55.** More than 25 checks
57. Gross sales greater than \$7000
59. Parties of more than 80   **61.** At least 625 people
63. (a) $\left\{x \mid x < 8181\frac{9}{11}\right\}$, or $\{x \mid x \leq 8181\}$;
(b) $\left\{x \mid x > 8181\frac{9}{11}\right\}$, or $\{x \mid x \geq 8182\}$ **65.** 🖉
67. $\{x \mid x$ is a real number *and* $x \neq 2\}$
68. $\{x \mid x$ is a real number *and* $x \neq -3\}$
69. $\left\{x \mid x$ is a real number *and* $x \neq \frac{7}{2}\right\}$
70. $\left\{x \mid x$ is a real number *and* $x \neq \frac{9}{4}\right\}$ **71.** $7x + 10$
72. $22x - 7$ **73.** 🖉   **75.** $\left\{x \mid x \leq \dfrac{2}{a - 1}\right\}$
77. $\left\{y \mid y \geq \dfrac{2a + 5b}{b(a - 2)}\right\}$ **79.** $\left\{x \mid x > \dfrac{4m - 2c}{d - (5c + 2m)}\right\}$
81. False; $2 < 3$ and $4 < 5$, but $2 - 4 = 3 - 5$.   **83.** 🖉
85. $\mathbb{R}$
87. $\{x \mid x$ is a real number *and* $x \neq 0\}$
89. 📈

Exercise Set 9.2, pp. 594–597

1. (h)   **3.** (f)   **5.** (e)   **7.** (b)   **9.** (c)   **11.** $\{9, 11\}$
13. $\{0, 5, 10, 15, 20\}$ **15.** $\{b, d, f\}$ **17.** $\{r, s, t, u, v\}$
19. $\varnothing$ **21.** $\{3, 5, 7\}$
23. $(3, 7)$
25. $[-6, -2]$
27. $(-\infty, -1) \cup (4, \infty)$
29. $(-\infty, -2] \cup (1, \infty)$
31. $(-2, 4]$
33. $(-2, 4)$

35. 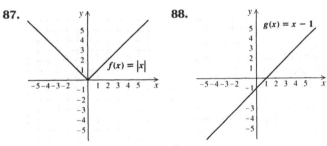 $(-\infty, 5) \cup (7, \infty)$
(number line: -1 0 1 2 3 4 5 6 7 8 9)

37. $(-\infty, -4] \cup [5, \infty)$
(number line: -5 -4 -3 -2 -1 0 1 2 3 4 5)

39. $[-3, 7)$
(number line: -3 -2 -1 0 1 2 3 4 5 6 7)

41. $[3, 7)$
(number line: -2 -1 0 1 2 3 4 5 6 7 8)

43. $(-\infty, 5)$
(number line: -4 -3 -2 -1 0 1 2 3 4 5 6)

45. $\{t \mid -3 < t < 7\}$, or $(-3, 7)$ (number line: -3 0 7)

47. $\{x \mid -1 < x \le 4\}$, or $(-1, 4]$ (number line: -1 0 4)

49. $\{a \mid -2 \le a < 2\}$, or $[-2, 2)$ (number line: -2 0 2)

51. $\mathbb{R}$, or $(-\infty, \infty)$ (number line: 0)

53. $\{x \mid 7 < x < 23\}$, or $(7, 23)$ (number line: 0 7 23)

55. $\{x \mid -3 \le x \le 2\}$, or $[-3, 2]$ (number line: -3 0 2)

57. $\{x \mid 1 \le x \le 3\}$, or $[1, 3]$ (number line: 0 1 3)

59. $\{x \mid -\frac{7}{2} < x \le 7\}$, or $\left(-\frac{7}{2}, 7\right]$ (number line: $-\frac{7}{2}$ 0 7)

61. $\{x \mid x \le 1 \text{ or } x \ge 3\}$, or $(-\infty, 1] \cup [3, \infty)$
(number line: 0 1 3)

63. $\{x \mid x < 2 \text{ or } x > 6\}$, or $(-\infty, 2) \cup (6, \infty)$
(number line: 0 2 6)

65. $\{a \mid a < \frac{7}{2}\}$, or $\left(-\infty, \frac{7}{2}\right)$ (number line: 0 $\frac{7}{2}$)

67. $\{a \mid a < -5\}$, or $(-\infty, -5)$ (number line: -5 0)

69. $\mathbb{R}$, or $(-\infty, \infty)$ (number line: 0)

71. $\{t \mid t \le 6\}$, or $(-\infty, 6]$ (number line: 0 6)

73. $(-\infty, -8) \cup (-8, \infty)$ **75.** $[6, \infty)$
77. $(-\infty, 4) \cup (4, \infty)$ **79.** $\left[-\frac{7}{2}, \infty\right)$ **81.** $(-\infty, 4]$
83. ▨
85.
(graph with $y = 5$)

86.
(graph with $y = -2$)

87.
(graph of $f(x) = |x|$)

88.
(graph of $g(x) = x - 1$)

89. $(8, 5)$ **90.** $(-5, -3)$ **91.** ▨   **93.** $(-1, 6)$
95. From 2000 to 2025   **97.** Sizes between 6 and 13
99. $1965 \le y \le 1981$ **101.** Between 12 and 240 trips
103. $\{m \mid m < \frac{6}{5}\}$, or $\left(-\infty, \frac{6}{5}\right)$ (number line: 0 $\frac{6}{5}$)

105. $\{x \mid -\frac{1}{8} < x < \frac{1}{2}\}$, or $\left(-\frac{1}{8}, \frac{1}{2}\right)$ (number line: $-\frac{1}{8}$ 0 $\frac{1}{2}$)

107. False   **109.** True   **111.** $\left(-\infty, -7\right) \cup \left(-7, \frac{3}{4}\right]$
113. ▨   **115.** ▨

Technology Connection, p. 599

1. The graphs of $y_1 = \text{abs}(4 - 7x)$ and $y_2 = -8$ do not intersect.

Technology Connection, p. 603

1. The x-values on the graph of $y_1 = |4x + 2|$ that are *below* the line $y = 6$ solve the inequality $|4x + 2| < 6$. The x-values on the graph of $y_1 = |4x + 2|$ that are *on* the line $y = 6$ solve the equation $|4x + 2| = 6$.   **2.** The x-values on the graph of $y_1 = |3x - 2|$ that are below the line $y = 4$ are in the interval $\left(-\frac{2}{3}, 2\right)$.

Exercise Set 9.3, pp. 604–606

1. True   **3.** False   **5.** True   **7.** False   **9.** $\{-7, 7\}$ **11.** $\emptyset$
13. $\{0\}$ **15.** $\{-5.5, 5.5\}$ **17.** $\left\{-\frac{1}{2}, \frac{7}{2}\right\}$ **19.** $\emptyset$ **21.** $\{-4, 8\}$
23. $\{2, 8\}$ **25.** $\{-2, 16\}$ **27.** $\{-8, 8\}$ **29.** $\left\{-\frac{11}{7}, \frac{11}{7}\right\}$
31. $\{-7, 8\}$ **33.** $\{-12, 2\}$ **35.** $\left\{-\frac{1}{3}, 3\right\}$ **37.** $\{-7, 1\}$
39. $\{-8.7, 8.7\}$ **41.** $\left\{-\frac{8}{3}, 4\right\}$ **43.** $\{1, 11\}$ **45.** $\left\{-\frac{1}{2}\right\}$
47. $\left\{-\frac{3}{5}, 5\right\}$ **49.** $\mathbb{R}$ **51.** $\{1\}$ **53.** $\left\{32, \frac{8}{3}\right\}$
55. $\{a \mid -9 \le a \le 9\}$, or $[-9, 9]$ (number line: -9 0 9)

57. $\{x \mid x < -8 \text{ or } x > 8\}$, or $(-\infty, -8) \cup (8, \infty)$
(number line: -8 0 8)

59. $\{t \mid t < 0 \text{ or } t > 0\}$, or $(-\infty, 0) \cup (0, \infty)$
(number line: 0)

61. $\{x \mid -3 < x < 5\}$, or $(-3, 5)$ (number line: -3 0 5)

63. $\{x \mid -8 \le x \le 4\}$, or $[-8, 4]$ (number line: -8 4)

65. $\{x \mid x < -2 \ or \ x > 8\}$, or $(-\infty, -2) \cup (8, \infty)$

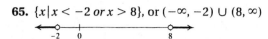

67. $\mathbb{R}$, or $(-\infty, \infty)$

69. $\{a \mid a \le -\frac{2}{3} \ or \ a \ge \frac{10}{3}\}$, or $(-\infty, -\frac{2}{3}] \cup [\frac{10}{3}, \infty)$

71. $\{y \mid -9 < y < 15\}$, or $(-9, 15)$

73. $\{x \mid x \le -8 \ or \ x \ge 0\}$, or $(-\infty, -8] \cup [0, \infty)$

75. $\{y \mid y < -\frac{4}{3} \ or \ y > 4\}$, or $(-\infty, -\frac{4}{3}) \cup (4, \infty)$

77. $\varnothing$

79. $\{x \mid x \le -\frac{2}{15} \ or \ x \ge \frac{14}{15}\}$, or $(-\infty, -\frac{2}{15}] \cup [\frac{14}{15}, \infty)$

81. $\{m \mid -9 \le m \le 3\}$, or $[-9, 3]$

83. $\{a \mid -6 < a < 0\}$, or $(-6, 0)$

85. $\{x \mid -\frac{1}{2} \le x \le \frac{7}{2}\}$, or $[-\frac{1}{2}, \frac{7}{2}]$

87. $\{x \mid x \le -\frac{7}{3} \ or \ x \ge 5\}$, or $(-\infty, -\frac{7}{3}] \cup [5, \infty)$

89. $\{x \mid -4 < x < 5\}$, or $(-4, 5)$

91.   **93.** $(-\frac{16}{13}, -\frac{41}{13})$ **94.** $(-2, -3)$ **95.** $(10, 4)$
96. $(-1, 7)$ **97.** $(1, 4)$ **98.** $(24, -41)$ **99.**
101. $\{t \mid t \ge \frac{5}{3}\}$, or $[\frac{5}{3}, \infty)$ **103.** $\mathbb{R}$, or $(-\infty, \infty)$ **105.** $\{-\frac{1}{7}, \frac{7}{3}\}$
107. $|x| < 3$ **109.** $|x| \ge 6$ **111.** $|x + 3| > 5$
113. $|x - 7| < 2$, or $|7 - x| < 2$ **115.** $|x - 3| \le 4$
117. $|x + 4| < 3$ **119.** Between 80 ft and 100 ft
121. $\{x \mid 1 \le x \le 5\}$, or $[1, 5]$ **123.** 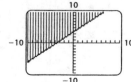 **125.**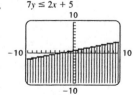

Technology Connection, p. 610

1. $y > x + 3.5$

2. $7y \le 2x + 5$

3. $8x - 2y < 11$

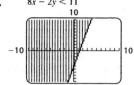

4. $11x + 13y + 4 \ge 0$

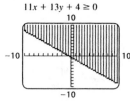

Technology Connection, p. 613

1. $y_1 \le 4 - x, \ y_2 > x - 4$

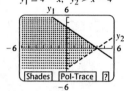

Exercise Set 9.4, pp. 615–617

1. (e) **3.** (d) **5.** (b) **7.** Yes **9.** No
11.

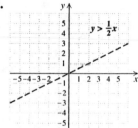

$y > \frac{1}{2}x$

13.

$y \ge x - 3$

15.

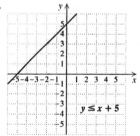

$y \le x + 5$

17.

$x - y \le 4$

19.

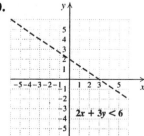

$2x + 3y < 6$

21.

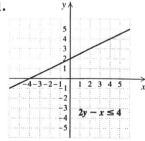

$2y - x \le 4$

23.

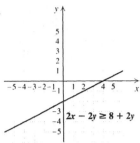

$2x - 2y \geq 8 + 2y$

25.

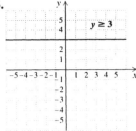

$y \geq 3$

43.

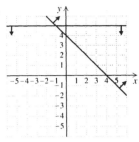

45.

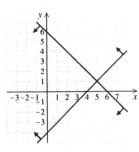

27.

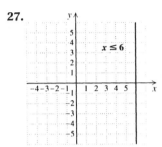

$x \leq 6$

29.

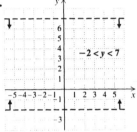

$-2 < y < 7$

47.

49.

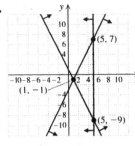

(5, 7)

(1, −1)

(5, −9)

31.

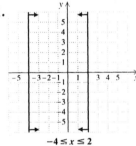

$-4 \leq x \leq 2$

33.

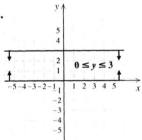

$0 \leq y \leq 3$

51.

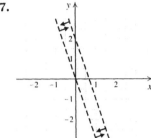

(0, 6)

(4, 4)

(0, 0)   (6, 0)

53.

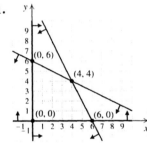

(0, 4)

$\left(\frac{40}{11}, \frac{24}{11}\right)$

(0, 0)

(5, 0)

35.

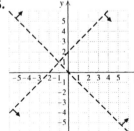

37.

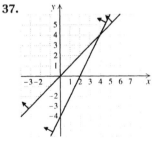

55.

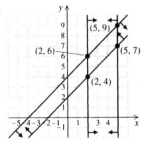

(5, 9)

(2, 6)

(5, 7)

(2, 4)

57. 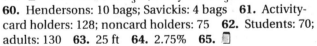   **59.** Peanuts: $6\frac{2}{3}$ lb; fancy nuts: $3\frac{1}{3}$ lb
60. Hendersons: 10 bags; Savickis: 4 bags   **61.** Activity-card holders: 128; noncard holders: 75   **62.** Students: 70; adults: 130   **63.** 25 ft   **64.** 2.75%   **65.**

39.

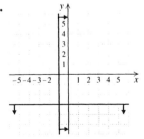

41.

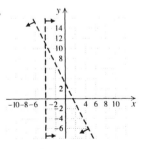

67.

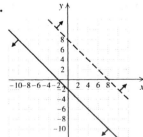

69.

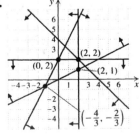

(2, 2)

(0, 2)

(2, 1)

$\left(-\frac{4}{3}, -\frac{2}{3}\right)$

71. $w > 0,$
$h > 0,$
$w + h + 30 \leq 62,$ or
$w + h \leq 32,$
$2w + 2h + 30 \leq 130,$ or
$w + h \leq 50$

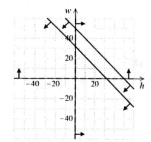

73. $35c + 75a > 1000,$
$c \geq 0,$
$a \geq 0$

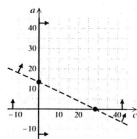

75. (a) $3x + 6y > 2$ **(b)** $x - 5y \leq 10$

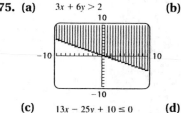

(c) $13x - 25y + 10 \leq 0$ **(d)** $2x + 5y > 0$

Exercise Set 9.5, pp. 623–625

1. Minimized **3.** Constraints **5.** Feasible
7. Maximum 84 when $x = 0, y = 6$; minimum 0 when
$x = 0, y = 0$ **9.** Maximum 76 when $x = 7, y = 0$;
minimum 16 when $x = 0, y = 4$ **11.** Maximum 5 when
$x = 3, y = 7$; minimum -15 when $x = 3, y = -3$
13. Car: 9 gal; moped: 3 gal; maximum: 480 mi
15. Lumber: 100 units; plywood: 300 units
17. Corporate bonds: $22,000; municipal bonds: $18,000;
maximum: $3110
19. Matching: 5; essay: 15; maximum: 425 **21.** Merlot:
80 acres; Cabernet: 160 acres **23.** Knit suits: 2; worsted
suits: 4 **25.** ▨ **27.** -40 **28.** 46 **29.** $10x + 5$
30. $26t + 20$ **31.** $3x - 6$ **32.** $2t + 2$ **33.** ▨ **35.** T3's:
30; S5's: 10 **37.** Chairs: 25; sofas: 9

Review Exercises: Chapter 9, pp. 627–628

1. True **2.** False **3.** True **4.** False **5.** True **6.** True
7. True **8.** False **9.** False **10.** False
11. $\{x \mid x \leq -2\}$, or $(-\infty, -2]$;
12. $\{a \mid a \leq -21\}$, or $(-\infty, -21]$;
13. $\{y \mid y \geq -7\}$, or $[-7, \infty)$;
14. $\left\{y \mid y > -\frac{15}{4}\right\}$, or $\left(-\frac{15}{4}, \infty\right)$;
15. $\{y \mid y > -30\}$, or $(-30, \infty)$;
16. $\left\{x \mid x > -\frac{3}{2}\right\}$, or $\left(-\frac{3}{2}, \infty\right)$;
17. $\{x \mid x < -3\}$, or $(-\infty, -3)$;
18. $\left\{y \mid y > -\frac{220}{23}\right\}$, or $\left(-\frac{220}{23}, \infty\right)$;
19. $\left\{x \mid x \leq -\frac{5}{2}\right\}$, or $\left(-\infty, -\frac{5}{2}\right]$;
20. $\{x \mid x \leq 4\}$, or $(-\infty, 4]$
21. More than 125 hr **22.** $3000 **23.** $\{1, 5, 9\}$
24. $\{1, 2, 3, 5, 6, 9\}$
25. $(-5, 3]$
26. $(-\infty, \infty)$
27. $\{x \mid -12 < x \leq -3\}$, or $(-12, -3]$
28. $\left\{x \mid -\frac{5}{4} < x < \frac{5}{2}\right\}$, or $\left(-\frac{5}{4}, \frac{5}{2}\right)$
29. $\{x \mid x < -3 \text{ or } x > 1\}$, or $(-\infty, -3) \cup (1, \infty)$
30. $\{x \mid x < -11 \text{ or } x \geq -6\}$, or $(-\infty, -11) \cup [-6, \infty)$
31. $\{x \mid x \leq -6 \text{ or } x \geq 8\}$, or $(-\infty, -6] \cup [8, \infty)$
32. $\left\{x \mid x < -\frac{2}{5} \text{ or } x > \frac{8}{5}\right\}$, or $\left(-\infty, -\frac{2}{5}\right) \cup \left(\frac{8}{5}, \infty\right)$
33. $(-\infty, 8) \cup (8, \infty)$ **34.** $[-5, \infty)$ **35.** $\left(-\infty, \frac{8}{3}\right]$
36. $\{-5, 5\}$ **37.** $\{t \mid t \leq -3.5 \text{ or } t \geq 3.5\}$, or
$(-\infty, -3.5] \cup [3.5, \infty)$ **38.** $\{-4, 10\}$
39. $\left\{x \mid -\frac{17}{2} < x < \frac{7}{2}\right\}$, or $\left(-\frac{17}{2}, \frac{7}{2}\right)$
40. $\left\{x \mid x \leq -\frac{11}{3} \text{ or } x \geq \frac{19}{3}\right\}$, or $\left(-\infty, -\frac{11}{3}\right] \cup \left[\frac{19}{3}, \infty\right)$
41. $\left\{-14, \frac{4}{3}\right\}$ **42.** $\varnothing$ **43.** $\{x \mid -16 \leq x \leq 8\}$, or $[-16, 8]$
44. $\{x \mid x < 0 \text{ or } x > 10\}$, or $(-\infty, 0) \cup (10, \infty)$ **45.** $\varnothing$

46.

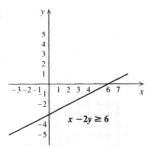

$x - 2y \geq 6$

47.

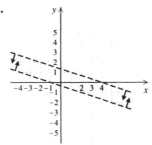

48.

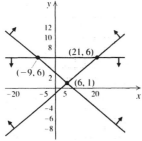

$(21, 6)$
$(-9, 6)$
$(6, 1)$

49. Maximum 40 when $x = 7$, $y = 15$; minimum 10 when $x = 1$, $y = 3$ **50.** Ohio plant: 120; Oregon plant: 40
51. 🖉 The equation $|X| = p$ has two solutions when p is positive because X can be either p or $-p$. The same equation has no solution when p is negative because no number has a negative absolute value.   **52.** 🖉 The solution set of a system of inequalities is all ordered pairs that make *all* the individual inequalities true. This consists of ordered pairs that are common to all the individual solution sets, or the intersection of the graphs.
53. $\{x | -\frac{8}{3} \leq x \leq -2\}$, or $\left[-\frac{8}{3}, -2\right]$ **54.** False; $-4 < 3$ is true, but $(-4)^2 < 9$ is false.   **55.** $|d - 1.1| \leq 0.03$

Test: Chapter 9, p. 629

1. [9.1] $\{x | x < 12\}$, or $(-\infty, 12)$

2. [9.1] $\{y | y > -50\}$, or $(-50, \infty)$

3. [9.1] $\{y | y \leq -2\}$, or $(-\infty, -2]$

4. [9.1] $\left\{a | a \leq \frac{11}{5}\right\}$, or $\left(-\infty, \frac{11}{5}\right]$

5. [9.1] $\left\{x | x > \frac{16}{5}\right\}$, or $\left(\frac{16}{5}, \infty\right)$

6. [9.1] $\left\{x | x \leq \frac{7}{4}\right\}$, or $\left(-\infty, \frac{7}{4}\right]$

7. [9.1] $\{x | x > 1\}$, or $(1, \infty)$ **8.** [9.1] More than $166\frac{2}{3}$ mi
9. [9.1] Less than or equal to 2.5 hr   **10.** [9.2] $\{3, 5\}$
11. [9.2] $\{1, 3, 5, 7, 9, 11, 13\}$ **12.** [9.2] $(-\infty, 4]$
13. [9.2] $\{x | 1 < x < 8\}$, or $(1, 8)$

14. [9.2] $\left\{t | -\frac{2}{5} < t \leq \frac{9}{5}\right\}$, or $\left(-\frac{2}{5}, \frac{9}{5}\right]$

15. [9.2] $\{x | x < 3 \ or \ x > 6\}$, or $(-\infty, 3) \cup (6, \infty)$

16. [9.2] $\left\{x | x < -4 \ or \ x > -\frac{5}{2}\right\}$, or $(-\infty, -4) \cup \left(-\frac{5}{2}, \infty\right)$

17. [9.2] $\left\{x | 4 \leq x < \frac{15}{2}\right\}$, or $\left[4, \frac{15}{2}\right)$

18. [9.3] $\{-13, 13\}$

19. [9.3] $\{a | a < -7 \ or \ a > 7\}$, or $(-\infty, -7) \cup (7, \infty)$

20. [9.3] $\left\{x | -2 < x < \frac{8}{3}\right\}$, or $\left(-2, \frac{8}{3}\right)$

21. [9.3] $\left\{t | t \leq -\frac{13}{5} \ or \ t \geq \frac{7}{5}\right\}$, or $\left(-\infty, -\frac{13}{5}\right] \cup \left[\frac{7}{5}, \infty\right)$

22. [9.3] $\varnothing$
23. [9.2] $\left\{x | x < \frac{1}{2} \ or \ x > \frac{7}{2}\right\}$, or $\left(-\infty, \frac{1}{2}\right) \cup \left(\frac{7}{2}, \infty\right)$

24. [9.3] $\{1\}$
25. [9.4]   **26.** [9.4]

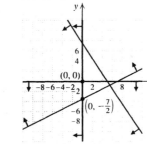

$(4, -1)$ $(0, 0)$ $\left(0, -\frac{7}{2}\right)$

27. [9.5] Maximum 57 when $x = 6$, $y = 9$; minimum 5 when $x = 1$, $y = 0$ **28.** [9.5] Manicures: 35; haircuts: 15; maximum: \$690   **29.** [9.3] $[-1, 0] \cup [4, 6]$ **30.** [9.2] $\left(\frac{1}{5}, \frac{4}{5}\right)$
31. [9.3] $|x + 3| \leq 5$

Cumulative Review: Chapters 1–9, pp. 630–631

1. 10   **2.** 3.91×10^8 **3.** Slope: $\frac{7}{4}$; y-intercept: $(0, -3)$
4. $y = -\frac{10}{3}x + \frac{11}{3}$ **5.** $(-3, 4)$ **6.** $(-2, -3, 1)$
7. Small: 16; large: 29   **8.** $12, \frac{1}{2}, 7\frac{1}{2}$
9. \$28.36 million per year   **10.** (a) $V(t) = \frac{5}{18}t + 15.4$;
(b) about 19.8 min   **11.** (a) $-\frac{1}{2}$;
(b) $\{x | x$ is a real number $and \ x \neq 5\}$ **12.** $\frac{1}{4}$

13. $-\frac{12}{7}, \frac{12}{7}$ **14.** $\{x \mid x > -3\}$, or $(-3, \infty)$ **15.** $\{x \mid x \geq -1\}$, or $[-1, \infty)$ **16.** $\{x \mid -10 < x < 13\}$, or $(-10, 13)$
17. $\left\{x \mid x < -\frac{4}{3} \, or \, x > 6\right\}$, or $\left(-\infty, -\frac{4}{3}\right) \cup (6, \infty)$
18. $\{x \mid x < -6.4 \, or \, x > 6.4\}$, or $(-\infty, -6.4) \cup (6.4, \infty)$
19. $\left\{x \mid -4 \leq x \leq \frac{16}{3}\right\}$, or $\left[-4, \frac{16}{3}\right]$ **20.** 2 **21.** -1
22. No solution **23.** $\frac{1}{3}$ **24.** $1, \frac{7}{3}$ **25.** $[9, \infty)$
26. $n = \dfrac{m - 12}{3}$ **27.** $a = \dfrac{Pb}{4 - P}$

28. 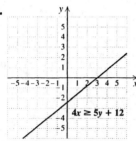 **29.**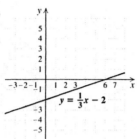

30. $-3x^3 + 11x^2 - 2x + 3$ **31.** $-24x^4 y^4$
32. $5a + 5b - 5c$ **33.** $15x^4 - x^3 - 9x^2 + 5x - 2$
34. $9x^4 + 6x^2 y + y^2$ **35.** $4x^4 - y^2$
36. $-m^3 n^2 - m^2 n^2 - 5mn^3$ **37.** $\dfrac{y - 6}{2}$ **38.** $x - 1$
39. $\dfrac{a^2 + 7ab + b^2}{(a - b)(a + b)}$ **40.** $\dfrac{-m^2 + 5m - 6}{(m + 1)(m - 5)}$ **41.** $\dfrac{3y^2 - 2}{3y}$
42. $\dfrac{y - x}{xy(x + y)}$ **43.** $9x^2 - 13x + 26 + \dfrac{-50}{x + 2}$
44. $2x^2(2x - 7)$ **45.** $(x - 6)(x + 14)$
46. $(4y - 9)(4y + 9)$ **47.** $8(2x + 1)(4x^2 - 2x + 1)$
48. $(t - 8)^2$ **49.** $x^2(x - 1)(x + 1)(x^2 + 1)$
50. $(0.3b - 0.2c)(0.09b^2 + 0.06bc + 0.04c^2)$
51. $(4x + 1)(5x - 3)$ **52.** $(3t - 4)(t + 7)$
53. $(x^2 - y)(x^3 + y)$
54. $\{x \mid x$ is a real number $and \, x \neq 2 \, and \, x \neq 5\}$
55. $3\frac{1}{3}$ sec **56.** 30 ft **57.** All such sets of even integers satisfy this condition. **58.** 25 ft
59. $x^3 - 12x^2 + 48x - 64$ **60.** $-3, 3, -5, 5$
61. $\{x \mid -3 \leq x \leq -1 \, or \, 7 \leq x \leq 9\}$, or $[-3, -1] \cup [7, 9]$
62. All real numbers except 9 and -5 **63.** $-\frac{1}{4}, 0, \frac{1}{4}$

CHAPTER 10

Technology Connection, p. 637

1. False **2.** True **3.** False

Exercise Set 10.1, pp. 641–642

1. Two **3.** Positive **5.** Irrational **7.** Nonnegative
9. $7, -7$ **11.** $12, -12$ **13.** $20, -20$ **15.** $30, -30$
17. $-\frac{6}{7}$ **19.** 21 **21.** $-\frac{4}{9}$ **23.** 0.2 **25.** -0.05

27. $p^2 + 4$; 2 **29.** $\dfrac{x}{y + 4}$; 3 **31.** $\sqrt{20}$; 0; does not exist; does not exist **33.** -3; -1; does not exist; 0
35. 1; $\sqrt{2}$; $\sqrt{101}$ **37.** 1; does not exist; 6 **39.** $6|x|$
41. $6|b|$ **43.** $|8 - t|$ **45.** $|y + 8|$ **47.** $|2x + 7|$
49. 4 **51.** -1 **53.** $-\frac{2}{3}$ **55.** $|x|$ **57.** $6|a|$ **59.** 6
61. $|a + b|$ **63.** $|a^{11}|$ **65.** Cannot be simplified
67. $4x$ **69.** $3t$ **71.** $a + 1$ **73.** $2(x + 1)$, or $2x + 2$
75. $3t - 2$ **77.** 3 **79.** $2x$ **81.** -6 **83.** $5y$ **85.** t^9
87. $(x - 2)^4$ **89.** 2; 3; -2; -4 **91.** 2; does not exist; does not exist; 3 **93.** $\{x \mid x \geq 6\}$, or $[6, \infty)$ **95.** $\{t \mid t \geq -8\}$, or $[-8, \infty)$ **97.** $\{x \mid x \geq 5\}$, or $[5, \infty)$ **99.** $\mathbb{R}$ **101.** $\left\{z \mid z \geq -\frac{2}{5}\right\}$, or $\left[-\frac{2}{5}, \infty\right)$ **103.** $\mathbb{R}$ **105.** ▨ **107.** $a^9 b^6 c^{15}$ **108.** $10a^{10} b^9$
109. $\dfrac{a^6 c^{12}}{8b^9}$ **110.** $\dfrac{x^6 y^2}{25z^4}$ **111.** $2x^4 y^5 z^2$ **112.** $\dfrac{5c^3}{a^4 b^7}$
113. ▨ **115.** (a) 34.6 lb; (b) 10.0 lb; (c) 24.9 lb; (d) 42.3 lb
117. $\{x \mid x \geq -5\}$, or $[-5, \infty)$ **119.** $\{x \mid x \geq 0\}$, or $[0, \infty)$

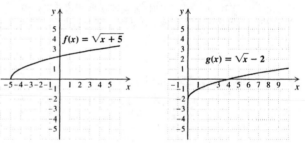

121. $\{x \mid -3 \leq x < 2\}$, or $[-3, 2)$
123. $\{x \mid x < -1 \, or \, x > 6\}$, or $(-\infty, -1) \cup (6, \infty)$ **125.** ▨

Technology Connection, p. 645

1. Without parentheses, the expression entered would be $\dfrac{7^2}{3}$. **2.** For $x = 0$ or $x = 1$, $y_1 = y_2 = y_3$; on $(0, 1)$, $y_1 > y_2 > y_3$; on $(1, \infty)$, $y_1 < y_2 < y_3$.

Technology Connection, p. 647

1. Most graphing calculators do not have keys for radicals of index 3 or higher. On those graphing calculators that offer $\sqrt[x]{\ }$ in a MATH menu, rational exponents still require fewer keystrokes.

Exercise Set 10.2, pp. 647–650

1. (g) **3.** (e) **5.** (a) **7.** (b) **9.** $\sqrt[6]{x}$ **11.** 4 **13.** 3
15. 3 **17.** $\sqrt[3]{xyz}$ **19.** $\sqrt[5]{a^2 b^2}$ **21.** $\sqrt[5]{t^2}$ **23.** 8 **25.** 81
27. $27\sqrt[4]{x^3}$ **29.** $125x^6$ **31.** $20^{1/3}$ **33.** $17^{1/2}$ **35.** $x^{3/2}$
37. $m^{2/5}$ **39.** $(cd)^{1/4}$ **41.** $(xy^2 z)^{1/5}$ **43.** $(3mn)^{3/2}$
45. $(8x^2 y)^{5/7}$ **47.** $\dfrac{2x}{z^{2/3}}$ **49.** $\dfrac{1}{x^{1/3}}$ **51.** $\dfrac{1}{(2rs)^{3/4}}$ **53.** 8

55. $2a^{3/5}c$ **57.** $\dfrac{5y^{4/5}z}{x^{2/3}}$ **59.** $\dfrac{a^3}{3^{5/2}b^{7/3}}$ **61.** $\left(\dfrac{3c}{2ab}\right)^{5/6}$

63. $\dfrac{6a}{b^{1/4}}$ **65.** $7^{7/8}$ **67.** $3^{3/4}$ **69.** $5.2^{1/2}$ **71.** $10^{6/25}$

73. $a^{23/12}$ **75.** 64 **77.** $\dfrac{m^{1/3}}{n^{1/8}}$ **79.** $\sqrt[3]{x^2}$ **81.** a^3

83. a^2 **85.** x^2y^2 **87.** $\sqrt{7a}$ **89.** $\sqrt[4]{8x^3}$ **91.** $\sqrt[18]{a}$

93. x^3y^3 **95.** a^6b^{12} **97.** $\sqrt[12]{xy}$ **99.** 🖿

101. $11x^4 + 14x^3$ **102.** $-3t^6 + 28t^5 - 20t^4$

103. $15a^2 - 11ab - 12b^2$ **104.** $49x^2 - 14xy + y^2$

105. \$93,500   **106.** $0, 1$ **107.** 🖿   **109.** $\sqrt[6]{x^5}$

111. $\sqrt[6]{p+q}$ **113.** $2^{7/12} \approx 1.498 \approx 1.5$ **115.** 53.0%

117. About 7.937×10^{-13} to 1   **119.** 🖿

Technology Connection, p. 652

1. The graphs differ in appearance because the domain of y_1 is the intersection of $[-3, \infty)$ and $[3, \infty)$, or $[3, \infty)$. The domain of y_2 is $(-\infty, -3] \cup [3, \infty)$.

Exercise Set 10.3, pp. 655–657

1. True   **3.** False   **5.** True   **7.** $\sqrt{35}$ **9.** $\sqrt[3]{14}$ **11.** $\sqrt[4]{18}$

13. $\sqrt{26xy}$ **15.** $\sqrt[5]{80y^4}$ **17.** $\sqrt{y^2 - b^2}$ **19.** $\sqrt[3]{0.21y^2}$

21. $\sqrt[5]{(x-2)^3}$ **23.** $\sqrt{\dfrac{7s}{11t}}$ **25.** $\sqrt[7]{\dfrac{5x-15}{4x+8}}$ **27.** $3\sqrt{2}$

29. $3\sqrt{3}$ **31.** $2\sqrt{2}$ **33.** $3\sqrt{22}$ **35.** $6a^2\sqrt{b}$ **37.** $2x\sqrt[3]{y^2}$

39. $-2x^2\sqrt[3]{2}$ **41.** $f(x) = 5x\sqrt[3]{x^2}$ **43.** $f(x) = |7(x-3)|$, or $7|x-3|$ **45.** $f(x) = |x-1|\sqrt{5}$ **47.** $a^3b^3\sqrt{b}$

49. $xy^2z^3\sqrt[3]{x^2z}$ **51.** $-2ab^2\sqrt[5]{a^2b}$ **53.** $x^2yz^3\sqrt[5]{x^3y^3z^2}$

55. $-2a^4\sqrt[3]{10a^2}$ **57.** $3\sqrt{2}$ **59.** $3\sqrt{35}$ **61.** 3 **63.** $18a^3$

65. $a\sqrt[3]{10}$ **67.** $2x^3\sqrt{5x}$ **69.** $s^2t^3\sqrt[3]{t}$ **71.** $(x+5)^2$

73. $2ab^3\sqrt[4]{5a}$ **75.** $x(y+z)^2\sqrt[5]{x}$ **77.** 🖿

79. $\dfrac{12x^2 + 5y^2}{64xy}$ **80.** $\dfrac{2a + 6b^3}{a^4b^4}$ **81.** $\dfrac{-7x - 13}{2(x-3)(x+3)}$

82. $\dfrac{-3x + 1}{2(x-5)(x+5)}$ **83.** $3a^2b^2$ **84.** $3ab^5$ **85.** 🖿

87. 175.6 mi   **89.** (a) $-3.3°$C; (b) $-16.6°$C; (c) $-25.5°$C; (d) $-54.0°$C   **91.** $25x^5\sqrt[3]{25x}$ **93.** $a^{10}b^{17}\sqrt{ab}$

95.

$f(x) = h(x); f(x) \neq g(x)$

97. $\{x \mid x \le 2 \text{ or } x \ge 4\}$, or $(-\infty, 2] \cup [4, \infty)$ **99.** 6

101. 🖿, 🖿

Exercise Set 10.4, pp. 663–665

1. (e)   **3.** (f)   **5.** (h)   **7.** (a)   **9.** $\dfrac{6}{5}$ **11.** $\dfrac{4}{3}$ **13.** $\dfrac{7}{y}$

15. $\dfrac{6y\sqrt{y}}{x^2}$ **17.** $\dfrac{3a\sqrt[3]{a}}{2b}$ **19.** $\dfrac{2a}{bc^2}$ **21.** $\dfrac{ab^2}{c^2}\sqrt[4]{\dfrac{a}{c^2}}$

23. $\dfrac{2x}{y^2}\sqrt[5]{\dfrac{x}{y}}$ **25.** $\dfrac{xy}{z^2}\sqrt[6]{\dfrac{y^2}{z^3}}$ **27.** $\sqrt{5}$ **29.** 3 **31.** $y\sqrt{5y}$

33. $2\sqrt[3]{a^2b}$ **35.** $\sqrt{2ab}$ **37.** $2x^2y^3\sqrt[4]{y^3}$

39. $\sqrt[3]{x^2 + xy + y^2}$ **41.** $\dfrac{\sqrt{6}}{2}$ **43.** $\dfrac{2\sqrt{15}}{21}$ **45.** $\dfrac{2\sqrt[3]{6}}{3}$

47. $\dfrac{\sqrt[3]{75ac^2}}{5c}$ **49.** $\dfrac{y\sqrt[3]{180x^2y}}{6x^2}$ **51.** $\dfrac{\sqrt[3]{2xy^2}}{xy}$ **53.** $\dfrac{\sqrt{14a}}{6}$

55. $\dfrac{3\sqrt{5y}}{10xy}$ **57.** $\dfrac{\sqrt{5b}}{6a}$ **59.** $\dfrac{5}{\sqrt{35x}}$ **61.** $\dfrac{2}{\sqrt{6}}$ **63.** $\dfrac{52}{3\sqrt{91}}$

65. $\dfrac{7}{\sqrt[3]{98}}$ **67.** $\dfrac{7x}{\sqrt{21xy}}$ **69.** $\dfrac{2a^2}{\sqrt[3]{20ab}}$ **71.** $\dfrac{x^2y}{\sqrt{2xy}}$ **73.** 🖿

75. $\dfrac{3(x-1)}{(x-5)(x+5)}$ **76.** $\dfrac{7(x-2)}{(x+4)(x-4)}$ **77.** $\dfrac{a-1}{a+7}$

78. $\dfrac{t+11}{t+2}$ **79.** $125a^9b^{12}$ **80.** $225x^{10}y^6$ **81.** 🖿

83. (a) 1.62 sec; (b) 1.99 sec; (c) 2.20 sec   **85.** $9\sqrt[3]{9n^2}$

87. $\dfrac{-3\sqrt{a^2-3}}{a^2-3}$, or $\dfrac{-3}{\sqrt{a^2-3}}$ **89.** Step 1: $\sqrt[n]{a} = a^{1/n}$, by definition; Step 2: $\left(\dfrac{a}{b}\right)^n = \dfrac{a^n}{b^n}$, raising a quotient to a power; Step 3: $a^{1/n} = \sqrt[n]{a}$, by definition

91. $(f/g)(x) = 3x$, where x is a real number and $x > 0$

93. $(f/g)(x) = \sqrt{x+3}$, where x is a real number and $x > 3$

Exercise Set 10.5, pp. 670–672

1. Radicands, indices   **3.** Bases   **5.** Numerator, conjugate

7. $9\sqrt{5}$ **9.** $2\sqrt[3]{4}$ **11.** $10\sqrt[3]{y}$ **13.** $7\sqrt{2}$

15. $13\sqrt[3]{7} + \sqrt{3}$ **17.** $9\sqrt{3}$ **19.** $23\sqrt{5}$ **21.** $9\sqrt[3]{2}$

23. $(1 + 6a)\sqrt{5a}$ **25.** $(x + 2)\sqrt[3]{6x}$ **27.** $3\sqrt{a-1}$

29. $(x + 3)\sqrt{x-1}$ **31.** $4\sqrt{3} + 3$ **33.** $15 - 3\sqrt{10}$

35. $6\sqrt{5} - 4$ **37.** $3 - 4\sqrt[3]{63}$ **39.** $a + 2a\sqrt[3]{3}$

41. $4 + 3\sqrt{6}$ **43.** $\sqrt{6} - \sqrt{14} + \sqrt{21} - 7$ **45.** 4

47. -2 **49.** $2 - 8\sqrt{35}$ **51.** $7 + 4\sqrt{3}$ **53.** $5 - 2\sqrt{6}$

55. $2t + 5 + 2\sqrt{10t}$ **57.** $14 + x - 6\sqrt{x+5}$

59. $6\sqrt[4]{63} + 4\sqrt[4]{35} - 3\sqrt[4]{54} - 2\sqrt[4]{30}$ **61.** $\dfrac{20 + 5\sqrt{3}}{13}$

63. $\dfrac{12 - 2\sqrt{3} + 6\sqrt{5} - \sqrt{15}}{33}$ **65.** $\dfrac{a - \sqrt{ab}}{a - b}$ **67.** -1

69. $\dfrac{12 - 3\sqrt{10} - 2\sqrt{14} + \sqrt{35}}{6}$ **71.** $\dfrac{3}{5\sqrt{7} - 10}$

73. $\dfrac{2}{14 + 2\sqrt{3} + 3\sqrt{2} + 7\sqrt{6}}$ **75.** $\dfrac{x - y}{x + 2\sqrt{xy} + y}$

77. $\dfrac{1}{\sqrt{a+h}+\sqrt{a}}$ **79.** $a\sqrt[4]{a}$ **81.** $b\sqrt[10]{b^9}$
83. $xy\sqrt[6]{xy^5}$ **85.** $3a^2b\sqrt[4]{ab}$ **87.** $a^2b^2c^2\sqrt[6]{a^2bc^2}$
89. $\sqrt[12]{a^5}$ **91.** $\sqrt[12]{x^2y^5}$ **93.** $\sqrt[10]{ab^9}$ **95.** $\sqrt[20]{(3x-1)^3}$
97. $\sqrt[15]{(2x+1)^4}$ **99.** $x\sqrt[6]{xy^5}-\sqrt[15]{x^{13}y^{14}}$
101. $2m^2+m\sqrt[4]{n}+2m\sqrt[3]{n^2}+\sqrt[12]{n^{11}}$ **103.** $\sqrt[4]{2x^2}-x^3$
105. x^2-7 **107.** $27+10\sqrt{2}$ **109.** $8-2\sqrt{15}$ **111.** 🖊
113. 8   **114.** $\frac{15}{2}$ **115.** $\frac{1}{5},1$ **116.** $\frac{1}{7},1$ **117.** $-5,4$
118. Length: 20 units; width: 5 units   **119.** 🖊
121. $f(x)=-6x\sqrt{5+x}$ **123.** $f(x)=(x+3x^2)\sqrt[4]{x-1}$
125. $ac^2\big[(3a+2c)\sqrt{ab}-2\sqrt[3]{ab}\big]$
127. $9a^2(b+1)\sqrt[6]{243a^5(b+1)^5}$ **129.** $1-\sqrt{w}$
131. $(\sqrt{x}+\sqrt{5})(\sqrt{x}-\sqrt{5})$
133. $(\sqrt{x}+\sqrt{a})(\sqrt{x}-\sqrt{a})$ **135.** $2x-2\sqrt{x^2-4}$

Technology Connection, p. 675

1. The x-coordinates of the points of intersection should approximate the solutions of the examples.

Exercise Set 10.6, pp. 677–679

1. False   **3.** True   **5.** True   **7.** $\frac{51}{5}$ **9.** $\frac{25}{3}$ **11.** 168
13. 56   **15.** 3   **17.** 82   **19.** 0, 9   **21.** 64   **23.** -27
25. 125   **27.** No solution   **29.** $\frac{80}{3}$ **31.** 57   **33.** $-\frac{5}{3}$
35. 1   **37.** $\frac{106}{27}$ **39.** 4   **41.** 3, 7   **43.** $\frac{80}{9}$ **45.** -1
47. No solution   **49.** 2, 6   **51.** 2   **53.** 4   **55.** 🖊
57. Height: 7 in.; base: 9 in.   **58.** 8 60-sec commercials
59.
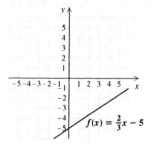
60.
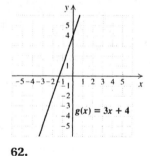
61.
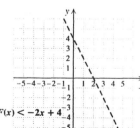
62.
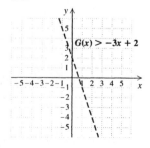
63. 🖊   **65.** 524.8°C   **67.** $t=\dfrac{1}{9}\left(\dfrac{S^2\cdot 2457}{1087.7^2}-2617\right)$

69. 4480 rpm   **71.** $r=\dfrac{v^2h}{2gh-v^2}$ **73.** 72.25 ft   **75.** $-\frac{8}{9}$
77. $-8,8$ **79.** 1, 8   **81.** $\left(\frac{1}{36},0\right),(36,0)$ **83.** 🖊   **85.** 🖊

Exercise Set 10.7, pp. 685–688

1. Right, hypotenuse   **3.** Square roots
5. 30°, 60°, 90°, leg   **7.** $\sqrt{34}$; 5.831   **9.** $9\sqrt{2}$; 12.728
11. 5   **13.** 4 m   **15.** $\sqrt{19}$ in.; 4.359 in.   **17.** 1 m
19. 250 ft   **21.** $\sqrt{8450}$, or $65\sqrt{2}$ ft; 91.924 ft   **23.** 12 in.
25. $\left(\sqrt{340}+8\right)$ ft; 26.439 ft   **27.** $\left(110-\sqrt{6500}\right)$ paces; 29.377 paces   **29.** Leg = 5; hypotenuse = $5\sqrt{2}\approx 7.071$
31. Shorter leg = 7; longer leg = $7\sqrt{3}\approx 12.124$
33. Leg = $5\sqrt{3}\approx 8.660$; hypotenuse = $10\sqrt{3}\approx 17.321$
35. Both legs = $\dfrac{13\sqrt{2}}{2}\approx 9.192$
37. Leg = $14\sqrt{3}\approx 24.249$; hypotenuse = 28
39. $3\sqrt{3}\approx 5.196$ **41.** $13\sqrt{2}\approx 18.385$
43. $\dfrac{19\sqrt{2}}{2}\approx 13.435$ **45.** $\sqrt{10561}$ ft ≈ 102.767 ft
47. $h=2\sqrt{3}$ ft ≈ 3.464 ft   **49.** $(0,-4),(0,4)$ **51.** 🖊
53. -47 **54.** 5   **55.** $x(x-3)(x+3)$
56. $7a(a-2)(a+2)$ **57.** $\left\{-\frac{2}{3},4\right\}$ **58.** $\left\{-\frac{4}{3},10\right\}$
59. 🖊   **61.** $36\sqrt{3}$ cm²; 62.354 cm²   **63.** $d=s+s\sqrt{2}$
65. 5 gal. The total area of the doors and windows is 134 ft² or more.   **67.** 60.28 ft by 60.28 ft

Exercise Set 10.8, pp. 695–696

1. False   **3.** True   **5.** True   **7.** False   **9.** $6i$ **11.** $i\sqrt{13}$, or $\sqrt{13}i$ **13.** $3i\sqrt{2}$, or $3\sqrt{2}i$ **15.** $i\sqrt{3}$, or $\sqrt{3}i$ **17.** $9i$
19. $-10i\sqrt{3}$, or $-10\sqrt{3}i$ **21.** $6-2i\sqrt{21}$, or $6-2\sqrt{21}i$
23. $\left(-2\sqrt{19}+5\sqrt{5}\right)i$ **25.** $\left(3\sqrt{2}-10\right)i$ **27.** $11+10i$
29. $4+5i$ **31.** $2-i$ **33.** $-12-5i$ **35.** -42 **37.** -24
39. -18 **41.** $-\sqrt{10}$ **43.** $-3\sqrt{14}$ **45.** $-30+10i$
47. $-28-21i$ **49.** $1+5i$ **51.** $38+9i$ **53.** $2-46i$
55. $-11-16i$ **57.** $13-47i$ **59.** $12-16i$
61. $-5+12i$ **63.** $-5-12i$ **65.** $\frac{28}{17}-\frac{7}{17}i$ **67.** $\frac{6}{13}+\frac{4}{13}i$
69. $\frac{3}{17}+\frac{5}{17}i$ **71.** $-\frac{5}{6}i$ **73.** $-\frac{3}{4}-\frac{5}{4}i$ **75.** $1-2i$
77. $-\frac{23}{58}+\frac{43}{58}i$ **79.** $\frac{19}{29}-\frac{4}{29}i$ **81.** $\frac{6}{25}-\frac{17}{25}i$ **83.** $-i$ **85.** 1
87. $-i$ **89.** i **91.** -1 **93.** $-125i$ **95.** 0   **97.** 🖊
99.
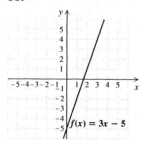
100.
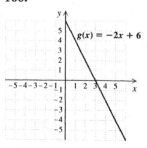

101. **102.**

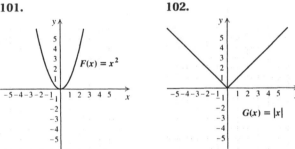

103. $-\frac{4}{3}, 7$ **104.** $\{x|-\frac{29}{3} < x < 5\}$, or $\left(-\frac{29}{3}, 5\right)$ **105.**
107. $-9 - 27i$ **109.** $50 - 120i$ **111.** $\frac{250}{41} + \frac{200}{41}i$ **113.** 8
115. $\frac{3}{5} + \frac{9}{5}i$ **117.** 1

Review Exercises: Chapter 10, pp. 700–701

1. True **2.** False **3.** True **4.** True **5.** True **6.** True
7. True **8.** False **9.** $\frac{7}{3}$ **10.** -0.5 **11.** 5
12. $\{x|x \geq \frac{7}{2}\}$, or $\left[\frac{7}{2}, \infty\right)$ **13.** $5|t|$ **14.** $|c + 8|$
15. $|x - 3|$ **16.** $|2x + 1|$ **17.** -2 **18.** $-\frac{4x^2}{3}$
19. $|x^3y^2|$, or $|x^3|y^2$ **20.** $2x^2$ **21.** $(5ab)^{4/3}$
22. $8a^4\sqrt{a}$ **23.** x^3y^5 **24.** $\sqrt[3]{x^2y}$ **25.** $\frac{1}{x^{2/5}}$ **26.** $7^{1/6}$
27. $f(x) = 5|x - 6|$ **28.** $\sqrt{6xy}$ **29.** $3a\sqrt[3]{a^2b^2}$
30. $-6x^5y^4\sqrt[3]{2x^2}$ **31.** $y\sqrt[3]{6}$ **32.** $\frac{5\sqrt{x}}{2}$ **33.** $\frac{2a^2\sqrt[4]{3a^3}}{c^2}$
34. $7\sqrt[3]{x}$ **35.** $\sqrt{3}$ **36.** $(2x + y^2)\sqrt[3]{x}$ **37.** $15\sqrt{2}$
38. $\sqrt{15} + 4\sqrt{6} - 6\sqrt{10} - 48$ **39.** $\sqrt[4]{x^3}$ **40.** $\sqrt[12]{x^5}$
41. $a^2 - 2a\sqrt{2} + 2$ **42.** $-4\sqrt{10} + 4\sqrt{15}$
43. $\frac{20}{\sqrt{10} + \sqrt{15}}$ **44.** 19 **45.** -126 **46.** 4 **47.** 14
48. $5\sqrt{2}$ cm; 7.071 cm **49.** $\sqrt{32}$ ft; 5.657 ft
50. Short leg = 10; long leg = $10\sqrt{3} \approx 17.321$
51. $-2i\sqrt{2}$, or $-2\sqrt{2}i$ **52.** $-2 - 9i$ **53.** $6 + i$ **54.** 29
55. -1 **56.** 3 **57.** $-\frac{2}{5} + \frac{9}{10}i$ **58.** $9 - 12i$ **59.** $\frac{13}{25} - \frac{34}{25}i$
60. A complex number $a + bi$ is real when $b = 0$. It is imaginary when $b \neq 0$.
61. An absolute-value sign must be used to simplify $\sqrt[n]{x^n}$ when n is even, since x may be negative. If x is negative while n is even, the radical expression cannot be simplified to x, since $\sqrt[n]{x^n}$ represents the principal, or positive, root. When n is odd, there is only one root, and it will be positive or negative depending on the sign of x. Thus there is no absolute-value sign when n is odd.
62. $\frac{2i}{3i}$; answers may vary

Test: Chapter 10, p. 702

1. [10.3] $5\sqrt{2}$ **2.** [10.4] $-\frac{2}{x^2}$ **3.** [10.1] $9|a|$
4. [10.1] $|x - 4|$ **5.** [10.3] $x^2y\sqrt[5]{x^2y^3}$ **6.** [10.4] $\left|\frac{5x}{6y^2}\right|$, or $\frac{5|x|}{6y^2}$ **7.** [10.3] $\sqrt[3]{15y^2z}$ **8.** [10.4] $\sqrt[5]{x^2y^2}$
9. [10.5] $xy\sqrt[4]{x}$ **10.** [10.5] $\sqrt[20]{a^3}$ **11.** [10.5] $6\sqrt{2}$
12. [10.5] $(x^2 + 3y)\sqrt{y}$ **13.** [10.5] $14 - 19\sqrt{x} - 3x$
14. [10.2] $(7xy)^{1/2}$ **15.** [10.2] $\sqrt[6]{(4a^3b)^5}$
16. [10.1] $\{x|x \geq 5\}$, or $[5, \infty)$ **17.** [10.5] $27 + 10\sqrt{2}$
18. [10.5] $\frac{5\sqrt{3} - \sqrt{6}}{23}$ **19.** [10.6] 7 **20.** [10.6] No solution
21. [10.7] $7\sqrt{3}$ cm or 12.124 cm (if the shorter leg is 7 cm); $\frac{7}{\sqrt{3}}$ cm or 4.041 cm (if the longer leg is 7 cm)
22. [10.7] $\sqrt{10,600}$ ft; 102.956 ft **23.** [10.8] $5i\sqrt{2}$, or $5\sqrt{2}i$
24. [10.8] $12 + 2i$ **25.** [10.8] -24 **26.** [10.8] $15 - 8i$
27. [10.8] $-\frac{11}{34} - \frac{7}{34}i$ **28.** [10.8] i **29.** [10.6] 3
30. [10.8] $-\frac{17}{4}i$ **31.** [10.7] The isosceles right triangle is larger by 1.206 ft^2.

CHAPTER 11

Technology Connection, p. 713

1. The right-hand x-intercept should be an approximation of $4 + \sqrt{23}$. **2.** x-intercepts should be approximations of $-3 + \sqrt{5}$ and $-3 - \sqrt{5}$ for Example 7; approximations of $(-5 + \sqrt{37})/2$ and $(-5 - \sqrt{37})/2$ for Example 9(b)
3. Most graphing calculators can give only rational-number approximations of the two irrational solutions. An *exact* solution cannot be found with a graphing calculator.
4. The graph of $y = x^2 - 6x + 11$ has no x-intercepts.

Exercise Set 11.1, pp. 713–715

1. $\sqrt{k}; -\sqrt{k}$ **3.** $t + 3; t + 3$ **5.** 25; 5 **7.** $\pm\sqrt{5}$ **9.** $\pm\frac{4}{3}i$
11. $\pm\sqrt{\frac{7}{5}}$, or $\pm\frac{\sqrt{35}}{5}$ **13.** $-6, 8$ **15.** $13 \pm 3\sqrt{2}$
17. $-1 \pm 3i$ **19.** $-\frac{3}{4} \pm \frac{\sqrt{17}}{4}$, or $\frac{-3 \pm \sqrt{17}}{4}$
21. $-3, 13$ **23.** 1, 9 **25.** $-4 \pm \sqrt{13}$ **27.** $-14, 0$
29. $x^2 + 16x + 64 = (x + 8)^2$
31. $t^2 - 10t + 25 = (t - 5)^2$ **33.** $x^2 + 3x + \frac{9}{4} = (x + \frac{3}{2})^2$
35. $t^2 - 9t + \frac{81}{4} = (t - \frac{9}{2})^2$ **37.** $x^2 + \frac{2}{5}x + \frac{1}{25} = (x + \frac{1}{5})^2$
39. $t^2 - \frac{5}{6}t + \frac{25}{144} = (t - \frac{5}{12})^2$ **41.** $-7, 1$ **43.** 4, 6
45. $-9, -1$ **47.** $-4 \pm \sqrt{19}$
49. $(-3 - \sqrt{2}, 0), (-3 + \sqrt{2}, 0)$

51. $\left(-6 - \sqrt{11}, 0\right), \left(-6 + \sqrt{11}, 0\right)$
53. $\left(5 - \sqrt{47}, 0\right), \left(5 + \sqrt{47}, 0\right)$ **55.** $-\frac{4}{3}, -\frac{2}{3}$ **57.** $-\frac{1}{3}, 2$
59. $-\frac{2}{5} \pm \frac{\sqrt{19}}{5}$, or $\frac{-2 \pm \sqrt{19}}{5}$
61. $\left(-\frac{1}{4} - \frac{\sqrt{13}}{4}, 0\right), \left(-\frac{1}{4} + \frac{\sqrt{13}}{4}, 0\right)$, or
$\left(\frac{-1 - \sqrt{13}}{4}, 0\right), \left(\frac{-1 + \sqrt{13}}{4}, 0\right)$
63. $\left(\frac{3}{4} - \frac{\sqrt{17}}{4}, 0\right), \left(\frac{3}{4} + \frac{\sqrt{17}}{4}, 0\right)$, or
$\left(\frac{3 - \sqrt{17}}{4}, 0\right), \left(\frac{3 + \sqrt{17}}{4}, 0\right)$ **65.** 10%   **67.** 18.75%
69. 4%   **71.** About 8.1 sec   **73.** About 9.5 sec   **75.**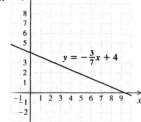
77. 28   **78.** -92 **79.** $3\sqrt[3]{10}$ **80.** $4\sqrt{5}$ **81.** 5   **82.** 7
83. ⬚   **85.** ± 18 **87.** $-\frac{7}{2}, -\sqrt{5}, 0, \sqrt{5}, 8$
89. Barge: 8 km/h; fishing boat: 15 km/h
91. ⬚   **93.** ⬚, ⬚

Exercise Set 11.2, pp. 720–722

1. True   **3.** False   **5.** False   **7.** $-\frac{7}{2} \pm \frac{\sqrt{61}}{2}$ **9.** $3 \pm \sqrt{7}$
11. $-\frac{1}{2} \pm \frac{\sqrt{3}}{2}i$ **13.** $2 \pm 3i$ **15.** $3 \pm \sqrt{5}$
17. $-\frac{4}{3} \pm \frac{\sqrt{19}}{3}$ **19.** $-\frac{1}{2} \pm \frac{\sqrt{17}}{2}$ **21.** $-\frac{3}{8} \pm \frac{\sqrt{129}}{24}$
23. $\frac{2}{5}$ **25.** $-\frac{11}{8} \pm \frac{\sqrt{41}}{8}$ **27.** 5, 10   **29.** $\frac{13}{10} \pm \frac{\sqrt{509}}{10}$
31. $2 \pm \sqrt{5}i$ **33.** $2, -1 \pm \sqrt{3}i$ **35.** $\frac{2}{3}, 1$ **37.** $5 \pm \sqrt{53}$
39. $\frac{7}{2} \pm \frac{\sqrt{85}}{2}$ **41.** $\frac{3}{2}, 6$ **43.** $-5.31662479, 1.31662479$
45. 0.7639320225, 5.236067978   **47.** -1.265564437,
2.765564437   **49.** ⬚   **51.** Kenyan: 30 lb; Kona: 20 lb
52. Cream-filled: 46; glazed: 44   **53.** $9a^2b^3\sqrt{2a}$
54. $4a^2b^3\sqrt{6}$ **55.** $\frac{3(x + 1)}{3x + 1}$ **56.** $\frac{4b}{3ab^2 - 4a^2}$ **57.** ⬚
59. $(-2, 0), (1, 0)$ **61.** $4 - 2\sqrt{2}, 4 + 2\sqrt{2}$
63. $-1.1792101, 0.3392101$ **65.** $\frac{-5\sqrt{2} \pm \sqrt{34}}{4}$ **67.** $\frac{1}{2}$
69. ⬚

Exercise Set 11.3, pp. 726–729

1. First part: 60 mph; second part: 50 mph   **3.** 40 mph
5. Cessna: 150 mph, Beechcraft: 200 mph; or
Cessna: 200 mph, Beechcraft: 250 mph
7. To Hillsboro: 10 mph; return trip: 4 mph
9. About 14 mph   **11.** 12 hr   **13.** About 3.24 mph
15. $r = \frac{1}{2}\sqrt{\frac{A}{\pi}}$ **17.** $r = \frac{-\pi h + \sqrt{\pi^2 h^2 + 2\pi A}}{2\pi}$

19. $s = \sqrt{\frac{kQ_1Q_2}{N}}$ **21.** $g = \frac{4\pi^2 l}{T^2}$
23. $c = \sqrt{d^2 - a^2 - b^2}$ **25.** $t = \frac{-v_0 + \sqrt{v_0^2 + 2gs}}{g}$
27. $n = \frac{1 + \sqrt{1 + 8N}}{2}$ **29.** $h = \frac{V^2}{12.25}$
31. $t = \frac{-b \pm \sqrt{b^2 - 4ac}}{2a}$ **33.** (a) 10.1 sec; (b) 7.49 sec;
(c) 272.5 m   **35.** 2.9 sec   **37.** 0.968 sec   **39.** 2.5 m/sec
41. 7%   **43.** ⬚   **45.** -104 **46.** $2i\sqrt{11}$ **47.** $\frac{x + y}{2}$
48. $\frac{a^2 - b^2}{b}$ **49.** $\frac{1 + \sqrt{5}}{2}$ **50.** $\frac{1 - \sqrt{7}}{5}$ **51.** ⬚
53. $t = \frac{-10.2 + 6\sqrt{-A^2 + 13A - 39.36}}{A - 6.5}$
55. $\pm\sqrt{2}$ **57.** $l = \frac{w + w\sqrt{5}}{2}$
59. $n = \pm\sqrt{\frac{r^2 \pm \sqrt{r^4 + 4m^4r^2p - 4mp}}{2m}}$
61. $A(S) = \frac{\pi S}{6}$

Technology Connection, p. 732

1. $(-0.4, 0)$ is the other x-intercept of $y = 5x^2 - 13x - 6$.
2. The x-intercepts of $y = x^2 - 175$ are $(-13.22875656, 0)$
and $(13.22875656, 0)$, or $(-5\sqrt{7}, 0)$ and $(5\sqrt{7}, 0)$.
3. The x-intercepts of $y = x^3 + 3x^2 - 4x$ are $(-4, 0)$,
$(0, 0)$, and $(1, 0)$.

Exercise Set 11.4, pp. 733–735

1. Discriminant   **3.** Two   **5.** Rational   **7.** Two irrational
9. Two imaginary   **11.** Two irrational   **13.** Two rational
15. Two imaginary   **17.** One rational   **19.** Two rational
21. Two rational   **23.** Two irrational   **25.** Two imaginary
27. Two irrational   **29.** $x^2 + 4x - 21 = 0$
31. $x^2 - 6x + 9 = 0$ **33.** $x^2 + 4x + 3 = 0$
35. $4x^2 - 23x + 15 = 0$ **37.** $8x^2 + 6x + 1 = 0$
39. $x^2 - 2x - 0.96 = 0$ **41.** $x^2 - 3 = 0$
43. $x^2 - 20 = 0$ **45.** $x^2 + 16 = 0$
47. $x^2 - 4x + 53 = 0$ **49.** $x^2 - 6x - 5 = 0$
51. $3x^2 - 6x - 4 = 0$ **53.** $x^3 - 4x^2 - 7x + 10 = 0$
55. $x^3 - 2x^2 - 3x = 0$ **57.** ⬚   **59.** $81a^8$ **60.** $16x^6$
61. $(-1, 0), (8, 0)$ **62.** $(2, 0), (4, 0)$ **63.** 6 commercials
64.

[Graph showing line $y = -\frac{3}{7}x + 4$ with y-axis marked 1–8 and x-axis marked 1–9]

65. 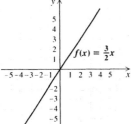   **67.** $a = 1, b = 2, c = -3$ **69. (a)** $-\frac{3}{5}$; **(b)** $-\frac{1}{3}$
71. (a) $9 + 9i$; **(b)** $3 + 3i$
73. The solutions of $ax^2 + bx + c = 0$ are
$x = \dfrac{-b \pm \sqrt{b^2 - 4ac}}{2a}$. When there is just one solution,
$b^2 - 4ac$ must be 0, so $x = \dfrac{-b \pm 0}{2a} = \dfrac{-b}{2a}$.
75. $a = 8, b = 20, c = -12$
77. $x^4 - 8x^3 + 21x^2 - 2x - 52 = 0$ **79.**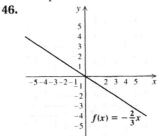

Exercise Set 11.5, pp. 739–741

1. (f)   **3.** (h)   **5.** (g)   **7.** (e)   **9.** $\pm 1, \pm 2$ **11.** $\pm\sqrt{5}, \pm 2$
13. $\pm\dfrac{\sqrt{3}}{2}, \pm 2$ **15.** $8 + 2\sqrt{7}$ **17.** $\pm 2\sqrt{2}, \pm 3$
19. No solution   **21.** $-\frac{1}{2}, \frac{1}{3}$ **23.** $-\frac{4}{5}, 1$ **25.** $-27, 8$
27. 729   **29.** 1   **31.** No solution   **33.** $\frac{12}{5}$ **35.** $\left(\frac{4}{25}, 0\right)$
37. $\left(\dfrac{3}{2} + \dfrac{\sqrt{33}}{2}, 0\right), \left(\dfrac{3}{2} - \dfrac{\sqrt{33}}{2}, 0\right), (4, 0), (-1, 0)$
39. $(-243, 0), (32, 0)$ **41.** No x-intercepts   **43.**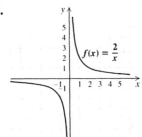
45.

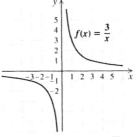

46.

47.

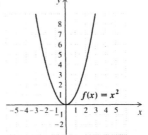

48.

49. Hiker's Mix: 4 lb; Trail Snax: 8 lb   **50.** $a^2 + a$ **51.**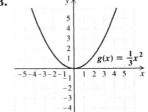
53. $\pm\sqrt{\dfrac{7 \pm \sqrt{29}}{10}}$ **55.** $-2, -1, 5, 6$ **57.** $\frac{100}{99}$
59. $-5, -3, -2, 0, 2, 3, 5$ **61.** $1, 3, -\dfrac{1}{2} + \dfrac{\sqrt{3}}{2}i$,
$-\dfrac{1}{2} - \dfrac{\sqrt{3}}{2}i, -\dfrac{3}{2} + \dfrac{3\sqrt{3}}{2}i, -\dfrac{3}{2} - \dfrac{3\sqrt{3}}{2}i$
63. 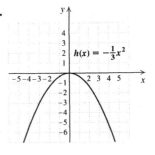   **65.**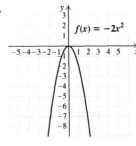

Technology Connection, p. 742

1. The graphs of y_1, y_2, and y_3 open upward. The graphs of y_4, y_5, and y_6 open downward. The graph of y_1 is wider

than the graph of y_2. The graph of y_3 is narrower than the graph of y_2. Similarly, the graph of y_4 is wider than the graph of y_5, and the graph of y_6 is narrower than the graph of y_5.   **2.** If A is positive, the graph opens upward. If A is negative, the graph opens downward. Compared with the graph of $y = x^2$, the graph of $y = Ax^2$ is wider if $|A| < 1$ and narrower if $|A| > 1$.

Technology Connection, p. 744

1. Compared with the graph of $y = ax^2$, the graph of $y = a(x - h)^2$ is shifted left or right. It is shifted left if h is negative and right if h is positive.   **2.** The value of A makes the graph wider or narrower, and makes the graph open downward if A is negative. The value of B shifts the graph left or right.

Technology Connection, p. 745

1. The graph of y_2 looks like the graph of y_1 shifted up 2 units, and the graph of y_3 looks like the graph of y_1 shifted down 4 units.   **2.** Compared with the graph of $y = a(x - h)^2$, the graph of $y = a(x - h)^2 + k$ is shifted up or down. It is shifted down if k is negative and up if k is positive.   **3.** The value of A makes the graph wider or narrower, and makes the graph open downward if A is negative. The value of B shifts the graph left or right. The value of C shifts the graph up or down.

Exercise Set 11.6, pp. 747–749

1. (h)   **3.** (f)   **5.** (b)   **7.** (e)
9.

11.

13.

15.

17.

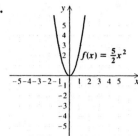

$f(x) = \frac{5}{2}x^2$

19. Vertex: $(-1, 0)$;
axis of symmetry: $x = -1$

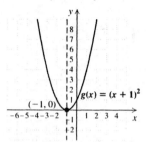

$g(x) = (x + 1)^2$

21. Vertex $(2, 0)$;
axis of symmetry: $x = 2$

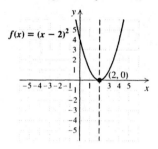

$f(x) = (x - 2)^2$

23. Vertex: $(3, 0)$;
axis of symmetry: $x = 3$

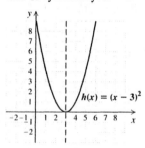

$h(x) = (x - 3)^2$

25. Vertex: $(-1, 0)$;
axis of symmetry: $x = -1$

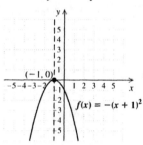

$f(x) = -(x + 1)^2$

27. Vertex: $(2, 0)$;
axis of symmetry: $x = 2$

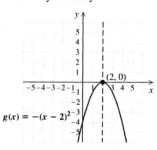

$g(x) = -(x - 2)^2$

29. Vertex: $(-1, 0)$;
axis of symmetry: $x = -1$

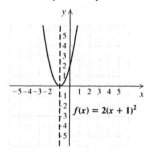

$f(x) = 2(x + 1)^2$

31. Vertex: $(4, 0)$;
axis of symmetry: $x = 4$

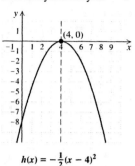

$h(x) = -\frac{1}{2}(x - 4)^2$

33. Vertex: $(1, 0)$;
axis of symmetry: $x = 1$

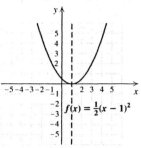

$f(x) = \frac{1}{2}(x - 1)^2$

35. Vertex: $(-5, 0)$;
axis of symmetry: $x = -5$

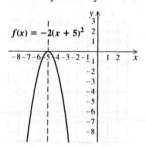

$f(x) = -2(x + 5)^2$

37. Vertex: $\left(\frac{1}{2}, 0\right)$;
axis of symmetry: $x = \frac{1}{2}$

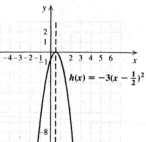

$h(x) = -3(x - \frac{1}{2})^2$

39. Vertex: $(5, 2)$;
axis of symmetry: $x = 5$;
minimum: 2

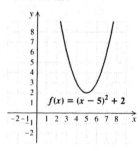

$f(x) = (x - 5)^2 + 2$

41. Vertex: $(-1, -3)$;
axis of symmetry: $x = -1$;
minimum: -3

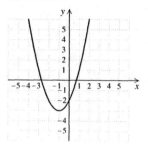

$f(x) = (x + 1)^2 - 3$

43. Vertex: $(-4, 1)$;
axis of symmetry: $x = -4$;
minimum: 1

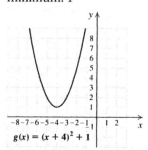

$g(x) = (x + 4)^2 + 1$

45. Vertex: $(1, -3)$;
axis of symmetry: $x = 1$;
maximum: -3

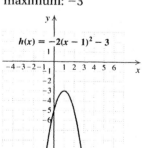

$h(x) = -2(x - 1)^2 - 3$

47. Vertex: $(-4, 1)$; axis of symmetry: $x = -4$; minimum: 1

49. Vertex: $(1, 4)$; axis of symmetry: $x = 1$; maximum: 4

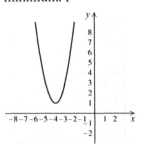

$f(x) = 2(x + 4)^2 + 1$

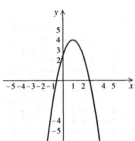

$g(x) = -\frac{3}{2}(x - 1)^2 + 4$

51. Vertex: $(8, 7)$; axis of symmetry: $x = 8$; minimum: 7
53. Vertex: $(-6, 11)$; axis of symmetry: $x = -6$; maximum: 11   **55.** Vertex: $\left(-\frac{1}{4}, -13\right)$; axis of symmetry: $x = -\frac{1}{4}$; minimum: -13
57. Vertex: $(-4.58, 65\pi)$; axis of symmetry: $x = -4.58$; minimum: 65π **59.**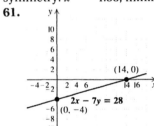

61.
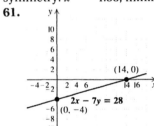

62.

63. $(-5, -1)$ **64.** $(-1, 2)$
65. $x^2 + 5x + \frac{25}{4} = \left(x + \frac{5}{2}\right)^2$
66. $x^2 - 9x + \frac{81}{4} = \left(x - \frac{9}{2}\right)^2$ **67.**
69. $f(x) = \frac{3}{5}(x - 4)^2 + 1$ **71.** $f(x) = \frac{3}{5}(x - 3)^2 - 1$
73. $f(x) = \frac{3}{5}(x + 2)^2 - 5$ **75.** $f(x) = 2(x - 2)^2$
77. $g(x) = -2x^2 + 3$ **79.** $F(x) = 3(x - 5)^2 + 1$
81.
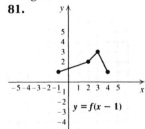
$y = f(x - 1)$

83.
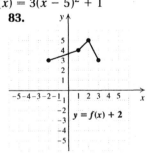
$y = f(x) + 2$

85.
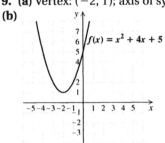
$y = f(x + 3) - 2$

87. 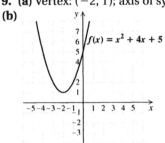   **89.**

Exercise Set 11.7, pp. 754–755

1. 9   **3.** 9   **5.** 3   **7.** $\frac{5}{2}, (-4)$
9. (a) Vertex: $(-2, 1)$; axis of symmetry: $x = -2$;
(b)
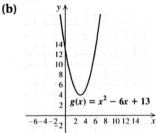
$f(x) = x^2 + 4x + 5$

11. (a) Vertex: $(3, 4)$; axis of symmetry: $x = 3$;
(b)
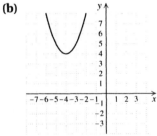
$g(x) = x^2 - 6x + 13$

13. (a) Vertex: $(-4, 4)$; axis of symmetry: $x = -4$;
(b)
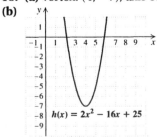
$f(x) = x^2 + 8x + 20$

15. (a) Vertex: $(4, -7)$; axis of symmetry: $x = 4$;
(b)
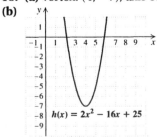
$h(x) = 2x^2 - 16x + 25$

17. (a) Vertex: $(1, 6)$; axis of symmetry: $x = 1$;
(b)

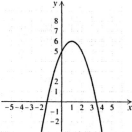

$$f(x) = -x^2 + 2x + 5$$

19. (a) Vertex: $\left(-\frac{3}{2}, -\frac{49}{4}\right)$; axis of symmetry: $x = -\frac{3}{2}$;
(b)

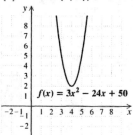

$$g(x) = x^2 + 3x - 10$$

21. (a) Vertex: $(4, 2)$; axis of symmetry: $x = 4$;
(b)

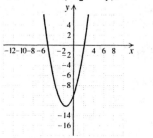

$$f(x) = 3x^2 - 24x + 50$$

23. (a) Vertex: $\left(-\frac{7}{2}, -\frac{49}{4}\right)$; axis of symmetry: $x = -\frac{7}{2}$;
(b)

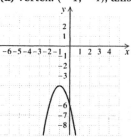

$$h(x) = x^2 + 7x$$

25. (a) Vertex: $(-1, -4)$; axis of symmetry: $x = -1$;
(b)

$$f(x) = -2x^2 - 4x - 6$$

27. (a) Vertex: $(2, -5)$; axis of symmetry: $x = 2$;
(b)

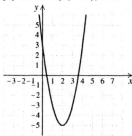

$$g(x) = 2x^2 - 8x + 3$$

29. (a) Vertex: $\left(\frac{5}{6}, \frac{1}{12}\right)$; axis of symmetry: $x = \frac{5}{6}$;
(b)

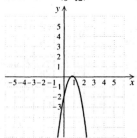

$$f(x) = -3x^2 + 5x - 2$$

31. (a) Vertex: $\left(-4, -\frac{5}{3}\right)$; axis of symmetry: $x = -4$;
(b)

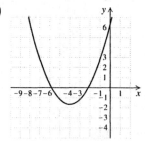

$$h(x) = \frac{1}{2}x^2 + 4x + \frac{19}{3}$$

33. $(3 - \sqrt{6}, 0), (3 + \sqrt{6}, 0)$; $(0, 3)$ **35.** $(-1, 0), (3, 0)$; $(0, 3)$ **37.** $(0, 0), (9, 0)$; $(0, 0)$ **39.** $(2, 0)$; $(0, -4)$ **41.** No x-intercept; $(0, 6)$ **43.** ▨   **45.** $(2, -2)$ **46.** $(7, 1)$ **47.** $(3, 2, 1)$ **48.** $(1, -3, 2)$ **49.** 5   **50.** 4   **51.** ▨   **53.** (a) Minimum: -6.953660714; (b) $(-1.056433682, 0)$, $(2.413576539, 0)$; $(0, -5.89)$ **55.** (a) $-2.4, 3.4$;
(b) $-1.3, 2.3$ **57.** $f(x) = m\left(x - \dfrac{n}{2m}\right)^2 + \dfrac{4mp - n^2}{4m}$
59. $f(x) = \frac{5}{16}x^2 - \frac{15}{8}x - \frac{35}{16}$, or $f(x) = \frac{5}{16}(x - 3)^2 - 5$
61.

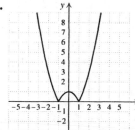

$$f(x) = |x^2 - 1|$$

63.

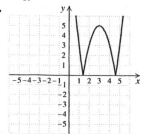

$$f(x) = |2(x - 3)^2 - 5|$$

Technology Connection, p. 760

1. 32.7%

Exercise Set 11.8, pp. 761–766

1. (e)   **3.** (c)   **5.** (d)   **7.** 11 days after the concert was announced; about 62 tickets   **9.** $120/Dobro; 350 Dobros   **11.** 32 in. by 32 in.   **13.** 450 ft^2; 15 ft by 30 ft (The house serves as a 30-ft side.)   **15.** 3.5 in.   **17.** 81; 9 and 9   **19.** -16; 4 and -4 **21.** 25; -5 and -5 **23.** $f(x) = mx + b$ **25.** $f(x) = ax^2 + bx + c, a < 0$ **27.** $f(x) = ax^2 + bx + c, a > 0$ **29.** $f(x) = ax^2 + bx + c, a < 0$ **31.** $f(x) = ax^2 + bx + c, a > 0$ **33.** $f(x) = mx + b$ **35.** $f(x) = 2x^2 + 3x - 1$ **37.** $f(x) = -\frac{1}{4}x^2 + 3x - 5$ **39.** (a) $A(s) = \frac{3}{16}s^2 - \frac{135}{4}s + 1750$; (b) about 531 accidents   **41.** $h(d) = -0.0068d^2 + 0.8571d$ **43.**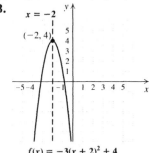

45. $\dfrac{x - 9}{(x + 9)(x + 7)}$ **46.** $\dfrac{(x - 3)(x + 1)}{(x - 7)(x + 3)}$

47. $\dfrac{(t + 2)(t + 8)}{(t - 3)(t + 1)}$ **48.** $\dfrac{2t(t + 2)}{(t - 7)(t - 3)(t + 7)}$

49. $\{x \mid x < 8\}$, or $(-\infty, 8)$ **50.** $\{x \mid x \geq 10\}$, or $[10, \infty)$ **51.** ▨   **53.** 158 ft   **55.** $15   **57.** The radius of the circular portion of the window and the height of the rectangular portion should each be $\dfrac{24}{\pi + 4}$ ft.   **59.** (a) $c(x) = 261.875x^2 - 882.5642857x + 2134.571429$; (b) 55,053 cars

Technology Connection, p. 771

1. $\{x \mid -0.78 \leq x \leq 1.59\}$, or $[-0.78, 1.59]$
2. $\{x \mid x \leq -0.21 \text{ or } x \geq 2.47\}$, or $(-\infty, -0.21] \cup [2.47, \infty)$
3. $\{x \mid x < -1.26 \text{ or } x > 2.33\}$, or $(-\infty, -1.26) \cup (2.33, \infty)$
4. $\{x \mid x > -1.37\}$, or $(-1.37, \infty)$

Exercise Set 11.9, pp. 774–775

1. True   **3.** True   **5.** True   **7.** False
9. $(-4, 3)$, or $\{x \mid -4 < x < 3\}$
11. $(-\infty, -7] \cup [2, \infty)$, or $\{x \mid x \leq -7 \text{ or } x \geq 2\}$
13. $(-\infty, -1) \cup (2, \infty)$, or $\{x \mid x < -1 \text{ or } x > 2\}$ **15.** $\varnothing$
17. $(-2, 6)$, or $\{x \mid -2 < x < 6\}$
19. $(-\infty, -2) \cup (0, 2)$, or $\{x \mid x < -2 \text{ or } 0 < x < 2\}$
21. $[-2, 1] \cup [4, \infty)$, or $\{x \mid -2 \leq x \leq 1 \text{ or } x \geq 4\}$
23. $[-2, 2]$, or $\{x \mid -2 \leq x \leq 2\}$ **25.** $(-1, 2) \cup (3, \infty)$, or $\{x \mid -1 < x < 2 \text{ or } x > 3\}$ **27.** $(-\infty, 0] \cup [2, 5]$, or $\{x \mid x \leq 0 \text{ or } 2 \leq x \leq 5\}$ **29.** $(-\infty, -5)$, or $\{x \mid x < -5\}$
31. $(-\infty, -1] \cup (3, \infty)$, or $\{x \mid x \leq -1 \text{ or } x > 3\}$
33. $(-\infty, -6)$, or $\{x \mid x < -6\}$ **35.** $(-\infty, -1] \cup [2, 5)$, or $\{x \mid x \leq -1 \text{ or } 2 \leq x < 5\}$ **37.** $(-\infty, -3) \cup [0, \infty)$, or $\{x \mid x < -3 \text{ or } x \geq 0\}$ **39.** $(0, \infty)$, or $\{x \mid x > 0\}$
41. $(-\infty, -4) \cup [1, 3)$, or $\{x \mid x < -4 \text{ or } 1 \leq x < 3\}$

43. $\left(-\frac{3}{4}, \frac{5}{2}\right]$, or $\left\{x \mid -\frac{3}{4} < x \leq \frac{5}{2}\right\}$ **45.** $(-\infty, 2) \cup [3, \infty)$, or $\{x \mid x < 2 \text{ or } x \geq 3\}$ **47.** ▨   **49.** $8a^9b^6c^{12}$ **50.** $25a^8b^{14}$ **51.** $\frac{1}{32}$ **52.** $\frac{1}{81}$ **53.** $3a^2 + 6a + 3$ **54.** $5a + 7$ **55.** ▨   **57.** $\left(-1 - \sqrt{6}, -1 + \sqrt{6}\right)$, or $\left\{x \mid -1 - \sqrt{6} < x < -1 + \sqrt{6}\right\}$ **59.** $\{0\}$ **61.** (a) $(10, 200)$, or $\{x \mid 10 < x < 200\}$; (b) $[0, 10) \cup (200, \infty)$, or $\{x \mid 0 \leq x < 10 \text{ or } x > 200\}$ **63.** $\{n \mid n \text{ is an integer } and\ 12 \leq n \leq 25\}$ **65.** $f(x) = 0$ for $x = -2, 1, 3$; $f(x) < 0$ for $(-\infty, -2) \cup (1, 3)$, or $\{x \mid x < -2 \text{ or } 1 < x < 3\}$; $f(x) > 0$ for $(-2, 1) \cup (3, \infty)$, or $\{x \mid -2 < x < 1 \text{ or } x > 3\}$ **67.** $f(x)$ has no zeros; $f(x) < 0$ for $(-\infty, 0)$, or $\{x \mid x < 0\}$; $f(x) > 0$ for $(0, \infty)$, or $\{x \mid x > 0\}$ **69.** $f(x) = 0$ for $x = -1, 0$; $f(x) < 0$ for $(-\infty, -3) \cup (-1, 0)$, or $\{x \mid x < -3 \text{ or } -1 < x < 0\}$; $f(x) > 0$ for $(-3, -1) \cup (0, 2) \cup (2, \infty)$, or $\{x \mid -3 < x < -1 \text{ or } 0 < x < 2 \text{ or } x > 2\}$ **71.** ▨

Review Exercises: Chapter 11, pp. 778–779

1. False   **2.** True   **3.** True   **4.** True   **5.** True   **6.** False   **7.** True   **8.** True   **9.** True   **10.** True   **11.** $\pm\frac{3}{2}$ **12.** $0, -\frac{3}{4}$
13. 3, 9   **14.** $2 \pm 2i$ **15.** 3, 5   **16.** $-\dfrac{9}{2} \pm \dfrac{\sqrt{85}}{2}$
17. $-0.3722813233, 5.3722813233$ **18.** $-\frac{1}{4}, 1$
19. $x^2 - 12x + 36 = (x - 6)^2$
20. $x^2 + \frac{3}{5}x + \frac{9}{100} = \left(x + \frac{3}{10}\right)^2$ **21.** $3 \pm 2\sqrt{2}$
22. 10%   **23.** 6.7 sec   **24.** About 153 mph   **25.** 6 hr
26. Two irrational   **27.** Two imaginary   **28.** $x^2 - 5 = 0$
29. $x^2 + 8x + 16 = 0$ **30.** $(-3, 0), (-2, 0), (2, 0), (3, 0)$
31. $-5, 3$ **32.** $\pm\sqrt{2}, \pm\sqrt{7}$
33.

$x = -2$
$(-2, 4)$

$f(x) = -3(x + 2)^2 + 4$
Maximum: 4

34. (a) Vertex: $(3, 5)$; axis of symmetry: $x = 3$;
(b)

$f(x) = 2x^2 - 12x + 23$

35. $(2, 0), (7, 0); (0, 14)$ **36.** $p = \dfrac{9\pi^2}{N^2}$

37. $T = \dfrac{1 \pm \sqrt{1 + 24A}}{6}$ **38.** Quadratic   **39.** Linear

40. 225 ft^2; 15 ft by 15 ft

41. **(a)** $f(x) = -42x^2 + 167x + 281$;
(b) 277 million books

42. $(-1, 0) \cup (3, \infty)$, or $\{x \mid -1 < x < 0 \; or \; x > 3\}$

43. $(-3, 5]$, or $\{x \mid -3 < x \le 5\}$

44. ▨ The x-coordinate of the maximum or minimum point lies halfway between the x-coordinates of the x-intercepts.

45. ▨ Yes; if the discriminant is a perfect square, then the solutions are rational numbers, p/q and r/s. (Note that if the discriminant is 0, then $p/q = r/s$.) Then the equation can be written in factored form, $(qx - p)(sx - r) = 0$.

46. ▨ Four; let $u = x^2$. Then $au^2 + bu + c = 0$ has at most two solutions, $u = m$ and $u = n$. Now substitute x^2 for u and obtain $x^2 = m$ or $x^2 = n$. These equations yield the solutions $x = \pm\sqrt{m}$ and $x = \pm\sqrt{n}$. When $m \ne n$, the maximum number of solutions, four, occurs.

47. ▨ Completing the square was used to solve quadratic equations and to graph quadratic functions by rewriting the function in the form $f(x) = a(x - h)^2 + k$.

48. $f(x) = \frac{7}{15}x^2 - \frac{14}{15}x - 7$ **49.** $h = 60, k = 60$

50. $18, 324$

Test: Chapter 11, p. 780

1. $[11.1] \pm \dfrac{\sqrt{11}}{2}$ **2.** $[11.2] \; 2, 9$ **3.** $[11.2] \; -1 \pm \sqrt{2}i$

4. $[11.2] \; 1 \pm \sqrt{6}$ **5.** $[11.5] \; -2, \frac{2}{3}$

6. $[11.2] \; -4.192582404, \; 1.192582404$ **7.** $[11.2] \; -\frac{3}{4}, \frac{7}{3}$

8. $[11.1] \; x^2 - 16x + 64 = (x - 8)^2$

9. $[11.1] \; x^2 + \frac{2}{7}x + \frac{1}{49} = \left(x + \frac{1}{7}\right)^2$ **10.** $[11.1] \; -5 \pm \sqrt{10}$

11. $[11.3] \; 16 \text{ km/h}$ **12.** $[11.3] \; 2 \text{ hr}$

13. $[11.4]$ Two imaginary   **14.** $[11.4] \; 3x^2 + 5x - 2 = 0$

15. $[11.5] \; (-4, 0), (4, 0)$

16. $[11.6]$

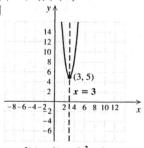

$f(x) = 4(x - 3)^2 + 5$
Minimum: 5

17. $[11.7]$ **(a)** $(-1, -8), x = -1$;
(b)

$f(x) = 2x^2 + 4x - 6$

18. $[11.7] \; (-2, 0), (3, 0); (0, -6)$

19. $[11.3] \; r = \sqrt{\dfrac{3V}{\pi} - R^2}$ **20.** $[11.8]$ Neither

21. $[11.8]$ Minimum: \$129/cap when 325 caps are built

22. $[11.8] \; f(x) = \frac{1}{5}x^2 - \frac{3}{5}x$ **23.** $[11.9] \; (-6, 1)$, or $\{x \mid -6 < x < 1\}$ **24.** $[11.9] \; [-1, 0) \cup [1, \infty)$, or $\{x \mid -1 \le x < 0 \; or \; x \ge 1\}$ **25.** $[11.4] \; \frac{1}{2}$

26. $[11.4] \; x^4 - 14x^3 + 67x^2 - 114x + 26 = 0$; answers may vary

27. $[11.4] \; x^6 - 10x^5 + 20x^4 + 50x^3 - 119x^2 - 60x + 150 = 0$; answers may vary

CHAPTER 12

Technology Connection, p. 784

1. To check $(f \circ g)(x)$, we use a table to show that $y_2 = y_3$.

$y_1 = x - 1; \; y_2 = \sqrt{y_1};$
$y_3 = \sqrt{x - 1}$

X	Y2	Y3
1	0	0
2	1	1
3	1.4142	1.4142
4	1.7321	1.7321
5	2	2
6	2.2361	2.2361
7	2.4495	2.4495
X =		

A similar table shows that for $y_2 = \sqrt{x}$ and $y_4 = y_2(y_1)$, we have $y_3 = y_4$. The check for $(g \circ f)(x)$ is similar. A graph can also be used.

Technology Connection, p. 790

1. Graph each pair of functions in a square window along with the line $y = x$ and determine whether the first two functions are reflections of each other across $y = x$. For further verification, examine a table of values for each pair of functions.   **2.** Yes; most graphing calculators do not require that the inverse relation be a function.

Exercise Set 12.1, pp. 791–793

1. True   **3.** False   **5.** False   **7.** True
9. $(f \circ g)(1) = 2; (g \circ f)(1) = 1;$
$(f \circ g)(x) = 4x^2 - 12x + 10;$
$(g \circ f)(x) = 2x^2 - 1$ **11.** $(f \circ g)(1) = -8; (g \circ f)(1) = 1;$
$(f \circ g)(x) = 2x^2 - 10; (g \circ f)(x) = 2x^2 - 12x + 11$
13. $(f \circ g)(1) = 8; (g \circ f)(1) = \frac{1}{64};$

$(f \circ g)(x) = \dfrac{1}{x^2} + 7; (g \circ f)(x) = \dfrac{1}{(x + 7)^2}$

15. $(f \circ g)(1) = 2; (g \circ f)(1) = 4;$
$(f \circ g)(x) = \sqrt{x + 3}; (g \circ f)(x) = \sqrt{x} + 3$

17. $(f \circ g)(1) = 2; (g \circ f)(1) = \frac{1}{2}; (f \circ g)(x) = \sqrt{\dfrac{4}{x}};$

$(g \circ f)(x) = \dfrac{1}{\sqrt{4x}}$ **19.** $(f \circ g)(1) = 4; (g \circ f)(1) = 2;$

$(f \circ g)(x) = x + 3; (g \circ f)(x) = \sqrt{x^2 + 3}$
21. $f(x) = x^2; g(x) = 7 + 5x$

23. $f(x) = \sqrt{x}; g(x) = 2x + 7$ **25.** $f(x) = \dfrac{2}{x}; g(x) = x - 3$

27. Yes   **29.** No   **31.** Yes   **33.** No   **35.** (a) Yes;

(b) $f^{-1}(x) = x - 4$ **37.** (a) Yes; (b) $f^{-1}(x) = \dfrac{x}{2}$

39. (a) Yes; (b) $g^{-1}(x) = \dfrac{x + 1}{3}$ **41.** (a) Yes;

(b) $f^{-1}(x) = 2x - 2$ **43.** (a) No   **45.** (a) Yes;

(b) $h^{-1}(x) = \dfrac{x - 4}{-2}$ **47.** (a) Yes; (b) $f^{-1}(x) = \dfrac{1}{x}$

49. (a) No   **51.** (a) Yes; (b) $f^{-1}(x) = \dfrac{3x - 1}{2}$ **53.** (a) Yes;

(b) $f^{-1}(x) = \sqrt[3]{x + 5}$ **55.** (a) Yes; (b) $g^{-1}(x) = \sqrt[3]{x} + 2$
57. (a) Yes; (b) $f^{-1}(x) = x^2, x \geq 0$
59.

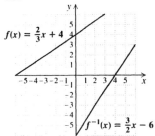
$f(x) = \frac{2}{3}x + 4$
$f^{-1}(x) = \frac{3}{2}x - 6$

61.

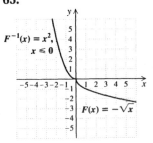
$f(x) = x^3 + 1$
$f^{-1}(x) = \sqrt[3]{x - 1}$

63.

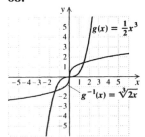
$g(x) = \frac{1}{2}x^3$
$g^{-1}(x) = \sqrt[3]{2x}$

65.

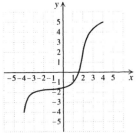
$F^{-1}(x) = x^2,$
$x \leq 0$
$F(x) = -\sqrt{x}$

67.

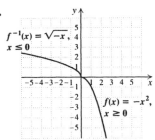
$f^{-1}(x) = \sqrt{-x},$
$x \leq 0$
$f(x) = -x^2,$
$x \geq 0$

69. (1) $(f^{-1} \circ f)(x) = f^{-1}(f(x))$
$= f^{-1}(\sqrt[3]{x - 4}) = (\sqrt[3]{x - 4})^3 + 4$
$= x - 4 + 4 = x;$
(2) $(f \circ f^{-1})(x) = f(f^{-1}(x))$
$= f(x^3 + 4) = \sqrt[3]{x^3 + 4 - 4}$
$= \sqrt[3]{x^3} = x$

71. (1) $(f^{-1} \circ f)(x) = f^{-1}(f(x)) = f^{-1}\left(\dfrac{1 - x}{x}\right)$

$= \dfrac{1}{\left(\dfrac{1 - x}{x}\right) + 1}$

$= \dfrac{1}{\dfrac{1 - x + x}{x}}$

$= x;$

(2) $(f \circ f^{-1})(x) = f(f^{-1}(x)) = f\left(\dfrac{1}{x + 1}\right)$

$= \dfrac{1 - \left(\dfrac{1}{x + 1}\right)}{\left(\dfrac{1}{x + 1}\right)}$

$= \dfrac{\dfrac{x + 1 - 1}{x + 1}}{\dfrac{1}{x + 1}} = x$

73. (a) 40, 44, 52, 60; (b) $f^{-1}(x) = (x - 24)/2;$
(c) 8, 10, 14, 18   **75.** ▨   **77.** $a^{13}b^{13}$ **78.** $x^{10}y^{12}$

79. 81   **80.** 125   **81.** $y = \frac{3}{2}(x + 7)$ **82.** $y = \dfrac{10 - x}{3}$
83. ▨
85.

87. $g(x) = \dfrac{x}{2} + 20$ **89.** ▨

91. Suppose that $h(x) = (f \circ g)(x)$. First, note that for $I(x) = x$, $(f \circ I)(x) = f(I(x)) = f(x)$ for any function f.
(i) $((g^{-1} \circ f^{-1}) \circ h)(x) = ((g^{-1} \circ f^{-1}) \circ (f \circ g))(x)$
$= ((g^{-1} \circ (f^{-1} \circ f)) \circ g)(x)$
$= ((g^{-1} \circ I) \circ g)(x)$
$= (g^{-1} \circ g)(x) = x$
(ii) $(h \circ (g^{-1} \circ f^{-1}))(x) = ((f \circ g) \circ (g^{-1} \circ f^{-1}))(x)$
$= ((f \circ (g \circ g^{-1})) \circ f^{-1})(x)$
$= ((f \circ I) \circ f^{-1})(x)$
$= (f \circ f^{-1})(x) = x.$
Therefore, $(g^{-1} \circ f^{-1})(x) = h^{-1}(x)$.   **93.** Yes   **95.** No
97. **(1)** C; **(2)** A; **(3)** B; **(4)** D   **99.** 📖

Technology Connection, p. 796

1. $y_1 = \left(\frac{5}{2}\right)^x$; $y_2 = \left(\frac{2}{5}\right)^x$

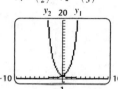

2. $y_1 = 3.2^x$; $y_2 = 3.2^{-x}$

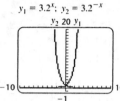

3. $y_1 = \left(\frac{3}{7}\right)^x$; $y_2 = \left(\frac{7}{3}\right)^x$

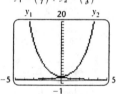

4. $y_1 = 5000(1.08)^x$; $y_2 = 5000(1.08)^{x-3}$

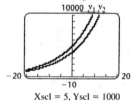
Xscl = 5, Yscl = 1000

Exercise Set 12.2, pp. 800–802

1. True   **3.** True   **5.** False
7.

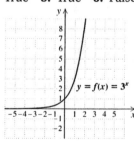
$y = f(x) = 3^x$

9.

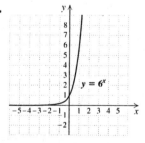
$y = 6^x$

11.

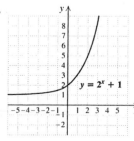
$y = 2^x + 1$

13.

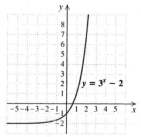
$y = 3^x - 2$

15.

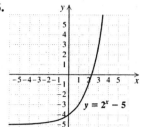
$y = 2^x - 5$

17.

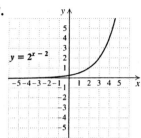
$y = 2^{x-2}$

19.

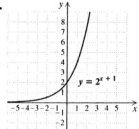
$y = 2^x + 1$

21.

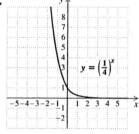
$y = \left(\frac{1}{4}\right)^x$

23.

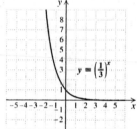
$y = \left(\frac{1}{3}\right)^x$

25.

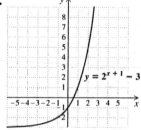
$y = 2^{x+1} - 3$

27.

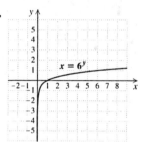
$x = 6^y$

29.

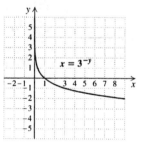
$x = 3^{-y}$

31.

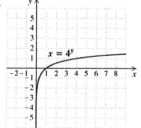
$x = 4^y$

33.

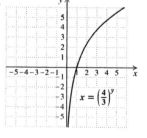
$x = \left(\frac{4}{3}\right)^y$

35.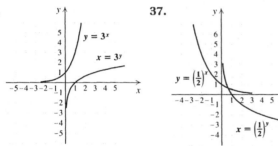

37.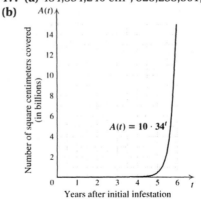

39. (a) About 6.8 billion; about 7.2 billion; about 7.7 billion;

(b)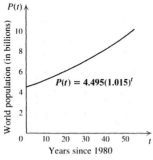

41. (a) 19.6%; 16.3%; 7.3%;

(b)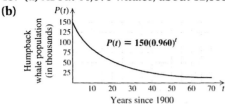

43. (a) About 44,079 whales; about 12,953 whales;

(b)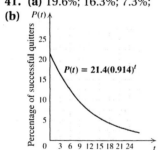

45. (a) About 8706 whales; about 15,107 whales;

(b)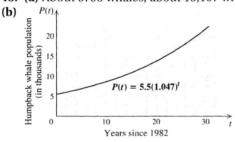

47. (a) 454,354,240 cm²; 525,233,501,400 cm²;

(b)

49.   **51.** $\frac{1}{25}$ **52.** $\frac{1}{32}$ **53.** 100   **54.** $\frac{1}{125}$ **55.** $5a^{6}b^{3}$

56. $6x^{4}y$ **57.**   **59.** $\pi^{2.4}$

61.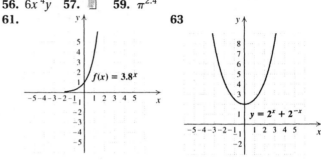

63

65.

67.

69.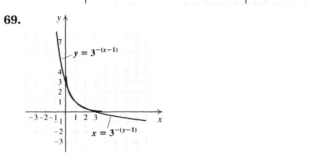

71. $A(t) = 200.7624553(1.992834389)^{t}$, where $A(t)$ is total sales, in millions of dollars, t years after 1997; $395,244,465,700

73. (a)

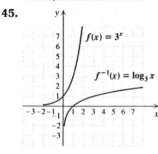

(b) linear; the points appear to lie on a straight line.
75.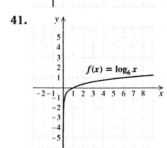

Exercise Set 12.3, pp. 808–809

1. (g)   **3.** (a)   **5.** (b)   **7.** (e)   **9.** 3   **11.** 4   **13.** 4
15. -2 **17.** -1 **19.** 4   **21.** 1   **23.** 0   **25.** 5   **27.** -2
29. $\frac{1}{2}$ **31.** $\frac{3}{2}$ **33.** $\frac{2}{3}$ **35.** 7
37.

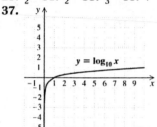

39.

41.

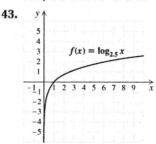

43.

45.

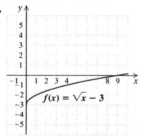

47. $5^t = 9$ **49.** $5^2 = 25$ **51.** $10^{-1} = 0.1$ **53.** $10^{0.845} = 7$
55. $c^8 = m$ **57.** $t^r = Q$ **59.** $e^{-1.3863} = 0.25$
61. $r^{-x} = T$ **63.** $2 = \log_{10} 100$ **65.** $-5 = \log_4 \frac{1}{1024}$
67. $\frac{3}{4} = \log_{16} 8$ **69.** $0.4771 = \log_{10} 3$ **71.** $m = \log_z 6$
73. $m = \log_p V$ **75.** $3 = \log_e 20.0855$
77. $-4 = \log_e 0.0183$ **79.** 9   **81.** 3   **83.** 4   **85.** 7
87. $\frac{1}{9}$ **89.** 4   **91.** 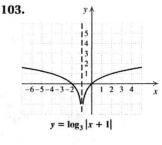   **93.** x^8 **94.** a^{12} **95.** a^7b^8
96. x^5y^{12} **97.** $\dfrac{x(3y-2)}{2y+x}$ **98.** $\dfrac{x+2}{x+1}$ **99.**

101.

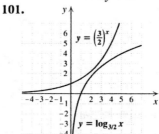

103.

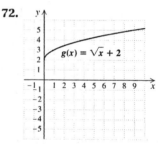

105. 6   **107.** $-25, 4$ **109.** -2 **111.** 0   **113.** Let $b = 0$, and suppose that $x_1 = 1$ and $x_2 = 2$. Then $0^1 = 0^2$, but $1 \neq 2$. Then let $b = 1$, and suppose that $x_1 = 1$ and $x_2 = 2$. Then $1^1 = 1^2$, but $1 \neq 2$.

Exercise Set 12.4, pp. 815–817

1. (e)   **3.** (a)   **5.** (c)   **7.** $\log_3 81 + \log_3 27$
9. $\log_4 64 + \log_4 16$ **11.** $\log_c r + \log_c s + \log_c t$
13. $\log_a (5 \cdot 14)$, or $\log_a 70$ **15.** $\log_c (t \cdot y)$ **17.** $8 \log_a r$
19. $6 \log_c y$ **21.** $-3 \log_b C$ **23.** $\log_2 25 - \log_2 13$
25. $\log_b m - \log_b n$ **27.** $\log_a \frac{17}{6}$ **29.** $\log_b \frac{36}{4}$, or $\log_b 9$
31. $\log_a \frac{7}{18}$ **33.** $\log_a x + \log_a y + \log_a z$
35. $3 \log_a x + 4 \log_a z$ **37.** $2 \log_a x - 2 \log_a y + \log_a z$
39. $4 \log_a x - 3 \log_a y - \log_a z$
41. $\log_b x + 2 \log_b y - \log_b w - 3 \log_b z$
43. $\frac{1}{2}(7 \log_a x - 5 \log_a y - 8 \log_a z)$
45. $\frac{1}{3}(6 \log_a x + 3 \log_a y - 2 - 7 \log_a z)$ **47.** $\log_a (x^8 z^3)$
49. $\log_a x$ **51.** $\log_a \dfrac{y^5}{x^{3/2}}$ **53.** $\log_a (x - 2)$ **55.** 1.953
57. -0.369 **59.** -1.161 **61.** $\frac{3}{2}$ **63.** Cannot be found
65. 7   **67.** m **69.**
71.

72.

73.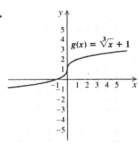

74.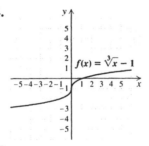

75. $a^{17}b^{17}$ **76.** $x^{11}y^6z^8$ **77.**
79. $\log_a(x^6 - x^4y^2 + x^2y^4 - y^6)$
81. $\frac{1}{2}\log_a(1-s) + \frac{1}{2}\log_a(1+s)$ **83.** $\frac{10}{3}$ **85.** -2
87. True

Technology Connection, p. 818

1.

Technology Connection, p. 819

1. As x gets larger, the value of y_1 approaches 2.7182818284.... **2.** For large values of x, the graphs of y_1 and y_2 will be very close or appear to be the same line, depending on the window chosen. **3.** Using TRACE, no y-value is given for $x = 0$. Using a table, an error message appears for y_1 when $x = 0$. The domain does not include 0 because division by 0 is undefined.

Technology Connection, p. 822

1. $y = \log x / \log 7$
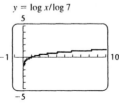

2. $y = \log(x+2)/\log 5$
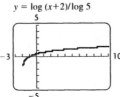

3. $y = \log x / \log 7 + 2$
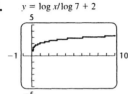

Exercise Set 12.5, pp. 822–824

1. True **3.** True **5.** True **7.** True **9.** 0.7782
11. 1.8621 **13.** 3 **15.** -0.2782 **17.** 1.7986
19. 199.5262 **21.** 1.4894 **23.** 0.0011 **25.** 1.6094
27. 4.0431 **29.** -5.0832 **31.** 96.7583 **33.** 15.0293

35. 0.0305 **37.** 109.9472 **39.** 2.5237 **41.** 6.6439
43. 2.1452 **45.** -2.3219 **47.** -2.3219 **49.** 3.5471
51. 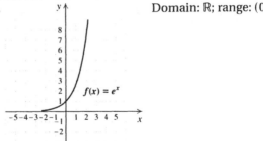 Domain: $\mathbb{R}$; range: $(0, \infty)$

53. 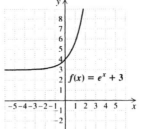 Domain: $\mathbb{R}$; range: $(3, \infty)$

55. 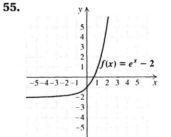 Domain: $\mathbb{R}$; range: $(-2, \infty)$

57. 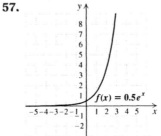 Domain: $\mathbb{R}$; range: $(0, \infty)$

59. 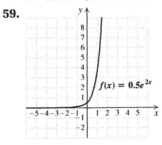 Domain: $\mathbb{R}$; range: $(0, \infty)$

61.

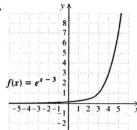

Domain: $\mathbb{R}$; range: $(0, \infty)$

63.

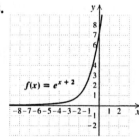

Domain: $\mathbb{R}$; range: $(0, \infty)$

65.

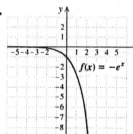

Domain: $\mathbb{R}$; range: $(-\infty, 0)$

67.

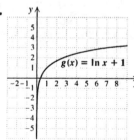

Domain: $(0, \infty)$; range: $\mathbb{R}$

69.

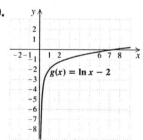

Domain: $(0, \infty)$; range: $\mathbb{R}$

71.

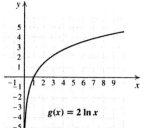

Domain: $(0, \infty)$; range: $\mathbb{R}$

73.

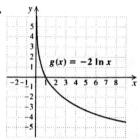

Domain: $(0, \infty)$; range: $\mathbb{R}$

75.

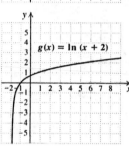

Domain: $(-2, \infty)$; range: $\mathbb{R}$

77.

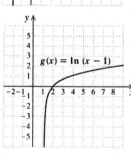

Domain: $(1, \infty)$; range: $\mathbb{R}$

79.   **81.** $-\frac{5}{2}, \frac{5}{2}$ **82.** $0, \frac{7}{5}$ **83.** $\frac{15}{17}$ **84.** $\frac{9}{13}$ **85.** $16, 256$
86. $\frac{1}{4}, 9$ **87.**   **89.** 2.452 **91.** 1.442

93. $\log M = \dfrac{\ln M}{\ln 10}$ **95.** 1086.5129 **97.** 4.9855

99. (a) Domain: $\{x \mid x > 0\}$, or $(0, \infty)$;
range: $\{y \mid y < 0.5135\}$, or $(-\infty, 0.5135)$; **(b)** $[-1, 5, -10, 5]$;
(c) $y = 3.4 \ln x - 0.25 e^x$

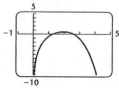

101. (a) Domain: $\{x \mid x > 0\}$, or $(0, \infty)$;
range: $\{y \mid y > -0.2453\}$, or $(-0.2453, \infty)$;
(b) $[-1, 5, -1, 10]$;
(c) $y = 2x^3 \ln x$

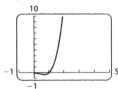

103.

Technology Connection, p. 829

1. 0.38 **2.** -1.96 **3.** 0.90 **4.** -1.53 **5.** 0.13, 8.47
6. $-0.75, 0.75$

Exercise Set 12.6, pp. 830–831

1. (e) **3.** (f) **5.** (b) **7.** (g) **9.** $\dfrac{\log 19}{\log 2} \approx 4.248$

11. $\dfrac{\log 17}{\log 8} + 1 \approx 2.362$ **13.** $\ln 1000 \approx 6.908$

15. $\dfrac{\ln 5}{0.03} \approx 53.648$ **17.** $\dfrac{\log 5}{\log 3} - 1 \approx 0.465$ **19.** 1

21. $\dfrac{\log 87}{\log 4.9} \approx 2.810$ **23.** $\dfrac{\ln\left(\frac{19}{2}\right)}{4} \approx 0.563$ **25.** $\dfrac{\ln 2}{5} \approx 0.139$

27. 81 **29.** $\frac{1}{8}$ **31.** $e^5 \approx 148.413$ **33.** 2 **35.** $\dfrac{e^3}{4} \approx 5.021$

37. $10^{2.5} \approx 316.228$ **39.** $\dfrac{e^4 - 1}{2} \approx 26.799$ **41.** $e \approx 2.718$

43. $e^{-3} \approx 0.050$ **45.** -4 **47.** 10 **49.** No solution
51. $\frac{83}{15}$ **53.** 1 **55.** 6 **57.** 1 **59.** 5 **61.** $\frac{17}{2}$ **63.** 4

65.   **67.** $y = 9x$ **68.** $y = \dfrac{21.35}{x}$ **69.** $L = \dfrac{8T^2}{\pi^2}$

70. $c = \sqrt{\dfrac{E}{m}}$ **71.** $1\frac{1}{5}$ hr **72.** $9\frac{3}{8}$ min **73.**   **75.** $\frac{12}{5}$

77. $\sqrt[3]{3}$ **79.** -1 **81.** $-3, -1$ **83.** $-625, 625$
85. $\frac{1}{2}, 5000$ **87.** $-3, -1$ **89.** $\frac{1}{100,000}, 100,000$ **91.** $-\frac{1}{3}$
93. 38 **95.** 1

Exercise Set 12.7, pp. 839–844

1. (a) About 2001; **(b)** 1 yr **3. (a)** 146,293; **(b)** 51
5. (a) 6.4 yr; **(b)** 23.4 yr **7. (a)** 2005; **(b)** 2018
9. (a) 2019; **(b)** 15.1 yr **11.** 4.9 **13.** 10^{-7} moles per liter
15. 65 dB **17.** $10^{-1.5}$ W/m^2 **19. (a)** $P(t) = P_0 e^{0.025t}$;
(b) \$5126.58; \$5256.36; **(c)** 27.7 yr
21. (a) $P(t) = 292.80 e^{0.009t}$, where t is the number of years
after 2004 and $P(t)$ is in millions; **(b)** 295.45 million;
(c) 2016 **23.** 6.7 months
25. (a) About 2010; **(b)** about 2019;

(c)

Y(x)
Years since 1980
$Y(x) = 67.17 \ln \dfrac{x}{4.5}$
World population (in billions)

27. (a) 68%; **(b)** 54%, 40%
(c) **(d)** 6.9 months

S(t)
Score (in percents)
$S(t) = 68 - 20 \log (t + 1), t \geq 0$
Months

29. (a) $N(t) = 17e^{0.534t}$, where t is the number of years
since 2000; **(b)** about 419
31. (a) $k \approx 0.004$; $P(t) = 987 e^{-0.004t}$, where t is the
number of years after 1990 and $P(t)$ is in millions;
(b) 918 million acres; **(c)** about 2043 **33.** About 2103 yr
35. About 7.2 days **37.** 69.3% per year
39. (a) $k \approx 0.099$; $V(t) = 451,000 e^{0.099t}$, where t is the
number of years after 1991; **(b)** about \$1.99 million;
(c) 7.0 yr; **(d)** 2010 **41.**
43.

$y = x^2 - 8x$

44.

$y = x^2 - 5x - 6$

45.

$f(x) = 3x^2 - 5x - 1$

46.

$g(x) = 2x^2 - 6x + 3$

47. $4 \pm \sqrt{23}$ **48.** $-5 \pm \sqrt{31}$ **49.** 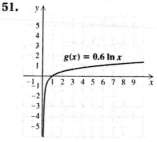 **51.** $18.9 million
53. $P(t) = 100 - 63.03(0.95)^t$ **55.** About 80,922 yr, or
with rounding of k, about 80,792 yr **57.** Consider an
exponential growth function $P(t) = P_0 e^{kt}$. At time T,
$P(T) = 2P_0$.
Solve for T:
$$2P_0 = P_0 e^{kT}$$
$$2 = e^{kT}$$
$$\ln 2 = kT$$
$$\frac{\ln 2}{k} = T.$$

59. (a)

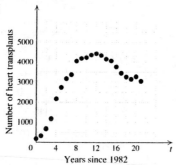

(b) 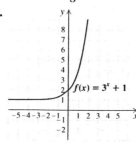; **(c)**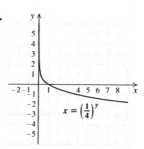

Review Exercises: Chapter 12, pp. 849–850

1. True **2.** True **3.** True **4.** False **5.** False **6.** True
7. False **8.** False **9.** True **10.** False
11. $(f \circ g)(x) = 4x^2 - 12x + 10$; $(g \circ f)(x) = 2x^2 - 1$
12. $f(x) = \sqrt{x}$; $g(x) = 3 - x$ **13.** No
14. $f^{-1}(x) = x + 8$ **15.** $g^{-1}(x) = \dfrac{2x - 1}{3}$
16. $f^{-1}(x) = \dfrac{\sqrt[3]{x}}{3}$

17.

$f(x) = 3^x + 1$

18.

$x = \left(\frac{1}{4}\right)^y$

19.

$y = \log_5 x$

20. 2 **21.** -2 **22.** 7 **23.** $\frac{1}{2}$ **24.** $\log_{10} \frac{1}{100} = -2$
25. $\log_{25} 5 = \frac{1}{2}$ **26.** $16 = 4^x$ **27.** $1 = 8^0$
28. $4 \log_a x + 2 \log_a y + 3 \log_a z$
29. $5 \log_a x - (\log_a y + 2 \log_a z)$, or
$5 \log_a x - \log_a y - 2 \log_a z$ **30.** $\frac{1}{4}(2 \log z - 3 \log x - \log y)$
31. $\log_a (7 \cdot 8)$, or $\log_a 56$ **32.** $\log_a \frac{72}{12}$, or $\log_a 6$
33. $\log \dfrac{a^{1/2}}{bc^2}$ **34.** $\log_a \sqrt[3]{\dfrac{x}{y^2}}$ **35.** 1 **36.** 0
37. 17 **38.** 6.93 **39.** -3.2698 **40.** 8.7601 **41.** 3.2698
42. 2.54995 **43.** -3.6602 **44.** 1.8751 **45.** 61.5177
46. -2.9957 **47.** 0.3753 **48.** 0.4307 **49.** 1.7097
50.   Domain: $\mathbb{R}$; range: $(-1, \infty)$

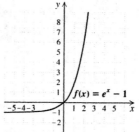

$f(x) = e^x - 1$

51.   Domain: $(0, \infty)$; range: $\mathbb{R}$

$g(x) = 0.6 \ln x$

52. 5 **53.** -2 **54.** $\frac{1}{81}$ **55.** 2 **56.** $\frac{1}{1000}$
57. $e^{-2} \approx 0.1353$ **58.** $\dfrac{1}{2}\left(\dfrac{\log 19}{\log 4} + 5\right) \approx 3.5620$
59. $-5, 1$ **60.** $\dfrac{\log 8.3}{\log 4} \approx 1.5266$ **61.** $\dfrac{\ln 0.03}{-0.1} \approx 35.0656$
62. $e^{-3} \approx 0.0498$ **63.** 4 **64.** 8 **65.** 20 **66.** $\sqrt{43}$
67. (a) 82; **(b)** 66.8; **(c)** 35 months **68. (a)** 6.6 yr; **(b)** 3.1 yr
69. (a) $k \approx 0.128$; $C(t) = 10e^{0.128t}$, where t is the number
of years after 1999 and $C(t)$ is in thousands; **(b)** $35,966;
(c) 2009 **70.** 23.105% per year **71.** 16.5 yr **72.** 3463 yr
73. 6.6 **74.** 90 dB
75. 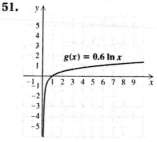 Negative numbers do not have logarithms because
logarithm bases are positive, and there is no exponent to
which a positive number can be raised to yield a negative
number. **76.** 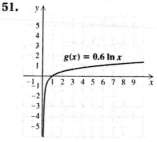 Taking the logarithm on each side of an
equation produces an equivalent equation because the
logarithm function is one-to-one. If two quantities are
equal, their logarithms must be equal, and if the
logarithms of two quantities are equal, the quantities must
be the same. **77.** e^{e^3} **78.** $-3, -1$ **79.** $\left(\frac{8}{3}, -\frac{2}{3}\right)$

Test: Chapter 12, pp. 851–852

1. [12.1] $(f \circ g)(x) = 2 + 6x + 4x^2$;

$(g \circ f)(x) = 2x^2 + 2x + 1$ **2.** [12.1] $f(x) = \dfrac{1}{x}$;

$g(x) = 2x^2 + 1$ **3.** [12.1] No   **4.** [12.1] $f^{-1}(x) = \dfrac{x - 4}{3}$

5. [12.1] $g^{-1}(x) = \sqrt[3]{x} - 1$

6. [12.2]   **7.** [12.3]

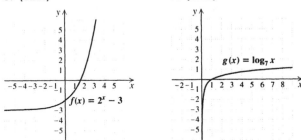

$f(x) = 2^x - 3$ $g(x) = \log_7 x$

8. [12.3] 3   **9.** [12.3] $\frac{1}{2}$ **10.** [12.3] 18
11. [12.3] $\log_4 \frac{1}{64} = -3$ **12.** [12.3] $\log_{256} 16 = \frac{1}{2}$
13. [12.3] $49 = 7^m$ **14.** [12.3] $81 = 3^4$
15. [12.4] $3 \log a + \frac{1}{2} \log b - 2 \log c$
16. [12.4] $\log_a (z^2 \sqrt[3]{x})$ **17.** [12.4] 1   **18.** [12.4] 23
19. [12.4] 0   **20.** [12.4] 1.146   **21.** [12.4] 0.477
22. [12.4] 1.204   **23.** [12.5] 1.0899   **24.** [12.5] 0.1585
25. [12.5] -3.3524 **26.** [12.5] 121.5104   **27.** [12.5] 2.4022
28. [12.5]

$f(x) = e^x + 3$

Domain: $\mathbb{R}$;
range: $(3, \infty)$

29. [12.5]

$g(x) = \ln (x - 4)$

Domain: $(4, \infty)$;
range: $\mathbb{R}$

30. [12.6] -5 **31.** [12.6] 5   **32.** [12.6] 2

33. [12.6] 10,000   **34.** [12.6] $-\dfrac{1}{3} \left(\dfrac{\log 87}{\log 5} - 4 \right) \approx 0.4084$

35. [12.6] $\dfrac{\log 1.2}{\log 7} \approx 0.0937$ **36.** [12.6] $e^{1/4} \approx 1.2840$

37. [12.6] 4   **38.** [12.7] **(a)** 2.56 ft/sec; **(b)** 711,637
39. [12.7] **(a)** $P(t) = 130.5e^{0.024t}$, where t is the number of
years after 2002 and $P(t)$ is in millions; **(b)** 147.1 million;
165.9 million; **(c)** 2014; **(d)** 28.9 yr
40. [12.7] **(a)** $k \approx 0.031$; $C(t) = 19,070e^{0.031t}$, where t is the
number of years after 1997; **(b)** \$28,535; **(c)** 2028
41. [12.7] 4.6%   **42.** [12.7] 4684 yr
43. [12.7] $10^{-4.5} \, \text{W/m}^2$ **44.** [12.7] 7.0
45. [12.6] $-309, 316$ **46.** [12.4] 2

Cumulative Review: Chapters 1–12, pp. 852–854

1. 2   **2.** 6   **3.** $\dfrac{y^{12}}{16x^8}$ **4.** $\dfrac{20x^6z^2}{y}$ **5.** $\dfrac{-y^4}{3z^5}$ **6.** $-2x - 1$

7. 25   **8.** $\frac{14}{5}$ **9.** $(3, -1)$ **10.** $(1, -2, 0)$ **11.** $-2, 5$
12. $\frac{9}{2}$ **13.** $\frac{5}{8}$ **14.** $\frac{3}{4}$ **15.** $\frac{1}{2}$ **16.** $\pm 5i$ **17.** 9, 25
18. $\pm 2, \pm 3$ **19.** 7   **20.** 6   **21.** $\frac{3}{2}$ **22.** $\dfrac{\log 7}{5 \log 3} \approx 0.3542$

23. $\dfrac{8e}{e - 1} \approx 12.6558$ **24.** $(-\infty, -5) \cup (1, \infty)$, or
$\{x \mid x < -5 \text{ or } x > 1\}$ **25.** $-3 \pm 2\sqrt{5}$
26. $\{x \mid x \le -2 \text{ or } x \ge 5\}$, or $(-\infty, -2] \cup [5, \infty)$
27. $a = \dfrac{Db}{b - D}$ **28.** $q = \dfrac{pf}{p - f}$ **29.** $B = \dfrac{3M - 2A}{2}$, or
$B = \frac{3}{2}M - A$ **30.** 2   **31.** 3
32. $\{x \mid x$ is a real number $and\ x \ne -\frac{1}{3} \ and\ x \ne 2\}$
33. **(a)** $\dfrac{1.7 \text{ million barrels}}{13 \text{ yr}}$, or approximately

130,769 barrels/yr; **(b)** $g(t) = \dfrac{1.7}{13}t + 7.2$, where $g(t)$ is in
millions of barrels; **(c)** $G(t) = 7.2e^{0.016t}$, where t is the
number of years after 1990 and $G(t)$ is in millions of barrels
34. Length: 36 m; width: 20 m   **35.** A: 15°; B: 45°; C: 120°
36. $5\frac{5}{11}$ min   **37.** Thick and Tasty: 6 oz;
Light and Lean: 9 oz   **38.** $2\frac{7}{9}$ km/h   **39.** -49; -7 and 7
40. 78   **41.** 67.5   **42.** $P(t) = 33.7e^{0.01t}$
43. 35.8 million; 38.0 million   **44.** 69.3 yr   **45.** 18
46. $7p^2q^3 + pq + p - 9$ **47.** $8x^2 - 11x - 1$
48. $9x^4 - 12x^2y + 4y^2$ **49.** $10a^2 - 9ab - 9b^2$
50. $\dfrac{(x + 4)(x - 3)}{2(x - 1)}$ **51.** $\dfrac{1}{x - 4}$ **52.** $\dfrac{a + 2}{6}$
53. $\dfrac{7x + 4}{(x + 6)(x - 6)}$ **54.** $x(y + 2z - w)$
55. $(2 - 5x)(4 + 10x + 25x^2)$ **56.** $2(3x - 2y)(x + 2y)$
57. $(x^3 + 7)(x - 4)$ **58.** $2(m + 3n)^2$
59. $(x - 2y)(x + 2y)(x^2 + 4y^2)$ **60.** -12
61. $x^3 - 2x^2 - 4x - 12 + \dfrac{-42}{x - 3}$ **62.** 1.8×10^{-1}
63. $2y^2\sqrt[3]{y}$ **64.** $14xy^2\sqrt{x}$ **65.** $81a^8b\sqrt[3]{b}$
66. $\dfrac{6 + \sqrt{y} - y}{4 - y}$ **67.** $\sqrt[10]{(x + 5)^3}$ **68.** $18 - 2\sqrt{3}i$

69. $13 - i$ **70.** $f^{-1}(x) = \dfrac{x-9}{-2}$, or $f^{-1}(x) = \dfrac{9-x}{2}$

71. $y = -10x - 8$ **72.** $y = \frac{1}{2}x + 7$

73.
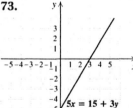

74.
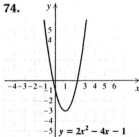

75.
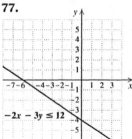

76.
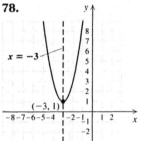

77.
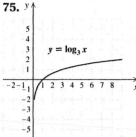

78.
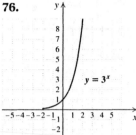

$f(x) = 2(x+3)^2 + 1$
Minimum: 1

79.
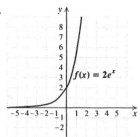

Domain: ℝ; range: $(0, \infty)$

80. $2\log a + 3\log c - \log b$ **81.** $\log\left(\dfrac{x^3}{y^{1/2}z^2}\right)$

82. $a^x = 5$ **83.** $\log_x t = 3$ **84.** -1.2545 **85.** 776.2471
86. 2.5479   **87.** 0.2466   **88.** All real numbers except
1 and -2 **89.** $\frac{1}{3}, \frac{10,000}{3}$ **90.** 35 mph

CHAPTER 13

Technology Connection, p. 863

1. $x^2 + y^2 - 16 = 0$
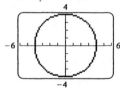

2. $(x-1)^2 + (y-2)^2 = 25$
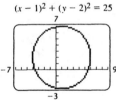

3. $(x+3)^2 + (y-5)^2 = 16$
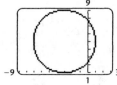

4. $(x-5)^2 + (y+6)^2 = 49$
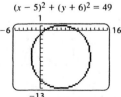

Exercise Set 13.1, pp. 864–868

1. (f)   **3.** (g)   **5.** (c)   **7.** (d)

9.
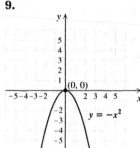

11.
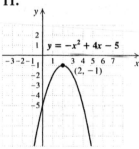

$y = -x^2 + 4x - 5$

13.
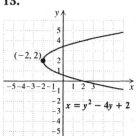

$x = y^2 - 4y + 2$

15.
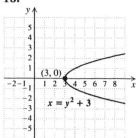

$x = y^2 + 3$

17.
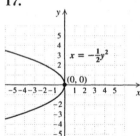

$x = -\frac{1}{2}y^2$

19.
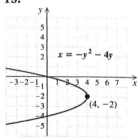

$x = -y^2 - 4y$

21.

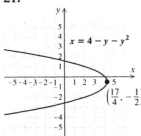

$x = 4 - y - y^2$

$\left(\frac{17}{4}, -\frac{1}{2}\right)$

23.

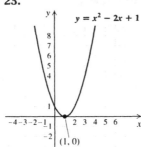

$y = x^2 - 2x + 1$

$(1, 0)$

25.

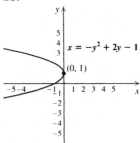

$x = -y^2 + 2y - 1$

$(0, 1)$

27.

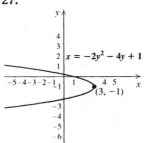

$x = -2y^2 - 4y + 1$

$(3, -1)$

29. 5 **31.** $\sqrt{18} \approx 4.243$ **33.** $\sqrt{200} \approx 14.142$ **35.** 17.8

37. $\dfrac{\sqrt{41}}{7} \approx 0.915$ **39.** $\sqrt{8} \approx 2.828$ **41.** $\sqrt{90} \approx 9.487$

43. $(1, 4)$ **45.** $\left(\frac{7}{2}, \frac{7}{2}\right)$ **47.** $(-1, -3)$

49. $(-0.25, -0.3)$ **51.** $\left(-\frac{1}{12}, \frac{1}{24}\right)$ **53.** $\left(\dfrac{\sqrt{2} + \sqrt{3}}{2}, \dfrac{3}{2}\right)$

55. $x^2 + y^2 = 36$ **57.** $(x - 7)^2 + (y - 3)^2 = 5$

59. $(x + 4)^2 + (y - 3)^2 = 48$

61. $(x + 7)^2 + (y + 2)^2 = 50$ **63.** $x^2 + y^2 = 25$

65. $(x + 4)^2 + (y - 1)^2 = 20$

67. $(0, 0);\ 8$

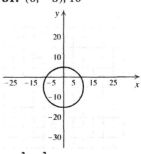

$x^2 + y^2 = 64$

69. $(-1, -3);\ 6$

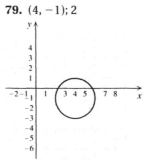

$(x + 1)^2 + (y + 3)^2 = 36$

71. $(4, -3);\ \sqrt{10}$

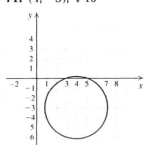

$(x - 4)^2 + (y + 3)^2 = 10$

73. $(0, 0);\ \sqrt{10}$

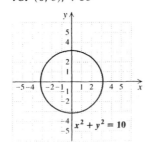

$x^2 + y^2 = 10$

75. $(5, 0);\ \frac{1}{2}$

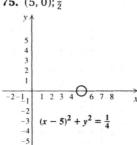

$(x - 5)^2 + y^2 = \frac{1}{4}$

77. $(-4, 3);\ \sqrt{40},$ or $2\sqrt{10}$

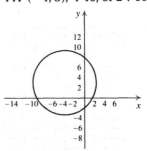

$x^2 + y^2 + 8x - 6y - 15 = 0$

79. $(4, -1);\ 2$

$x^2 + y^2 - 8x + 2y + 13 = 0$

81. $(0, -5);\ 10$

$x^2 + y^2 + 10y - 75 = 0$

83. $\left(-\dfrac{7}{2}, \dfrac{3}{2}\right);\ \sqrt{\dfrac{98}{4}},$ or $\dfrac{7\sqrt{2}}{2}$ **85.** $(0, 0);\ \frac{1}{6}$

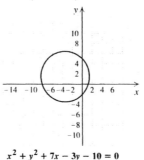

$x^2 + y^2 + 7x - 3y - 10 = 0$

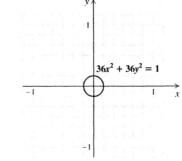

$36x^2 + 36y^2 = 1$

87. ▢ **89.** $-\frac{2}{3}$ **90.** $\frac{25}{6}$ **91.** 4 in. **92.** 2640 mi

93. $\left(\frac{35}{17}, \frac{5}{34}\right)$ **94.** $\left(0, -\frac{9}{5}\right)$ **95.** ▢

97. $(x - 3)^2 + (y + 5)^2 = 9$ **99.** $(x - 3)^2 + y^2 = 25$

101. $(0, 4)$ **103.** $\frac{17}{4}\pi\ \text{m}^2,$ or approximately $13.4\ \text{m}^2$

105. 7451.2 mm **107. (a)** $(0, -3);$ **(b)** 5 ft

109. $x^2 + (y - 30.6)^2 = 590.49$

111.

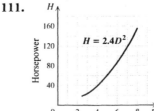

$H = 2.4D^2$

Horsepower

Diameter of piston (in inches)

113. (a) $y = -1 \pm \sqrt{-x^2 + 6x + 7}$; (b) 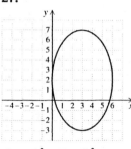 115. ▯

Exercise Set 13.2, pp. 872–874

1. True   3. True   5. False   7. True

9.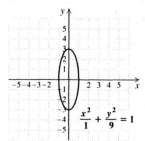
$$\frac{x^2}{1} + \frac{y^2}{9} = 1$$

11.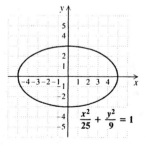
$$\frac{x^2}{25} + \frac{y^2}{9} = 1$$

13.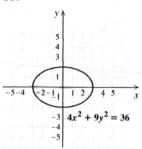
$4x^2 + 9y^2 = 36$

15.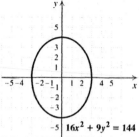
$16x^2 + 9y^2 = 144$

17.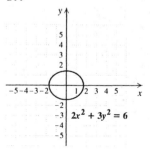
$2x^2 + 3y^2 = 6$

19.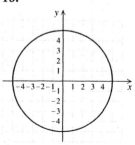
$5x^2 + 5y^2 = 125$

21.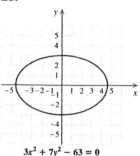
$3x^2 + 7y^2 - 63 = 0$

23.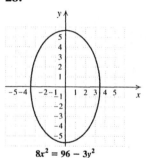
$8x^2 = 96 - 3y^2$

25.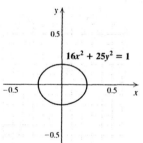
$16x^2 + 25y^2 = 1$

27.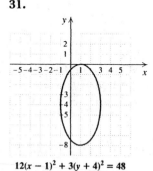
$$\frac{(x-3)^2}{9} + \frac{(y-2)^2}{25} = 1$$

29.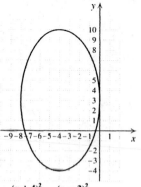
$$\frac{(x+4)^2}{16} + \frac{(y-3)^2}{49} = 1$$

31.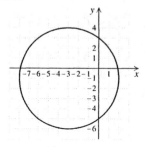
$12(x-1)^2 + 3(y+4)^2 = 48$

33.

$4(x+3)^2 + 4(y+1)^2 - 10 = 90$

35. ▯   37. $\frac{16}{9}$ 38. $-\frac{19}{8}$ 39. $5 \pm \sqrt{3}$ 40. $3 \pm \sqrt{7}$

41. $\frac{3}{2}$ 42. No solution   43. ▯   45. $\frac{x^2}{81} + \frac{y^2}{121} = 1$

47. $\frac{(x-2)^2}{16} + \frac{(y+1)^2}{9} = 1$ 49. $\frac{x^2}{9} + \frac{y^2}{25} = 1$

51. (a) Let $F_1 = (-c, 0)$ and $F_2 = (c, 0)$. Then the sum of the distances from the foci to P is $2a$. By the distance formula,

$$\sqrt{(x+c)^2 + y^2} + \sqrt{(x-c)^2 + y^2} = 2a, \text{ or}$$
$$\sqrt{(x+c)^2 + y^2} = 2a - \sqrt{(x-c)^2 + y^2}.$$

Squaring, we get

$$(x+c)^2 + y^2 = 4a^2 - 4a\sqrt{(x-c)^2 + y^2} + (x-c)^2 + y^2,$$

or

$$x^2 + 2cx + c^2 + y^2 = 4a^2 - 4a\sqrt{(x-c)^2 + y^2}$$
$$+ x^2 - 2cx + c^2 + y^2.$$

Thus

$$-4a^2 + 4cx = -4a\sqrt{(x-c)^2 + y^2}$$
$$a^2 - cx = a\sqrt{(x-c)^2 + y^2}.$$

Squaring again, we get

$$a^4 - 2a^2cx + c^2x^2 = a^2(x^2 - 2cx + c^2 + y^2)$$
$$a^4 - 2a^2cx + c^2x^2 = a^2x^2 - 2a^2cx + a^2c^2 + a^2y^2,$$

or

$$x^2(a^2 - c^2) + a^2y^2 = a^2(a^2 - c^2)$$
$$\frac{x^2}{a^2} + \frac{y^2}{a^2 - c^2} = 1.$$

(b) When P is at $(0, b)$, it follows that $b^2 = a^2 - c^2$.
Substituting, we have

$$\frac{x^2}{a^2} + \frac{y^2}{b^2} = 1.$$

53. 5.66 ft
55.

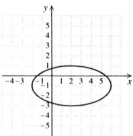

$$\frac{(x-2)^2}{16} + \frac{(y+1)^2}{4} = 1$$

57.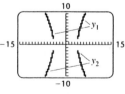

Technology Connection, p. 880

1. $y_1 = \dfrac{\sqrt{15x^2 - 240}}{2};$
$y_2 = -\dfrac{\sqrt{15x^2 - 240}}{2}$

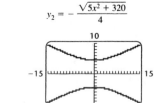

2. $y_1 = \sqrt{\dfrac{16x^2 - 64}{3}};$
$y_2 = -\sqrt{\dfrac{16x^2 - 64}{3}}$

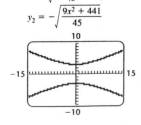

3. $y_1 = \dfrac{\sqrt{5x^2 + 320}}{4};$
$y_2 = -\dfrac{\sqrt{5x^2 + 320}}{4}$

4. $y_1 = \sqrt{\dfrac{9x^2 + 441}{45}};$
$y_2 = -\sqrt{\dfrac{9x^2 + 441}{45}}$

Exercise Set 13.3, pp. 885–886

1. (d)   **3.** (h)   **5.** (g)   **7.** (c)
9.

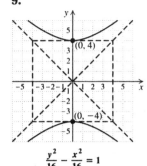

$$\frac{y^2}{16} - \frac{x^2}{16} = 1$$

11.

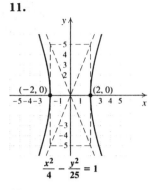

$$\frac{x^2}{4} - \frac{y^2}{25} = 1$$

13.

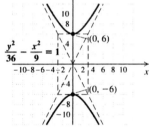

$$\frac{y^2}{36} - \frac{x^2}{9} = 1$$

15.

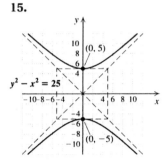

$$y^2 - x^2 = 25$$

17.

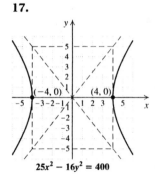

$$25x^2 - 16y^2 = 400$$

19.

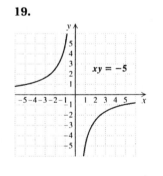

$$xy = -5$$

21.

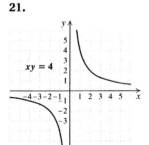

$$xy = 4$$

23.

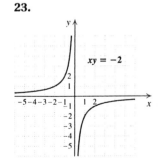

$$xy = -2$$

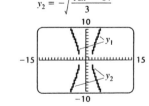

25.

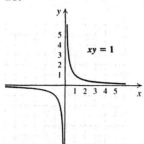

27. Circle **29.** Ellipse **31.** Hyperbola **33.** Circle
35. Ellipse **37.** Hyperbola **39.** Parabola
41. Hyperbola **43.** Circle **45.** Ellipse **47.** ▨
49. $\left(-\frac{22}{3}, \frac{37}{9}\right)$ **50.** $(9, -4)$ **51.** $-3, 3$ **52.** $-1, 1$
53. $35 **54.** 69 **55.** ▨ **57.** $\dfrac{y^2}{36} - \dfrac{x^2}{4} = 1$
59. C: $(5, 2)$; V: $(-1, 2), (11, 2)$;
asymptotes: $y - 2 = \frac{5}{6}(x - 5), y - 2 = -\frac{5}{6}(x - 5)$

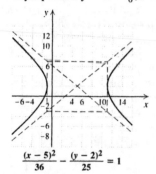

$$\frac{(x-5)^2}{36} - \frac{(y-2)^2}{25} = 1$$

61. $\dfrac{(y + 3)^2}{4} - \dfrac{(x - 4)^2}{16} = 1$; C: $(4, -3)$; V: $(4, -5), (4, -1)$;
asymptotes: $y + 3 = \frac{1}{2}(x - 4), y + 3 = -\frac{1}{2}(x - 4)$

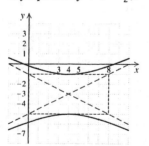

$$8(y + 3)^2 - 2(x - 4)^2 = 32$$

63. $\dfrac{(x + 3)^2}{1} - \dfrac{(y - 2)^2}{4} = 1$; C: $(-3, 2)$; V: $(-4, 2), (-2, 2)$;
asymptotes: $y - 2 = 2(x + 3), y - 2 = -2(x + 3)$

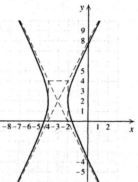

$$4x^2 - y^2 + 24x + 4y + 28 = 0$$

65. ▨

Technology Connection, p. 889

1. $(-1.50, -1.17)$; $(3.50, 0.50)$
2. $(-2.77, 2.52)$; $(-2.77, -2.52)$

Technology Connection, p. 891

1. $y_1 = \sqrt{(20 - x^2)/4}$; $y_2 = -\sqrt{(20 - x^2)/4}$; $y_3 = 4/x$

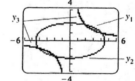

Exercise Set 13.4, pp. 894–896

1. True **3.** False **5.** True **7.** $(-4, -3), (3, 4)$
9. $(0, 2), (3, 0)$ **11.** $(-2, 1)$
13. $\left(\dfrac{5 + \sqrt{70}}{3}, \dfrac{-1 + \sqrt{70}}{3}\right), \left(\dfrac{5 - \sqrt{70}}{3}, \dfrac{-1 - \sqrt{70}}{3}\right)$
15. $\left(4, \frac{3}{2}\right), (3, 2)$ **17.** $\left(\frac{7}{3}, \frac{1}{3}\right), (1, -1)$ **19.** $\left(\frac{11}{4}, -\frac{5}{4}\right), (1, 4)$
21. $\left(\dfrac{7 - \sqrt{33}}{2}, \dfrac{7 + \sqrt{33}}{2}\right), \left(\dfrac{7 + \sqrt{33}}{2}, \dfrac{7 - \sqrt{33}}{2}\right)$
23. $(3, -5), (-1, 3)$ **25.** $(-5, -8), (8, 5)$ **27.** $(0, 0), (1, 1)$,
$\left(-\dfrac{1}{2} + \dfrac{\sqrt{3}}{2}i, -\dfrac{1}{2} - \dfrac{\sqrt{3}}{2}i\right), \left(-\dfrac{1}{2} - \dfrac{\sqrt{3}}{2}i, -\dfrac{1}{2} + \dfrac{\sqrt{3}}{2}i\right)$
29. $(-3, 0), (3, 0)$ **31.** $(-4, -3), (-3, -4), (3, 4), (4, 3)$
33. $\left(\dfrac{16}{3}, \dfrac{5\sqrt{7}}{3}i\right), \left(\dfrac{16}{3}, -\dfrac{5\sqrt{7}}{3}i\right), \left(-\dfrac{16}{3}, \dfrac{5\sqrt{7}}{3}i\right)$,
$\left(-\dfrac{16}{3}, -\dfrac{5\sqrt{7}}{3}i\right)$ **35.** $(-3, -\sqrt{5}), (-3, \sqrt{5}), (3, -\sqrt{5})$,
$(3, \sqrt{5})$ **37.** $(4, 2), (-4, -2), (2, 4), (-2, -4)$
39. $(4, 1), (-4, -1), (2, 2), (-2, -2)$ **41.** $(2, 1), (-2, -1)$
43. $\left(2, -\frac{4}{5}\right), \left(-2, -\frac{4}{5}\right), (5, 2), (-5, 2)$

45. $\left(-\sqrt{2}, \sqrt{2}\right), \left(\sqrt{2}, -\sqrt{2}\right)$
47. Length: 8 cm; width: 6 cm
49. Length: 5 in.; width: 4 in.
51. Length: 12 ft; width: 5 ft   **53.** 6 and 10; −6 and −10
55. 24 ft, 16 ft   **57.** 13 and 12   **59.** 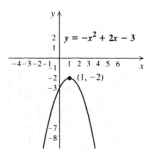   **61.** −16
62. −32   **63.** 1   **64.** −$\frac{1}{4}$ **65.** 44   **66.** 28   **67.**
69. $(x + 2)^2 + (y - 1)^2 = 4$
71. $(-2, 3), (2, -3), (-3, 2), (3, -2)$ **73.** Length: 55 ft;
width: 45 ft   **75.** 10 in. by 7 in. by 5 in.
77. Length: 61.02 in.; height: 34.32 in.   **79.**

Review Exercises: Chapter 13, pp. 898–899

1. True   **2.** False   **3.** False   **4.** False   **5.** True   **6.** True
7. False   **8.** True   **9.** 4   **10.** 5   **11.** $\sqrt{90.1} \approx 9.492$
12. $\sqrt{9 + 4a^2}$ **13.** $\left(\frac{9}{2}, -1\right)$ **14.** $(-3, 7)$
15. $\left(\frac{3}{4}, \frac{\sqrt{3} - \sqrt{2}}{2}\right)$ **16.** $\left(\frac{1}{2}, 2a\right)$ **17.** $(-3, 2), \sqrt{7}$
18. $(5, 0), 7$ **19.** $(3, 1), 3$ **20.** $(-4, 3), \sqrt{35}$
21. $(x + 4)^2 + (y - 3)^2 = 48$
22. $(x - 7)^2 + (y + 2)^2 = 20$
23. Circle   **24.** Ellipse

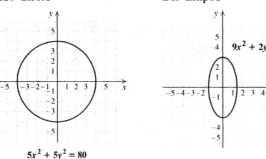

$5x^2 + 5y^2 = 80$ $9x^2 + 2y^2 = 18$

25. Parabola   **26.** Hyperbola

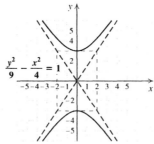

$y = -x^2 + 2x - 3$ $\frac{y^2}{9} - \frac{x^2}{4} = 1$

27. Hyperbola   **28.** Parabola

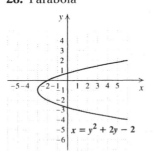

$xy = 9$ $x = y^2 + 2y - 2$

29. Ellipse   **30.** Circle

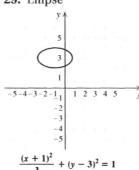

$\frac{(x + 1)^2}{3} + (y - 3)^2 = 1$ $x^2 + y^2 + 6x - 8y - 39 = 0$

31. $(7, 4)$ **32.** $(2, 2), \left(\frac{32}{9}, -\frac{10}{9}\right)$ **33.** $(0, -3), (2, 1)$
34. $(4, 3), (4, -3), (-4, 3), (-4, -3)$
35. $(2, 1), \left(\sqrt{3}, 0\right), (-2, 1), \left(-\sqrt{3}, 0\right)$ **36.** $(3, -3), \left(-\frac{3}{5}, \frac{21}{5}\right)$
37. $(6, 8), (6, -8), (-6, 8), (-6, -8)$
38. $(2, 2), (-2, -2), \left(2\sqrt{2}, \sqrt{2}\right), \left(-2\sqrt{2}, -\sqrt{2}\right)$
39. Length: 12 m; width: 7 m   **40.** Length: 12 in.;
width: 9 in.   **41.** 32 cm, 20 cm   **42.** 3 ft, 11 ft
43. 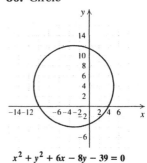 The graph of a parabola has one branch whereas
the graph of a hyperbola has two branches. A hyperbola
has asymptotes, but a parabola does not.
44. 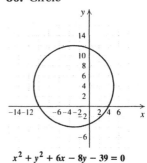 Function notation rarely appears in this chapter
because many of the relations are not functions. Function
notation could be used for vertical parabolas and for
hyperbolas that have the axes as asymptotes.
45. $\left(-5, -4\sqrt{2}\right), \left(-5, 4\sqrt{2}\right), \left(3, -2\sqrt{2}\right), \left(3, 2\sqrt{2}\right)$
46. $(0, 6), (0, -6)$ **47.** $(x - 2)^2 + (y + 1)^2 = 25$
48. $\frac{x^2}{81} + \frac{y^2}{25} = 1$ **49.** $\left(\frac{9}{4}, 0\right)$

Test: Chapter 13, p. 900

1. [13.1] $9\sqrt{2} \approx 12.728$ **2.** [13.1] $2\sqrt{9 + a^2}$
3. [13.1] $\left(-\frac{1}{2}, \frac{7}{2}\right)$ **4.** [13.1] $(0, 0)$ **5.** [13.1] $(-5, 1), 9$
6. [13.1] $(-2, 3), 3$
7. [13.1], [13.3] Parabola   **8.** [13.1], [13.3] Circle

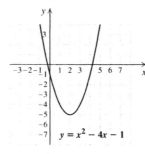

$y = x^2 - 4x - 1$ $x^2 + y^2 + 2x + 6y + 6 = 0$

9. [13.3] Hyperbola

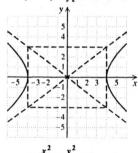

$$\frac{x^2}{16} - \frac{y^2}{9} = 1$$

10. [13.2], [13.3] Ellipse

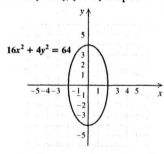

$16x^2 + 4y^2 = 64$

11. [13.3] Hyperbola

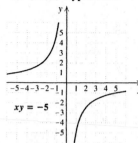

$xy = -5$

12. [13.1], [13.3] Parabola

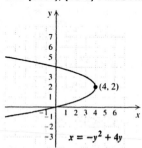

$x = -y^2 + 4y$

13. [13.4] $(0, 3)$, $\left(\frac{8}{5}, \frac{9}{5}\right)$ **14.** [13.4] $(4, 0)$, $(-4, 0)$

15. [13.4] $(3, 2)$, $(-3, -2)$

16. [13.4] $\left(\sqrt{6}, 2\right), \left(\sqrt{6}, -2\right), \left(-\sqrt{6}, 2\right), \left(-\sqrt{6}, -2\right)$

17. [13.4] 2 by 11   **18.** [13.4] $\sqrt{5}$ m, $\sqrt{3}$ m

19. [13.4] Length: 32 ft; width: 24 ft

20. [13.4] $1200, 6\%$ **21.** [13.2] $\dfrac{(x-6)^2}{25} + \dfrac{(y-3)^2}{9} = 1$

22. [13.1] $\left(0, -\frac{31}{4}\right)$ **23.** [13.4] 9   **24.** [13.2] $\dfrac{x^2}{16} + \dfrac{y^2}{49} = 1$

CHAPTER 14

Exercise Set 14.1, pp. 906–908

1. (f)   **3.** (d)   **5.** (c)   **7.** 5, 7, 9, 11; 23; 33

9. 3, 6, 11, 18; 102; 227   **11.** $0, \frac{3}{5}, \frac{4}{17}, \frac{15}{101}; \frac{99}{113}; \frac{112}{113}$

13. $1, -\frac{1}{2}, \frac{1}{4}, -\frac{1}{8}; -\frac{1}{512}; \frac{1}{16,384}$ **15.** $-4, 5, -6, 7; 13; -18$

17. $0, 7, -26, 63; 999; -3374$ **19.** 13   **21.** 364

23. -23.5 **25.** -363 **27.** $\dfrac{441}{400}$ **29.** $2n$ **31.** $(-1)^{n+1}$

33. $(-1)^n \cdot n$ **35.** $2n + 1$ **37.** $(-1)^n \cdot 2 \cdot (3)^{n-1}$

39. $\dfrac{n}{n+1}$ **41.** 5^n **43.** $(-1)^n \cdot n^2$ **45.** 4   **47.** 30

49. $\dfrac{1}{2} + \dfrac{1}{4} + \dfrac{1}{6} + \dfrac{1}{8} + \dfrac{1}{10} = \dfrac{137}{120}$

51. $3^0 + 3^1 + 3^2 + 3^3 + 3^4 = 121$

53. $2 + \dfrac{3}{2} + \dfrac{4}{3} + \dfrac{5}{4} + \dfrac{6}{5} + \dfrac{7}{6} + \dfrac{8}{7} = \dfrac{1343}{140}$

55. $(-1)^2 2^1 + (-1)^3 2^2 + (-1)^4 2^3 + (-1)^5 2^4 + (-1)^6 2^5 + (-1)^7 2^6 + (-1)^8 2^7 + (-1)^9 2^8 = -170$

57. $(0^2 - 2 \cdot 0 + 3) + (1^2 - 2 \cdot 1 + 3) + (2^2 - 2 \cdot 2 + 3) + (3^2 - 2 \cdot 3 + 3) + (4^2 - 2 \cdot 4 + 3) + (5^2 - 2 \cdot 5 + 3) = 43$

59. $\dfrac{(-1)^3}{3 \cdot 4} + \dfrac{(-1)^4}{4 \cdot 5} + \dfrac{(-1)^5}{5 \cdot 6} = -\dfrac{1}{15}$ **61.** $\displaystyle\sum_{k=1}^{5} \dfrac{k+1}{k+2}$

63. $\displaystyle\sum_{k=1}^{6} k^2$ **65.** $\displaystyle\sum_{k=2}^{n} (-1)^k k^2$ **67.** $\displaystyle\sum_{k=1}^{\infty} 5k$

69. $\displaystyle\sum_{k=1}^{\infty} \dfrac{1}{k(k+1)}$ **71.** ▨   **73.** 77   **74.** 23

75. $x^3 + 3x^2 y + 3xy^2 + y^3$ **76.** $a^3 - 3a^2 b + 3ab^2 - b^3$

77. $8a^3 - 12a^2 b + 6ab^2 - b^3$

78. $8x^3 + 12x^2 y + 6xy^2 + y^3$ **79.** ▨

81. 1, 3, 13, 63, 313, 1563   **83.** $5200, $3900, $2925, $2193.75, $1645.31, $1233.98, $925.49, $694.12, $520.59, $390.44   **85.** $S_{100} = 0$; $S_{101} = -1$ **87.** $i, -1, -i, 1, i; i$

89. 11th term

Exercise Set 14.2, pp. 915–917

1. True   **3.** False   **5.** True   **7.** False   **9.** $a_1 = 2, d = 4$

11. $a_1 = 7, d = -4$ **13.** $a_1 = \frac{3}{2}, d = \frac{3}{4}$

15. $a_1 = $5.12, d = 0.12 **17.** 49   **19.** -94

21. $-$1628.16$ **23.** 26th   **25.** 57th   **27.** 82   **29.** 5

31. 28   **33.** $a_1 = 8; d = -3; 8, 5, 2, -1, -4$

35. $a_1 = 1; d = 1$ **37.** 780   **39.** 31,375   **41.** 2550

43. 918   **45.** 1030   **47.** 35 marchers; 315 marchers

49. 180 stones   **51.** $49.60   **53.** 722 seats   **55.** ▨

57. $\dfrac{13}{30x}$ **58.** $\dfrac{23}{36t}$ **59.** $a^k = P$ **60.** $e^a = t$

61. $x^2 + y^2 = 81$ **62.** $(x + 2)^2 + (y - 5)^2 = 18$

63. ▨   **65.** 33 jumps   **67.** $8760, $7961.77, $7163.54, $6365.31, $5567.08; $4768.85, $3970.62, $3172.39, $2374.16, $1575.93   **69.** Let $d = $ the common difference. Since p, m, and q form an arithmetic sequence, $m = p + d$ and $q = p + 2d$. Then $\dfrac{p+q}{2} = \dfrac{p + (p + 2d)}{2} = p + d = m$.

71. 156,375

Exercise Set 14.3, pp. 925–927

1. Geometric sequence   **3.** Arithmetic sequence

5. Geometric series   **7.** Geometric series   **9.** 2

11. -0.1 **13.** $-\frac{1}{2}$ **15.** $\frac{1}{5}$ **17.** $\dfrac{6}{m}$ **19.** 192

21. $112\sqrt{2}$ **23.** 52,488   **25.** $2331.64   **27.** $a_n = 5^{n-1}$

29. $a_n = (-1)^{n-1}$, or $a_n = (-1)^{n+1}$

31. $a_n = \dfrac{1}{x^n}$, or $a_n = x^{-n}$ **33.** 3066   **35.** $\dfrac{547}{18}$ **37.** $\dfrac{1 - x^8}{1 - x}$, or $(1 + x)(1 + x^2)(1 + x^4)$ **39.** $5134.51   **41.** $\dfrac{64}{3}$ **43.** $\dfrac{49}{4}$

45. No   **47.** No   **49.** $\dfrac{43}{99}$ **51.** $25,000   **53.** $\dfrac{7}{9}$ **55.** $\dfrac{830}{99}$

57. $\dfrac{5}{33}$ **59.** $\dfrac{5}{1024}$ ft   **61.** 155,797   **63.** 2710 flies

65. 10,723,491 apartments and houses   **67.** 3100.35 ft
69. 20.48 in.   **71.** ▨   **73.** $x^3 + 3x^2y + 3xy^2 + y^3$
74. $a^3 - 3a^2b + 3ab^2 - b^3$ **75.** $\left(-\frac{63}{29}, -\frac{114}{29}\right)$
76. $(-1, 2, 3)$ **77.** ▨   **79.** 54   **81.** $\dfrac{x^2[1 - (-x)^n]}{1 + x}$
83. 512 cm^2 **85.** ▨, ◪

Technology Connection, p. 933

1. 479,001,600   **2.** 56; 792

Exercise Set 14.4, pp. 936–937

1. 2^5, or 32   **3.** 9   **5.** $\dbinom{8}{5}$ **7.** x^7y^2 **9.** 362,880
11. 39,916,800   **13.** 56   **15.** 3024   **17.** 35   **19.** 126
21. 4060   **23.** 780   **25.** $a^4 - 4a^3b + 6a^2b^2 - 4ab^3 + b^4$
27. $p^7 + 7p^6q + 21p^5q^2 + 35p^4q^3 + 35p^3q^4 + 21p^2q^5 + 7pq^6 + q^7$
29. $2187c^7 - 5103c^6d + 5103c^5d^2 - 2835c^4d^3 + 945c^3d^4 - 189c^2d^5 + 21cd^6 - d^7$
31. $t^{-12} + 12t^{-10} + 60t^{-8} + 160t^{-6} + 240t^{-4} + 192t^{-2} + 64$
33. $x^5 - 5x^4y + 10x^3y^2 - 10x^2y^3 + 5xy^4 - y^5$
35. $19{,}683s^9 + \dfrac{59{,}049s^8}{t} + \dfrac{78{,}732s^7}{t^2} + \dfrac{61{,}236s^6}{t^3} + \dfrac{30{,}618s^5}{t^4} + \dfrac{10{,}206s^4}{t^5} + \dfrac{2268s^3}{t^6} + \dfrac{324s^2}{t^7} + \dfrac{27s}{t^8} + \dfrac{1}{t^9}$
37. $x^{15} - 10x^{12}y + 40x^9y^2 - 80x^6y^3 + 80x^3y^4 - 32y^5$
39. $125 + 150\sqrt{5}t + 375t^2 + 100\sqrt{5}t^3 + 75t^4 + 6\sqrt{5}t^5 + t^6$
41. $x^{-3} - 6x^{-2} + 15x^{-1} - 20 + 15x - 6x^2 + x^3$
43. $15a^4b^2$ **45.** $-64{,}481{,}508a^3$ **47.** $1120x^{12}y^2$
49. $1{,}959{,}552u^5v^{10}$ **51.** y^8 **53.** ▨   **55.** 4   **56.** $\frac{5}{2}$
57. 5.6348   **58.** ± 5 **59.** ▨
61. List all the subsets of size 3: $\{a, b, c\}, \{a, b, d\}, \{a, b, e\},$
$\{a, c, d\}, \{a, c, e\}, \{a, d, e\}, \{b, c, d\}, \{b, c, e\}, \{b, d, e\}, \{c, d, e\}.$
There are exactly 10 subsets of size 3 and $\dbinom{5}{3} = 10$, so
there are exactly $\dbinom{5}{3}$ ways of forming a subset of size 3
from $\{a, b, c, d, e\}$.
63. $\dbinom{8}{5}(0.15)^3(0.85)^5 \approx 0.084$
65. $\dbinom{8}{6}(0.15)^2(0.85)^6 + \dbinom{8}{7}(0.15)(0.85)^7 + \dbinom{8}{8}(0.85)^8 \approx 0.89$
67. $\dbinom{n}{n-r} = \dfrac{n!}{[n-(n-r)]!\,(n-r)!}$
$= \dfrac{n!}{r!\,(n-r)!} = \dbinom{n}{r}$

69. $\dfrac{-\sqrt[3]{q}}{2p}$ **71.** $x^7 + 7x^6y + 21x^5y^2 + 35x^4y^3 + 35x^3y^4 + 21x^2y^5 + 7xy^6 + y^7$

Review Exercises: Chapter 14, pp. 939–940

1. False   **2.** True   **3.** True   **4.** False   **5.** True   **6.** True
7. False   **8.** False   **9.** 1, 5, 9, 13; 29; 45
10. $0, \frac{1}{5}, \frac{1}{5}, \frac{3}{17}, \frac{7}{65}; \frac{11}{145}$ **11.** $a_n = 7n$
12. $a_n = (-1)^n(2n - 1)$
13. $-2 + 4 + (-8) + 16 + (-32) = -22$
14. $-3 + (-5) + (-7) + (-9) + (-11) + (-13) = -48$
15. $\sum_{k=1}^{5} 4k$ **16.** $\sum_{k=1}^{5} \dfrac{1}{(-2)^k}$ **17.** 85   **18.** $\frac{8}{3}$
19. $a_1 = \frac{45}{4}, d = \frac{5}{4}$ **20.** -544 **21.** 8580   **22.** $1024\sqrt{2}$
23. $\frac{2}{3}$ **24.** $a_n = 2(-1)^n$ **25.** $a_n = 3\left(\dfrac{x}{4}\right)^{n-1}$ **26.** 4095
27. $-4095x$ **28.** 12   **29.** $\frac{49}{11}$ **30.** No   **31.** No
32. \$40,000   **33.** $\frac{5}{9}$ **34.** $\frac{46}{33}$ **35.** \$24.30   **36.** 903 poles
37. \$15,791.18   **38.** 6 m   **39.** 5040   **40.** 56
41. $190a^{18}b^2$ **42.** $x^4 - 8x^3y + 24x^2y^2 - 32xy^3 + 16y^4$
43. ▨ For a geometric sequence with $|r| < 1$, as n gets larger, the absolute value of the terms gets smaller, since $|r^n|$ gets smaller.
44. ▨ The first form of the binomial theorem draws the coefficients from Pascal's triangle; the second form uses factorial notation. The second form avoids the need to compute all preceding rows of Pascal's triangle, and is generally easier to use when only one term of an expression is needed. When several terms of an expansion are needed and n is not large (say, $n \le 8$), it is often easier to use Pascal's triangle.
45. $\dfrac{1 - (-x)^n}{x + 1}$
46. $x^{-15} + 5x^{-9} + 10x^{-3} + 10x^3 + 5x^9 + x^{15}$

Test: Chapter 14, pp. 940–941

1. [14.1] 1, 7, 13, 19, 25; 67   **2.** [14.1] $a_n = 4\left(\frac{1}{3}\right)^n$
3. [14.1] $-1 + (-5) + (-13) + (-29) + (-61) = -109$
4. [14.1] $\sum_{k=1}^{5} (-1)^{k+1}k^3$ **5.** [14.2] -51 **6.** [14.2] $\frac{3}{8}$
7. [14.2] $a_1 = 31.2; d = -3.8$ **8.** [14.2] 2508   **9.** [14.3] $\frac{9}{128}$
10. [14.3] $\frac{2}{3}$ **11.** [14.3] 3^n **12.** [14.3] $511 + 511x$
13. [14.3] 1   **14.** [14.3] No   **15.** [14.3] $\frac{\$25{,}000}{23} \approx \$1086.96$
16. [14.3] $\frac{85}{99}$ **17.** [14.2] 63 seats   **18.** [14.2] \$17,100
19. [14.3] \$8981.05   **20.** [14.3] 36 m   **21.** [14.4] 220
22. [14.4] $x^{10} - 15x^8y + 90x^6y^2 - 270x^4y^3 + 405x^2y^4 - 243y^5$ **23.** [14.4] $220a^9x^3$ **24.** [14.2] $n(n+1)$

25. [14.3] $\dfrac{1 - \left(\dfrac{1}{x}\right)^n}{1 - \dfrac{1}{x}}$, or $\dfrac{x^n - 1}{x^{n-1}(x - 1)}$

Cumulative Review: Chapters 1–14, pp. 941–943

1. $-35x^6 y^{-4}$, or $\dfrac{-35x^6}{y^4}$ **2.** 6.3   **3.** $-4y + 17$ **4.** 280

5. $\frac{7}{6}$ **6.** $3a^2 - 8ab - 15b^2$ **7.** $13x^3 - 7x^2 - 6x + 6$

8. $6a^2 + 7a - 5$ **9.** $9a^4 - 30a^2 y + 25y^2$ **10.** $\dfrac{4}{x + 2}$

11. $\dfrac{x - 4}{4(x + 2)}$ **12.** $\dfrac{(x + y)(x^2 + xy + y^2)}{x^2 + y^2}$ **13.** $x - a$

14. $(2x - 3)^2$ **15.** $(3a - 2)(9a^2 + 6a + 4)$

16. $(a + 3)(a^2 - b)$ **17.** $3(y^2 + 3)(5y^2 - 4)$ **18.** 20

19. $7x^3 + 9x^2 + 19x + 38 + \dfrac{72}{x - 2}$ **20.** $\frac{3}{5}$ **21.** $-\frac{6}{5}, 4$

22. $\mathbb{R}$, or $(-\infty, \infty)$ **23.** $(-1, 1)$ **24.** $(2, -1, 1)$ **25.** 2

26. $\pm 2, \pm 5$ **27.** $(\sqrt{5}, \sqrt{3}), (\sqrt{5}, -\sqrt{3}), (-\sqrt{5}, \sqrt{3}),$
$(-\sqrt{5}, -\sqrt{3})$ **28.** 1.4037   **29.** 1005   **30.** $\frac{1}{25}$ **31.** $-\frac{1}{2}$

32. $\{x \,|\, -2 \le x \le 3\}$, or $[-2, 3]$ **33.** $\pm i\sqrt{2}$

34. $-2 \pm \sqrt{7}$ **35.** $\{y \,|\, y < -5 \text{ or } y > 2\}$, or
$(-\infty, -5) \cup (2, \infty)$ **36.** $\{a \,|\, -6 \le a \le 8\}$, or $[-6, 8]$ **37.** 3

38. 5 ft by 12 ft   **39.** More than 4 purchases

40. 65, 66, 67   **41.** $11\frac{3}{7}$ **42.** \$2.68 herb: 10 oz;
\$4.60 herb: 14 oz   **43.** 350 mph   **44.** $8\frac{2}{5}$ hr, or 8 hr 24 min

45. 20   **46.** 5000 ft^2

47.

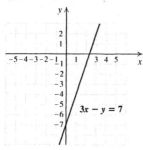

48.

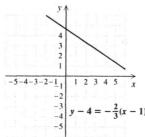

49.

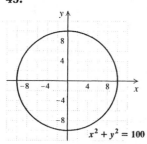

50.

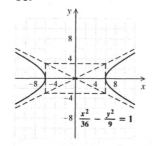

51.

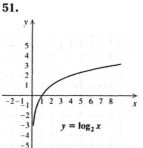

52.

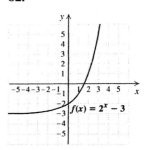

53.

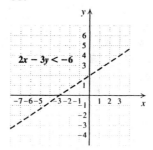

54.

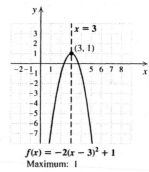

55. $r = \dfrac{V - P}{-Pt}$, or $\dfrac{P - V}{Pt}$ **56.** $R = \dfrac{Ir}{1 - I}$ **57.** $y = 3x - 8$

58. $\left\{x \,\middle|\, x \le \frac{3}{4}\right\}$, or $\left(-\infty, \frac{3}{4}\right]$

59. $\{x \,|\, x \text{ is a real number } and \ x \ne 1\}$

60. 6.8×10^{-12} **61.** $8x^2\sqrt{y}$ **62.** $125x^2 y^{3/4}$ **63.** $\dfrac{\sqrt[3]{5xy}}{y}$

64. $\dfrac{1 - 2\sqrt{x} + x}{1 - x}$ **65.** $26 - 13i$ **66.** $x^2 - 50 = 0$

67. $(2, -3); 6$ **68.** $\log_a \dfrac{\sqrt[3]{x^2} \cdot z^5}{\sqrt{y}}$ **69.** $a^5 = c$

70. 3.7541   **71.** 0.0003   **72.** 8.6442   **73.** 0.0277

74. (a) $k \approx 0.219$; $C(t) = 0.12e^{0.219t}$; (b) about 29 million
computers   **75.** 5   **76.** -121 **77.** 875

78. $16\left(\frac{1}{4}\right)^{n-1}$ **79.** $13{,}440a^4 b^6$ **80.** $74.88671875x$

81. \$652.39   **82.** All real numbers except 0 and -12

83. 81   **84.** y gets divided by 8   **85.** $-\dfrac{7}{13} + \dfrac{2\sqrt{30}}{13}i$

86. 84 yr

CHAPTER R

Exercise Set R.1, pp. 953–954

1. False   **3.** True   **5.** True   **7.** 4   **9.** 1.3   **11.** -25

13. $-\frac{11}{15}$ **15.** -6.5 **17.** -15 **19.** 0   **21.** $-\frac{1}{2}$

23. 5.8   **25.** -3 **27.** 39   **29.** 175   **31.** -32

33. 16   **35.** -6 **37.** 9   **39.** -3 **41.** -16

43. 100   **45.** 2   **47.** -23 **49.** 36   **51.** 10   **53.** 10

55. 7 **57.** 32 **59.** 28 cm^2 **61.** 8x + 28
63. 5x − 50 **65.** −30 + 6x **67.** 8a + 12b − 6c
69. 2(4x + 3y) **71.** 3(1 + w) **73.** 10(x + 5y + 10)
75. p **77.** −m + 22 **79.** 3x + 7 **81.** 6p − 7
83. −5x + 12y **85.** 36a − 48b **87.** −10x + 104y + 9
89. Yes **91.** No **93.** Yes **95.** Let n represent the
number; 3n = 348 **97.** Let c represent the number of
calories in a Taco Bell Beef Burrito; c + 69 = 500
99. Let l represent the amount of water used to produce
1 lb of lettuce; 42 = 2l

Exercise Set R.2, pp. 961–963

1. 8 **3.** 12 **5.** −$\frac{1}{12}$ **7.** −0.8 **9.** $\frac{13}{3}$ **11.** −$\frac{5}{3}$
13. 42 **15.** −5 **17.** 2 **19.** $\frac{25}{3}$ **21.** −$\frac{4}{9}$
23. −4 **25.** $\frac{69}{5}$ **27.** $\frac{9}{32}$ **29.** −2 **31.** −15
33. $\frac{43}{2}$ **35.** −$\frac{61}{115}$ **37.** $l = \dfrac{A}{w}$ **39.** $q = \dfrac{p}{30}$
41. $P = IV$ **43.** $p = 2q - r$ **45.** $\pi = \dfrac{A}{r^2 + r^2h}$
47. **(a)** No; **(b)** yes; **(c)** no; **(d)** yes
49. $\{x \mid x \leq 12\}$

51. $\{m \mid m > 12\}$

53. $\{x \mid x \geq -\frac{3}{2}\}$

55. $\{t \mid t < -3\}$

57. $\{y \mid y > 10\}$ **59.** $\{a \mid a \geq 1\}$ **61.** $\{x \mid x \geq \frac{64}{17}\}$
63. $\{x \mid x > \frac{39}{11}\}$ **65.** $\{x \mid x \leq -10.875\}$ **67.** 7
69. 16, 18 **71.** 166$\frac{2}{3}$ pages **73.** 4.5 cm, 9.5 cm
75. 900 cubic feet **77.** 80¢

Exercise Set R.3, pp. 969–970

1.

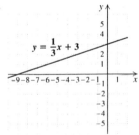

3. I **5.** IV

7. I, IV **9.** No **11.** Yes **13.**

15.

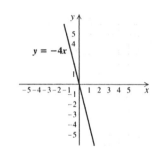

17. 1 **19.** 0 **21.** Slope: 2; y-intercept: (0, −5)
23. Slope: −2; y-intercept: (0, 1)

25.

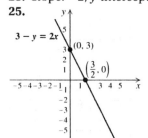

27.

29.

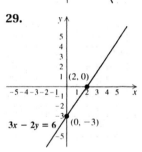

31.

33.

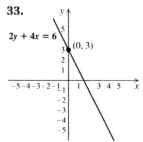

35. 0

37. Undefined

39. $y = \frac{1}{3}x + 1$ **41.** $y = -x + 3$
43. Perpendicular **45.** Neither

Exercise Set R.4, pp. 978–979

1. 1 **3.** -3 **5.** $\dfrac{1}{8^2}=\dfrac{1}{64}$ **7.** $\dfrac{1}{(-2)^3}=-\dfrac{1}{8}$

9. $\dfrac{1}{(ab)^2}$ **11.** y^{10} **13.** y^{-4} **15.** x^{-t} **17.** x^{13}

19. a^6 **21.** $(4x)^8$ **23.** 7^{40} **25.** x^8y^{12} **27.** $\dfrac{y^6}{64}$

29. $\dfrac{9q^8}{4p^6}$ **31.** $8x^3,\,-6x^2,\,x,\,-7$ **33.** 18, 36, -7, 3; 3, 9, 1,

0; 9 **35.** -1, 4, -2; 3, 3, 2; 3 **37.** $8p^4$; 8
39. x^4+3x^3 **41.** $-7t^2+5t+10$ **43.** 36
45. -14 **47.** 144 ft **49.** $4x^3-3x^2+8x+7$
51. $-y^2+5y-2$ **53.** $-3x^2y-y^2+8y$
55. $12x^5-28x^3+28x^2$ **57.** $8a^2+2ab+4ay+by$
59. $x^3+4x^2-20x+7$ **61.** x^2-49
63. $x^2+2xy+y^2$ **65.** $6x^4+17x^2-14$
67. $a^2-6ab+9b^2$ **69.** $42a^2-17ay-15y^2$
71. $-t^4-3t^2+2t-5$ **73.** $5x+3$

75. $2x^2-3x+3+\dfrac{-2}{x+1}$ **77.** $5x+3+\dfrac{3}{x^2-1}$

Exercise Set R.5, pp. 989–990

1. $3x(x-1)(x+3)$ **3.** $(y-3)^2$
5. $(p+2)(2p^3+1)$ **7.** Prime
9. $(2t+3)(4t^2-6t+9)$ **11.** $(m+6)(m+7)$
13. $(x^2+9)(x+3)(x-3)$ **15.** $(2x+3)(4x+5)$
17. $(x+2)(x+1)(x-1)$
19. $(0.1t^2-0.2)(0.01t^4+0.02t^2+0.04)$
21. $\left(x^2+\frac14\right)\left(x+\frac12\right)\left(x-\frac12\right)$ **23.** $(a+3+y)(a+3-y)$
25. $(m+15n)(m-10n)$ **27.** $2y(3x+1)(4x-3)$
29. $(y-11)^2$ **31.** $-7,2$ **33.** $0,4.7$ **35.** $-10,10$
37. $-\frac52,7$ **39.** $0,5$ **41.** $-2,6$ **43.** $-11,5$
45. -5 **47.** Base: 8 ft; height: 5 ft **49.** 8 ft, 15 ft

Exercise Set R.6, pp. 1001–1002

1. $-\frac23$ **3.** $-10,10$ **5.** $\dfrac{8x}{9y}$ **7.** $\dfrac{t+2}{t+4}$ **9.** $\dfrac{-1}{x+2}$

11. $\dfrac{6}{x}$ **13.** $\dfrac{(a+1)^3(a-1)}{a^3}$ **15.** 1 **17.** $\dfrac{5x+6}{x^2}$

19. $\dfrac{6a+3b-4}{3a-3b}$ **21.** $\dfrac{-3}{5x(x+2)}$ **23.** $\dfrac{(x+1)^2}{x^2(x+2)}$

25. $\dfrac{x+3}{(x+1)^2}$ **27.** $\dfrac{-3x}{2}$ **29.** $\dfrac{-14x-7}{(x+5)(x-4)}$

31. $\dfrac{8x-4}{x^3}$ **33.** $\dfrac{3(x+1)}{(x-7)(4x+3)}$ **35.** $\dfrac{(x+1)^2}{(x-2)(x+4)}$

37. $\dfrac{-1}{x}$ **39.** $\dfrac65$ **41.** 1 **43.** $\dfrac{31}{2}$ **45.** $-4,4$
47. $22\frac29$ hr **49.** Jessica: 45 km/h; Josh: 25 km/h
51. 50

APPENDIXES

Exercise Set A, pp. 1006–1007

1. Mean: 21; median: 18.5; mode: 29 **3.** Mean: 21;
median: 20; mode: 5, 20 **5.** Mean: 5.2; median: 5.7;
mode: 7.4 **7.** Mean: 239.5; median: 234; mode: 234
9. Average: 23.8; median: 15; mode: 1 **11.** Mean: 897.2;
median: 798; mode: none **13.** Average: $8.19;
median: $8.49; mode: $6.99 **15.** 10 home runs
17. $a=30, b=58$

Exercise Set B, pp. 1010–1011

1. $\{3,4,5,6,7\}$ **3.** $\{41,43,45,47,49\}$ **5.** $\{-3,3\}$
7. False **9.** True **11.** True **13.** True **15.** True
17. False **19.** $\{c,d,e\}$ **21.** $\{1,10\}$ **23.** $\varnothing$
25. $\{a,e,i,o,u,q,c,k\}$ **27.** $\{0,1,2,5,7,10\}$
29. $\{a,e,i,o,u,m,n,f,g,h\}$ **31.** ▨ **33.** The set of
integers **35.** The set of real numbers **37.** $\varnothing$ **39.** (a) A;
(b) A; (c) A; (d) $\varnothing$ **41.** True

Exercise Set C, pp. 1015–1016

1. $x^2-3x+5+\dfrac{-12}{x+1}$ **3.** $a+5+\dfrac{-4}{a+3}$

5. $x^2-5x-23+\dfrac{-43}{x-2}$ **7.** $3x^2-2x+2+\dfrac{-3}{x+3}$

9. $y^2+2y+1+\dfrac{12}{y-2}$ **11.** $x^4+2x^3+4x^2+8x+16$

13. $3x^2+6x-3+\dfrac{2}{x+\frac13}$ **15.** 6 **17.** 1 **19.** 54 **21.** ▨
23. (a) The degree of R must be less than 1, the degree of
$x-r$; (b) Let $x=r$. Then
$$\begin{aligned}P(r)&=(r-r)\cdot Q(r)+R\\&=0\cdot Q(r)+R\\&=R.\end{aligned}$$
25. $0; -\frac72, \frac53, 4$ **27.** 0

Index

Quadratic functions, 470, 471, 472, 501
  completing the square and, 750–753
  finding intercepts and, 753–754
  fitting to data, 758–760
  of form $f(x) = a(x - h)^2$, graphing, 743–744, 777
  of form $f(x) = a(x - h)^2 + k$, graphing, 744–746, 777
  of form $f(x) = ax^2$, graphing, 741–743, 777
  graphing, 741–747
  problem solving and, 756–760
    fitting quadratic functions to data and, 758–760
    maximum and minimum problems and, 756–758, 777
  zeros of, 769, 777
Quadratic inequalities, 767–771
Quotient rule, 232
  for exponents, 971
  for logarithms, 812
  for radicals, 658, 697
Quotients. *See also* Division
  raising to a power, 235–236, 971

R

Radical equations, 673–677
  principle of powers and, 673–675, 698
  reducible to quadratic, 736–739
  with two radical terms, 676–677
Radical expressions, 634–640. *See also* Roots; Square roots
  containing several radical terms, 665–669
    addition of, 665–666
    division of, 666–667
    multiplication of, 666–667
    rationalizing denominators and numerators and, 667–668, 698
    subtraction of, 665–666
    terms with differing indices and, 668–669
  cube roots and, 638–639
  division of, 658–662, 697
    rationalizing denominators and numerators and, 660–662
    simplifying and, 658–660
  of form $\sqrt{a^2}$, 636–637

  geometric applications of, 680–684
    Pythagorean theorem and, 360–362, 368, 680–682, 699, 988
    special triangles and, 682–684, 699
  like radicals, 666
  multiplication of, 651–655, 697
    multiplying and simplifying and, 654–655
    simplifying by factoring and, 652–654
  odd and even nth roots and, 639–640
  simplifying
    division and, 658–660
    of expressions of form $\sqrt{a^2}$, 636–637
    by factoring, 652–654
    multiplying and, 654–655
Radicals, quotient rule for, 658, 697
Radical sign, 635, 697
Radicand, 635, 697
Radius of a circle, 861
Range of functions, 442, 501
  determining, 454–458
  linear, 470
Rates, 177–181
  visualizing, 179–181
Rational equations
  problem solving with, 420–428
  reducible to quadratic, 736–739
  solving, 412–418, 997–1000
Rational exponents, 643–647, 697
  laws of exponents and, 646, 647
  negative, 645, 647
  positive, 643–644, 647
  simplifying radical expressions with, 646–647, 698
Rational expressions, 374–379, 435, 990–997
  addition of, 992–995
    with like denominators, 387–388, 435
    with unlike denominators, 397–401
  complex. *See* Complex rational expressions
  division of, 382–384, 435, 991–992
  with factors that are opposites, 378–379
  least common multiples and denominators of, 389–394, 993–995

  multiplication of, 381–382, 435, 991–992
    when factors are opposites, 401–403
  simplifying, 375–379, 435
  subtraction of, 992–995
    with like denominators, 388–389, 435
    with unlike denominators, 397–401
Rational functions, 470, 471, 472, 501
Rational inequalities, 771–773, 777
Rationalizing the denominator, 660–662, 667, 698
Rationalizing the numerator, 662, 667–668, 698
Rational numbers, 31–33, 74, 946
  as exponents. *See* Rational exponents
Real numbers, 33–36, 74, 946–949
  addition of, 39–43, 947
  associative laws and, 950
  commutative laws and, 950
  distributive law, 950
  division of, 57–60, 948
  identity property of one and, 950
  identity property of zero and, 950
  law of opposites, 950
  multiplication of, 54–56, 57, 948
  multiplicative property of zero and, 950
  opposite of a sum, 950
  ordering, 946
  property of -1, 950
  subtraction of, 46–51, 948
Real-number system, 34
Recalling calculations using graphing calculator, 98
Reciprocals, 23, 84
  negative exponents and, 291
  opposites versus, 60
Rectangles, area of, 3, 75
Relations, 443–444
Remainder theorem, 1014–1015
Repeating decimals, 33, 74, 946
Revenue, total, 565, 572
Right triangles, 360–362, 368
  isosceles, 682–683, 699
  Pythagorean theorem and, 360–362, 368, 680–682, 699, 988
  30°–60°–90°, 683–684, 699

INDEX OF APPLICATIONS

Selected Keys of the Scientific Calculator

This secondary function takes the square root of number displayed.

Squares number displayed.

Activates secondary functions printed above certain keys. Also denoted INV or 2nd.

Used when entering numbers in scientific notation. Also denoted EXP.

Finds reciprocal of number displayed.

Used to raise any base to a power. Also denoted y^x, a^x, or ⌃.

Stores number displayed in memory. Also denoted MIN or M.

Recalls number stored in memory. Also denoted MR.

Clears last number displayed but not preceding operations.

Used when entering decimal notation.

This secondary function raises 10 to any power entered.

Clears all preceding numbers and operations. Also used to turn calculator on.

Used as an approximation for pi.

Used to perform indicated operation.

Used to control order in which certain operations are performed.

Used to change sign of number displayed.

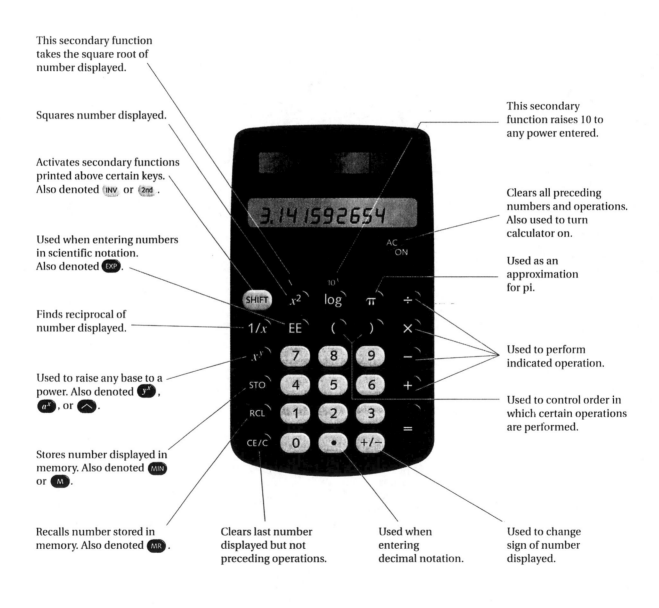

Selected Keys of the Graphing Calculator*

Controls the values that are used when creating a table.

Determines the portion of the curve(s) shown and the scale of the graph.

Used to enter the equation(s) that is to be graphed.

Controls whether graphs are drawn sequentially or simultaneously and if the window is split.

Activates the secondary functions printed above many keys in blue or green.

Used to delete previously entered characters.

Accesses pre-programmed applications and tutorials.

These keys are similar to those found on a scientific calculator.

Magnifies or reduces a portion of the curve being viewed and can "square" the graph to reduce distortion.

Used to determine certain important values associated with a graph.

Used to display the coordinates of points on a curve.

Used to display x- and y-values in a table.

Used to graph equations that were entered using the ⬛ key.

Used to move the cursor and adjust contrast.

Used to fit curves to data.

Used to access a previously named function or equation.

Used to raise a base to a power.

Used to write the variable, x.

Used as a negative sign.

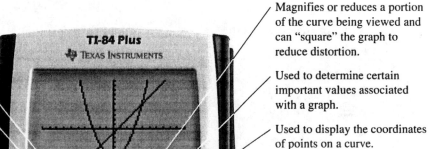

*Key functions and locations are the same for the TI-83 Plus.

Frequently Used Symbols and Formulas

SYMBOLS

$=$	Is equal to
$\approx$	Is approximately equal to
$>$	Is greater than
$<$	Is less than
$\geq$	Is greater than or equal to
$\leq$	Is less than or equal to
$\in$	Is an element of
$\subseteq$	Is a subset of
$|x|$	The absolute value of x
$\{x \mid x...\}$	The set of all x such that $x...$
$-x$	The opposite of x
$\sqrt{x}$	The square root of x
$\sqrt[n]{x}$	The nth root of x
LCM	Least Common Multiple
LCD	Least Common Denominator
π	Pi
i	$\sqrt{-1}$
$f(x)$	f of x, or f at x
$f^{-1}(x)$	f inverse of x
$(f \circ g)(x)$	$f(g(x))$
e	Approximately 2.7
Σ	Summation
$n!$	Factorial notation

FORMULAS

$m = \dfrac{y_2 - y_1}{x_2 - x_1}$	Slope of a line
$y = mx + b$	Slope–intercept form of a linear equation
$y - y_1 = m(x - x_1)$	Point–slope form of a linear equation
$(A + B)(A - B) = A^2 - B^2$	Product of the sum and difference of the same two terms
$\left.\begin{array}{l} (A + B)^2 = A^2 + 2AB + B^2, \\ (A - B)^2 = A^2 - 2AB + B^2 \end{array}\right\}$	Square of a binomial
$d = rt$	Formula for distance traveled
$\dfrac{1}{a} \cdot t + \dfrac{1}{b} \cdot t = 1$	Work principle
$s = 16t^2$	Free-fall distance
$y = kx$	Direct variation
$y = \dfrac{k}{x}$	Inverse variation
$x = \dfrac{-b \pm \sqrt{b^2 - 4ac}}{2a}$	Quadratic formula
$P(t) = P_0 e^{kt}, k > 0$	Exponential growth
$P(t) = P_0 e^{-kt}, k > 0$	Exponential decay
$d = \sqrt{(x_2 - x_1)^2 + (y_2 - y_1)^2}$	Distance formula
$\dbinom{n}{r} = \dfrac{n!}{(n - r)!\,r!}$	$\dbinom{n}{r}$ notation